Arktis

Quality of Endurance

DESIGNED IN BRITAIN

ARKTIS KA-330

NATO
OTAN

Innovators of foul weather
& protective clothing

T: +44 (0)1392 2   @arktisltd.co.uk

POLICE AND CONSTABULARY ALMANAC 2013

OFFICIAL REGISTER

SWEET & MAXWELL

THOMSON REUTERS

Published in 2013 by Sweet & Maxwell, 100 Avenue Road, London NW3 3PF
part of Thomson Reuters (Professional) UK Limited
(Registered in England & Wales, Company No 1679046.
Registered Office and address for service:
Aldgate House, 33 Aldgate High Street, London EC3N 1DL)

For further information on our products and services, visit
www.sweetandmaxwell.co.uk

Typeset by Letterpart Limited, Reigate, Surrey
Printed and bound by CPI Group (UK) Ltd, Croydon, CR0 4YY

No natural forests were destroyed to make this product;
only farmed timber was used and re-planted.

A CIP catalogue record for this book
is available from the British Library

ISBN 9780 4140 27466

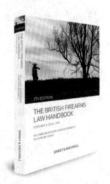

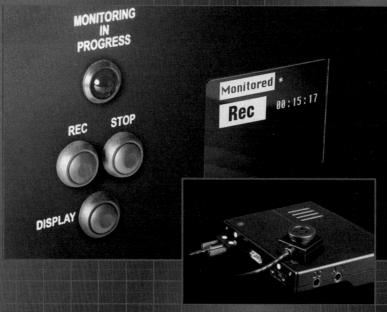

CONTENTS

CONTENTS

FOREWORD

Welcome to the 2013 edition of the *Police and Constabulary Almanac*.

As always, accuracy is our prime objective. The *Almanac* contains a vast amount of detailed information, all of which has been checked, cross-checked and updated. The police forces are invited to revise their entries as many times as necessary and to submit further changes until the book goes to press. The format of these entries is not prescriptive, nor are they limited in length. This allows the forces to submit as much information as they want in a format that suits their structure.

April 1, 2013 saw the launch of Scotland's new national police service, Police Scotland, which replaces the eight Scottish police forces, the Scottish Police Services Authority and the Scottish Crime and Drug Enforcement Agency. We have included the most up-to-date information on Police Scotland – which consists of more than 25,000 police officers – available as the *Almanac* goes to press. Next year, when the new service has become established, we expect to be able to publish much more detail.

In November 2012, the police authorities in England and Wales were replaced by the police and crime commissioners. Details of these can be found at the top of each force's entry.

Apart from the police forces themselves, a glance at the contents page will show that the book includes a wide range of other information of use to police officers and staff, public authorities, HMCTS, probation trusts and other public bodies, as well as many private sector organisations and individuals.

Ease of use is our second main objective. The book's layout is deliberately utilitarian, designed for speed and simplicity of use. You will not find pictures or colour within the body of the directory but you will find clear and accurate information logically arranged, supported by a detailed list of contents and index.

As ever, I would like to thank the police forces and other organisations who put so much effort into providing detailed information for inclusion each year; without them, it would not be possible to produce this book.

Helen Gough
Editor

2012

JANUARY 2012
Sun.	1	8	15	22	29
Mon.	2	9	16	23	30
Tue.	3	10	17	24	31
Wed.	4	11	18	25	
Thu.	5	12	19	26	
Fri.	6	13	20	27	
Sat.	7	14	21	28	

FEBRUARY 2012
Sun.	5	12	19	26
Mon.	6	13	20	27
Tue.	7	14	21	28
Wed.	1	8	15	22	29
Thu.	2	9	16	23	
Fri.	3	10	17	24	
Sat.	4	11	18	25	

MARCH 2012
Sun.	4	11	18	25
Mon.	5	12	19	26
Tue.	6	13	20	27
Wed.	7	14	21	28
Thu.	1	8	15	22	29
Fri.	2	9	16	23	30
Sat.	3	10	17	24	31

APRIL 2012
Sun.	1	8	15	22	29
Mon.	2	9	16	23	30
Tue.	3	10	17	24	
Wed.	4	11	18	25	
Thu.	5	12	19	26	
Fri.	6	13	20	27	
Sat.	7	14	21	28	

MAY 2012
Sun.	6	13	20	27
Mon.	7	14	21	28
Tue.	1	8	15	22	29
Wed.	2	9	16	23	30
Thu.	3	10	17	24	31
Fri.	4	11	18	25	
Sat.	5	12	19	26	

JUNE 2012
Sun.	3	10	17	24
Mon.	4	11	18	25
Tue.	5	12	19	26
Wed.	6	13	20	27
Thu.	7	14	21	28
Fri.	1	8	15	22	29
Sat.	2	9	16	23	30

JULY 2012
Sun.	1	8	15	22	29
Mon.	2	9	16	23	30
Tue.	3	10	17	24	31
Wed.	4	11	18	25	
Thu.	5	12	19	26	
Fri.	6	13	20	27	
Sat.	7	14	21	28	

AUGUST 2012
Sun.	5	12	19	26
Mon.	6	13	20	27
Tue.	7	14	21	28
Wed.	1	8	15	22	29
Thu.	2	9	16	23	30
Fri.	3	10	17	24	31
Sat.	4	11	18	25	

SEPTEMBER 2012
Sun.	2	9	16	23	30
Mon.	3	10	17	24	
Tue.	4	11	18	25	
Wed.	5	12	19	26	
Thu.	6	13	20	27	
Fri.	7	14	21	28	
Sat.	1	8	15	22	29

OCTOBER 2012
Sun.	7	14	21	28
Mon.	1	8	15	22	29
Tue.	2	9	16	23	30
Wed.	3	10	17	24	31
Thu.	4	11	18	25	
Fri.	5	12	19	26	
Sat.	6	13	20	27	

NOVEMBER 2012
Sun.	4	11	18	25
Mon.	5	12	19	26
Tue.	6	13	20	27
Wed.	7	14	21	28
Thu.	1	8	15	22	29
Fri.	2	9	16	23	30
Sat.	3	10	17	24	

DECEMBER 2012
Sun.	2	9	16	23	30
Mon.	3	10	17	24	31
Tue.	4	11	18	25	
Wed.	5	12	19	26	
Thu.	6	13	20	27	
Fri.	7	14	21	28	
Sat.	1	8	15	22	29

2013

JANUARY 2013
Sun.	6	13	20	27
Mon.	7	14	21	28
Tue.	1	8	15	22	29
Wed.	2	9	16	23	30
Thu.	3	10	17	24	31
Fri.	4	11	18	25	
Sat.	5	12	19	26	

FEBRUARY 2013
Sun.	3	10	17	24
Mon.	4	11	18	25
Tue.	5	12	19	26
Wed.	6	13	20	27
Thu.	7	14	21	28
Fri.	1	8	15	22	
Sat.	2	9	16	23	

MARCH 2013
Sun.	3	10	17	24	31
Mon.	4	11	18	25	
Tue.	5	12	19	26	
Wed.	6	13	20	27	
Thu.	7	14	21	28	
Fri.	1	8	15	22	29
Sat.	2	9	16	23	30

APRIL 2013
Sun.	7	14	21	28
Mon.	1	8	15	22	29
Tue.	2	9	16	23	30
Wed.	3	10	17	24	
Thu.	4	11	18	25	
Fri.	5	12	19	26	
Sat.	6	13	20	27	

MAY 2013
Sun.	5	12	19	26
Mon.	6	13	20	27
Tue.	7	14	21	28
Wed.	1	8	15	22	29
Thu.	2	9	16	23	30
Fri.	3	10	17	24	31
Sat.	4	11	18	25	

JUNE 2013
Sun.	2	9	16	23	30
Mon.	3	10	17	24	
Tue.	4	11	18	25	
Wed.	5	12	19	26	
Thu.	6	13	20	27	
Fri.	7	14	21	28	
Sat.	1	8	15	22	29

JULY 2013
Sun.	7	14	21	28
Mon.	1	8	15	22	29
Tue.	2	9	16	23	30
Wed.	3	10	17	24	31
Thu.	4	11	18	25	
Fri.	5	12	19	26	
Sat.	6	13	20	27	

AUGUST 2013
Sun.	4	11	18	25
Mon.	5	12	19	26
Tue.	6	13	20	27
Wed.	7	14	21	28
Thu.	1	8	15	22	29
Fri.	2	9	16	23	30
Sat.	3	10	17	24	31

SEPTEMBER 2013
Sun.	1	8	15	22	29
Mon.	2	9	16	23	30
Tue.	3	10	17	24	
Wed.	4	11	18	25	
Thu.	5	12	19	26	
Fri.	6	13	20	27	
Sat.	7	14	21	28	

OCTOBER 2013
Sun.	6	13	20	27
Mon.	7	14	21	28
Tue.	1	8	15	22	29
Wed.	2	9	16	23	30
Thu.	3	10	17	24	31
Fri.	4	11	18	25	
Sat.	5	12	19	26	

NOVEMBER 2013
Sun.	3	10	17	24
Mon.	4	11	18	25
Tue.	5	12	19	26
Wed.	6	13	20	27
Thu.	7	14	21	28
Fri.	1	8	15	22	29
Sat.	2	9	16	23	30

DECEMBER 2013
Sun.	1	8	15	22	29
Mon.	2	9	16	23	30
Tue.	3	10	17	24	31
Wed.	4	11	18	25	
Thu.	5	12	19	26	
Fri.	6	13	20	27	
Sat.	7	14	21	28	

2014

JANUARY 2014
Sun.	5	12	19	26
Mon.	6	13	20	27
Tue.	7	14	21	28
Wed.	1	8	15	22	29
Thu.	2	9	16	23	30
Fri.	3	10	17	24	31
Sat.	4	11	18	25	

FEBRUARY 2014
Sun.	2	9	16	23
Mon.	3	10	17	24
Tue.	4	11	18	25
Wed.	5	12	19	26
Thu.	6	13	20	27
Fri.	7	14	21	28
Sat.	1	8	15	22	

MARCH 2014
Sun.	2	9	16	23	30
Mon.	3	10	17	24	31
Tue.	4	11	18	25	
Wed.	5	12	19	26	
Thu.	6	13	20	27	
Fri.	7	14	21	28	
Sat.	1	8	15	22	29

APRIL 2014
Sun.	6	13	20	27
Mon.	7	14	21	28
Tue.	1	8	15	22	29
Wed.	2	9	16	23	30
Thu.	3	10	17	24	
Fri.	4	11	18	25	
Sat.	5	12	19	26	

MAY 2014
Sun.	4	11	18	25
Mon.	5	12	19	26
Tue.	6	13	20	27
Wed.	7	14	21	28
Thu.	1	8	15	22	29
Fri.	2	9	16	23	30
Sat.	3	10	17	24	31

JUNE 2014
Sun.	1	8	15	22	29
Mon.	2	9	16	23	30
Tue.	3	10	17	24	
Wed.	4	11	18	25	
Thu.	5	12	19	26	
Fri.	6	13	20	27	
Sat.	7	14	21	28	

JULY 2014
Sun.	6	13	20	27
Mon.	7	14	21	28
Tue.	1	8	15	22	29
Wed.	2	9	16	23	30
Thu.	3	10	17	24	31
Fri.	4	11	18	25	
Sat.	5	12	19	26	

AUGUST 2014
Sun.	3	10	17	24	31
Mon.	4	11	18	25	
Tue.	5	12	19	26	
Wed.	6	13	20	27	
Thu.	7	14	21	28	
Fri.	1	8	15	22	29
Sat.	2	9	16	23	30

SEPTEMBER 2014
Sun.	7	14	21	28
Mon.	1	8	15	22	29
Tue.	2	9	16	23	30
Wed.	3	10	17	24	
Thu.	4	11	18	25	
Fri.	5	12	19	26	
Sat.	6	13	20	27	

OCTOBER 2014
Sun.	5	12	19	26
Mon.	6	13	20	27
Tue.	7	14	21	28
Wed.	1	8	15	22	29
Thu.	2	9	16	23	30
Fri.	3	10	17	24	31
Sat.	4	11	18	25	

NOVEMBER 2014
Sun.	2	9	16	23	30
Mon.	3	10	17	24	
Tue.	4	11	18	25	
Wed.	5	12	19	26	
Thu.	6	13	20	27	
Fri.	7	14	21	28	
Sat.	1	8	15	22	29

DECEMBER 2014
Sun.	7	14	21	28
Mon.	1	8	15	22	29
Tue.	2	9	16	23	30
Wed.	3	10	17	24	31
Thu.	4	11	18	25	
Fri.	5	12	19	26	
Sat.	6	13	20	27	

CALENDAR 2013

CHRONOLOGICAL CYCLES AND ERAS

Dominical Letter	F	Julian Period (year of)		6726
Epact	17	Roman Indiction		6
Golden Number (Lunar Cycle)	XIX	Solar Cycle		6

Era	Year	Begins		Era	Year	Begins	
Byzantine	7522	Sept.	14	Grecian (Seleucidae)	2325	Sept.	14
Roman (AUC)	27656	Jan.	14			(or Oct.	14)
Nabonassar	2762	Apr.	20	Indian (Saka)	1935	Mar.	22
Japanese	2673	Jan.	1	Diocletian	1730	Sept.	11

RELIGIOUS CALENDARS

Epiphany	Jan.	6	Easter Day	Mar.	31
Septuagesima Sunday	Jan.	27	Low Sunday	Apr.	7
Quinquagesima Sunday	Feb.	10	Rogation Sunday	May	5
Ash Wednesday	Feb.	1322	Ascension Day – Holy Thursday	May	9
Quadragesima Sunday	Feb.	17	Whit Sunday – Pentecost	May	19
Fourth Sunday in Lent	Mar.	10	Trinity Sunday	May	26
(Mothering Sunday)			Corpus Christi	May	30
Palm Sunday	Mar.	24	First Sunday in Advent	Dec.	1
Good Friday	Mar.	29	Christmas Day (Tuesday)	Dec.	25

Passover, First day of (Pesach)	Mar.	26	Day of Atonement	Sept.	14
Feast of Weeks (Shavuot)	May	15	(Yom Kippur)		
Jewish New Year (5774	Sept.	5	Tabernacles, First day of	Sept.	19
(Rosh Hashanah))			(Succoth)		

First day of Ramadan	July	9	Islamic New Year (1435)	Nov.	5

All Jewish and Islamic dates above are tabular dates, which begin at sunset on the previous evening and end at sunset on the day tabulated. In practice, the dates of Islamic fasts and festivals are determined by an actual sighting of the appropriate new Moon.

CIVIL CALENDAR: UNITED KINGDOM

Accession of Queen Elizabeth II	Feb.	6	The Queen's Official Birthday	June	8
St David (Wales)	Mar.	1	Birthday of Prince Philip, Duke of	June	10
Commonwealth Day	Mar.	11	Edinburgh		
St Patrick (Ireland)	Mar.	17	Remembrance Sunday	Nov.	10
Birthday of Queen Elizabeth II	Apr.	21	Birthday of the Prince of Wales	Nov.	14
St George (England)	Apr	23	St Andrew (Scotland)	Nov.	30
Coronation Day	June	2			

SEASONS

Vernal Equinox:	Spring begins 20 March 0102 hrs.
Summer Solstice:	Summer begins 21 June 0504 hrs.
Autumnal Equinox:	Autumn begins 22 Sept. 2044 hrs.
Winter Solstice:	Winter begins 21 Dec. 1711 hrs.

BRITISH SUMMER TIME

In the United Kingdom BST, one hour in advance of GMT, will be kept from 0100 hrs. on 31 March to 0100 hrs. on 27 October.

The times of sunrise and sunset, of moonrise and moonset that follow, prepared by Her Majesty's Nautical Almanac Office, are given in Greenwich Mean Time (GMT) or, appropriately, in British Summer Time at Greenwich. To estimate the times of sunrise and sunset for other places from the tabulations requires a correction in both longitude and latitude. The rule for the longitude correction is simple: add four minutes of time for every degree of longitude west of Greenwich, and subtract four minutes if east. However, there is no simple rule for the latitude correction which depends upon the calendar date. As a guide, the times could vary by up to four minutes for every degree of latitude north or south of Greenwich.

In general, the times of moonrise and moonset for other places estimated from the tabulations will be less precise than the corresponding times estimated for sunrise and sunset. The beginning and end of the lighting-up period, as defined by the Road Traffic Acts, occur at half-an-hour after sunset and half-an-hour before sunrise. These times are always within the period of civil twilight, but the corresponding depression of the Sun, and hence the illumination conditions at these times, vary considerably throughout the year even when the sky is clear.

Astronomical information that is required for legal and other purposes may be supplied in appropriate circumstances by H.M. Nautical Almanac Office, Rutherford Appleton Laboratory, Chilton, Didcot OX11 0QX from whom a schedule of charges can be obtained.

JANUARY 2013 XXXI DAYS

HOLIDAYS: New Year — England & Wales 1st; Scotland 1st & 2nd; Northern Ireland 1st

PHASES OF THE MOON
Last Quarter	5th	0358
New Moon	11th	1944
First Quarter	18th	2345
Full Moon	27th	0438

Day of Year	Day of Month	Day of Week	SUN Rise	SUN Set	MOON Rise	MOON Set
1	1	Tu	08 05	16 02	20 51	09 41
2	2	W	08 05	16 03	22 01	10 03
3	3	Th	08 05	16 04	23 13	10 24
4	4	F	08 05	16 05	** **	10 47
5	5	Sa	08 04	16 06	00 26	11 12
6	6	Su	08 04	16 08	01 42	11 40
7	7	M	08 04	16 09	02 59	12 16
8	8	Tu	08 03	16 10	04 15	13 00
9	9	W	08 03	16 12	05 26	13 56
10	10	Th	08 03	16 13	06 28	15 04
11	11	F	08 02	16 15	07 18	16 21
12	12	Sa	08 01	16 16	07 58	17 41
13	13	Su	08 00	16 18	08 31	19 01
14	14	M	07 59	16 19	08 58	20 19
15	15	Tu	07 58	16 21	09 22	21 33
16	16	W	07 58	16 22	09 44	22 45
17	17	Th	07 57	16 24	10 07	23 55
18	18	F	07 56	16 26	10 30	** **
19	19	Sa	07 55	16 27	10 55	01 02
20	20	Su	07 54	16 29	11 25	02 06
21	21	M	07 53	16 31	11 59	03 04
22	22	Tu	07 52	16 32	12 39	04 04
23	23	W	07 51	16 34	13 26	04 56
24	24	Th	07 49	16 36	14 20	05 41
25	25	F	07 48	16 37	15 20	06 20
26	26	Sa	07 47	16 39	16 24	06 53
27	27	Su	07 45	16 41	17 32	07 21
28	28	M	07 44	16 43	18 41	07 46
29	29	Tu	07 42	16 44	19 51	08 10
30	30	W	07 41	16 46	21 03	08 32
31	31	Th	07 40	16 48	22 16	08 54

LIGHTING-UP TIMES: BEGIN and END with SUNSET and SUNRISE times.

FEBRUARY 2013 XXVIII DAYS

HOLIDAYS: Nil

PHASES OF THE MOON
Last Quarter	3rd	1356
New Moon	10th	0720
First Quarter	17th	2031
Full Moon	25th	2026

Day of Year	Day of Month	Day of Week	SUN Rise	SUN Set	MOON Rise	MOON Set
32	1	F	07 38	16 50	23 30	09 18
33	2	Sa	07 36	16 52	** **	09 45
34	3	Su	07 35	16 54	00 45	10 17
35	4	M	07 33	16 55	01 59	10 57
36	5	Tu	07 32	16 57	03 10	11 46
37	6	W	07 30	16 59	04 13	12 46
38	7	Th	07 28	17 01	05 05	13 56
39	8	F	07 26	17 03	05 51	15 13
40	9	Sa	07 25	17 04	06 27	16 32
41	10	Su	07 23	17 06	06 57	17 51
42	11	M	07 21	17 08	07 23	19 08
43	12	Tu	07 19	17 10	07 47	20 22
44	13	W	07 17	17 12	08 08	21 34
45	14	Th	07 15	17 14	08 33	22 44
46	15	F	07 12	17 15	08 58	23 50
47	16	Sa	07 10	17 17	09 26	** **
48	17	Su	07 08	17 19	09 59	00 54
49	18	M	07 06	17 21	10 36	01 53
50	19	Tu	07 04	17 23	11 21	02 47
51	20	W	07 02	17 25	12 11	03 35
52	21	Th	07 00	17 26	13 09	04 16
53	22	F	06 58	17 28	14 04	04 52
54	23	Sa	06 56	17 30	15 17	05 22
55	24	Su	06 53	17 32	16 26	05 49
56	25	M	06 51	17 33	17 37	06 03
57	26	Tu	06 49	17 35	18 49	06 36
58	27	W	06 47	17 37	20 03	06 59
59	28	Th	06 44	17 39	21 18	07 24

LIGHTING-UP TIMES: BEGIN and END with SUNSET and SUNRISE times.

MARCH 2013 XXXI DAYS

HOLIDAYS: St Patrick & Good Friday
- St Patrick – Northern Ireland: 17th & 18th
- Good Friday: England & Wales Mar 29th; Scotland Mar 29th; Northern Ireland Mar 29th

PHASES OF THE MOON
Last Quarter	4th	2153
New Moon	11th	1951
First Quarter	19th	1727
Full Moon	27th	0927

Day of Year	Day of Month	Day of Week	SUN Rise	SUN Set	MOON Rise	MOON Set
60	1	F	06 45	17 41	22 34	07 50
61	2	Sa	06 43	17 43	23 49	08 21
62	3	Su	06 41	17 44	** **	08 59
63	4	M	06 38	17 46	01 00	09 44
64	5	Tu	06 36	17 48	02 05	10 40
65	6	W	06 34	17 49	03 01	11 45
66	7	Th	06 32	17 51	03 47	12 56
67	8	F	06 30	17 53	04 25	14 12
68	9	Sa	06 27	17 54	04 56	15 29
69	10	Su	06 25	17 56	05 23	16 45
70	11	M	06 23	17 58	05 48	17 59
71	12	Tu	06 21	18 00	06 11	19 12
72	13	W	06 18	18 01	06 35	20 23
73	14	Th	06 16	18 03	07 00	21 32
74	15	F	06 14	18 05	07 27	22 38
75	16	Sa	06 12	18 07	07 58	23 39
76	17	Su	06 09	18 08	08 34	** **
77	18	M	06 07	18 10	09 15	00 36
78	19	Tu	06 05	18 12	10 02	01 26
79	20	W	06 03	18 13	10 58	02 10
80	21	Th	06 00	18 15	11 57	02 48
81	22	F	05 58	18 17	13 03	03 20
82	23	Sa	05 56	18 18	14 08	03 49
83	24	Su	05 53	18 20	15 17	04 14
84	25	M	05 51	18 22	16 29	04 38
85	26	Tu	05 49	18 23	17 43	05 01
86	27	W	05 47	18 25	18 59	05 26
87	28	Th	05 44	18 27	20 17	05 52
88	29	F	05 42	18 28	21 34	06 22
89	30	Sa	05 40	18 30	22 49	06 58
90	31	Su	06 38	19 32	** **	08 42

LIGHTING-UP TIMES: BEGIN and END with SUNSET and SUNRISE times.

APRIL 2013 XXX DAYS

PHASES OF THE MOON

Phase	Day	Time
Last Quarter	3rd	0437
New Moon	10th	0935
First Quarter	18th	1231
Full Moon	25th	1957

HOLIDAYS: Easter Monday
England & Wales 1st
Northern Ireland 1st

Day of Year	Day of Month	Day of Week	SUN Rise h m	SUN Set h m	MOON Rise h m	MOON Set h m	LIGHTING UP TIMES
91	1	M	06 35	19 33	30	09 36	BEGIN and END with SUNSET and SUNRISE times
92	2	Tu	06 33	19 35	31	10 38	
93	3	W	06 31	19 37	32	11 48	
94	4	Th	06 28	19 38	33	13 02	
95	5	F	06 26	19 40	33	14 16	
96	6	Sa	06 24	19 42	04 26	15 31	
97	7	Su	06 22	19 43	04 51	16 44	
98	8	M	06 20	19 45	05 14	17 56	
99	9	Tu	06 17	19 47	05 37	19 07	
100	10	W	06 15	19 48	06 01	20 16	
101	11	Th	06 13	19 50	06 28	21 23	
102	12	F	06 11	19 52	06 57	22 26	
103	13	Sa	06 09	19 53	07 31	23 25	
104	14	Su	06 06	19 55	08 11	** **	
105	15	M	06 04	19 57	08 57	00 18	
106	16	Tu	06 02	19 58	09 48	01 05	
107	17	W	06 00	20 00	10 45	01 45	
108	18	Th	05 58	20 02	11 46	02 18	
109	19	F	05 56	20 03	12 51	02 48	
110	20	Sa	05 54	20 05	13 58	03 14	
111	21	Su	05 52	20 07	15 07	03 38	
112	22	M	05 50	20 08	16 19	04 02	
113	23	Tu	05 48	20 10	17 33	04 25	
114	24	W	05 45	20 12	18 51	04 50	
115	25	Th	05 43	20 13	20 10	05 19	
116	26	F	05 42	20 15	21 19	05 53	
117	27	Sa	05 40	20 17	22 42	06 35	
118	28	Su	05 38	20 18	23 47	07 26	
119	29	M	05 36	20 20	** **	08 28	
120	30	Tu	05 34	20 22	00 42	09 37	

MAY 2013 XXXI DAYS

PHASES OF THE MOON

Phase	Day	Time
Last Quarter	2nd	1114
New Moon	10th	0028
First Quarter	18th	0435
Full Moon	25th	0425
Last Quarter	31st	1858

HOLIDAYS: Early Spring & Spring

		LIGHTING UP TIMES
England & Wales	6th & 27th	6th & 27th
Scotland	6th & 27th	6th & 27th
Northern Ireland	6th & 27th	6th & 27th

Day of Year	Day of Month	Day of Week	SUN Rise h m	SUN Set h m	MOON Rise h m	MOON Set h m	LIGHTING UP TIMES
121	1	W	05 32	20 23	01 26	10 51	BEGIN and END with SUNSET and SUNRISE times
122	2	Th	05 30	20 25	02 01	12 07	
123	3	F	05 28	20 27	02 30	13 22	
124	4	Sa	05 27	20 28	02 56	14 35	
125	5	Su	05 25	20 30	03 19	15 46	
126	6	M	05 23	20 31	03 42	16 56	
127	7	Tu	05 21	20 33	04 05	18 04	
128	8	W	05 19	20 35	04 30	19 11	
129	9	Th	05 18	20 36	04 58	20 16	
130	10	F	05 16	20 38	05 30	21 16	
131	11	Sa	05 14	20 39	06 08	22 11	
132	12	Su	05 13	20 41	06 51	23 00	
133	13	M	05 11	20 42	07 41	23 43	
134	14	Tu	05 10	20 44	08 36	** **	
135	15	W	05 08	20 45	09 35	00 19	
136	16	Th	05 07	20 47	10 38	00 50	
137	17	F	05 05	20 48	11 43	01 16	
138	18	Sa	05 04	20 50	12 49	01 41	
139	19	Su	05 03	20 51	13 58	02 04	
140	20	M	05 01	20 53	15 10	02 26	
141	21	Tu	05 00	20 54	16 24	02 50	
142	22	W	04 59	20 55	17 42	03 16	
143	23	Th	04 58	20 57	19 01	03 47	
144	24	F	04 56	20 58	20 18	04 24	
145	25	Sa	04 55	20 59	21 26	05 09	
146	26	Su	04 54	21 01	22 22	06 09	
147	27	M	04 53	21 02	23 07	07 18	
148	28	Tu	04 52	21 03	23 42	08 33	
149	29	W	04 51	21 04	** **	09 51	
150	30	Th	04 50	21 05	00 09	11 09	
151	31	F	04 49	21 07	00 33	12 24	

JUNE 2013 XXX DAYS

PHASES OF THE MOON

Phase	Day	Time
New Moon	8th	1556
First Quarter	16th	1724
Full Moon	23rd	1132
Last Quarter	30th	0454

HOLIDAYS: Nil

Day of Year	Day of Month	Day of Week	SUN Rise h m	SUN Set h m	MOON Rise h m	MOON Set h m	LIGHTING UP TIMES
152	1	Sa	04 49	21 08	01 25	13 37	BEGIN and END with SUNSET and SUNRISE times
153	2	Su	04 48	21 09	01 48	14 47	
154	3	M	04 47	21 10	02 11	15 56	
155	4	Tu	04 47	21 11	02 35	17 03	
156	5	W	04 46	21 12	03 02	18 09	
157	6	Th	04 45	21 13	03 32	19 09	
158	7	F	04 45	21 14	04 07	20 04	
159	8	Sa	04 44	21 14	04 48	20 57	
160	9	Su	04 44	21 15	05 36	21 42	
161	10	M	04 44	21 16	06 29	22 20	
162	11	Tu	04 43	21 16	07 28	22 53	
163	12	W	04 43	21 17	08 28	23 21	
164	13	Th	04 43	21 18	09 32	23 46	
165	14	F	04 43	21 18	10 37	** **	
166	15	Sa	04 42	21 19	11 44	00 08	
167	16	Su	04 42	21 19	12 53	00 30	
168	17	M	04 42	21 20	14 04	00 53	
169	18	Tu	04 42	21 20	15 17	01 17	
170	19	W	04 42	21 20	16 33	01 44	
171	20	Th	04 43	21 21	17 50	02 17	
172	21	F	04 43	21 21	19 05	02 58	
173	22	Sa	04 43	21 21	20 12	03 49	
174	23	Su	04 43	21 21	21 03	04 52	
175	24	M	04 44	21 21	21 55	06 06	
176	25	Tu	04 44	21 21	22 32	07 25	
177	26	W	04 45	21 21	23 03	08 46	
178	27	Th	04 45	21 21	23 29	10 05	
179	28	F	04 46	21 21	23 53	11 21	
180	29	Sa	04 46	21 21	** **	12 35	
181	30	Su	04 47	21 20	00 17	13 46	

JULY 2013 XXXI DAYS

HOLIDAYS: Battle of the Boyne 12th — Northern Ireland

PHASES OF THE MOON

New Moon	8th	0714
First Quarter	16th	0318
Full Moon	12nd	1816
Last Quarter	29th	1743

LIGHTING UP TIMES: BEGIN and END with SUNSET and SUNRISE times

Day of Year	Month	Week	Sun Rise h m	Sun Set h m	Moon Rise h m	Moon Set h m
182	1	M	04 47	21 20	00 41	14 54
183	2	Tu	04 48	21 20	01 07	16 00
184	3	W	04 49	21 19	01 36	17 02
185	4	Th	04 50	21 19	02 09	18 01
186	5	F	04 50	21 18	02 48	18 54
187	6	Sa	04 51	21 18	03 33	19 41
188	7	Su	04 52	21 17	04 24	20 21
189	8	M	04 53	21 17	05 20	20 56
190	9	Tu	04 54	21 16	06 21	21 26
191	10	W	04 55	21 15	07 24	21 52
192	11	Th	04 56	21 14	08 28	22 14
193	12	F	04 57	21 13	09 35	22 37
194	13	Sa	04 58	21 12	10 42	22 59
195	14	Su	05 00	21 12	11 51	23 22
196	15	M	05 01	21 11	13 02	23 47
197	16	Tu	05 02	21 10	14 14	** **
198	17	W	05 03	21 08	15 29	00 16
199	18	Th	05 04	21 07	16 42	00 52
200	19	F	05 06	21 06	17 51	01 35
201	20	Sa	05 07	21 05	18 52	02 32
202	21	Su	05 08	21 04	19 44	03 39
203	22	M	05 10	21 02	20 26	04 55
204	23	Tu	05 11	21 01	21 00	06 16
205	24	W	05 12	21 00	21 30	07 37
206	25	Th	05 14	20 58	21 56	08 57
207	26	F	05 15	20 57	22 10	10 14
208	27	Sa	05 17	20 55	22 45	11 28
209	28	Su	05 18	20 53	23 11	12 40
210	29	M	05 19	20 52	23 39	13 48
211	30	Tu	05 21	20 50	** **	14 52
212	31	W	05 22	20 49	00 11	15 53

AUGUST 2013 XXXI DAYS

HOLIDAYS: Summer — England & Wales 26th, Scotland 5th, Northern Ireland 26th

PHASES OF THE MOON

New Moon	6th	2151
First Quarter	14th	1056
Full Moon	21st	0145
Last Quarter	28th	0935

LIGHTING UP TIMES: BEGIN and END with SUNSET and SUNRISE times

Day of Year	Month	Week	Sun Rise h m	Sun Set h m	Moon Rise h m	Moon Set h m
213	1	Th	05 24	20 48	00 48	16 48
214	2	F	05 25	20 46	01 30	17 37
215	3	Sa	05 27	20 44	02 18	18 20
216	4	Su	05 29	20 43	03 14	18 57
217	5	M	05 30	20 41	04 14	19 29
218	6	Tu	05 32	20 39	05 15	19 56
219	7	W	05 33	20 37	06 20	20 21
220	8	Th	05 35	20 35	07 26	20 44
221	9	F	05 36	20 34	08 33	21 06
222	10	Sa	05 38	20 32	09 42	21 29
223	11	Su	05 39	20 30	10 52	21 53
224	12	M	05 41	20 28	12 03	22 21
225	13	Tu	05 43	20 26	13 14	22 53
226	14	W	05 44	20 24	14 22	23 33
227	15	Th	05 46	20 22	15 26	** **
228	16	F	05 47	20 20	16 38	00 22
229	17	Sa	05 49	20 18	17 33	01 22
230	18	Su	05 50	20 16	18 16	02 31
231	19	M	05 52	20 14	18 56	03 48
232	20	Tu	05 54	20 12	19 29	05 08
233	21	W	05 55	20 10	19 56	06 29
234	22	Th	05 57	20 08	20 21	07 48
235	23	F	05 58	20 06	20 47	09 05
236	24	Sa	06 00	20 04	21 13	10 19
237	25	Su	06 02	20 01	21 41	11 30
238	26	M	06 03	19 59	22 12	12 37
239	27	Tu	06 05	19 57	22 47	13 41
240	28	W	06 06	19 55	23 28	14 39
241	29	Th	06 08	19 53	** **	15 31
242	30	F	06 10	19 51	00 14	16 16
243	31	Sa	06 11	19 48	01 07	16 56

SEPTEMBER 2013 XXX DAYS

HOLIDAYS: Nil

PHASES OF THE MOON

New Moon	5th	1136
First Quarter	12th	1708
Full Moon	19th	1113
Last Quarter	22nd	0355

LIGHTING UP TIMES: BEGIN and END with SUNSET and SUNRISE times

Day of Year	Month	Week	Sun Rise h m	Sun Set h m	Moon Rise h m	Moon Set h m
244	1	Su	06 13	19 46	02 04	17 29
245	2	M	06 14	19 44	03 05	17 58
246	3	Tu	06 16	19 42	04 09	18 25
247	4	W	06 18	19 39	05 15	18 48
248	5	Th	06 19	19 37	06 22	19 11
249	6	F	06 21	19 35	07 31	19 35
250	7	Sa	06 22	19 33	08 41	19 59
251	8	Su	06 24	19 30	09 53	20 26
252	9	M	06 25	19 28	11 05	20 57
253	10	Tu	06 27	19 26	12 17	21 34
254	11	W	06 29	19 23	13 26	22 20
255	12	Th	06 30	19 21	14 30	23 15
256	13	F	06 32	19 19	15 26	** **
257	14	Sa	06 33	19 17	16 13	00 19
258	15	Su	06 35	19 14	16 52	01 30
259	16	M	06 37	19 12	17 26	02 47
260	17	Tu	06 38	19 10	17 55	04 05
261	18	W	06 40	19 07	18 21	05 23
262	19	Th	06 41	19 05	18 47	06 40
263	20	F	06 43	19 03	19 13	07 55
264	21	Sa	06 45	19 00	19 40	09 08
265	22	Su	06 46	18 58	20 10	10 18
266	23	M	06 48	18 56	20 45	11 25
267	24	Tu	06 49	18 54	21 24	12 26
268	25	W	06 51	18 51	22 08	13 21
269	26	Th	06 53	18 49	23 00	14 10
270	27	F	06 54	18 47	23 58	14 52
271	28	Sa	06 56	18 44	** **	15 27
272	29	Su	06 57	18 42	00 58	15 58
273	30	M	06 59	18 40	01 55	16 26

OCTOBER 2013 XXXI DAYS — HOLIDAYS: Nil

PHASES OF THE MOON

	Day of Month	
New Moon	5th	0035
First Quarter	11th	2302
Full Moon	18th	2338
Last Quarter	26th	2340

Day of Year	Day of Month	Day of Week	SUN Rise h m	SUN Set h m	MOON Rise h m	MOON Set h m	LIGHTING-UP TIMES
274	1	Tu	07 01	18 38	03 00	16 50	BEGIN and END with SUNSET and SUNRISE times
275	2	W	07 02	18 35	04 06	17 14	
276	3	Th	07 04	18 33	05 05	17 37	
277	4	F	07 06	18 31	06 26	18 02	
278	5	Sa	07 07	18 28	07 38	18 28	
279	6	Su	07 09	18 26	08 52	18 59	
280	7	M	07 11	18 24	10 05	19 35	
281	8	Tu	07 12	18 22	11 17	20 24	
282	9	W	07 14	18 20	12 23	21 08	
283	10	Th	07 16	18 17	13 22	22 12	
284	11	F	07 17	18 15	14 11	23 21	
285	12	Sa	07 19	18 13	14 52	** **	
286	13	Su	07 21	18 11	15 27	00 35	
287	14	M	07 22	18 09	15 56	01 50	
288	15	Tu	07 24	18 07	16 23	03 06	
289	16	W	07 26	18 04	16 48	04 22	
290	17	Th	07 27	18 02	17 13	05 36	
291	18	F	07 29	18 00	17 41	06 49	
292	19	Sa	07 31	17 58	18 09	07 59	
293	20	Su	07 33	17 56	18 41	09 08	
294	21	M	07 34	17 54	19 19	10 12	
295	22	Tu	07 36	17 52	20 01	11 10	
296	23	W	07 38	17 50	20 50	12 02	
297	24	Th	07 40	17 48	21 43	12 47	
298	25	F	07 41	17 46	22 41	13 25	
299	26	Sa	07 43	17 44	23 44	13 58	
300	27	Su	07 45	17 42	** **	14 26	
301	28	M	06 47	16 40	00 49	14 51	
302	29	Tu	06 48	16 38	01 56	15 13	
303	30	W	06 50	16 37	03 05	15 38	
304	31	Th	06 52	16 35	** **	15 02	

NOVEMBER 2013 XXX DAYS — HOLIDAYS: Nil

PHASES OF THE MOON

	Day of Month	
New Moon	3rd	1250
First Quarter	10th	0557
Full Moon	17th	1516
Last Quarter	25th	1928

Day of Year	Day of Month	Day of Week	SUN Rise h m	SUN Set h m	MOON Rise h m	MOON Set h m	LIGHTING-UP TIMES
305	1	F	06 54	16 33	04 16	15 27	BEGIN and END with SUNSET and SUNRISE times
306	2	Sa	06 55	16 31	05 30	15 56	
307	3	Su	06 57	16 29	06 45	16 30	
308	4	M	06 59	16 28	08 00	17 12	
309	5	Tu	07 01	16 26	09 11	18 02	
310	6	W	07 04	16 24	10 14	19 03	
311	7	Th	07 06	16 23	11 08	20 11	
312	8	F	07 06	16 21	11 56	21 25	
313	9	Sa	07 08	16 19	12 29	22 41	
314	10	Su	07 10	16 18	12 59	23 56	
315	11	M	07 11	16 16	13 27	** **	
316	12	Tu	07 13	16 15	13 53	01 10	
317	13	W	07 15	16 14	14 17	02 24	
318	14	Th	07 16	16 12	14 42	03 35	
319	15	F	07 18	16 11	15 10	04 46	
320	16	Sa	07 20	16 09	15 40	05 59	
321	17	Su	07 21	16 08	16 15	07 08	
322	18	M	07 23	16 07	16 58	08 08	
323	19	Tu	07 25	16 06	17 42	09 00	
324	20	W	07 26	16 04	18 33	09 54	
325	21	Th	07 28	16 03	19 29	10 42	
326	22	F	07 30	16 02	20 30	11 28	
327	23	Sa	07 31	16 01	21 34	12 11	
328	24	Su	07 33	16 00	22 38	12 54	
329	25	M	07 34	15 59	23 38	13 12	
330	26	Tu	07 36	15 58	** **	13 40	
331	27	W	07 37	15 57	00 45	14 03	
332	28	Th	07 39	15 57	01 53	14 13	
333	29	F	07 40	15 56	03 04	14 53	
334	30	Sa	07 42	15 55	04 18	14 24	

DECEMBER 2013 XXXI DAYS

HOLIDAYS: Christmas Day & Boxing Day — England & Wales; Scotland; Northern Ireland

PHASES OF THE MOON

	Day of Month	
New Moon	3rd	0022
First Quarter	9th	1512
Full Moon	17th	0928
Last Quarter	25th	1348

Day of Year	Day of Month	Day of Week	SUN Rise h m	SUN Set h m	MOON Rise h m	MOON Set h m	LIGHTING-UP TIMES
335	1	Su	07 43	15 55	05 33	15 01	BEGIN and END with SUNSET and SUNRISE times. 25th & 26th (×3)
336	2	M	07 45	15 54	06 47	15 48	
337	3	Tu	07 46	15 53	07 57	16 45	
338	4	W	07 47	15 53	08 58	17 52	
339	5	Th	07 49	15 52	09 48	19 07	
340	6	F	07 50	15 52	10 29	20 21	
341	7	Sa	07 51	15 52	11 03	21 32	
342	8	Su	07 52	15 52	11 32	22 43	
343	9	M	07 53	15 51	11 58	23 58	
344	10	Tu	07 54	15 51	12 23	** **	
345	11	W	07 55	15 51	12 48	01 26	
346	12	Th	07 56	15 51	13 14	02 36	
347	13	F	07 57	15 51	13 43	03 44	
348	14	Sa	07 58	15 51	14 15	04 50	
349	15	Su	07 59	15 51	14 53	05 51	
350	16	M	08 00	15 51	15 37	06 48	
351	17	Tu	08 01	15 52	16 26	07 38	
352	18	W	08 01	15 52	17 19	08 22	
353	19	Th	08 02	15 52	18 19	08 59	
354	20	F	08 03	15 53	19 22	09 31	
355	21	Sa	08 03	15 53	20 22	09 58	
356	22	Su	08 04	15 54	21 26	10 23	
357	23	M	08 04	15 54	22 36	10 45	
358	24	Tu	08 04	15 55	23 36	11 07	
359	25	W	08 05	15 56	** **	11 30	
360	26	Th	08 05	15 57	00 44	11 54	
361	27	F	08 05	15 57	01 54	12 21	
362	28	Sa	08 05	15 58	03 03	12 54	
363	29	Su	08 05	15 59	04 20	13 34	
364	30	M	08 06	16 00	05 31	14 24	
365	31	Tu	08 06	16 01	06 37	15 26	

ENGLAND AND WALES

HOME OFFICE

2 Marsham Street, London SW1P 4DF. Tel: 020 7035 4848.
Website: www.homeoffice.gov.uk

Home Secretary: Theresa May MP.
Minister for Immigration: Mark Harper MP.
Minister for Policing & Criminal Justice: Damian Green MP.
Minister for Crime Prevention: Jeremy Browne MP.
Security Minister: James Brokenshire MP.
Lords Minister & Minister for Criminal Information: Lord Taylor of Holbeach.
Permanent Secretary for the Home Office: Mark Sedwill.
Legal Adviser: David Seymour CB.
Chief Executive of the UK Border Agency: Rob Whiteman.
Chief Executive of the Identity & Passport Service: Sarah Rapson.
Director General Office for Security & Counter-terrorism: Charles Blandford Farr OBE.
Director General of the Crime & Policing Group: Stephen Rimmer.

CRIME & POLICING GROUP

2 Marsham Street, London SW1P 4DF. Tel: 020 7035 4848.

Director General: Stephen Rimmer. Tel: 020 7035 1439.
National Crime Agency Programme Director: Gareth Hills.
CRIME DIRECTORATE
Director, Crime: Jaee Samant. Tel: 020 7035 0443.
Senior Personal Secretary: Sonia O'Reilly. Tel: 020 7035 0413.

Heads of Units
Crime & Anti-social Behaviour Reduction Unit: Mike Warren. Tel: 020 7035 6517.
Violent & Youth Crime Prevention Unit: Mark Cooper. Tel: 020 7035 1827.
Drug & Alcohol Unit: Daniel Greaves. Tel: 020 7035 5315.
Reducing Reoffending Unit: Sally Richards. Tel: 020 7035 0518.
POLICING DIRECTORATE
Director, Policing: Emily Miles. Tel: 020 7035 8708.
Executive Assistant: Dino Besirevic. Tel: 020 7035 0190.

Heads of Units
Police Productivity Unit: Richard Pickering. Tel: 020 7035 1869.
Police Reform Unit: Ann-Marie Field. Tel: 020 7035 3128.
Public Order Unit: Sarah Severn CBE. Tel: 020 7035 1793.
Police Transparency Unit: Gareth Redmond. Tel: 020 7035 0897.
FINANCE & STRATEGY DIRECTORATE
A/Director, Finance & Strategy: Ziggy MacDonald. Tel: 020 7035 0396.
Senior Personal Secretary: Dina Maher. Tel: 020 7035 0590.

Heads of Units
Group Finance Unit: Ziggy MacDonald. Tel: 020 7035 0396.
Strategy, Skills & Planning Unit: Dee O'Connell. Tel: 020 7035 4861.
EMERGENCY SERVICES MOBILE COMMUNICATIONS PROGRAMME (ESMCP)
SRO/Interim Director, ESMCP: Stephen Webb. Tel: 020 7035 0591.
Senior Personal Secretary: Esther Aryeetey. Tel: 020 7035 0592.
Head Programme Management Office: Stephen Lyttleton. Tel: 07920 577058
Programme Support Officer: Gemma Trickey. Tel: 020 7035 3961.
Programme Management Office Administrator: Caroline Lockwood. Tel: 020 7035 3013.

CENTRE FOR APPLIED SCIENCE AND TECHNOLOGY (CAST)
Woodcock Hill, Sandridge, St Albans, Hertfordshire AL4 9HQ.
Tel: 01727 865051; 816400 (information service). Fax: 01727 816233.
Email: cast@homeoffice.gsi.gov.uk. Website: www.homeoffice.gov.uk
Langhurst House, Langhurstwood Road, Horsham, West Sussex RH12 4WX. Tel:
01403 213800. Fax: 01403 213827.

Other offices: Harperley Hall, Fir Tree, Crook, Co Durham DL15 8DS. Tel: 01388 744100. Fax: 01388 768016. Yew Tree Lane, Pannal Ash, Harrogate, North Yorkshire. Tel: 01423 876999. Fax 01423 876800. 2 Marsham Street, London SW1P 4DF. Tel: 020 3113 6000. 3 Leamington Road, Ryton-on-Dunsmore, Coventry CV8 3EN. Fax: 02476 639172.
Director: Rob Coleman. Tel: 01727 816299.
Staff Officer: Lynne Head. Tel: 01727 816336.
Diary Manager: Mandy Church. Tel: 01727 816261.
ASSISTANT DIRECTORS
Strategic Engagement: David Williams. Tel: 01727 815443.
Strategy & Plans: Mark Stroud. Tel: 01403 213816/01727 816339.
Operations: Michael Horner. Tel: 01403 213888.
Chief Technical Officer: Steve Barber. Tel: 01727 816350.
Transition Group: Shaun Mallinson. Tel: 01388 744002
CAPABILITY ADVISERS
Contraband Detection: Prof Dick Lacey. Tel: 01727 816330.
Crime Investigation: Neil Cohen. Tel: 01727 816321.
Crime Prevention & Community Safety: Colin Wilson. Tel: 01727 816271.
Identity Assurance & Senior Biometrics Adviser: Marek Rejman-Greene. Tel: 01727 816352.
Protective Security: David Spence. Tel: 01403 213860.
Public Order: Graham Smith. Tel: 01727 816332.
Surveillance: Chris Rampton. 01727 816224.
POLICE ADVISERS
Senior Police Adviser: Chief Supt Dave Wharton. Tel: 01727 816300.
Crime & Counter Terrorism: Det Supt Peter Fulham. Tel: 01727 816354
Uniformed Operations: Chief Insp Andy Mellows. Tel: 01727 816239.
CBRN & Operational Support: Chief Insp Malcolm Peattie. Tel: 01727 816282.
Previously known as the Home Office Scientific Development Branch, the Centre for Applied Science and Technology is a unique team of scientists and engineers providing expert advice, innovation and frontline support in the areas of policing and tackling crime, counter-terrorism, border security and controlling immigration. CAST is the primary science and technology interface between Home Office ministers and policy-makers, frontline partners such as the police, and suppliers of science and technology.

HOME OFFICE SCIENCE
Chief Scientific Advisor: Professor Bernard Silverman FRS.
PA: Christina Goodwin. Tel: 020 7035 3345.
This group is responsible for the conduct and management of social science research and statistics relevant to crime reduction and policing.
HOME OFFICE SCIENCE: CRIME AND POLICING ANALYSIS UNIT
Head of Unit: Amanda White. Tel: 020 7035 0261.
Programme Directors: Robert Street. Tel: 020 7035 0412. Andy Feist. Tel: 020 7035 1710.
HOME OFFICE STATISTICS
Chief Statistician & Head of Profession for Statistics: David Blunt. Tel: 020 7035 3402.
Programme Directors: **Crime:** Damon Wingfield. Tel: 020 7035 0277. **Policing:** Chris Kershaw. Tel: 020 7035 0275.

HM INSPECTORATE OF CONSTABULARY ENGLAND WALES AND NORTHERN IRELAND

HM Inspectorate of Constabulary, 6th Floor, Globe House, 89 Eccleston Square, London SW1V 1PN.
Tel: 020 3513 plus extension. Fax: 020 3513 0650.
Email: firstname.surname@hmic.gsi.gov.uk, unless otherwise shown.
Website: www.hmic.gov.uk

HM Chief Inspector of Constabulary: Thomas P Winsor.
Executive PA: Rebecca Robinson. Ext: 0503.
Private Secretary: Harriet Bradley. Ext: 0502.
HM Inspector of Constabulary Northern Region: Roger Baker QPM. Unit 2, Wakefield Office Village, Fryers Way, Silkwood Park, Wakefield, West Yorkshire WF5 9TJ. **Forces inspected:** Cheshire; Cleveland; Cumbria; Durham; Greater Manchester; Humberside; Lancashire; Merseyside; North Yorkshire; Northumbria; South Yorkshire; West Yorkshire. *Senior Personal Secretary:* Andrea Ryder. Tel: 01924 237722. Fax: 01924 237705. **General Office.** Tel: 01924 237700.
HM Inspector of Constabulary Eastern Region: Zoë Billingham. 6th Floor, Globe House, as above. **Forces inspected:** Bedfordshire; Cambridgeshire; Derbyshire; Essex; Hampshire; Hertfordshire; Kent; Leicestershire; Lincolnshire; Norfolk; Northamptonshire; Nottinghamshire; Suffolk; Surrey; Sussex; Thames Valley. *Senior Personal Secretary:* Val Protts. Ext: 0507.
HM Inspector of Constabulary National Team: Stephen Otter QPM. 6th Floor, Globe House, as above. **Forces inspected:** Metropolitan; City of London; Police Service of Northern Ireland; British Transport Police; Civil Nuclear Constabulary; MOD Police and Guarding Agency; HM Revenue & Customs; Serious Organised Crime Agency. Undertaking national responsibilities and other force inspections otherwise unallocated. *Personal Assistant:* Rhys Cullen. Ext: 0506.
HM Inspector of Constabulary Wales and the Western Region: Dru Sharpling CBE. 4th Floor, 5 St Philips Place, Colmore Row, Birmingham, B3 2PW Email: drusilla.sharpling@hmic.gsi.gov.uk. **Forces inspected:** Avon and Somerset; Devon and Cornwall; Dorset; Dyfed-Powys; Gloucestershire; Gwent; North Wales; South Wales; Staffordshire; Warwickshire; West Mercia; West Midlands; Wiltshire. *Senior Personal Secretary:* Karen Aslett. Tel: 0303 444 4702. **General Office.** Tel: 0303 444 4700. Fax: 020 3513 0650.

HM Assistant Inspectors of Constabulary: Vacant. Ext: 0515/6.
A/HM Assistant Inspector of Constabulary Western Region: Steve Blake. Ext: 0513. Email: steve.blake4@hmic.gsi.gov.uk

Chief Operating Officer: Steve Blake. Ext: 0513. Email: steve.blake4@hmic.gsi.gov.uk
Personal Secretary: Geraldine Bradley. Ext: 0505.
Head of Analysis & Performance: Lawrence Morris. Ext: 0517.
Executive PA: Yvonne Henry. Ext: 0617.
Head of HR: Nick White. Ext: 0618.
HR Manager: Kate Gregory. Ext: 0547. Email: katherine.gregory@hmic.gsi.gov.uk
HR Support: Delores Stratton. Ext: 0594. Katherine Hagestadt. Ext: 0548. Jayashree Chellappa. Ext: 0532. Sangita Shah. Ext: 0586.
HR enquiries. Ext: 0500.
Finance Manager: Mark Tooze ACMA CGMA. Ext: 0565.
Finance Officer: Debbie Jamieson. Ext: 0621. Email: debbie.jamieson1@hmic.gsi.gov.uk
Finance enquiries. Ext: 0621.
Deputy Chief Operating Officer: Katherine Savage. Ext: 0604.
Press Manager: Ruth Allman. Ext: 0603.
Press Officer: Phil Gillen. Ext: 0601.
Press Office. Ext: 0600. Email: hmicpressoffice@hmic.gsi.gov.uk

THE SERIOUS ORGANISED CRIME AGENCY (SOCA)

PO Box 8000, London SE11 5EN.
Tel: 0370 496 7622 (24 hrs).
Website: www.soca.gov.uk

Chair: Sir Ian Andrews CBE TD.
Director General: Trevor Pearce QPM.
Director Capability & Service Delivery: Malcolm Cornberg OBE.
Director Strategy & Prevention: Gerry Liddell.
Director Operational Delivery: Brad Jones.
SARS Helpdesk. Tel: 020 7238 8282.
Recruitment Team. Tel: 0117 372 0000.
Media Enquiries. Tel: 0870 268 8100.
SOCA International & Interpol UK National Central Bureau (NCB–24 hrs). Tel: 020 7238 8115.
SOCA tackles serious organised crime affecting the United Kingdom and its citizens and is the custodian of a large range of national and international capabilities. SOCA works to priorities set by the Home Secretary which currently includes Class A drugs, people smuggling and human trafficking, major gun crime, fraud, cyber crime and money laundering. SOCA works to bring serious criminals to justice and uses many other tactics to disrupt crime – to ensure it doesn't pay and to make it harder to commit.

SERIOUS FRAUD OFFICE

Elm House, 10–16 Elm Street, London WC1X OBJ.
Tel: 020 7239 7272 (switchboard and enquiries); 020 7239 plus extension (direct lines). Fax: 020 7278 5721.

Director: David Green CB. Tel: 020 7239 7101. Fax: 020 7833 5479.
Chief Operating Officer: Chris Bailes. Tel: 020 7239 73855.
General Counsel: Alun Milford. Tel: 020 7239 7051. Fax: 020 7833 5479.
Special Adviser: His Hon Geoffrey Rivlin QC. Tel: 020 7239 4585. Fax: 020 7833 5479.
Head of Policy & Strategic Relations: Kristin Jones. Tel: 020 7239 7474.
Heads of Bribery & Corruption Divisions: Matthew Wagstaff. Tel: 020 7239 7061. Patrick Rappo. Tel: 020 7239 7475.
Heads of Fraud Divisions: Jane de Lozey. Tel: 020 7239 7386. Clare Whitaker. Tel: 020 7239 7391.
Chief Investigator: Kevin Davis. Tel: 020 7239 7188.
Head of External Communications: David Jones. Tel: 020 7239 7001.

NATIONAL DOMESTIC EXTREMISM UNIT (NDEU)

PO Box 61701, London SW1H 0XN.
Tel: 020 3276 1616. Fax: 020 7084 8577.
Email: so15mailbox-ndeu@met.police.uk

The National Domestic Extremism Unit (NDEU), a dedicated unit within the Metropolitan Police, is the sole UK collection, assessment and dissemination agency for intelligence in relation to domestic extremism. It works to support UK police in tackling domestic extremism across England, Scotland, Wales and Northern Ireland. Forces and regional officers pass intelligence on domestic extremism and strategic public order to the NDEU, which assesses and collates intelligence at a national level to produce UK-wide strategic assessments for a range of partners including police, businesses and government.

ACPO CRIMINAL RECORDS OFFICE

PO Box 481, Fareham, Hampshire PO14 9FS.
Tel: 01489 569800.
Email: enquiries@acro.pnn.police.uk
Individual email: firstname.lastname@acro.pnn.police.uk

ACPO Director of Information: Ian Readhead. Tel: 023 8074 5143.
Head of ACRO: Supt Philip Winchester. Tel: 01489 569804.
Senior Management Team: Michael McMullen. Tel: 01489 569811. Nicholas Apps. Tel: 01489 569844. David McKinney. Tel: 01489 569834. Andrea Jackson. Tel: 01489 569800.
Finance Advisor: Susan Francis. Tel: 01489 569841.

Media & Communications Officer: Lindsey Eudo-Mitchell. Tel: 023 8074 4635.
International Criminal Conviction Exchange (ICCE) (including the UK Central Authority for the Exchange of Criminal Records (UKCA-ECR). Tel: 01489 569805. Email: ukca@acro.pnn.police.uk
The ACPO Criminal Records Office (ACRO) provides operational support and guidance to the police service concerning legislation and policy on matters relating to criminal records held on the police national computer (PNC) and associated biometric data. ACRO also manages the International Criminal Conviction Exchange (ICCE). This portfolio includes the UK Central Authority for the Exchange of Criminal Records (UKCA-ECR), which facilitates the exchange of criminal conviction information with other EU member states.

NATIONAL POLICING IMPROVEMENT AGENCY (NPIA)

Fry Building, 2 Marsham Street, London SW1P 4DF.
Tel: 0800 496 3322; (from outside the UK) +44(0) 1423 876817.
Email: enquiries@npia.pnn.police.uk
Website: www.npia.police.uk

Chairman: Chris Hughes CBE.
Board: Chief Chief Constable Jim Barker-McCardle QPM; Mark Castle OBE; Stephen Webb.
Chief Executive: Michael Romberg.
Subject to legislation, the NPIA is to be abolished when the new National Crime Agency is set up, planned to be by the end of 2013, and a small team remains to manage the final closedown. It has transferred all but one of its functions to its successor bodies (the Home Office, College of Policing and Serious Organised Crime Agency), but retains responsibility for the accreditation and training of financial investigators, carried out by the Proceeds of Crime Centre hosted by SOCA on the NPIA's behalf.

POLICE NATIONAL CBRN CENTRE

College of Policing, Leamington Road, Ryton-on-Dunsmore, Coventry CV8 3EN.
Tel: 02476 516333. Fax: 02476 826146.
Email: firstname.lastname-cbrn@npia.pnn.police.uk
Website (accessible only via the PNN network): https://polka.pnn.police.uk
Head of Centre: **Supt Paul Granger. Tel: 02476 516228.**

Capabilities Lead: Chief Insp Ian Stubbs. Tel: 02476 516276.
Operations, Communications & Exercising: Chief Insp Patricia Foy. Tel: 02476 516359.
Head of Training: Chief Insp Nigel Tottie. Tel: 02476 516385.
Business Manager: David Edwards. Tel: 02476 825962.
Operations Centre. 24-hour hotline tel: 08450 006382. Email: cbrnopscentre@npia.pnn.police.uk
Administration. Tel: 02476 516333. Email: cbrnadmin@npia.pnn.police.uk
The Police National CBRN Centre is committed to meeting the threat of CBRN terrorism. It will achieve this through the delivery of comprehensive doctrine and tactics in a nationally recognised format; professionally designed and delivered training, sound procurement, and the effective co-ordination of national assets. The centre also provides advice and guidance on CBRN operational matters through the PN CBRN Operations Centre.

THE COLLEGE OF POLICING

Tel: 0800 496 3322. Media enquiries: 020 3113 7241; (out of hours) 07827 309361.
Email: contactus@college.pnn.police.uk Twitter: @CollegeofPolice
Website: www.college.police.uk

Chief Executive: Chief Constable Alex Marshall.
PA: Catriona Lang. Tel: 020 3113 7211.
Staff Officer: Stephanie Dormer. Tel: 020 3113 7073.
Service Director: David Peacock.
PA: Gill Baker. Tel: 020 3113 7960.
Build Director: David Horne.
PA: Catriona Lang. Tel: 020 3113 7211.

Launched in February 2013 as the professional body for policing, the College of Policing will set high professional standards to assist forces in cutting crime and protecting the public. It will work to equip all who work in policing with the tools, skills and knowledge they need to succeed. The College's intention is to replace bureaucracy and unnecessary policies in policing with practical, common sense approaches based on the evidence of what works. Registered company number 8235199, VAT registered number 152023949. Registered office: College of Policing Limited, Leamington Road, Ryton-on-Dunsmore, Coventry CV8 3EN.

THE POLICE ICT COMPANY LTD

Police ICT Company Directorate (PCD), Home Office, 2 Marsham Street, London SW1P 4DF. Tel: 020 7035 4848.

Email: policeictcompany@homeoffice.gsi.gov.uk

Website: www.gov.uk/home-office

As part of the coalition government's police reform agenda, announced in July 2010, The Police ICT Company Ltd was incorporated on 20 June 2012 as a company limited by guarantee. The Company will: deliver better value for forces in their ICT spend; stimulate innovation, providing officers and staff with the best technologies; free chief officers from in-depth involvement in ICT management; deliver services and products that support interoperability. Registered address: 10 Dean Farrar Street, London SW1H 0NY.

The Police ICT Company Directorate
The directorate has been set up to support development of the new company and deliver ICT procurement, implementation and management services to police forces and other law enforcement agencies in support of policing outcomes.

A/Director: Jennie Cronin.
Executive Assistant to the Director: Jen Parr. Tel: 020 7035 3311.
Chief of Staff: Tracey Eaton. Tel: 020 7035 3548.
Head of Ownership & Governance: Alan Bucknall.
Head of Company Build & Ownership: Vacant.
Head of Organisational Design: Keith Lambert.
Head of Projects & Services: Andrew Goodman.
Head of Police Commercial & Procurement: Ian Currie.

REGIONAL ASSET RECOVERY TEAMS (RARTS)

The RARTs are multi-agency units staffed by investigators from regional police forces and HM Revenue and Customs. A CPS lawyer is attached to each team. The principal role of the RARTs is to conduct criminal confiscation investigations and criminal money-laundering investigations in support of drug-trafficking investigations at NIM Levels 2 & 3 and to conduct investigations into serious and organised crime by law enforcement agencies in their regions.

RART NATIONAL CO-ORDINATOR'S OFFICE
ACPO Financial Investigation & Proceeds of Crime Portfolio, Derbyshire Constabulary Q, Butterley Hall, Ripley, Derbyshire DE5 3RS. Tel: 01773 572279.
SRO: Chief Constable Mick Creedon.
National Co-ordinator: Det Supt Ian Davidson. Email: ian.davidson.1242@derbyshire.pnn.police.uk
Support: John Dayman. Email: john.dayman.3719@derbyshire.pnn.police.uk
PA: Rachel Watson. Email: rachel.watson.3803@derbyshire.pnn.police.uk
EASTERN RART
Hertfordshire Police HQ, Stanborough Road, Welwyn Garden City AL8 6XF. Fax: 01438 757979.
Head: Det Chief Insp Andrew Theakston. Tel: 01438 757947.
   Email: andrew.theakston@herts.pnn.police.uk
Deputy Head & Operational Team Leader: Det Insp Liz Fernandes. Tel: 01438 757983.
   Email: liz.fernandes@herts.pnn.police.uk
Team Leaders: Financial Investigation Manager: Chris Saunders. Tel: 01438 757984.
   Email: christopher.saunders@herts.pnn.police.uk. Det Sgt Emma Harwood. Tel: 01438 757943.
   Email: emma.harwood@herts.pnn.police.uk
CPS Lawyer: Vacant.
HMRC: Warren Mitchell. Tel: 01733 866167. Email: warren.mitchell@hmrc.gsi.gov.uk
EAST MIDLANDS RART
PO Box 9557, Nottingham NG15 5BU. Fax: 01623 608167.
Head: Det Chief Insp Mick Beattie. Tel: 01623 608160.
   Email: michael.beattie@leicestershire.pnn.police.uk
Deputy Head & Operational Team Leader: Det Insp Nick Allwood. Tel: 01623 608161.
   Email: nicholas.allwood@leicestershire.pnn.police.uk

Team Leaders: Det Sgt Pete Sihota. Tel: 01623 608239.
  Email: peter.sihota@leicestershire.pnn.police.uk. Vacant.
CPS Lawyer: Sonia Gilhespy. Tel: 01623 608210. Email: sonia.gilhespy@cps.pnn.police.uk
HMRC: Kelvin Frost. Tel: 01623 608039. Email: kelvin.frost@leicestershire.pnn.police.uk

LONDON RART
Victoria Block, New Scotland Yard, Broadway, London SW1H 0BG. Fax: 020 7230 2770.
Head: Det Chief Insp Simon Welch. Tel: 020 7230 2065. Email: simon.welch@met.police.uk
Deputy Head & Operational Team Leader: Det Insp Andrew Mahoney. Tel: 020 7230 6932.
  Email: andrew.mahoney@met.police.uk
Team Leaders: Det Sgt Jim Shingler. Tel: 020 7230 1385. Email: jim.shingler@met.police.uk.
  Det Sgt Pete Ward. Tel: 020 7230 4387. Email: pete.ward@met.police.uk

NORTH EAST RART
PO Box 229, Leeds LS15 8GX. Fax: 0113 260 8760.
Head: Vacant.
Deputy Head & Operational Team Leader: Det Insp Andrew Eaton. Tel: 0113 260 9551.
  Email: andrew.eaton@westyorkshire.pnn.police.uk
Team Leaders: Heather Forrest. Tel: 0113 260 5535.
  Email: heather.forrest@westyorkshire.pnn.police.uk. Det Sgt Tommy Maughan. Tel: 0191 375 2634.
  Email: thomas.maughan@durham.pnn.police.uk
CPS Lawyer: Mr David Mattan. Tel: 0113 260 7554.
  Email: david.mattan@westyorkshire.pnn.police.uk
HMRC: Warren Mitchell. Tel: 0113 260 7398. Email: warren.mitchell@westyorkshire.pnn.police.uk

NORTH WEST RART
Lancashire Constabulary Headquarters, PO Box 77, Hutton, Preston PR4 5SB. Fax: 0151 777 7649.
Head: Vacant.
Deputy Head & Operational Team Leader: Det Insp Tim Dean. Tel: 0151 777 7640.
  Email: tim.dean@merseyside.pnn.police.uk
Team Leaders: Det Sgt Mark Unsworth. Tel: 0151 777 7636.
  Email: mark.unsworth@merseyside.pnn.police.uk. Det Sgt Alison Cooke. Tel: 0151 777 7641.
  Email: alison.cooke@merseyside.pnn.police.uk
CPS Lawyer: Ms Tracey Ames. Tel: 0151 777 7625. Email: tracey.ames@merseyside.pnn.police.uk

SOUTH EAST RART
Criminal Finances Team (SE RART), Top Floor, Horsham Police Station, Hurst Road, Horsham,
  West Sussex RH12 2DJ. Tel: 01273 470101. Fax: 01293 583379.
Head: Det Chief Insp Paul Furnell. Mob: 07876 137224. Email: paul.furnell@sussex.pnn.police.uk
Deputy Head & Operational Team Leader: Det Insp Simon Harsley. Ext: 30506.
  Email: simon.harsley@sussex.pnn.police.uk
Team Leaders: Det Sgt Dennis Phelan. Ext: 30384. Email: dennis.phelan@sussex.pnn.police.uk.
  Det Sgt Ian Ball. Ext: 30371. Email: ian.ball@sussex.pnn.police.uk
CPS Lawyer: Viv Pearson. Mob: 07795 486229. Email: vivienne.pearson@sussex.pnn.police.uk

SOUTH WEST RART
PO Box 169, Bristol BS20 1AJ. Fax: 01275 841749.
Head: Det Chief Insp Will White. Tel: 01275 841706.
  Email: will.white@avonandsomerset.pnn.police.uk
Deputy Head & Operational Team Leader: Det Insp Tony Hubbard. Tel: 01275 841753.
  Email: tony.hubbard@avonandsomerset.pnn.police.uk
Team Leaders: Det Sgt Ian Tyers. Tel: 01275 841735.
  Email: ian.tyers@avonandsomerset.pnn.police.uk. Det Sgt Matt Piggot. Tel: 01275 841734.
  Email: matt.piggot@avonandsomerset.pnn.police.uk
CPS Lawyer: Philip Tew. Tel: 01275 841736. Email: philip.tew@avonandsomerset.pnn.police.uk
HMRC: Craig Carscadden. Tel: 01275 841751.
  Email: craig.carscadden@avonandsomerset.pnn.police.uk

WALES RART
South Wales Police HQ, Cowbridge Road, Bridgend CF31 3SU. Fax: 01656 305834.
Head: Det Chief Insp Lian Penhale. Tel: 01656 310101.
  Email: lian.penhale@south-wales.pnn.police.uk
Deputy Head & Operational Team Leader. Mr Stuart Slyman (HMRC). Tel: 01656 310102.
  Email: stuart.slyman@south-wales.pnn.police.uk
Team Leaders: Det Sgt Barry McGregor. Tel: 01656 310104.
  Email: barry.mcgregor@south-wales.pnn.police.uk. Det Sgt Richie O'Neill. Tel: 01656 310215.
CPS Lawyer: Mr Norman (Brin) Hurford. Tel: 01656 310112.
  Email: brinley.hurford@south-wales.pnn.police.uk

WEST MIDLANDS RART
Aqua House, Lionel Street, Birmingham B3 1AQ. Fax: 0121 251 2182.
Head: Det Chief Insp Pete Murphy. Tel: 0121 251 2049.
    Email: p.murphy@west-midlands.pnn.police.uk
Deputy Head & Operational Team Leader: Det Insp Chris Berrow. Tel: 0121 251 2091.
    Email: c.berrow@west-midlands.pnn.police.uk
Team Leaders: Det Sgt Chris Bates. Tel: 0121 251 2062.
    Email: chris.bates@west-midlands.pnn.police.uk Det Sgt Dave Treacy. Tel: 0121 251 2067.
    Email: d.treacy@west-midlands.pnn.police.uk
CPS Lawyer: Don Knapper. Tel: 0121 251 2114. Email: don.knapper@west-midlands.pnn.police.uk
HMRC: Kelvin Frost. Tel: 0121 251 2049. Email: kelvin.frost@west-midlands.pnn.police.uk

NATIONAL VIPER BUREAU

(Video Identification Parades Electronic Recording)
PO Box 9, Laburnum Road, Wakefield WF1 3QP.
Tel: 01924 821330. Fax: 01924 821399.
Email: viper@westyorkshire.pnn.police.uk.
Email individuals: firstname.lastname@westyorkshire.pnn.police.uk.
Website: www.viper.police.uk

Bureau Manager: Wayne Collins. Tel: 01924 281354.
Service Capability Manager: Lindsey Jeffs. Tel: 01924 821360.
Service Support Manager: Steven Kenwright. Tel. 01924 821365.
Service Delivery Manager: Cliff Barr. Tel: 01924 821369.
Customer Service Manager: Joanne Bedingfield. Tel: 01924 821355.
Business Change Manager: Darran Joynson. Tel: 01924 821323.
Finance & Administration. Anita Haynes. Tel: 01924 821353.
Operational Enquiries. Tel: 01924 821330 (24 hours).
The National VIPER Bureau, owned and operated by West Yorkshire Police, supplies a managed video identification parade service to police forces throughout the UK via the PNN. VIPER specialises in applying advanced video editing techniques to obscure or replicate identifiable features in compliance with legislation. The managed service includes a fully supported IT infrastructure, training and development for users, and a dedicated team to maintain and enhance the volunteer database.

POLICE NATIONAL LEGAL DATABASE (PNLD)

Bishopgarth, Westfield Road, Wakefield WF1 3QZ.
Tel: 01924 208229.
Email: pnld@westyorkshire.pnn.police.uk
Websites: www.pnld.co.uk (for internet PNLD subscriptions); www.askthe.police.uk (frequently asked questions database); www.pnsd.co.uk (statistics database).

Chair: Assistant Chief Constable John Parkinson.
Head of Department: Nigel P Hughes.
PNLD Manager: Robin Green.
PNLD provides three databases for all the forces and the public, covering up-to-date law and procedure; answers to the public's most frequently asked questions about policing matters; and the role of Police and Crime Commissioners. A fourth database containing statistical information for analysts and performance managers is restricted to police forces.

UNITED KINGDOM BORDER AGENCY (UKBA)
Website: www.ukba.homeoffice.gov.uk

Chief Executive of the UK Border Agency: Rob Whiteman.

CRIME DIRECTORATE
Head of Crime Directorate: David Pennant. Peel Building, 2 Marsham Street, London SW1P 4DF. Tel: 020 7035 4515.

Deputy Director: Tony Erne. Mob: 07919 166557. Email: tony.erne2@homeoffice.gsi.gov.uk Out of hours tel: 07920 751493 (24/7).

Seconded Police HR Support. Tel: 020 8603/8125. Email: cfi.immigrationpolicehr@homeoffice.gsi.gov.uk

REGIONAL MANAGERS
London & South East Regions: *Assistant Director:* Rob Allen. Bedford Point, 34–35 Dingwall Road, Croydon CR9 2EF. Tel: 020 8603 8140.

North East & North West Regions: *A/Assistant Director:* David Magrath. Brookland House, Salford, Vere Street, Manchester M50 2GQ.

Scotland & Northern Ireland, Wales & South West and Midlands & Eastern Regions: A/Det Chief Supt Chris Foster. 2 Marsham Street, London SW1P 4DF. Mob: 07881 858275.

SPECIALIST TEAMS
Assistant Director: Dave Fairclough. Becket House, 60–68 St Thomas Street, London SE1 3QU. Tel: 020 3513 8413.

LONDON
HM Inspector: Hannah Shirley. Becket House, as above. Tel: 020 3513 8200. Email: cfiimmlondon@homeoffice.gsi.gov.uk

Professional Support to HM Inspector: A/Chief Insp Doug Rushworth. Becket House, as above. Tel: 020 3513 8434. **London North & East:** Det Insp Simon Prankard. Becket House, as above. Tel: 020 3513 8434. **London West:** Det Insp Andrew Shortland. Eaton House, Hounslow, Middlesex TW4 5DL. Tel: 020 8814 5122. **London South:** Det Insp (Vacant). Electric House, Croydon CR0 2AG. Tel: 020 8603 8648.

SOUTH EAST
HM Inspector: Mark Rickard. NPIA Bramshill, Hook, Hampshire RG27 0JW. Tel: 01256 730600. Email: cfiimmse@homeoffice.gsi.gov.uk

Professional support to HM Inspector: Det Insp Andrew Cummins. Ashdown House, South Terminal, Gatwick Airport RH6 0LX. Tel: 01293 501726.

WALES & SOUTH WEST
HM Inspector: Nick Jupp. Portishead Office Park, Conference Avenue, Bristol BS20 7LZ. Tel: 01275 841566. Email: cfiimmigration43@homeoffice.gsi.gov.uk
Professional support to HM Inspector: Vacant.

MIDLANDS & EAST OF ENGLAND
HM Inspector: Andy Radcliffe. Pembroke House, Castle Donington, Derby DE74 2TZ, Tel: 01332 442205. Email: cfiimmmidandeast@homeoffice.gsi.gov.uk

Professional support to HM Inspector: East Midlands: Det Insp Barry Gardner. Pembroke House, as above. Tel: 01332 442157. **West Midlands:** Det Insp Richard Meaden. Sandford House, Solihull B91 3QJ. Tel: 0121 713 3355.

NORTH WEST
A/HM Inspector: Nick Wood. Brookland House, Salford, Vere Street, Manchester M50 2GQ. Tel: 0161 880 5764. Email: nwimmigrationcrimeteam@homeoffice.gsi.gov.uk

Professional support to HM Inspector: Det Insp Paul Roche. Brookland House, as above. Tel: 0161 880 5760.

NORTH EAST, YORKSHIRE & THE HUMBER
HM Inspector: Janet Griffiths. PO Box 3468, Sheffield S3 8WA. Tel: 0114 297 1386. Email: cfiimmigrationnortheast@homeoffice.gsi.gov.uk

Professional support to HM Inspector: Tyne Tees: Det Insp Paul Foggin. PO Box 3468, as above. Tel: 0191 375 2630. **South Yorkshire:** Det Insp Mark Bates. PO Box 3468, as above. Tel: 0114 296 1391. **West Yorkshire:** Det Insp Adrian Watkins. PO Box 3468, as above. Tel: 01274 471 441.

SCOTLAND & NORTHERN IRELAND
HM Inspector: Carolyne Wallace. Festival Court, 200 Brand Street, Govan, Glasgow G51 1DH. Tel: 0141 555 1462. Email: cfiimmscotandni@homeoffice.gsi.gov.uk

Professional support to HM Inspector: Det Insp (Vacant). Festival Court, as above. Tel: 0141 555 1449.

IMMIGRATION ENQUIRIES
UKBA Command & Control Unit. Tel: 0161 261 1640 (24 hrs). Under no circumstances should CCU contact details be given to the public.

OFFICE OF THE IMMIGRATION SERVICES COMMISSIONER (OISC)

5th Floor, Counting House, 53 Tooley Street, London SE1 2QN.
Tel: 0845 000 0046. Fax: 020 7211 1553.

Website: http://oisc.homeoffice.gov.uk

Immigration Services Commissioner: Suzanne McCarthy. Tel: 020 7211 1525.
Deputy Immigration Services Commissioner: Dr Ian Leigh.
Director of Operations: Stephen Seymour. Tel: 020 7211 1638.
The OISC is responsible for regulating immigration advisers in the United Kingdom, investigating complaints about immigration advisers and others giving immigration advice or services, and undertaking criminal prosecutions against those giving immigration advice or services when not legally authorised to do so.

CROWN PROSECUTION SERVICE (CPS)

The Crown Prosecution Service is responsible for prosecuting cases investigated by the police in England and Wales (with the exception of cases conducted by the Serious Fraud Office and certain minor offences). The Director of Public Prosecutions is the head of the CPS and discharges his statutory functions under the superintendence of the Attorney General. The CPS comprises headquarters offices in London and York and 13 areas covering England and Wales, corresponding to each police force in England and Wales outside London and one for London. Each of the areas is led by a chief crown prosecutor supported by an area business manager.

CPS HEADQUARTERS
Rose Court, 2 Southward Bridge, London SE1 9HS.
Tel: 020 3357 0000. DX: 154263 Southwark 12.
Email: enquiries@cps.gsi.gov.uk
Website: www.cps.gov.uk
Director of Public Prosecutions (SCS): Keir Starmer QC.
Chief Executive (SCS): Peter Lewis.

CPS DIRECT
6th Floor, United House, Piccadilly, York YO1 9PQ.
Tel: 01904 545400. Fax: 01904 545698. DX: 65204 York 6.
Website: www.cps.gov.uk/direct
Deputy Chief Crown Prosecutor: Peter Swain.
Area Business Manager: Delphine Horner.

CPS AREAS

CPS EAST MIDLANDS
www.cps.gov.uk/eastmidlands
Chief Crown Prosecutor for CPS East Midlands: Judith Walker. *Area Business Manager:* Adele Clarke. 2 King Edward Court, King Edward Street, Nottingham NG1 1EL. Tel: 0115 852 3300. Fax: 0115 853 3314. DX: 729100 NOTTINGHAM 48.
Deputy Chief Crown Prosecutor for CPS East Midlands (North): Steve Chappell. 2 King Edward Court, King Edward Street, Nottingham NG1 1EL. Tel: 0115 852 3340. DX: 729100 NOTTINGHAM 48.
Deputy Chief Crown Prosecutor for CPS East Midlands (South): Richard Crowley. Princes Court, 34 York Road, Leicester LE1 5TU. Tel: 0116 204 6700. Fax: 0116 204 6799. DX: 10899 LEICESTER 1.

CPS EASTERN
www.cps.gov.uk/eastern
Chief Crown Prosecutor for CPS Eastern: Ken Caley. *Area Business Manager:* Susan Stovell. County House, 100 New London Road, Chelmsford, Essex CM2 0RG. Tel: 01245 455800. Fax: 01245 455964. DX: 139160 CHELMSFORD 11.
Deputy Chief Crown Prosecutor for CPS Eastern: Andrew Baxter. Carmelite House, St James' Court, White Friars, Norwich NR3 1SL. Tel: 01603 693000. Fax: 01603 693001. DX: 5299 NORWICH.
Deputy Chief Crown Prosecutor for CPS Eastern: Paula Abrahams. St Vincent's House, 9th Floor, 1 Cutler Street, Ipswich IP1 1UL. Tel: 01473 282100. Fax: 01473 282101. DX: 3266 IPSWICH.

CPS LONDON
www.cps.gov.uk/london
Chief Crown Prosecutor: Alison Saunders CB. *Deputy Chief Crown Prosecutors:* David Robinson; Grace Ononiwu; Jenny Hopkins. *Area Business Manager:* Jean Ashton. CPS London, 5th Floor, Rose Court, 2 Southwark Bridge, London SE1 9HS. Tel: 020 3357 0000. DX: 154263 SOUTHWARK 12.

CPS MERSEY/CHESHIRE
www.cps.gov.uk/mersey-cheshire
Chief Crown Prosecutor for CPS Mersey/Cheshire: Paul Whittaker. *Area Business Manager:* Angela Walsh. 7th Floor, Royal Liver Building, Pier Head, Liverpool L3 1HN. Tel: 0151 239 6400. Fax: 0151 239 6420. DX: 700596 LIVERPOOL 4.
Deputy Chief Crown Prosecutor for CPS Cheshire: Claire Lindley. 2nd Floor, Windsor House, Pepper Street, Chester CH1 1TD. Tel: 01244 408600. Fax: 01244 408657. DX: 20019 CHESTER.

CPS NORTH EAST
www.cps.gov.uk/northeast
Chief Crown Prosecutor for CPS North East: Wendy Williams. *Area Business Manager:* Ian Brown. St Ann's Quay, 122 Quayside, Newcastle-upon-Tyne NE1 3BD. Tel: 0191 260 4200. Fax: 0191 260 4240. DX: 61006 NEWCASTLE-UPON-TYNE.
Deputy Chief Crown Prosecutor for CPS North East: Chris Enzor. Elvet House, Hallgarth Street, Durham DH1 3AT. Tel: 0191 383 5800. Fax: 0191 383 5801. DX: 60227 DURHAM.

CPS NORTH WEST
www.cps.gov.uk/northwest

Chief Crown Prosecutor for CPS North West: Nazir Afzal. *Area Business Manager:* Louise Rice. PO Box 237, 8th Floor, Sunlight House, Quay Street, Manchester M60 3PS. Tel: 0161 827 4700. Fax: 0161 827 4931. DX: 744372 MANCHESTER 53.

Deputy Chief Crown Prosecutor for CPS North West: Christopher Long. 1st Floor, Stocklund House, Castle Street, Carlisle CA3 8SY. Tel: 01228 882900. Fax: 01228 882910. DX: 744700 CARLISLE 33.

Deputy Chief Crown Prosecutor for CPS North West: Ian Rushton. 2nd Floor Podium, The Unicentre, Lords Walk, Preston PR1 1DH. Tel: 01772 208100. Fax: 01772 208144. DX: 723740 PRESTON 20.

CPS SOUTH EAST

www.cps.gov.uk/southeast

Chief Crown Prosecutor for CPS South East: Roger Coe-Salazar. *Area Business Manager:* Julie Heron.. Priory Gate, 29 Union Street, Maidstone ME14 1PT. Tel: 01622 356300. Fax: 01622 356700. DX: 4830 MAIDSTONE.

Riding Gate House, 37 Old Dover Road, Canterbury CT1 3JG. Tel: 01227 866000. Fax: 01227 866001.

Deputy Chief Crown Prosecutor for CPS South East: Portia Ragnauth. Gateway, Power Close, Guildford GU1 1EJ. Tel: 01483 468200. Fax: 01483 468282. DX: 122041 GUILDFORD 10.

Deputy Chief Crown Prosecutor for CPS South East: Jaswant Narwal. City Gate, 185 Dyke Road, Brighton BN3 1TL. Tel: 01273 765600. Fax: 01273 765606. DX: 149840 HOVE 6.

CPS SOUTH WEST

www.cps.gov.uk/southwest

Chief Crown Prosecutor for CPS South West: Barry Hughes. *Area Business Manager:* Sarah Trevelyan. 2nd Floor, Froomsgate House, Rupert Street, Bristol BS1 2QJ. Tel: 0117 930 2800. Fax: 0117 930 2810. DX: 78120 BRISTOL.

Deputy Chief Crown Prosecutor for CPS South West: Tracy Easton. Hawkins House, Pynes Hill, Rydon Lane, Exeter EX2 5SS. Tel: 01392 288000. Fax: 01392 288008. DX: 135606 EXETER 16.

Deputy Chief Crown Prosecutor for CPS South West: Victoria Cook. 2 Kimbrose Way, Gloucester GL1 2DB. Tel: 01452 872400. Fax: 01452 872406. DX: 7544 GLOUCESTER.

CPS THAMES & CHILTERN

www.cps.gov.uk/thames_chiltern

Chief Crown Prosecutor for CPS Thames & Chiltern: Baljit Ubhey OBE. *Area Business Manager:* Karen Sawitzki. Eaton Court, 112 Oxford Road, Reading RG1 7LL. Tel: 0118 951 3600. Fax: 0118 951 3601. DX: 40104 READING (Castle Street).

Oxfordshire Branch, Gemini One, Oxford Business Park South, Garsington Road, Oxford OX4 2LL. Tel: 01865 233400. Fax: 01865 233401. DX: 45417 COWLEY.

Deputy Chief Crown Prosecutor for CPS Thames & Chiltern: Richard Newcombe. Sceptre House, 7–9 Castle Street, Luton LU1 3AJ. Tel: 01582 816600. Fax: 01582 816678. DX: 120503 LUTON 6.

Deputy Chief Crown Prosecutor for CPS Thames & Chiltern: Ruth Bowskill. Berkshire Branch, Eaton Court, 112 Oxford Road, Reading RG1 7LL. Tel: 01865 233434. DX: 40104 READING (CASTLE STREET).

CPS WESSEX

www.cps.gov.uk/wessex

Chief Crown Prosecutor for CPS Wessex: Nick Hawkins. *Area Business Manager:* Denise Meldrum. 3rd Floor, Black Horse House, 8–10 Leigh Road, Eastleigh SO50 9FH. Tel: 023 8067 3800. Fax: 023 8067 3854. DX: 148581 EASTLEIGH 4.

Deputy Chief Crown Prosecutor for CPS Wessex: Kate Brown. Ground Floor, Oxford House, Oxford Road, Bournemouth BH8 8HA. Tel: 01202 498700. Fax: 01202 498860. DX: 7699 BOURNEMOUTH.

CPS WEST MIDLANDS

www.cps.gov.uk/westmidlands

Chief Crown Prosecutor for CPS West Midlands: Harry Ireland. *Area Business Manager:* Laurence Sutton. Operations Centre, Colmore Gate, 2 Colmore Row, Birmingham B3 2QA. Tel: 0121 262 1300. Fax: 0121 262 1500. DX: 719540 BIRMINGHAM 45.

Email: contact.westmidlands@cps.gsi.gov.uk.

Deputy Chief Crown Prosecutors for CPS West Midlands: Nick Price; Zafar Siddique. Operations Centre, as above.

CPS YORKSHIRE & HUMBERSIDE

www.cps.gov.uk/yorkshire_humberside

Chief Crown Prosecutor for CPS Yorkshire & Humberside: Martin Goldman. *Area Business Manager:* Karen Wright. Jefferson House, 27 Park Place, Leeds LS1 2SZ. Tel: 0113 290 2700. Fax: 0113 290 2707. DX: 26435 LEEDS PARK SQUARE.

Deputy Chief Crown Prosecutor for CPS West & North Yorkshire: Barbara Petchey. Jefferson House, as above.

Deputy Chief Crown Prosecutor for CPS South Yorkshire & Humberside: Gerry Wareham. Greenfield House, 32 Scotland Street, Sheffield S3 7DQ. Tel: 0114 229 8600. Fax: 0114 229 8607. DX: 711830 SHEFFIELD 18. Email: info.southyorkshire@cps.gsi.gov.uk.

CPS CYMRU/WALES
www.cps.gov.uk/wales
Chief Crown Prosecutor for CPS Cymru/Wales: Jim Brisbane. *Area Business Manager:* Mike Grist. 20th Floor, Capital Tower, Greyfriars Road, Cardiff CF10 3PL. Tel: 029 2080 3800. Fax: 029 2080 3802. DX: 33056 CARDIFF 1. Email: wales.communications@cps.gsi.gov.uk.
Deputy Chief Crown Prosecutor for CPS Cymru/Wales: Naheed Hussain. Ty Coch Way, Cwmbran NP44 7XX. Tel: 01633 261100. Fax: 01633 261106. DX: 743270 CWMBRAN 4.
Deputy Chief Crown Prosecutor for CPS Cymru/Wales: Ed Beltrami. Bromfield House, Ellice Way, Wrexham LL13 7YW. Tel: 01978 346000. Fax: 01978 346001. DX: 723100 WREXHAM 5.

INDEPENDENT POLICE COMPLAINTS COMMISSION

90 High Holborn, London WC1V 6BH.
Tel: 0845 300 2002 (switchboard); 020 7166 plus extension (individuals).
Fax: 020 7404 0430.

Email: enquiries@ipcc.gsi.gov.uk

Website: www.ipcc.gov.uk

Chair: Dame Anne Owers. Ext: 3237.
Deputy Chair: Deborah Glass OBE. Ext: 3275.
Commission Secretary: Anna O'Rourke. Ext: 3179.
Chief Executive: Jane Furniss. Ext: 3075.
Private Secretary to the Chief Executive: Chris Simpson. Ext: 3175.

Management Board
Director of Casework & Customer Service: David Knight. Tel: 0161 246 8505.
Director of Investigations: Moir Stewart. Tel: 01530 258750.
Director of Standards & Quality: Mike Benbow. Tel: 029 2024 5406.
Director of Business Services: Amanda Kelly. Ext: 3171.

Central Region
East Midlands Commissioner: Amerdeep Somal. Tel: 01530 258741. **Forces:** Derbyshire, Leicestershire; Lincolnshire; Northamptonshire; Nottinghamshire; Staffordshire.
East England Commissioner: Rachel Cerfontyne. Ext: 3237. **Forces:** Essex; Warwickshire; West Mercia; West Midlands; Port of Tilbury; Ministry of Defence; MPS cases.

Wales & South West Region
Commissioner for Wales: Tom Davies OBE. Tel: 029 2024 5403. **Forces:** Dyfed-Powys; Gwent; North Wales; South Wales.
South West Commissioner: Rebecca Marsh (currently on loan to the Office for Nuclear Regulation and no longer has force responsibility). **Forces:** the Deputy Chair will allocate a commissioner on a case-by-case basis for the following forces: Avon and Somerset; Devon and Cornwall; Dorset; Gloucestershire; Wiltshire; Civil Nuclear Constabulary; Port of Bristol; Port of Portland.

North Region
Yorkshire & North East Commissioner: Nicholas Long. Tel: 0161 246 8551. **Forces:** Cleveland; Durham; Humberside; North Yorkshire; Northumbria; South Yorkshire; West Yorkshire; UKBA Port of Tees & Hartlepool.
North West Commissioner: Naseem Malik. Tel: 0161 246 8551. **Forces:** Cheshire; Cumbria; Greater Manchester; Lancashire; Merseyside; Port of Liverpool.

London & South East Region
London Commissioner: Deborah Glass OBE. Ext: 3275. **Forces:** Metropolitan Police Service; City of London Police.
London & South East Commissioner: Sarah Green. Ext: 3283. **Forces:** Bedfordshire; Cambridgeshire; Hertfordshire; Norfolk; Suffolk; Cambridge University; MPS cases; Port of Felixstowe; British Transport Police; HMRC.
South East Commissioner: Mike Franklin. Ext: 3283. **Forces:** Hampshire; Kent; Surrey; Sussex; Thames Valley; MPS cases; Port of Dover; SOCA.

Non-operational Commissioners
Chair of the IPCC Audit Committee & IPCC Quality Committee: Jonathan Tross.
Chair of the IPCC Remuneration Committee: Ruth Evans. Ext: 3237.

New Commissioners
Mary Cunneen; Jennifer Izekor; Cindy Butts; James Dipple-Johnstone; Derrick Campbell.

Senior Investigators: Simon Cousins. Ext: 3110. John Cummins. Ext: 3049. Paul Davies. Tel: 029 2024 5444. Anzac Evans. Tel: 029 2024 5445. Mike Grant. Tel: 01530 258706. Peter Orr. Ext: 3170. Joseph Penrose. Tel: 01924 811510. Steve Reynolds. Ext: 3910. Amanda Rowe. Tel: 0161 246 8529.
Heads of Casework: David Ford. Tel: 029 2024 5473. John Paul Napier. Tel: 0161 246 8541.
Head of News: Charlotte Phillips. Ext: 3932.
Regional Communications Officers: **Wales & South West:** David Nicholson. Tel: 029 2024 5464. **Central & Eastern England:** Mark Pearson. Ext: 3239. **North & North East:** Ian Christon. Tel: 0161 246 8582. **Corporate & Digital:** Danny Brierley. Ext: 8633. **London & South East:** Julia Davies. Ext: 3028. Caroline Craig. Ext: 3134.
Head of Analytical Services: Kathie Cashell. Ext: 3265.
Head of Strategy & Communications: Sadie East. Ext: 3940.

Head of Finance: Mike Benson. Ext: 3135.
Head of Human Resources: Colin Woodward. Ext: 3292.
Head of ICT: Bob Fox. Ext: 3166.
Head of Procurement & Estates: Javier Roig. Ext: 3050.
Head of Legal: David Emery. Ext: 3911.
Head of Change & Customer Service: Jason Taylor. Ext: 3966.
Parliamentary Officer: Lianne Corris. Ext: 3185.

POLICE INVESTIGATIONS AND REVIEW COMMISSIONER

(formerly Police Complaints Commissioner for Scotland)
Hamilton House, Hamilton Business Park, Caird Park, Hamilton ML3 0QA.
Freephone: 0808 178 5577.
Email: enquiries@pcc-scotland.org
Website: www.pcc-scotland.org

Police Complaints Commissioner for Scotland: Professor John McNeill.
Director of Investigations: John Mitchell.
Director of Reviews: Robin Johnston.
Head of Communications: Christine McAllister.

POLICE NEGOTIATING BOARD

Office of Manpower Economics, 6th Floor, Victoria House, Southampton Row, London WC1B 4AD.
Tel: 020 7271 0472. Fax: 020 7271 0499. Email: william.blase@bis.gsi.gov.uk

Chair: Mr John Randall.
Deputy Chair: Professor Gillian Morris.
Independent Secretary: William Blase. All correspondence for the Board should be addressed to the Independent Secretary at the above address.
The Board, described in the Police Act 1996, is the forum for negotiations between an official side (*Secretary:* S Messenger, Local Government Employers, 3rd Floor, Local Government House, Smith Square, London SW1P 3HZ. Tel: 020 7187 7342) and a staff side (*Secretary:* Mr I Rennie, Police Federation of England & Wales, Federation House, Highbury Drive, Leatherhead, Surrey KT22 7UY. Tel: 01372 352022). Queries relating to one side or the other should be addressed in the first instance to the secretary of the side concerned.

CRIMINAL INJURIES COMPENSATION AUTHORITY (CICA)

Tay House, 300 Bath Street, Glasgow G2 4LN.
Tel: 0300 003 3601.
Website: www.cica.gov.uk

Chief Executive: Carole Oatway.
Deputy Chief Executive: Rena Kinloch.
Chief Business Officer: Jackie Lockhart.
The government body responsible for administering the Criminal Injuries Compensation Scheme in England, Scotland and Wales, CICA provides a free service to victims of violent crime. It is part of the Ministry of Justice and also provides a service on behalf of the Scottish government.

HMCTS CRIMINAL INJURIES COMPENSATION APPEALS PANEL

Third Floor, Wellington House, 134–136 Wellington Street, Glasgow G2 2XL.

Tel: 0141 354 8555. Fax: 0141 354 8556.

Website: www.justice.gov.uk

Email: cic.enquiries@hmcts.gsi.gov.uk

Chair of the Criminal Injuries Compensation Appeals Panel: Anthony Summers.

HM REVENUE AND CUSTOMS
ENFORCEMENT & COMPLIANCE

100 Parliament Street, London SW1A 2BQ.
HMRC 24-hour contact point: National Co-ordination Unit (NCU): PO Box 440, Ipswich IP4 1WB.
Tel: 0870 785 3600 (24 hrs). Fax: 0870 240 3738. Email: ncu@hmrc.gsi.gov.uk

Director General Enforcement & Compliance: Jennie Granger.
PA: Gary Gatter. Tel: 020 7147 0716.
PS: Declan Greaney. Tel: 020 7147 0392.
DS: Susan Coles. Tel: 020 7147 0320.

CRIMINAL INVESTIGATION DIRECTORATE

Director, Criminal Investigation: Donald Toon. Custom House, London. *Support Officer:* Ayeisha Chaudhry. Tel: 0870 785 7436. *PA:* Ruth Edisbury. Tel: 0161 827 0071.

Deputy Director, Operational Tasking, Performance & Specialist Delivery: Chris Harrison. *Staff Officer:* Derek Dubery. Tel: 0289 035 8316. *Support Officer:* Lesley Lambert. Tel: 0870 785 4171.

Deputy Director, Scotland & East: Richard Las. *Support Officer:* Donna Farmer. Tel: 0870 785 8777.

Deputy Director, West, Wales & Northern Ireland: Alan Lee. *Support Officer:* Dave Smith. Tel: 0161 827 0628. *PA:* Kath Barker. Tel: 0161 827 0214.

Deputy Director, London & South: Duncan Stewart. *Support Officer:* Gayle Adam. Tel: 0870 785 7594.

Deputy Director, Planning & Change: Peter Robson. *Support Officer:* John O'Neill. Tel: 0870 785 7146.

Head of Professionalism & Capability: Mark Peterson. *Support Officer:* Paul Hutton. Tel: 0161 827 0686.

Deputy Director, Internal Governance : Ian Watson. *PA:* David Ellis. Tel: 0870 785 7525.

Criminal Investigation Communications Officer: Gina Tierney. Tel: 0870 785 7577.

RISK & INTELLIGENCE

Custom House, 20 Lower Thames Street, London EC3R 6EE (unless otherwise stated).

Director (Risk & Intelligence Service): Mike Wells CBE. 4E/14, 100 Parliament Street, London SW1A 2BQ. Tel: 020 7147 3357. **Private Office:** Ann Gibbard. Tel: 020 7147 3356. Simone Barnett. Tel: 020 7147 0210.

Deputy Director (Risk & Intelligence Service, Head of Integration and Intelligence Development): Euan Stewart OBE. Room W2/13. Tel: 0870 785 6717. **Private Office:** *Staff Officer:* Helen Chard. Tel: 0870 785 7287. *PA:* Audrey Brown. Tel: 0870 785 7413.

Assistant Director (Specific Intelligence): Nick Burris. Tel: 0300 056 3287. *Staff Officer:* Rose Daly. Tel: 0870 785 7877.

Assistant Director (Intelligence Development): Paul Golightly. Tel: 0870 785 7709. *Staff Officer:* Rachelle Ellenby. Tel: 0870 785 7245.

Assistant Director (Integration): Tom Gardiner. Tel: 0870 785 6806. *Staff Officer:* Karen Yaxley. Tel: 0870 785 7897

Assistant Director (Fiscal Crime Overseas Network Delivery): John Kay. Tel: 0870 785 2586.

Assistant Director (Intelligence Policy & Assurance): Barry Peterson. Tel: 0870 785 2894.

Assistant Director (Capability & Performance): Alex Mitham. Tel: 0870 785 2209.

Head of NCU & Information Management Unit: Julian Hurst. Haven House, PO Box 440, Ipswich IP4 1WB. Tel: 0870 785 3619.

MAP OF POLICE FORCES IN ENGLAND & WALES

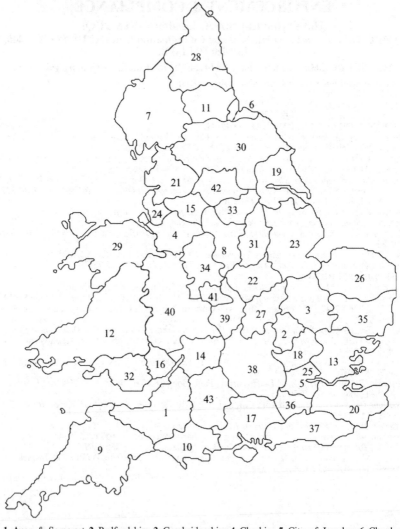

1 Avon & Somerset 2 Bedfordshire 3 Cambridgeshire 4 Cheshire 5 City of London 6 Cleveland 7 Cumbria 8 Derbyshire 9 Devon and Cornwall 10 Dorset 11 Durham 12 Dyfed-Powys 13 Essex 14 Gloucestershire 15 Greater Manchester 16 Gwent 17 Hampshire 18 Hertfordshire 19 Humberside 20 Kent 21 Lancashire 22 Leicestershire 23 Lincolnshire 24 Merseyside 25 Metropolitan 26 Norfolk 27 Northamptonshire 28 Northumbria 29 North Wales 30 North Yorkshire 31 Nottinghamshire 32 South Wales 33 South Yorkshire 34 Staffordshire 35 Suffolk 36 Surrey 37 Sussex 38 Thames Valley 39 Warwickshire 40 West Mercia 41 West Midlands 42 West Yorkshire 43 Wiltshire

METROPOLITAN POLICE
New Scotland Yard, Broadway, London SW1H 0BG.
Tel: 020 7230 1212. Telex: 893421/2/3 Metpol Gn.
Email for New Scotland Yard: mso@met.police.uk
Website: www.met.police.uk

Commissioner: Sir Bernard Hogan-Howe QPM MBA MA(Oxon).
Staff Officer. Ext: 2598.
Commissioner's Chief of Staff: Caroline Murdoch. Ext: 4402.
Private Secretary: Sharon East. Ext: 2346.
Head of Strategic Relationships: Judith Mullett. Ext: 2424.
Deputy Commissioner: Craig Mackey QPM.
Staff Officer. Sally Meaden. Ext: 2155.
Private Secretary: Clare O'Hara. Ext: 2636.

METROPOLITAN POLICE DISTRICT
The Metropolitan Police District includes the whole of Greater London, excluding the City of London, and comprises the following boroughs:

1. Barking & Dagenham	11. Hackney	19. Kensington & Chelsea (Royal Borough)	25. Redbridge
2. Barnet	12. Hammersmith & Fulham	20. Kingston-upon-Thames (Royal Borough)	26. Richmond-upon-Thames
3. Bexley	13. Haringey		27. Southwark
4. Brent	14. Harrow		28. Sutton
5. Bromley	15. Havering	21. Lambeth	29. Tower Hamlets
6. Camden	16. Hillingdon	22. Lewisham	30. Waltham Forest
7. Croydon	17. Hounslow	23. Merton	31. Wandsworth
8. Ealing	18. Islington	24. Newham	32. Westminster
9. Enfield			
10. Greenwich			

The following areas, although they have a Kent postal address, are in the Metropolitan Police District and are policed by the Metropolitan Police: Beckenham, Belvedere, Bexleyheath, Bromley, Chislehurst, Erith, Farnborough, St Mary Cray & Sidcup.

HQ ADDRESSES
Enquiries (all departments). Tel: 020 7230 1212 at all times.
Unless otherwise shown, telephone extensions in HQ buildings can be obtained direct by dialling 020 7230 followed by the extension number.

New Scotland Yard 10 Broadway, London SW1H 0BG.
Cobalt Square 1 South Lambeth Road, London SW8 1SU.
Edinburgh House 170 Kennington Lane, London SE11 5DP.
Empress State Building Empress Approach, Lillie Road, Earls Court, London SW16 1TR.
Jubilee House 230–232 Putney Bridge Road, London SW15 2PD. Tel: 020 8785 followed by extension number.

Lambeth Support Headquarters 109 Lambeth Road, London SE1 7JH.
Metropolitan Police Training Establishment (Peel Centre) Aerodrome Road, London NW9 5JE. Tel: 020 8358 followed by extension number.
Regency Street 105 Regency Street, London SW1P 4AN.
Tintagel House 92 Albert Embankment, London SE1 7TT.
Wellington House 67–73 Buckingham Gate, London SW1E 6BE.

CENTRAL SERVICES
COMMISSIONER'S PRIVATE OFFICE
Tel: 020 7230 plus extension number, unless otherwise stated.
Commissioner: Sir Bernard Hogan-Howe QPM MBA MA(Oxon).
Staff Officer. Ext: 2598.
Private Secretary: Sharon East. Ext: 2346.
Head of Strategic Relationships: Judith Mullett. Ext: 2424.
Deputy Commissioner: Craig Mackey QPM.
Staff Officer. Sally Meaden. Ext: 2155.
Private Secretary: Clare O'Hara. Ext: 2636.

DIVERSITY AND CITIZEN'S FOCUS DIRECTORATE
Tel: 020 7161 plus extension number, unless otherwise stated.
Structure & Personnel: *Director.* Denise Milani. Ext: 2828.

Staff Officer to Director: Insp David Antoine. Ext: 4963.
Strategic Support & Policy (including Governance, Advisors, Diversity Equality Performance & Communication): *Head of Delivery:* David Skelton. Ext: 3061.

DIRECTORATE OF INFORMATION
Edinburgh House, 170 Kennington Lane, London SE11 5DP, unless otherwise stated. Tel: 020 7091 plus extension number, unless otherwise stated.

Director of Information: Eur Ing Ailsa Beaton OBE BSc(Hons) CEng CITP FBCS. Rm 808 New Scotland Yard. Tel: 020 7230 5000.
Senior Staff Officer: Julia Ward. Rm 809 New Scotland Yard. Tel: 020 7230 3334.
Staff Officer: Mia Klasson. Rm 809 New Scotland Yard. Tel: 020 7230 3333.
Staff Officer ACPO: Alan Hadfield. Rm 809 New Scotland Yard. Tel: 020 7230 3335.
PA: Sylvia Moore. Rm 809, New Scotland Yard. Tel: 020 7230 3332.

DEPUTY DIRECTOR OF INFORMATION
Tel: 020 7091 plus extension number, unless otherwise stated.
Deputy Director of Information: Andrew Watson. Ext: 5200.
Deputy Director's Private Officer: Dawn Hudson. Ext: 5006.
Business Needs: Mark McLeod. Ext: 5929.
Head of Planning: Supt Adrian Hutchinson. Tel: 07825 833948.
Lean Team Programme Manager: Angela Emery. Ext: 5033.
Mission Control: Chris Nason. Ext: 5382.

INFORMATION SERVICES
Tel: 020 7091 plus extension number, unless otherwise stated.
Director of Information Services: Simon Davies. Ext: 5142.
Director's Private Officer: Dawn Hudson. Ext: 5006.
Reporting Services: Peter Emery. Empress State Building. Tel: 020 7161 3355.
Information Access Services: Merilyne Knox. Empress State Building. Tel: 020 7161 3554.
Digital Services: Carol McDonald. Ext: 3426.
Infrastructure Services: Paul Cripps. Tel: 07801 206245.
Crime & CJ Services: Jak Tourabaly. Ext: 5724.
Command & Control Services: Kim Brown. Ext: 5469.
Business Support Services: John Ferguson. Ext: 5061.
Secure Services: Brian Douglas. Rm 852, New Scotland Yard. Tel: 020 7230 3679

MAJOR CHANGE
Tel: 020 7091 plus extension number, unless otherwise stated.
Director of Major Change: Steve Whatson. Ext: 5498.
Director's Private Officer: Dawn Hudson. Ext: 5006.
Project Flow & Resources: Gary Fitzpatrick. Ext: 5100.
Head of In-house Stream: Mukesh Dev. Ext: 5060.
Head of Supplier Stream: Dave Rounds. Ext: 5459.
Head of Secure Stream: Steve Kearney. Ext: 5164.
Head of Estates Stream: Trevor Day. Tel: 07595 005383.
Head of S & ET: Les Ding. Denmark Hill. Tel: 020 7230 6837.
Operational Policing Systems Futures: Dawn Burroughs. Ext 5631.
C & C Futures: Nigel Lee. Tel: 07786 197108.

DIRECTORATE OF PROFESSIONAL STANDARDS
Tel: 020 7230 plus extension number, unless otherwise stated.
Director Professional Standards: Commander Allan Gibson. Ext: 1377.
Staff Officer: A/Det Sgt Julie Tweedy. Ext: 7908.
Staff Officer: A/Insp Matthew Talboys. Ext: 7907
PA: Binta Patel. Ext: 7325.
Directorate for Professional Standards: T/Chief Supt Nicola Dale. Tel: 020 7161 6633.
Business Manager: Marina Zarvou. Tel: 020 7161 6642.

DIRECTORATE OF LEGAL SERVICES
First Floor, Victoria Block, New Scotland Yard.

Director: H Giles.
Assistant Directors: G Morgan LLB; N F Saleh LLB; S D M Burrows BA; Mrs F Oliffe.
Senior Lawyers: J C Bergin BSc; S A Bird LLB; N Brannigan LLB; G M Carey-Yard LLB; S Castiglione LLB; S E C Catcheside BA; A Cunningham BA; A J Fairbrother LLB; T Fowler LLB; L M Gluck LLB; S Heron LLB; J Hickman BA; M Jones LLB; J M Leonard BSc; E McCafferty LLB; D McCahon BA; J R Morris BA MA; N Pierce BA; G Rai BA; S M Royan BA; R J Skipper LLB; M A Spanton LLB; S Winfield LLB.
Lawyers: R W Baker LLB; R A Barnes BA; D Blay BA; C A Boahen LLB; L A Collins BSc; V Cooper LLB; A E Coultas BA; H A Darr LLB; M F Davis BA; E L Harraway LLB; M T Knowles BA; J

Lloyd BA; P D Loose BA; P P S Mandair BA; S I Moxom; J M O'Dwyer LLB; A E Peacock BA; Z
L Roberts LLB; E J Scott LLB; V C Spencer LLB; T A Tuffuor LLB; T J Wisbey LLB; J M Wright
BA.
Legal Executives: S A Gilchrist FInstLEx; D Z Senior GInstLEx; L J Simpson FInstLEx; W P Sung.

DMC DIRECTORATE OF MEDIA AND COMMUNICATION
Tel: 020 7230 plus extension number, unless otherwise stated.
Director, Media & Communication: Mr Martin Fewell. Ext: 3272.
Personal Secretary: Mrs Teresa Want. Ext: 3272.
Deputy Director of Media & Communication: Vacant. Ext: 2675.
Assistant Director, Head of Engagement: Ruth Shulver. Ext: 2316.
Assistant Director, Head of Publicity: Stephanie Day. Ext: 0940.
Assistant Director, Head of Media: Ed Stearns. Ext: 2475.
Press Bureau. Tel: 020 7230 2171.
Specialist Operations Press Desk: *Senior Information Officer.* Ext: 4094.
E-comms: *Senior Information Officer.* Ext: 9607.
Publicity Branch: *Senior Information Officer.* Ext: 3509.

HUMAN RESOURCES DIRECTORATE
Director of Human Resources: Robin Wilkinson. Room 1015, New Scotland Yard. Tel: 020 7230 2912.
Staff Officer: Jo Smith. Room 1015, New Scotland Yard. Tel: 020 7230 1439.
PA: Diania Cork. Room 1015, New Scotland Yard. Tel: 020 7161 2912.
Director of HR Operations: Ellie Ryan. 3rd Floor North, Empress State Building. Tel: 020 7161 0441.
Director of HR Professional Services: Alexandra Walsh. 3rd Floor North, Empress State Building. Tel:
020 7161 3034.

SPECIALIST OPERATIONS DEPARTMENT
Tel: 020 7230 plus extension number, unless otherwise stated.
Assistant Commissioner, Specialist Operations has pan London responsibility for security and protection matters that
cannot effectively be dealt with territorially: this may be because of the high degree of specialism required; lack of
relevance of territorial boundaries; scale; or the national nature of the functions.
Assistant Commissioner: Cressida Dick QPM.
Staff Officers: Det Chief Supt Clarke Jarrett. Ext: 4051. Det Sgt Stephen Atkinson. Ext: 1375.
Private Secretaries: Mrs Karen Boyd. Ext: 1821. Miss Norah Healy. Ext: 3967.
Head of Strategic Briefing Team: Alison Duncan-Mercy. Ext: 1328.
PA: Sally Cox. Ext: 7143.

SUPPORT BRANCH
SPECIALIST OPERATIONS HEADQUARTERS
Tel: 020 7230 plus extension number, unless otherwise stated.
Director of Business Services (F & R): Brian Sweeting. Ext: 2970.
Deputy to Director (Finance): Stephanie O'Sullivan. Ext: 3092.
Deputy to Director (Resources): Martin Etherington. Ext: 3428.
SO HR Business Partner: Sandra Gavin. Ext: 3080.
SO Careers Consultancy. Ext: 3030.

SECURITY, ROYALTY & PERSONAL PROTECTION & CHANGE MANAGEMENT DIRECTORATE
Tel: 020 7230 plus extension number, unless otherwise stated.
Deputy Assistant Commissioner: Vacant.
Staff Officer. Ext: 6800.
PA: Lorraine Jones. Room 1806, New Scotland Yard. Ext: 6801.
SPECIAL OPERATIONS – PROTECTIVE SECURITY
Responsible for SO17, SO18, SO20.
Room 1805, New Scotland Yard. Tel: 020 7230 plus extension number, unless otherwise stated.
Commander: Richard Morris.
Staff Officer: PS Martin Griffin. Ext: 3324.
PA: Jenny Russell. Ext: 4372.
ROYALTY & SPECIALIST PROTECTION COMMAND
Responsible for SO1 protection, SO6 Diplomatic Protection Group & SO14 Royalty & Specialist Protection.
Tel: 020 8721 plus extension number, unless otherwise stated.
Commander: Peter Loughborough QPM. Ext: 5212.
Staff Officer: Insp Michael MacKenzie Ext: 5211.
Personal Secretary: June Lovelock. Ext: 5212.
SO1 SPECIALIST PROTECTION
Tel: 020 7230 plus extension number, unless otherwise stated.
OCU Commander: Det Chief Supt Claire Johnston. Ext: 6001.

Staff Officer: Insp Iain MacFarlane. Ext: 6210.
PA: Katrina Burke. Ext: 6207.
Operations Command Centre 24 Hours. Ground Floor, Victoria Block, New Scotland Yard. Ext: 6789.
SO6 DIPLOMATIC PROTECTION
Tel: 020 8721 plus extension number, unless otherwise stated.
OCU Commander: Chief Supt Andy Tarrant. Ext: 5351.
Staff Officer: Sarah Hine. Ext: 5358.
SO14 ROYALTY PROTECTION DEPARTMENT
Tel: 020 8721 plus extension number, unless otherwise stated.
OCU Commander: Chief Supt Des Stout. Ext: 5202.
Staff Officers: Sgt Jim Cook. Ext: 5222. Sheena Horbury. Ext: 5221.
24 Hour Control Room. Tel: 020 7321 7800/020 8721 8363.
SO17 PALACE OF WESTMINSTER
1 Canon Row, London SW1A 2JN.
Security Control Room. Tel: (24hrs): 020 7219 5311 ext 47267.
Police Operations Office. Tel: 020 7219 5350 ext 47264.
OCU Commander: Chief Supt Ed Bateman. Tel: 020 7219 5431 ext 47258.
SO18 AVIATION SECURITY
Tel: 020 3276 plus extension number, unless otherwise stated.
OCU Commander: Chief Supt Bert Moore. Ext: 1247.
Staff Officer: PS Richard Evans. Ext: 1249.
PA: Una Cripps. Ext: 1248.
SO20 CT PROTECTIVE SECURITY COMMAND
Tel: 0207 230 plus extension number, unless otherwise stated.
OCU Commander: Chief Supt Michael McDonagh. Ext: 3346.
Staff Officer: PS David Anderson. Ext: 7152.
PA: Debbie Geldard. Ext: 3572.

SO15 COUNTER TERRORISM COMMAND
Tel: 020 7230 plus extension number, unless otherwise stated.
Initial Response Co-ordination Cell (24 Hour Reserve Facility). Ext: 9015.
Deputy Assistant Commissioner: Stuart Osborne.
Senior National Co-ordinator: Room 1707, New Scotland Yard. Ext: 2310.
Staff Officer: Det Insp Peter Barber. Ext: 3235.
Staff Officer: Det Sgt Maria Lovegrove. Ext: 2444.
PA: Evelyn White. Ext: 2297.
Commander: Richard Walton. Head of SO15 Counter Terrorism Command, Room 1501, New Scotland Yard. Ext: 2302.
Det Chief Superintendent (Operations): Keith Surtees. Ext: (6)3012.
Det Chief Superintendent (Operational Support): Tom Manson. Ext: (6)9732.
Det Chief Superintendent (National CT Functions): Duncan Ball. Ext: (6)2293.
Det Chief Superintendent (National DE Functions): Chris Greany. Tel: 020 3276 1657.

SPECIALIST CRIME AND OPERATIONS
Individuals tel: 020 7230 plus extension number, unless otherwise stated.
Assistant Commissioner: Mark Rowley QPM. Room 1101, Tower Block, New Scotland Yard. Ext: 0341. Fax: 020 7230 4296.
Staff Officers: Chief Insp Alisa Newman. Ext: 0479. Det Insp Neil Matthews. Ext: 0480.
PA: Mini Jaideep. Ext: 0341.
Deputy Assistant Commissioner: Martin Hewitt. Room 1130, Tower Block, New Scotland Yard. Ext: 3756.
Staff Officer: A/Det Chief Insp Noel McHugh. Ext: 2110.
PA: Marion Simeone. Ext: 2422.
Deputy Assistant Commissioner: Maxine de Brunner. Room 933, Tower Block, New Scotland Yard.
Staff Officer: Insp Sarah Titterell. Ext: 2339.
SC&O1 HOMICIDE & SERIOUS CRIME, SC&O2 SAPPHIRE AND SC&O5 CHILD ABUSE INVESTIGATION
Tel: 020 7230 plus extension number, unless otherwise stated.
Commander: Peter Spindler. Ext: 3146.
Staff Officer: Det Sgt Imran Beg. Ext: 4052.
PA: Melanie Martin. Ext: 3467.
SC&O1 OCU Commander: Det Chief Supt Hamish Campbell. Ext: 4649.
SC&O2 OCU Commander: Det Chief Supt Mick Duthie. Tel: 020 8721 4681.
SC&O5 OCU Commander: Det Chief Supt Keith Niven. Tel: 020 7161 3311.

SC&O4 DIRECTORATE OF FORENSIC SERVICES
Tel: 020 7230 plus extension number, unless otherwise stated.
Director: Gary Pugh OBE BSc MSc CSci CChem MRSC. Ext: 2529.
PA: Karen A Moye. Ext: 3204. Fax: 020 7230 9974.
Personal Secretary: Rosie Rigg. Ext: 6372.
Head of Forensic Organisational Resilience: David Wheeler AdvDip. Ext: 3564.
Head of Forensic Operations: David Lloyd. Ext: 9676.
PA. Ext: 3978.
Forensic Operations Manager (North): Richard Deacon. Tel: 07768 145937.
Forensic Operations Manager (South): Phil Kaye. Mob: 07768 147094.
Forensic Operations Manager (Central): Leigh Fleeman. Tel: 020 7230 0097.
Head of Digital & Electronic Forensic Services (DEFS): Mark Stokes. Ext: 0051.
PA: Janet McNally. Ext: 3144.
Head of Quality & Performance: Edward Bennett. Ext: 3489.
Head of Specialist Evidence Recovery & Imaging Services: Chris Porter BSc(Hons). Ext: 1894.
PA: Annie Donelan. Ext: 1899. Fax: 0314.
Head of Counter Terrorist Forensic Services: Roger Baldwin. Ext: 2759.
Head of Forensic Development: Karen Georgiou. Ext: 2750.
Head of DNA Services Unit: Shazia Khan. Tel: 020 3276 1887.
Contracts Manager: Elaine Eastham. Tel: 020 3276 1780.
Forensic Monitoring Unit: *Office Manager.* Ext: 3164.

SC&O6 SPECIALIST & ECONOMIC CRIME, SC&O7 SERIOUS & ORGANISED CRIME, SC&O8 TRIDENT AND SC&O9 HUMAN EXPLOITATION & ORGANISED CRIME
Tel: 020 7230 plus extension number, unless otherwise stated.
Commander: Steve Rodhouse.
PA: Sue Farley. Ext: 3852.
Staff Officer: Det Insp Yasmin Lalani.
SC&O3 Head of Unit: Mike Taylor. Ext: 2501.
SC&O6 & SC&O9 OCU Commander: Det Chief Supt Stuart Macleod. Ext: 7277.
SC&O7 OCU Commander: Det Chief Supt Clive Timmons. Ext: 9493.
SC&O8 OCU Commander: Det Chief Supt Dean Haydon. Tel: 020 8785 8228.

SC&O10/11/14/16/25/27/33 INTELLIGENCE AND COVERT POLICING
Tel: 020 7230 plus extension number, unless otherwise stated.
Commander: Richard Martin. Ext: 2029.
Staff Officer: Louise Tuck. Ext: 2070.
PA: Diana Anthony. Ext: 1720.
SC&O10/11 OCU Commander: Det Chief Supt Phillip Williams. Ext: 0023.
SC&O14 Head of Unit: T/Det Supt Frankie Flood. Ext: 7116.
SC&O16 Head of Unit: Caroline Bridgman. Ext: 2836.
SC&O25 OCU Commander: Det Chief Supt Steve Dower. Ext: 8352.
24/7 Intelligence Support/Enquiries. Ext: 8400. Email: mib@met.pnn.police.uk
SC&O27 Head of Unit: Tracy Dancy. Tel: 020 7161 2839.
SC&O33 Head of Unit: Det Supt Stuart Dark. Ext: 7150.

SC&O12 BUSINESS SUPPORT
Tel: 020 7230 plus extension number, unless otherwise stated.
Deputy Director: Karen Russell. Ext: 3094.

SC&O15 TRAFFIC, SC&O20 TSG AND SC&O22 PUBLIC ORDER & OPERATIONAL SUPPORT
Tel: 020 7230 plus extension number, unless otherwise stated.
Commander: David Martin. Ext: 4310.
Staff Officers: PC Sara Tetlow. Ext: 4308. Sgt Anna McCartney. Ext: 4310.
SC&O15 OCU Commander: Chief Supt Scott Wilson. Ext: 1427.
SC&O20 OCU Commander: Chief Supt Mark Bird. Ext: 1845.
SC&O22 OCU Commander: Chief Supt Peter Terry. Ext: 4499.

SC&O19 SPECIALIST FIREARMS AND SC&O23 FIREARM COMMAND
Tel: 020 7230 plus extension number, unless otherwise stated.
Commander: Mark Streater. Ext: 1727.
Staff Officer: Sgt Marion Kent. Ext: 1727.
SC&O19 & SC&O23 OCU Commander: Chief Supt Alistair Sutherland. Tel: 020 7275 3500.

SC&O21/26 CRIME ACADEMY AND OPERATIONAL INFORMATION SERVICE
SC&O21 Director: Det Chief Supt Steve Lovelock. Tel: 020 8358 1049.
SC&O26 Head of Unit: Graham Morris. Ext: 2987. Fax: 0715.
CEC Production Manager: Stuart Gibson. Ext: 2980.

CEC/CRB Disclosure Manager. Ext: 3385.
CEC Liaison Team Enquiries. Ext: 2002, Fax: 4862.
Overseas Visitors Records Office (OVRO). Ext: 1222.
Personal Security Group (PSG) Vetting Manager. Ext: 6862.
Police National Computer (PNC) Bureau Manager. Ext: 3799.

TERRITORIAL POLICING
Based at 10th Floor, New Scotland Yard. Tel: 020 7230 plus extension number.
Assistant Commissioner Territorial Policing: Simon Byrne MA. Ext: 1613.
PA: Miss Siobhan Finn. Ext: 61613.
Staff Officers: Insp Kris Wright. Ext: 1558. Sgt Emma Gardiner. Ext: 69759.
Deputy Assistant Commissioner Territorial Policing North: Helen Ball. Ext: 1919.
Personal Secretary: Vacant. Ext: 1919.
Staff Officer: Mr Kerry Hutton. Ext: 0920.
Deputy Assistant Commissioner Territorial Policing South: Mark Simmons.
Personal Secretary: Mrs Elieen Lurcuck. Ext: 2964.
Staff Officer: Sgt Fiona McGrath. Ext: 2896.
Director of Operational Resourcing for Territorial Policing: Mrs Alex Morley. Ext: 0883.
PA: Joanne Langridge. Ext: 4692.
Programme Director TP Development: Dr Nina Cope. Ext: 3095.
PA: Vacant. Ext: 3095.
Staff Officer: Insp Annette Godfrey. Ext: 3096.
Chief Officer, Special Constabulary: John Conway. Ext: 0947.
Staff Officer: Tim Reason. Tel: 020 7161 2654.
Territorial Policing Chief of Staff: Mrs Poppy Walker. Ext: 0951.
Commanders' Suite, 2nd Floor, Lambeth CCC.
Commander Public Contact: Tony Eastaugh. Tel: 020 7109 6531.
Staff Officer: Sgt Steve Scott. Tel: 020 7109 6531.
Based at New Scotland Yard.
Commander North East: Stephen Watson. Tel: 020 8217 7801.
Staff Officer: Sgt Rob McElroy. Tel: 020 8217 7801.
Commander South West: Mak Chishty. Tel: 020 8358 1504.
Personal Secretary: Ingrid Weekes. Tel: 020 8358 1504.
Staff Officer: Sgt Lora John. Tel: 020 8358 1501.
Commander City of Westminster: Alison Newcomb. Tel: 020 7321 8209.
Staff Officer: Sgt Stephen Willers. Tel: 020 7321 7516.
PA: Sue Kilbey. Tel: 020 7321 7530.
Commander South East: Neil Basu. Tel: 020 7230 0669.
PA: Katie Bennett. Tel: 020 7230 0669.
Staff Officer: Insp Darren Murphy. Tel: 020 7230 0667.
Commander North West: Christine Jones. Tel: 020 7161 4503.
PA: Linda Glogg. Tel: 020 7161 4503.
Staff Officer: Sgt Liz Symmonds. Tel: 020 7161 4502.
Commander Crime & Customer Strategy: Nick Ephgrave. Tel: 020 7161 0724.
PA: Vacant. Tel: 020 7161 0724.
Staff Officer: Vacant.
Based at The Palestra, Blackfriars Road.
Commander Safer Transport Command: Fiona Taylor. Tel: 020 3054 0293.
PA: Sue Wood. Tel: 020 3054 4454.
Staff Officer: PS Christopher Lloyd. Tel: 020 3054 0293.

RESOURCES DIRECTORATE
New Scotland Yard. Tel: 020 7230 plus extension number.
Director of Resources: Tracie Evans. Rm 920. Ext: 4321.
Senior Staff Officer: Henry Pugh. Rm 920. Ext: 2178.
Staff Officer: Lorraine Goodfellow. Rm 920. Ext: 2077.
Senior Personal Secretary: Sue Gosbee. Rm 920. Ext: 2149.

CUSTOMER AND COMMERCIAL SERVICES
7th Floor North, Empress State Building. Tel: 020 7161 plus extension number.
Director of Customer & Commercial Services: Caroline Mortimer. Ext: 1301.
Staff Officer: Faye Robinson. Ext: 1404.
Director of Catering Services: Liz Church. Ext: 1310.
Director of Transport Services: Tony Marsh. Ext: 1424.

FINANCE SERVICES
Empress State Building. Tel: 020 7161 plus extension number.
Director of Finance Services: Nick Rogers. 9th Floor North. Ext: 1777.
Staff Officer: Roger Berry. 9th Floor North. Ext: 1778.
Director of Business Support: Karim Mahamdallie. 9th Floor West. Ext: 1683.
Director of Group Finance: Ian Percival. 9th Floor East. Ext: 4966.
Director of Exchequer Services: Paul Daly. 10th Floor North. Ext: 1820.

PROCUREMENT SERVICES
Empress State Building. Tel: 020 7161 plus extension number.
Director of Procurement Services: Lee Tribe. 8th Floor North. Ext: 1590.
Staff Officer: Debbie Sullivan. 8th Floor North. Ext: 1591.

PROPERTY SERVICES
Empress State Building. Tel: 020 7161 plus extension number.
Director of Property Services: Jane Bond. 11th Floor West. Ext: 2307.
Staff Officer: Nancy Ford. 11th Floor West. Ext: 2348.
Deputy Director of Property Services & Director of Resilience, Compliance & Operational Support: Phil Smith. 11th Floor West. Ext: 2069.
Director of Real Estate Construction: Roger Harding. 11th Floor West. Ext: 2338.
Director of Real Estate Facilities Management: Howard Evans. 11th Floor West. Ext: 2249.

METROPOLITAN POLICE STATIONS
All stations have been designated by the Commissioner under s. 35 of the Police and Criminal Evidence Act 1984. Except where marked ♦, all stations are authorised charging stations. Non-emergency number 101; in an emergency dial 999.

Acton (XA), 250 High Street, Acton, London W3 9BH.	020 8896 1212
♦ Addington (ZA), Addington Village Road, Croydon, Surrey CR0 5AQ. (Restricted opening hours.)	01689 842222
Albany Street (ED), 60 Albany Street, London NW1 4EE.	020 8733 6225
Barking (KB), 6 Ripple Road Barking, Essex IG11 7NP.	020 7230 1212
Barkingside (JB), 1 High Street Barkingside, Ilford, Essex IG4 1QB.	020 7230 1212
Barnet (SA), 26 The High Street Barnet EN5 5RU.	020 8733 5025
Battersea (WA), 112–118 Battersea Bridge Road, London SW11 3AF.	020 7230 1212
Beckenham Safer Neighbourhood base (PY) Albemarle House, Albemarle Road, Beckenham BR3 5LN. Safer Neighbourhood Team base for Copers Cope SNT and Shortlands SNT. (Closed to public.)	101
Belgravia (AB), 202–206 Buckingham Palace Road, London SW1V 6SX.	020 7230 1212
Bethnal Green (HT), 12 Victoria Park Square, London E2 9NZ.	020 7230 1212
Bexleyheath (RY), 2 Arnsberg Way, Bexleyheath, Kent DA7 4QS.	020 7230 1212
Bickley Safer Neighbourhood base (PY), 212 Widmore Road, Bickley, Kent BR1 2RH. Safer Neighbourhood Team base for Bickley SNT. (Closed to public.)	101
Biggin Hill Safer Neighbourhood base (PY), 192 Main Road, Biggin Hill, Kent TN16 5DT. Safer Neighbourhood Team base for Biggin Hill SNT and Darwin SNT. (Front counter service: Mon–Fri 1100–1300.)	101
♦ Bow (HW), 111 Bow Road, London E3 2AN. (Restricted opening hours.)	020 7230 1212
♦ Brentford (TB), The Half Acre, Brentford, Middlesex TW3 8BH.	101
♦ Brick Lane (HR), 25 Brick Lane, London E1 6PU. (Restricted opening hours.)	020 7230 1212
Brixton (LD), 367 Brixton Road, London SW9 7DD.	020 8649 2025/ 2029(Custody)/ 2045(Grip and Pace Centre)
♦ Brockley (PK), 4 Howson Road, London SE4 2AS. (Mon–Fri 1000–1400.)	101
Bromley Police Station (PY), High Street, Bromley, Kent BR1 1ER. (24 hours)	101
Brompton *see* Chelsea or Kensington	
Burnt Ash Lane Safer Neighbourhood base (PY), 121–123 Burnt Ash Lane, Plaistow, Bromley, Kent. Safer Neighbourhood Team base for Plaistow and Sundridge SNT. (Closed to public.)	101

◆Camberwell (MC), 22A Camberwell Church Street, London SE5   020 7232 6333
8QU. (Limited opening times.)
Canning Town (KT), 23 Tarling Road, London E16 1HN.   020 7230 1212
Carey Way (QR), Unit 5–8 Towers Business Park, Carey Way, Wembley,   020 7230 1212
Middlesex HA9 0LQ.
Catford (PD), 333 Bromley Road, London SE6 2RJ. (24 hours.)   101
Cavendish Road (LC), 47 Cavendish Parade, Clapham, London SW12   020 8649 2625
0BL. (Restricted opening hours)
◆Chadwell Heath (JH), 14 Wangey Road, Chadwell Heath, Essex RM6   020 7230 1212
4AJ.
Chalkhill Police Office, Ken Way, Chalkhill Estate, Chalkhill, Wembley,   020 7230 1212
Middlesex HA9 9DS. (Monday to Friday 1300–1500.)
Charing Cross, Agar Street, London WC2N 4JP.   020 7230 1212
Chelsea (BC), 2 Lucan Place, London SW3 3PB.   020 7230 1212
Chingford (JC), Kings Head Hill, London E4 7EA.   020 7230 1212
Chislehurst Safer Neighbourhood base (PY), 1a High Street,   101
Chislehurst BR7 5AB. Safer Neighbourhood Team base for
Chislehurst SNT and Mottingham & Chislehurst North SNT.
(Closed to public.)
Chiswick (TC), 205–211 Chiswick High Road, London W4 2DR.   101
Clapham (LM), 51 Union Grove, London SW8 2QU.   020 8649 2525
Colindale (SC), Grahame Park Way, Colindale, London NW9 5TW.   020 8733 4425
Coney Hall Safer Neighbourhood base (PY), 6 Coney Hall Parade,   101
Kingsway, West Wickham BR4 9JB. Safer Neighbourhood Team
base for Hayes and Coney Hall SNT. (Closed to public.)
Cray Valley Safer Neighbourhood base (PY), 43–45 High Street, St   101
Mary Cray BR5 3NJ. Safer Neighbourhood Team base for Cray
Valley East SNT and Cray Valley West SNT. (Closed to public.)
Croydon (ZD), 71 Park Lane, Croydon, Surrey CR9 1BP.   020 8667 1212
Dagenham (KG), 561 Rainham Road South, Dagenham, Essex RM10   020 7230 1212
7TU.
Deptford (PP), 116 Amersham Vale, London SE14 6LG. (24 hours.)   101
Ealing (XD), 67–69 Uxbridge Road, London W5 5SJ.   020 8810 1212
Earlsfield (WF), 522 Garratt Lane, London SW17 0NZ.   020 7230 1212
East Dulwich (ME), 173–183 Lordship Lane, London SE2 8HA.   020 7232 7325
(Limited opening times.)
East Ham (KE), 4 High Street South, London E6 6ES.   020 7230 1212
Edmonton (YE), 462 Fore Street, Edmonton, London N9 0PW.   101
Elmers End Safer Neighbourhood base (PY), 80 Croydon Road, Elmers   101
End, Beckenham, Kent. Safer Neighbourhood Team base for Kelsey
and Eden Park SNT and Clock House SNT. (Closed to public.)
◆Eltham (RM), 20 Well Hall Road, London SE9 6SF. (Mon–Sat   020 8284 5625
0800–2000, Sun 1000–1800.)
Enfield (YF), 41 Baker Street, Enfield, Middlesex EN1 3EU.   101
◆Feltham (TF), 34 Hanworth Road, Feltham, Middlesex TW13 5BD.   101
Forest Gate (KF), 350–360 Romford Road, London E7 8BS.   020 7230 1212
Fresh Wharf (KW) Custody Centre & Patrol Base, Unit 24 Muirhead   020 7230 1212
Quay, Fresh Wharf Estate, Barking, Essex IG11 7BG.
Fulham (FF), Heckfield Place, London SW6 5NL.   020 7230 1212
Gipsy Hill (LG), 66 Central Hill, Gipsy Hill, London SE19 1DT.   020 8649 2325
Golders Green (SG), 1069 Finchley Road, London NW11 0QB.   020 8733 5525
Green Street Green Safer Neighbourhood base (PY), 49 High Street,   101
Green Street Green, Orpington BR6 6BG. Safer Neighbourhood
Team base for Chelsfield and Pratts Bottom SNT and Farnborough
and Crofton SNT. (Closed to public.)
◆Greenford (XG), 21 Oldfield Lane, Greenford, Middlesex UB6 9LQ.   020 8575 1212
Greenwich (RG), 31 Royal Hill, London SE10 8RR (24 hours.)   020 8248 5325
Hackney (GH), 2 Lower Clapton Road, London E5 0PA.   020 7230 1212
Haggerston (GR), 228 Haggerston Road, London E8 4HT. (Restricted   020 7230 1212
opening hours.)
Hammersmith (FH), 226 Shepherds Bush Road, London W6 7NX.   020 7230 1212
Hampstead (EH), 26 Rosslyn Hill, London NW3 1PD.   020 8733 6625
◆Harefield (XF), The Gatehouse, Harefield Hospital, Hill End Road,   020 7230 1212
Harefield, Middlesex UB9 6JH. (Restricted opening hours.)

Harlesden (QH), 76 Craven Park, London NW10 8RJ.	020 8733 3825
Harrow (QA), 74 Northolt Road, Harrow, Middlesex HA2 0DN.	020 7230 1212
Harrow Central Police Station, 11–15 Peterborough Road, Harrow, Middlesex HA1 2AX.	020 7230 1212
Harrow Road Safer Neighbourhood Team (DR), 325 Harrow Road, London W9 3RD.	020 7230 1212
Hayes (XY), 755 Uxbridge Road, Hayes, Middlesex UB4 8HU. (Restricted opening hours.)	020 7230 1212
Heathrow Airport (ID), Heathrow Police Station, Unit 3, Polar Park, Bath Road, Sipson, West Drayton UB7 0DG.	020 3276 1460 (24 hours)
Hillingdon (XH), 1 Warwick Place, Uxbridge, Middlesex UB8 1PG. (24 hours.)	020 7230 1212
Holborn (EO), 10 Lamb's Conduit Street, London WC1N 3NR.	020 8733 6556
Holloway (NH), 284 Hornsey Road, London N7 7QY.	020 7230 1212
Hornchurch (KC), 74 Station Road, Hornchurch, Essex RM12 6NA.	020 7230 1212
Hornsey (YR), 98 Tottenham Lane, Hornsey, London N8 7EJ.	020 7230 1212
Hounslow (TX), 5 Montague Road, Hounslow, Middlesex TW3 1LB.	101
Ilford (JI), 270–294 High Road, Ilford, Essex IG1 1GT.	020 7230 1212
◆Isle of Dogs (HI), 160–174 Manchester Road, London E14 9HW. (Restricted opening hours.)	020 7230 1212
◆Islington (NI), 2 Tolpuddle Street, London N1 0YY.	020 7230 1212
◆Kenley (ZK), 94–96 Godstone Road, Kenley, Surrey CR8 5AB. (Restricted opening hours.)	020 8763 9222
Kennington (LK), 49–51 Kennington Road, London SE1 7QA.	020 8649 2429 (Custody)
Kensington (BD), 72 Earls Court Road, London W8 6EQ.	020 7230 1212
Kentish Town (EK), 12A Holmes Road, London NW5 3AE.	020 8733 6025
Kilburn (QK), 38 Salisbury Road, London NW6 6NN.	080 8733 3725
◆Kingsbury (QY), 5 The Mall, Kenton, Harrow, Middlesex HA3 9TF. (Restricted opening hours.)	020 7230 1212
Kingston (VK), 5–7 High Street, Kingston-upon-Thames, Surrey KT1 1LB.	020 8247 5351
◆Lavender Hill (WL), 176 Lavender Hill, London SW11 1JX.	020 7230 1212
◆Lee Road (PE), 418 Lee High Road, London SE12 8RW.	020 7230 1212
Leman Street (HD), 74 Leman Street, London E1 8EU.	020 7230 1212
Lewisham (PL), 43 Lewisham High Street, London SE13 5HZ. (24 hours.)	101
Leyton (JL), 215 Francis Road, London E10 6NJ.	020 7230 1212
Limehouse (HH), 29 West India Dock Road, London E14 8EZ.	020 7230 1212
Maple Road Safer Neighbourhood base (PY), Maple Road, Penge SE20 8RE. Safer Neighbourhood Team base for Crystal Palace SNT and Penge and Cator SNT. (Front counter service 1100–1500 and 1600–1900 Mon–Fri.)	101
Marks Gate (KK), 78 Ross Lane, Marks Gate, Romford, Essex RM6 5JU.	020 7230 1212
Marylebone, 1–9 Seymour Street, London W1H 7BA.	020 7230 1212
Mitcham (VM), 58 Cricket Green, Mitcham, Surrey CR4 4LA.	020 8947 1212
Morden (VR), 4 Crown Parade, Crown Lane, Morden, Surrey SM4 5DA.	020 8947 1212
◆Muswell Hill (YM), 115 Fortis Green, Muswell Hill, London N2 9HW.	020 7230 1212
◆New Malden Police Community Office (VN) St George's Square, High Street, New Malden, Surrey KT3 4HH.	020 7230 1212
◆Norbury (ZY), 15167 London Road, Norbury, London SW16 4ES. (Restricted opening hours.)	020 8765 1212
◆North Woolwich (KN), Albert Road, London E16 2JJ.	020 7230 1212
Northwood (XN), 2 Murray Road, Northwood, Middlesex HA6 2YW. (Restricted opening hours.)	020 7230 1212
Notting Hill (BH), 101 Ladbroke Road, London W11 3PL.	020 7230 1212
Operational Parade Site (JU), Uplands Patrol Base, Unit 6B–7B Uplands Business Park, Blackhorse Lane, Walthamstow, London E17 5QJ.	020 7230 1212
Orpington Safer Neighbourhood base (PY), The Walnuts, Orpington, Kent BR6 0TW. Safer Neighbourhood Team base for Orpington SNT. (Front counter service 1000–1200 Mon, Wed, Fri.)	101

Paddington Green (DP), 2–4 Harrow Road, London W2 1XJ.	020 7230 1212
Peckham (MM), 171 Peckham High Street, London SE15 5SL. (24 hours.)	020 7232 7125
Petts Wood Safer Neighbourhood base (PY), 198 Petts Wood Road, Petts Wood, Orpington, Kent. Safer Neighbourhood Team base for Petts Wood and Knoll SNT. (Closed to public.)	101
♦Pinner (QP), 1 Waxwell Lane, Pinner, Middlesex HA5 3LA.	020 7230 1212
♦Plaistow (KO), 444 Barking Road, London E13 8HJ.	020 7230 1212
Plumstead (RA), 200 Plumstead High Street, London SE18 1JY. (24 hours.)	020 8284 9471
♦Poplar (HP), 2 Market Way, London E14 8ET. (Restricted opening hours.)	020 7230 1212
♦Richmond (TR), 8 Red Lion Street, Richmond, Surrey TW9 1RW. (Front counter services at Sovereign Gate, 18–20 Kew Road, Richmond, 0800–2000 except bank/public holidays.)	020 8607 9199
♦Roehampton Safer Neighbourhoods Team (WR), 37 Holybourne Avenue, Roehampton, London SW15 4JE.	020 8247 7681
Romford (KD), 19 Main Road, Romford, Essex RM1 3BJ.	020 7230 1212
Rotherhithe (MR), 99 Lower Road, London SE16 2XQ. (Limited opening times.)	020 7232 6825
Ruislip (XR), The Oaks, Manor Road, Ruislip, Middlesex HA4 7LE. (Restricted opening hours.)	020 7230 1212
Shepherds Bush (FS), 252–258 Uxbridge Road, London W12 7JB.	020 7230 1212
Shoreditch (GD), 4–6 Shepherdess Walk, London N1 7LF.	020 7230 1212
South Norwood (ZN), 11 Oliver Grove, London SE25 6ED.	020 8768 1212
Southall (XS), 67 High Street, Southall, Middlesex UB1 3HG.	020 8574 1212
♦Southgate (YS), 25 Chase Side, Southgate, London N14 5BW.	101
Southwark (MD), 323 Borough High Street, London SE1 1JL. (Borough Grip & Pace Centre 24 hours.)	020 7232 6625
♦St Ann's Road (YA), 289 St Ann's Road, London N15 5RD.	020 7230 1212
St John's Wood (DS), 20 Newcourt Street, London NW8 7AA.	020 7230 1212
Stoke Newington (GN), 33 High Street, London N16 8DS.	020 7230 1212
Stratford (KS), 18 West Ham Lane, London E15 4SG.	020 7230 1212
Streatham (LS), 101 Streatham High Road, London SW16 1HT.	020 8649 2225/ 2229 (Custody)
Sutton (ZT), 6 Carshalton Road West, Sutton, Surrey SM1 4RF	020 8643 1212
♦Sydenham (PS), 179 Dartmouth Road, London SE26 4RN. (Mon–Fri 1000–1800.)	101
♦Teddington (TT), 18 Park Road, Teddington, Middlesex TW11 0AQ. (Mon–Fri 1000–1700, Sat 1100–1400 except bank/public holidays.)	020 8607 9199
♦Thamesmead (RT), 11 Joyce Dawson Way, London SE28 8RA. (24 hours.)	020 8721 2286
Tooting (WD), 251 Mitcham Road, London SW17 9JQ.	020 7230 1212
Tottenham (YT), 398 High Road, Tottenham, London N17 9JA.	020 7230 1212
♦Tower Bridge (MT), 209 Tooley Street, London SE1 2JX.	020 7230 1212
Twickenham (TW), 41 London Road, Twickenham, Middlesex TW1 3SY. (24 hours.)	020 8607 9199
Vauxhall (LX) *see* Kennington	
♦Wallington (ZW), Crosspoint House, Stafford Road, Wallington, Surrey.	020 8643 1212 (switching centre)
Walpole Road Safer Neighbourhood base, 58–62 Walpole Road, Bromley BR2 9SF. Safer Neighbourhood Team base for Bromley Common & Keston SNT and Bromley Town SNT. (Closed to public.)	101
Waltham Forest Custody Centre (JP), Boreham Close, Leyton E1 6RN.	020 7230 1212
Waltham House (JM), 11 Kirkdale House, Leytonstone, London E11 1HP.	020 7230 1212
Walthamstow Market Office (JK), 191–193 High Street, Walthamstow, London E17 7BX.	020 7230 1212
Walworth (MS), 12–18 Manor Place, London SE17 3RL. (24 hours.)	020 7232 6225
Wandsworth (WW), 146 High Street, London SW18 4JJ.	020 7230 1212
♦Wanstead (JN), Spratt Hall Road, London E11 2RQ.	020 7230 1212
Wembley (QD), 603 Harrow Road, Wembley, Middlesex HA0 2HH.	020 8733 3125

West Drayton (XE), Station Road, West Drayton, Middlesex UB7 7JQ. (Not open to the public.)	020 7230 1212
West End Central (CD), 27 Savile Row, London W1S 2EX	020 7230 1212
West Hampstead (EW), 21 Fortune Green Road, London NW6 1DX.	020 8733 6825
West Hendon (SV), The Broadway, London NW9 7AL.	020 7230 1212
West Wickham Safer Neighbourhood base (PY), 9 High Street, West Wickham, Kent BR4 0LP. Safer Neighbourhood Team base for West Wickham SNT. (Front counter service 1000–1200 Mon–Fri.)	101
♦ Whetstone (ST), 1170 High Road, London N20 0LW.	020 8733 5225
Willesden Green (QL), 96 High Road, London NW10 2PP.	020 8733 3925
Wimbledon (VW), 15 Queen's Road, London SW19 8NN.	020 8947 1212
♦ Winchmore Hill (YW), 687 Green Lanes, London N21 3RS.	101
♦ Woodford (JF), 509 High Road, Woodford Green, Essex IG8 0SR.	020 7230 1212
Wood Green (YD), 347 High Road, London N22 4HZ.	020 7230 1212
Wood Green Patrol Base (YDQ), Units 1 & 2, Quicksilver Place, Western Road, Wood Green, London N22 6XH.	020 7230 1212
Woolwich (RW), 29 Market Street, London SE18 6QS. (Mon–Fri 0700–2000 weekends 1000–1800.)	020 8284 9826
♦ Worcester Park (ZR), 154 Central Road, Worcester Park, Surrey KT4 8HH.	020 8643 1212 (switching centre)
Marine Police Unit	
♦ Wapping (UD), 98 Wapping High Street, London E1W 2NE.	020 7275 4452 (general enquiries)/ 4402 (unit commander)/ 4850 (workshops (transport services))

WESTMINSTER BOROUGH

Charing Cross Police Station, Agar Street, London WC2N 4JP. Tel: 020 7321 7712. Individuals tel: 020 7321 plus last four digits of extension number.

Commander, City of Westminster: Alison Newcomb. Ext: 48209. Fax: 48292.
Staff Officer: Sgt Stephen Willers. Ext: 47516.
Personal Secretary: Sue Kilbey. Ext: 47530. Fax: 48282.
Chief Superintendent: Paul Rickett. Ext: 46703.
Borough Senior Finance & Resources Manager: Karen Seaman. Ext: 56776.

ROYAL PARKS OCU, METROPOLITAN POLICE SERVICE

Headquarters: Police Station, Hyde Park, London W2 2UH. Tel: 020 7298 2000. Fax: 020 7298 2005.
Responsible for policing the 17 royal parks, gardens and other open spaces within the Greater London area.

OCU Commander: Supt Colin Morgan. Tel: 020 7321 6703.
Deputy OCU Commander: Chief Insp Wayne Petford. Tel: 020 7161 9610.
Business Manager: Karen Seaman. Tel: 020 7231 6776
Operations Inspector: Insp Emma Richards. Tel: 020 7161 9601.
Crime Manager: Insp Scott McDonald. Tel: 020 7161 9633.

Stations Covering the City of Westminster
For details of the police stations listed below, refer to the table above.

Operational police stations: Belgravia; Charing Cross; Paddington.
Stations housing officers but not response officers: Harrow Road; Marylebone; West End Central.

EAST LONDON

East London consists of the London boroughs of Barking & Dagenham, Enfield, Hackney, Haringey, Havering, Islington, Newham, Redbridge, Tower Hamlets and Waltham Forest.

COMMUNITY LIAISON OFFICERS FOR THE BOROUGHS

Barking & Dagenham: Chief Insp Richard Goodwin. Tel: 020 8217 5545.
Hackney: Supt Richard Woolfrod. Tel: 020 7275 3272.
Haringey: Insp Tracey Tempest. Tel: 020 3276 0150.
Islington: Chief Insp Richard Padwell. Tel: 020 7421 0121.
Newham: Chief Insp Dave Moorhead. Tel: 020 8217 5374.
Redbridge: Chief Insp Michael Forbes. Tel: 020 8345 2771.
For details of the police stations listed below, refer to the table above.

Stations Covering the London Borough of Barking & Dagenham
Tel: 020 7230 1212.
Dagenham (KG); Barking (KB); Fresh Wharf (KW). *Borough Commander:* Chief Supt Andrew Ewing.
Stations Covering the London Borough of Enfield
Tel: 101.

Edmonton (YE); Enfield (YF); Southgate (YS); Winchmore Hill (YW). *Borough Commander:* Chief Supt Jane Johnson.

Stations Covering the London Borough of Hackney
Tel: 020 7230 1212
Shoreditch (GD) and Hackney (GH); Stoke Newington (GN). *Borough Commander:* Chief Supt Matthew Horne.

Stations Covering the London Borough of Haringey
Tel: 020 7230 1212.
Tottenham (YT); Wood Green (YD); St Ann's Road (YA); Hornsey (YR); Muswell Hill (YM), Wood Green Patrol Base (YDQ). *Borough Commander:* Det Chief Supt Sandra Looby.

Stations Covering the London Borough of Havering
Tel: 020 7230 1212.
Havering (KD); Hornchurch (KC). *Borough Commander:* Chief Supt Michael Smith.

Stations Covering the London Borough of Islington
Tel: 020 7230 1212.
Islington (NI); Holloway (NH). *Borough Commander:* Det Chief Supt Gerry Campbell.

Stations Covering the London Borough of Newham
Tel: 020 7230 1212.
Forest Gate (KF); Plaistow (KO); Stratford (KS); North Woolwich (KN); East Ham (KE). *Borough Commander:* Chief Supt Robert Jones. **Operations, Partnerships, Youth:** Supt Craig Haslam. Tel: 020 8217 5302. **Response Teams:** Chief Insp David Brewster. Tel: 020 8217 5204. **Neighbourhood Policing:** Chief Insp Dave Moorhead. Tel: 020 8217 5223. **Business Support:** Supt Ian Larnder. Tel: 020 8217 5209. Chief Insp Guy Wade; Chief Insp Rick Tyson. Tel: 020 8217 5372. **Crime Investigation:** Det Supt Helen Millichap. Tel: 020 8217 5264. **Acquisitive Crime:** Det Chief Insp Alan Moore. Tel: 020 8217 5406. **Public Protection:** Det Chief Insp Dave Rock. Tel: 020 8275 5878. **Forensics:** HEO David Bennett. Tel: 020 8345 4226. **Human Resources:** SHRM Minaxi Patel. Tel: 020 7232 6605. **Intelligence:** HEO Jon West. Tel: 020 8217 5014.

Stations Covering the London Borough of Redbridge
Tel: 020 7230 1212.
Ilford (JI); Wanstead (JN); Barkingside (JB); Woodford (JF). *Borough Commander:* Chief Supt Sue Williams.

Stations Covering the London Borough of Tower Hamlets
Tel: 020 7230 1212.
Bethnal Green (HT); Limehouse (HH); Brick Lane (HR); Isle of Dogs (HI); Bow (HW); Poplar (HP). *Borough Commander:* Chief Supt Dave Stringer.

Stations Covering the London Borough of Waltham Forest
Tel: 020 7230 1212.
Chingford (JC); Leyton (JL); Operational Parade Site (JU); Waltham Forest Custody Centre (JP); Waltham House (JM); Walthamstow Market Office (JK). *Borough Commander:* Chief Supt Mark Collins.

WEST LONDON
West London consists of the London boroughs of Barnet, Brent, Camden, Ealing, Hammersmith and Fulham, Hillingdon, Hounslow, Kensington & Chelsea and Richmond-upon-Thames.
COMMUNITY LIAISON OFFICERS FOR THE BOROUGHS
Camden: Supt Gary Buttercase. Tel: 020 8733 6003.
Ealing: Chief Insp Dan Thorpe. Tel: 020 8246 2080.
Harrow: Insp Stuart Ward. Tel: 020 8733 3477.
Hounslow: Chief Insp Robert Wilson. Tel: 020 8247 6200.
Richmond-upon-Thames: Chief Insp Steve Kyte. Tel: 020 8247 5801.
SAFER NEIGHBOURHOODS & PARTNERSHIP OFFICER
Hillingdon Borough: Chief Insp Nigel Quantrell. Tel: 020 8246 1473.
For details of the police stations listed below, refer to the table above.

Stations Covering the London Borough of Barnet
Tel: 020 7230 1212.
Colindale (SC); Golders Green (SG); Barnet (SA); Whetstone (ST). *Borough Commander:* Chief Supt Adrian Usher. All enquiries via the Staff Office tel: 020 8733 4005/4022.

Stations Covering the London Borough of Brent
Tel: 020 7230 1212.
Borough HQ: Wembley (QD). Other stations: Kilburn (QK); Willesden Green (QL); Harlesden (QH). *Borough Commander:* Chief Supt Matthew Gardner. All enquiries via the Secretariat tel: 020 8721 3124.

Stations Covering the London Borough of Camden
Tel: 020 7230 1212.
Albany Street (ED); Holborn (EO); Hampstead (EH); West Hampstead (EW); Kentish Town (EK). *Borough Commander:* Chief Supt John Sutherland.
Stations Covering the London Borough of Ealing
Tel: 020 7230 1212.
Southall (XS); Ealing (XD); Acton (XA); Greenford (XG). *Borough Commander:* Det Chief Supt Andy Rowell.
Stations Covering the London Borough of Hammersmith & Fulham
Tel: 020 7230 1212.
Hammersmith (FH); Shepherds Bush (FS); Fulham (FF). *Borough Commander:* Lucy D'Orsi.
Stations Covering the London Borough of Harrow
Tel: 020 7230 1212.
Harrow (QA); Pinner (QP). *Borough Commander:* Chief Supt Dalwardin Babu.
Heathrow & London City Airport Police (SO18 Aviation Security)
Tel: 020 3276 1460 (24 hours).
OCU Commander: Chief Supt Bert Moore. Tel: 020 3276 1248. *Superintendent Deputy to OCU Commander:* Martin Hendy.
Stations Covering the London Borough of Hillingdon
Tel: 020 7230 1212.
Hillingdon (XH); Ruislip (XR); Northwood (XN); Hayes (XY); West Drayton (XE); Harefield (XF). *Borough Commander:* Chief Supt Steve Kershaw.
Stations Covering the London Borough of Hounslow
Tel: 020 7230 1212.
Hounslow (TX); Feltham (TF); Chiswick (TC); Brentford (TB). *Borough Commander:* Det Chief Supt Carl Bussey. Supt Paul Martin.
Stations Covering the London Borough of Kensington & Chelsea
Tel: 020 7230 1212.
Kensington (BD); Chelsea (BC); Notting Hill (BH). *Divisional Command:* T/Chief Supt Alisdair Ferguson.
Stations Covering the London Borough of Richmond-upon-Thames
Tel: 020 7230 1212.
Twickenham (TW): *OCU Commander:* Chief Supt Clive Chalk. **Operational:** Det Supt Christos Kalamatianos. Teddington (TT); Richmond (TR).

SOUTH LONDON
South London consists of the London boroughs of Bexley, Bromley, Croydon, Greenwich, Kingston-upon-Thames, Lambeth, Lewisham, Merton, Southwark, Sutton and Wandsworth.
BOROUGH LIAISON OFFICERS
Bexley Safer Neighbourhoods and Partnership Manager: Chief Insp Ian Broadbridge. Tel: 020 8284 9114.
Croydon: Chief Insp Caroline Trevithick. Tel: 020 8649 0209.
Royal Borough of Kingston-upon-Thames: Chief Insp Bill Heasman. Tel: 020 8247 5124.
Lambeth: Chief Insp Robyn Williams. Tel: 07771 748069.
Lewisham: Chief Insp Shaun Willshire. Tel: 020 8284 8425.
Southwark: *Borough Commander Staff Officer:* Sgt Chris Scott. Tel: 020 7232 6653. *Business Support Team Manager:* Michelle Taylor. Tel: 020 7232 6654.
Sutton: Chief Insp Nick Collins. Tel: 020 8649 0499.
Wandsworth: Chief Insp Dale Anderton. Tel: 020 8247 8681. Based at Lavender Hill.
For details of the police stations listed below, refer to the table above.
Stations Covering the London Borough of Bexley
Tel: 020 7230 1212.
Bexleyheath (RY): Chief Supt Victor Olisa; Supt Peter Ayling.
Stations Covering the London Borough of Bromley
Tel: 101.
Bromley (PY): Det Chief Supt S Roberts; Det Supt J Oakley. Bromley Police Station; Beckenham Safer Neighbourhood base; Bickley Safer Neighbourhood base; Biggin Hill Safer Neighbourhood base; Burnt Ash Lane Safer Neighbourhood base; Chislehurst Safer Neighbourhood base; Coney Hall Safer Neighbourhood base; Cray Valley Safer Neighbourhood base; Elmers End Safer Neighbourhood base; Green Street Green Safer Neighbourhood base; Maple Road Safer Neighbourhood base; Orpington Safer Neighbourhood base; Petts Wood Safer Neighbourhood base; Walpole Road Safer Neighbourhood base; West Wickham Safer Neighbourhood base.

Stations Covering the London Borough of Croydon
Tel: 020 7230 1212.
Croydon (ZD): Chief Supt Dave Musker; Det Supt Simon Messinger; Supt Rob Atkin. Kenley (ZK); South Norwood (ZN); Norbury (ZY); Addington (ZA).

Stations Covering the London Borough of Greenwich
Tel: 020 7230 1212.
Greenwich (RG); Eltham (RM); Westcombe Park (RK); Thamesmead (RT); Plumstead (RA): Det Chief Supt Richard Wood; Woolwich (RW).

Stations Covering the Royal London Borough of Kingston-upon-Thames
Tel: 020 8247 5351. For further details and Safer Neighbourhood Teams see website: www.met.police.uk/kingston
Kingston (VK); *OCU Commander:* Martin Greenslade.

Stations Covering the London Borough of Lambeth
Tel: 020 7230 1212.
Borough Commander: Chief Supt Matt Bell. *Deputy Borough Commander:* Det Supt Martin Huxley. *Superintendent Operations:* Andy Howe. **CID:** Det Supt Martin Huxley. **Partnership:** Supt David McLaren. Tel: 07768 908495.

Stations Covering the London Borough of Lewisham
Tel: 020 7230 1212.
Lewisham (PL): *OCU Commander:* Chief Supt Russell Nyman; Supt Suzanne Wallace; Supt Michael Gallagher. Catford (PD); Sydenham (PS); Deptford (PP); Brockley (PK).

Stations Covering the London Borough of Merton
Tel: 020 7230 1212.
Wimbledon (VW): *OCU Commander:* Det Chief Supt Darren Williams; Supt David Palmer; Supt Pete Dobson. Mitcham (VM); Morden (VR).

Stations Covering the London Borough of Southwark
Tel: 020 7232 6007.
Southwark (MD): *OCU Commander:* Chief Supt John Sutherland. **Partnership:** Supt Cheryl Burden. **Crime:** Det Supt Neil Hutchison. **Operations:** A/Supt Neil Paton. Southwark (MD); East Dulwich (ME); Peckham (MM); Rotherhithe (MR); Camberwell (MC); Walworth (MS)

Stations Covering the London Borough of Sutton
Tel: 020 7230 1212.
Sutton (ZT): *OCU Commander:* Det Chief Supt Guy Ferguson. Supt Fran Smith. Wallington (ZW); Worcester Park (ZR).

Stations Covering the London Borough of Wandsworth
Tel: 020 7230 1212
Battersea (WA): *Borough Commander:* Chief Supt David Chinchen. Tel: 020 8247 8406. *Deputy Borough Commander:* Supt Paul McGregor. Tel: 020 8247 8406. *Det Chief Inspector Acquisitive Crime:* Jim Foley. Tel: 02 8247 8447. *A/Chief Inspector Partnership:* Gilbert Martin. Tel: 020 8247 8401. Earlsfield (WF): *Chief Inspector Operations:* Dawn Morris. Tel: 020 8247 8935. Lavender Hill (WL): *Chief Inspector Safer Neighbourhoods:* Dale Anderton. Tel: 020 8247 8681. Tooting (WD): no SLT presence. Wandsworth (WH): *Det Superintendent Crime:* Penny Banham. Tel: 020 3276 2553. *Det Chief Inspector Public Protection:* Brian McCluskey. Tel: 020 3276 2561.

REPRESENTATIVES
Police Superintendents' Association of England and Wales (Metropolitan and City of London Police Forces). *Secretary:* Chief Supt Joanna Young. Room 311, New Scotland Yard. Tel: 020 7230 3356/2771. Mob: 07799 476649.
Police Federation. York House, 2 Elmfield Park, Bromley, Kent BR1 1LU. *Joint Executive Committee General Secretary:* PC Neil Cratchley. Tel: 020 8464 2322. Email: n.cratchley@metfed.org.uk

THE MAYOR'S OFFICE FOR POLICING AND CRIME
(formerly the Metropolitan Police Authority)
10 Dean Farrar Street, London SW1H 0NY. Tel: 020 7202 0202. Individuals tel: 020 7202 plus extension number. Minicom: 020 7202 0173. Fax: 020 7202 0200.

Email: firstname.lastname@mopac.london.gov.uk, unless otherwise stated.

Website: www.london.gov.uk/policing

The Mayor's Office for Policing and Crime has been set up in response to the Police Reform and Social Responsibility Act (2011) which reforms the accountability of police services and replaces police authorities across England and Wales with elected individuals. The MOPAC is headed by the Mayor or, by his nomination, the appointed statutory Deputy Mayor for Policing and Crime. This means that the Mayor is directly accountable for policing performance in

London. The MOPAC makes this process and accountability clearer and gives Londoners a further voice in how their city is policed. Through the MOPAC the Mayor and Deputy Mayor will be directly accountable for police performance in the capital, setting the Metropolitan Police's strategic direction and allocating resources. Operational policing remains the responsibility of the Metropolitan Police Commissioner, Sir Bernard Hogan-Howe.

Occupant of the Mayor's Office for Policing & Crime: Boris Johnson, Mayor of London. Email: mayor@london.gov.uk

Deputy Mayor for Policing & Crime: Stephen Greenhalgh.

Chief Operating Officer: Helen Bailey. Ext: 0203.

Chief Finance Officer: Bob Atkins. Ext: 0209.

Deputy Chief Finance Officer: Annabel Adams. Ext: 0206.

Director of Audit, Risk & Assurance: Julie Norgrove. Ext: 0104.

HM CORONERS

East London: Mr Chinyere Inyama. Coroner's Court, Queen's Road, Walthamstow E17 8QP. Tel: 020 8496 5000. Fax: 020 8496 3378.

Inner North London: Dr A Scott Reid. St Pancras Coroner's Court, Camley Street, London N1C 4PP. Tel: 020 7387 4884/2. Fax: 020 7383 2485.

Inner South London: Dr Andrew Harris. Southwark Coroner's Court, 1 Tennis Street, London SE1 1YD. Tel: 020 7525 4200. Fax: 020 7525 6356. Email: andrew.harris@southwark.gov.uk

Inner West London: Fiona J Wilcox. Westminster Coroner's Court, 65 Horseferry Road, London SW1P 2ED. Tel: 020 7802 4750. Fax: 020 7828 2837.

North London: Andrew Walker. 29 Wood Street, Barnet, London EN5 4BE. Tel: 020 8447 7680. Fax: 020 8447 7690.

Southern District of London: Dr Roy Palmer. Croydon Coroner's Court, Barclay Road, Croydon CR9 3NE. Tel: 020 8681 5019. Fax: 020 8680 0999.

West London: Alison Mary Thompson. 25 Bagleys Lane, Fulham, London SW6 2QA. Tel: 020 8753 6800. Fax: 020 8753 6803.

YOUTH OFFENDING TEAMS

Youth Offending Team	Address	Phone	Fax
Barking & Dagenham	Bridge House, 150 London Road Barking, Essex IG11 8BB.	020 8227 3998	020 8227 3690
Barnet	North London Business Park, Oakleigh Road South, London N11 1NP.	020 8359 5535	020 8359 5530
Bexley	The Howbury Centre, Slade Green Road, Erith, Kent DA8 2HX.	020 8284 9207	020 8284 5560
Brent	Chesterfield House, 9 Park Lane, Wembley HA9 7RH.	020 8937 3810	020 8937 3811
Bromley	8 Masons Hill, Bromley, Kent BR2 9EY.	020 8466 3080	020 8466 3099
Camden	Crowndale Centre, 218 Eversholt Street, London NW1 1BD.	020 7974 1304	020 7974 7208
Croydon	Turnaround Centre, 51–55 Southend, Croydon CR0 1BF.	020 8404 5860	020 8404 5810
Ealing	Youth Justice Office, 2 Cheltenham Place, Acton W3 8JS.	020 8993 9555 Mob: 07769	020 8993 6292
Enfield	Claverings Industrial Estate, 3 South Way, London N9 0AB.	64254 020 8379 5805/07/30	020 8379 5801
Greenwich	The Woolwich Centre, 35 Wellington Street, Woolwich, London SE18 6HQ.	020 3276 0660/61/62	
Hackney	275 Mare Street, Hackney, London E8 1GR.	020 8356 1025/1014/1038/1062/1098	020 8356 1090
Hammersmith & Fulham	Cobbs Hall, Fulham Palace Road, Fulham, London SW6 0LL.	020 8753 6200	020 8753 6242
Haringey	48 Station Road, Wood Green, N22 7TY	020 8489 1596	020 8489 1588
Harrow	13 St John's Road, Harrow, Middlesex, HA1 2EE.	020 8901 4455	020 8901 4466
Havering	Portman House, Ground Floor, 16–20 Victoria Road, Romford, Essex RM1 2JH.	01708 436220	01708 436222
Hillingdon	Link 1A, Civic Centre, High Street, Uxbridge, Middlesex UB8 1UW.	01895 558203	01895 477946
Hounslow	Redlees Centre, Worton Road, Isleworth TW7 6DW.	020 8583 6363	020 8479 9418
Islington	London Borough of Islington Youth Centre Team, Dingley Centre, 27 Dingley Place, London EC1V 8BR.	020 7527 7059	020 7527 7066
Kensington & Chelsea	36C Oxford Gardens, London W10 5UQ.	020 7598 4734/4701	020 8598 4715
Kingston-upon-Thames	Ground Floor, Guildhall 1, Kingston-upon-Thames KT1 1EU.	020 8547 6920	020 8547 6959
Lambeth	Lambeth Young People Services, 392 Brixton Road, Brixton, London SW19 7AW.	020 7926 2644	020 7926 2639
Lewisham	23 Mercia Grove, Lewisham, London SE13 6BJ.	020 8314 6794/8565	020 8314 3505
Merton	1st Floor, Athena House, 86–88 London Road, Morden, Surrey SM4 5AZ.	020 8274 4949	020 8540 5829
Newham	192 Cumberland Road, Plaistow, London E13 8LT.	020 3373 3589/3462	020 8430 2299
Redbridge	Redbridge Youth Offending Team, Station Road Centre, Station Road, Barkingside, Essex IG6 1NB.	020 8708 7800	020 8708 7802
Richmond-upon-Thames	2nd Floor, 42 York Street, Twickenham, Middlesex TW1 3BW.	020 8891 7050	020 8891 7473
Southwark	1 Bradenham Close, Aylesbury Estate, Albany Road, London SE17 2QA.	020 7525 0919	020 7525 7876
Sutton	57 Montague Gardens, Wallington, Surrey SM6 8BP.	020 8773 6621	020 8773 6634
Tower Hamlets	5th Floor, Mulberry Place, 5 Clove Crescent, London E14 2BG.	020 7364 1099/1696	020 8983 9911
Waltham Forest	Rowan House, 1 Cecil Road, Leytonstone, London E11 3HF.	020 8496 5033/5002	020 8496 5052

Youth Offending Team	Address	Phone	Fax
Wandsworth	177 Blackshaw Road, Tooting, London SW17 0DJ.	020 8871 5554/5561/5574	020 8682 4255
Westminster	6a Crompton Street, London W2 1ND.	020 7641 7799/7782/6649	020 7641 5311

CITY OF LONDON POLICE
37 Wood Street, London EC2P 2NQ.
Tel: 020 7601 2222. Fax: 020 7601 2125 (24 hrs).
Email: Postmaster@cityoflondon.pnn.police.uk; staff email:
firstname.lastname@cityoflondon.pnn.police.uk
Website: www.cityoflondon.police.uk

Official communications to: The Commissioner of Police for the City of London, 37 Wood Street, London EC2P 2NQ.

Please note that some streets in the EC postal district are situated in the Metropolitan Police district. EC after an address does not necessarily indicate that it is in the City of London; for example, City Road EC1, Old Street EC1, Farringdon Road EC1, Finsbury Pavement EC2, and HM Tower of London EC3 are all in the Metropolitan Police District.

Lord Mayor: Alderman Roger Gifford.
Aldermanic Sheriff: Alderman Jeffery Evans.
Clerk to the Police Authority: John Barradell OBE.
Clerk to the Police Committee: Alex Orme.

Commissioner: Adrian Leppard QPM MBA.
PA: Mrs Sara Coker.
Assistant Commissioner: Ian Dyson.
PA: Mrs Josie Wheeler.
T/Commander Operations: Wayne Chance.
PA: Mrs Xa Naylor.
T/Commander National Coordinator Economic Crime: Steve Head.
ACPO Staff Officers: T/Sgt Jess Wynne; T/Sgt Jon Quin.
Chief of Staff: Ms Hayley Williams.

CORPORATE SERVICES DIRECTORATE
37 Wood Street, London EC2P 2NQ. Fax: 020 7601 2260.
ACPO Director of Corporate Services: Eric Nisbett BA(Hons) ACMA.
PA: Mrs Sheila McCullough.
T/Head of Shared Services: Ms Gillian Slipper.

PROFESSIONAL STANDARDS
PO Box 36451, London EC2M 4WN. Tel: 020 7601 2770. Fax: 020 7601 2711.
Director of Professional Standards: Det Supt Martin Kapp.
Force Vetting Manager: Mr Paul Holcroft.

CORPORATE COMMUNICATION
37 Wood Street, London EC2P 2NQ. Tel: 020 7601 2220. Fax: 020 7601 2236.
T/Corporate Communications Director: Jon Parker MCIPR.
Web Manager: Michael Frost.
Media Liaison Officer: Christine Townsend MCIPR. Tel: 020 7601 2220.
PR Manager: Tracey Woods.
Internal Communications Manager: Pamela Ray.

HUMAN RESOURCES
Human Resource Services Directorate, 5 Snow Hill, London EC1A 2DP.
Head of HR Services: Phil Pepper MCIPD.
Joint Heads of HR: Caroline Craigie MCIPD; Maria Harding FCIPD.
Head of Learning & Development: Jean Harper FCIPD BSc(Hons).
Head of Occupational Health: Ginny Giles RGN Bsc(Hons).
Recruitment Managers: Mary-Anne Blackburn; Jen Mitchell.
Workforce Career & Development Manager: Sgt Garry Freire.
Workforce Information Manager: Diego Leal.
PA: Fiona Ramsay.

FINANCIAL SERVICES
T/Head of Finance: Nina Van Markwijk ACCA BSc(Hons).
Senior Finance Manager: Meinir Hall BSc(Hons) Econ FCCA.
PA: Fiona Ramsay.

GENERAL SERVICES
21 New Street, London EC2M 4TP. Tel: 020 7601 6792.
General Services Director: Roger Archer-Reeves PGDip Eng MSc Eng CMILT.

Head of Facilities Management: Mr Mike Ward MBIFM.
Vehicle Fleet Manager: Arend Mouton.
Force Supplies Officer: Tim Higham.
Facilities Manager Wood Street: Mr Neil Hawkins.
Facilities Manager Bernard Morgan House: Mr Anthony Haynes.

STRATEGIC DEVELOPMENT

Head of Strategic Development: Supt Lorraine Cussen.
Deputy Head of Strategic Development: Mr Stuart Phoenix LLB(Hons).
Head of Corporate Programmes: Mr Brian Petty.
Head of Performance Information: Ms Fiona MacLeod BSc(Hons) MSc.
Head of Service Review & Development & EDHR: Chief Insp Tony Cairney.
Chief of Staff: Ms Hayley Williams.
Risk Advisor: Mr Paul Adams BA(Hons) MA(WBS).

INFORMATION TECHNOLOGY
21 New Street, London EC2M 4TP. Fax: 020 7601 2009.

Information Services & Information Technology Director: Mr Amrik Dosanjh.
Operations Manager. Tel: 0207 601 6776.
IT Service Desk. Tel: 0207 601 6744.

UNIFORM POLICING DIRECTORATE
37 Wood Street, London EC2P 2NQ. Fax: 020 7601 2510.

Head of Uniform Policing: Chief Supt Andrew Mellor.
Superintendent Operations: Dave Lawes.
Superintendent Communities: Norma Collicott.
Chief Inspector Support: Andrew Ricketts.
Chief Inspector Operations: T/Chief Insp Chris Rowbottom.
PA: Ms Margaret Raymond. Tel 020 7601 2128.
Staff Officer. Tel: 020 7601 2140.

CRIME INVESTIGATION DIRECTORATE
182 Bishopsgate, London EC2M 4NQ.

Head of Specialist Crime Operations: Det Chief Supt Ken Stewart.
Operations: T/Det Supt John Folan.
Counter-terrorism: Supt Dermont Robinson.
PA: Mrs Nadia Head.

INTELLIGENCE & INFORMATION DIRECTORATE
37 Wood Street, London EC2P 2NQ.

Head of Intelligence & Information Directorate: Det Chief Supt Jeff Davies.
Head of Information & Operational Planning: Supt Dave McGinley.
Director of Intelligence: Det Supt Julie MacFarlane
Deputy Head of Information & Operational Planning: Chief Insp Matt Burgess.
Deputy Director of Intelligence: Det Chief Insp Pete Digby.
Head of Information Management: Mr Gary Brailsford-Hart.
Information Access Manager (FoI/DPA/CRB): Insp David Lockyear.
PNC & PND: Ms Liz Newns.
PA: Ms Jane King.

ADMINISTRATION OF JUSTICE DEPARTMENT
PO Box 36428, London EC2M 4WG. Tel: 020 7601 2148.

Head of Criminal Justice: Ms Mairi Moore MCMI.
Deputy Head of Criminal Justice: T/Insp Nigel Howard.
Traffic Section Manager. Mrs Jacqui Adkin MCMI.
Crime Section Manager. Mrs Jennifer Harper.

ECONOMIC CRIME
21 New Street, London EC2M 4TP.

Head of Economic Crime: T/Det Chief Supt Oliver Shaw.
Head of Operations: Det Supt Bob Wishart.
Head of Sponsored Policing: Det Supt Paul Barnard.
Director of National Fraud Intelligence Bureau (NFIB): Det Supt Dave Clark.
Head of Fraud Investigation: Det Chief Insp Perry Stokes.
Head of Financial Investigation: Det Chief Insp Dave Manley.
Head of Dedicated Cheque & Plastic Crime Unit (DCPCU): Det Chief Insp Dave Carter.
Head of Insurance Fraud Enforcement Department (IFED): Det Chief Insp Dave Wood.
Head of Overseas Anti-corruption Unit (OACU): Det Chief Insp Sanjay Andersen.
Head of Economic Crime & Fraud Training Academy: Det Insp Steve Strickland.

PA: Ms Shade Idris.

CITY OF LONDON SPECIAL CONSTABULARY
37 Wood Street, London, EC2P 2NQ. Tel: 020 7601 2712.
Commandant: Ian Miller MBE.

STAFF ASSOCIATIONS
Superintendents' Association: *Secretary of City Branch:* Det Chief Supt Ken Stewart.
Police Federation: City of London JBB, Wood Street Police Office, London EC2P 2NQ.
Black Police Association: Mr John Awosoga.
Women's Network: Supt Lorraine Cussen.
Chorus (Gay Support Network): PC Richard Butcher.
Disability Network: Chief Insp Norma Collicott.
Christian Police Association: A/Sgt Mark Price.
Muslim Police Association: PC Asif Sadiq.
Sports & Social Club: Sgt Colin Norris.
General & Municipal Boilermakers (GMB): Mr Kevin Bedford.
Unite the Union: Mr Mick Cawston.

HM CORONER
Dr Paul Matthews. City of London Coroner's Court, Walbrook Wharf, 78–83 Upper Thames Street,
London EC4Y 3TD. Tel: 020 7332 1598. Fax: 020 7332 1800.
Email: paul.major@cityoflondon.gov.uk

AVON AND SOMERSET CONSTABULARY
PO Box No 37, Portishead, Bristol BS20 8QJ.
Tel: 101. Telex: 44–114. Fax: 01275 816890 (24 hrs).
The dialling code for all numbers is 01275, unless otherwise indicated.
Email: firstname.lastname@avonandsomerset.pnn.police.uk
Website: www.avonandsomerset.police.uk
Unless otherwise stated all personnel should be contacted via the Force Service Centre.

Lord Lieutenant: Mr Andrew Nisbet (Bristol); Mrs Sylvana Chandler (Somerset); Mr Duncan Clegg (Glos).
Police & Crime Commissioner: Ms Sue Mountstevens.
Chief Executive to the Police & Crime Commissioner: Mr J Smith.
Chief Financial Officer to the Police & Crime Commissioner: Mr M Simmonds.
Office of the Police & Crime Commissioner. Tel: 816377.

Chief Constable: Mr Nick Gargan.
Deputy Chief Constable: Mr R Beckley QPM.
Assistant Chief Constable Communications, Criminal Justice & Service Standards: Mr A Bangham.
Assistant Chief Constable Protective Services: Mr R Hansen.
Assistant Chief Constable Territorial Operations: Mr J Long.
Strategic Director of Finance: Mr J Kern.
Strategic Director of Human Resources: Mrs E Zeeman.
Chief Constable's Staff Officer: T/Chief Insp C Morgan.
Head of Legal Services: Ms S Dauncey LLB. Tel: 816270.
Head of Professional Standards Unit: Supt I Wylie. Tel: 816020.

ORGANISATIONAL DEVELOPMENT TEAM
Head of Organisational Development Team: Mr L Bohdan. Tel: 816191.
Performance & Process Improvement Unit: Mr S Price. Tel: 816323.
Change Management Unit: Mrs V Hext. Tel: 816228.
Force Inspection Unit: Chief Insp C Jennings. Tel: 816321.

EXECUTIVE SERVICES DEPARTMENT
Head of Corporate Communications: Mrs A Hirst.
Deputy Head of Corporate Communications: Mrs Z Heben. Tel: 816155.
Head of Corporate Information Management: Mrs K Ford MBE. Tel: 816183.
Head of Retained ICT: Mr M Bailey. Tel: 0845 456 700.

OPERATIONS
Head of Operations: Chief Supt C Peters. Tel: 816908.
Operations Training: Chief Insp R Hughes. Tel: 816892.
Firearms & Road Policing & Policy: Chief Insp J Holt. Tel: 816845.
Firearms Unit: Chief Insp J Holt. Tel: 816845.
Operations Management: Chief Insp Y Georgiou. Tel: 816845.
Operational Support: Chief Insp P Mogg. Tel: 816843.
Operational Planning: Chief Insp A Cohen. Tel: 816519.
Operational Training: Chief Insp R Hughes. Tel: 816292.
Roads Policing: *Head of Roads Policing:* T/Supt P Richards. Tel: 816519.
Traffic Management: Mr D Sheppard. Tel: 816854.
Head of Operations Planning: Supt K Instance. Tel: 816847.
Air Operations Unit: Insp B Thomas. Tel: 0117 936 3974.
Mounted & Dogs Units: Chief Insp P Mogg. Tel: 816843.

CRIMINAL INVESTIGATION
Head of CID: Chief Supt S Jeffries. Tel: 816594.
Head of Major Crime & Investigation Unit: Supt S Scott. Tel: 0117 945 5834.
Head of Public Protection Unit: Supt G Wessell. Tel: 816954.
Director of Intelligence: Supt M Saunders. Tel: 816653.
Head of Scientific Investigations: Mr M Bradford. Tel: 816522.
Authorising Officer: Det Supt M Courtiour. Tel: 816702.
Special Branch: Chief Insp D Kearney. Tel: 0845 456 7000.

PERSONNEL AND TRAINING
Head of HR Business Support: Mrs C Wood. Tel: 816079.
Head of People Development: Mrs C Dodsworth. Tel: 816983.

Senior HR Business Partner (Diversity): N F Saba LLB LLM LCIPD. Tel: 816181.
Head of Safety: Mr D Bray. Tel: 814934.
Corporate Learning & Development: Ms C Taylor. Tel: 816504.
Occupational Health & Welfare: Dr D Bulpitt. Tel: 814943.

COMMUNICATIONS
Head of Communications: Chief Supt A Francis. Tel: 816507.
Strategic Development: Chief Insp M Evans. Tel: 816508.
Force Control Room Manager: Chief Insp A Bennett. Tel: 816508.
Call Centre Manager: Ms A Barnfather. Tel: 816827.
HR Manager: Mrs Y Biggs. Tel: 814559.

CRIMINAL JUSTICE
Head of Criminal Justice: Chief Supt K Wozniak. Tel: 0117 952 9609.
Deputy Head of Criminal Justice: Supt I Smith. Tel: 0117 952 9612.
Criminal Justice Performance & Development: Mrs M Poole. Tel: 0117 952 9613.
Force Custody Manager: Chief Insp I Norrie. Tel: 0117 952 9674.
Licensing Bureau Manager: Mr M Cox. Tel: 0117 945 5157.
Prosecutions Unit Manager: Mrs Kathy Cadogan. Tel: 0117 952 9680.
Victim & Witness Champion: Ms J Land. Tel: 0117 930 2897.
Safety Camera Unit Manager: Ms S Kostanjsek. Tel: 0117 945 4743.
Trials Unit Manager: Mr M Flay. Tel: 0117 952 9833.
Identification Unit Manager: Mr C Parish. Tel: 0117 952 9761.
Criminal Justice Support Unit Manager: Ms S Dingley. Tel: 0117 952 9610.
HR Manager: Ms H Hodges. Tel: 0117 952 9611.

FINANCE & ADMINISTRATION
Deputy Director of Finance: Mrs M Hardwell. Tel: 816171.
Retained Head of Procurement: Mr M Dunphy BSc MCIPS. Tel: 816372.
Retained Head of Estates: Mr D Harley. Tel: 816491.
Southwest One Head of Estates: Mr M Halligan.
Transport Services: Vacant. Tel: 0117 952 9425.
Head of Corporate Support: Mrs S Quantick. Tel: 816280.
Superintendents' Association: *Secretary:* Chief Supt G Spicer.
Police Federation: *Secretary:* PC A Duncan. Tel: 878854.
UNISON: *Secretary:* Mr P Cooper. Tel: 0117 945 4473.

TERRITORIAL DISTRICTS
BRISTOL (B)
Trinity Road Police Station, St Phillips, Bristol BS2 0NW.
Commander: Assistant Chief Constable J Long. Tel: 0117 945 5701.
Deputy: Chief Supt Jon Stratford. Tel: 0117 945 5702.
Community Safety: Supt M Prior. Tel: 0117 945 5726.
Operations: Supt R Cadden. Tel: 0117 945 5885.
CID: Det Supt J Reilly. Tel: 0117 945 5767.
Finance Manager: Ms L Gerard. Tel: 0117 945 5790.
HR Manager: Ms R Bridgeman. Tel: 0117 945 5751.
Administration & Facilities Manager: Ms L Woodberg. Tel: 0117 945 5881.

SOUTH GLOUCESTERSHIRE (D)
Concorde House, Harlequin Office Park, Fieldfare, Emersons Green, Bristol BS16 7FN.
Commander: Chief Supt S Crew. Tel: 0117 928 6001.
Performance Support: Supt M Carter. Tel: 0117 928 6002.
Operations: Chief Insp N Pascal. Tel: 0117 928 6003.
CID: Carolyn Phillips. Tel: 0117 928 6004.
Administration & Finance Manager: A Houghton. Tel: 0117 928 6006.
HR Manager: N Plant. Tel: 0117 928 6005.

BATH & NORTH EAST SOMERSET (E)
Bath Police Station, Manvers Street, Bath BA1 1JN.
Commander: Chief Supt G Spicer. Tel: 01225 842508.
Operations: Chief Insp S Ellis. Tel: 01225 842402.
CID: Det Chief Insp N Papuca. Tel: 01225 842577.
Administration & Finance Manager: Mrs L Woudberg. Tel: 01225 842400.
HR Manager: Ms N Plant. Tel: 01225 842546.

SOMERSET EAST (F)
Yeovil Police Station, Horsey Lane, Yeovil BA20 1SN.
Commander: Chief Supt N Watson. Tel: 01935 402101.

Operations Performance: T/Supt R Corrigan. Tel: 01935 402102.
Operations South: Chief Insp R Hulin. Tel: 01935 402239.
Operations North: Chief Insp S Williams. Tel: 01823 363753.
CID: Det Chief Insp Warren. Tel: 01935 402151.
Administration & Finance Manager: Ms S Harze. Tel: 01935 402174/01823 363201.
HR Manager: Mrs S Innes. Tel: 01935 402118.

SOMERSET WEST (G)
Taunton Police Station, Shuttern, Taunton, Somerset TA1 3QA.
Commander: Chief Supt D Tilley. Tel: 01823 363001.
Operations: Supt K McCoubrey. Tel: 01823 363002. Chief Insp P Saban. Tel: 01823 363002.
CID: Chief Insp P Jones. Tel: 01823 363049.
Finance Manager: Ms S Harze. Tel: 01823 363201.
HR Manager: Mrs S Innes. Tel: 01823 363656.

NORTH SOMERSET (J)
Weston-super-Mare Police Station, Walliscote Road, Weston-super-Mare, North Somerset BS23 1UU.
Commander: Chief Supt J Moss. Tel: 01934 638101.
Operations: Chief Insp J Foreman. Tel: 01934 638102.
CID: Det Chief Insp S Wilshire. Tel: 01934 638215.
Administration & Finance Manager: Ms A Houghton. Tel: 01934 638202.
HR Manager: Mrs Y Biggs. Tel: 01934 638173.

Station	District	Station	District
Avonmouth	Bristol BCU	New Bridewell	Bristol BCU
*†Bath	Bath & North East Somerset	Newfoundland Road	Bristol BCU
		Portishead	North Somerset
Bishopsworth	Bristol BCU	Radstock	Bath & North East Somerset
*†Bridgwater	Somerset West		
Brislington	Bristol BCU	Redland	Bristol BCU
*†Broadbury Road	Bristol BCU	Shepton Mallet	Somerset East
Burnham-on-Sea	Somerset West	Somerton	South Gloucestershire
Chard	Somerset East		
Cheddar	Somerset West	*†Southmead Road	Bristol BCU
Chipping Sodbury	South Gloucestershire	*†Staple Hill	South Gloucestershire
Clevedon	North Somerset	Street	Somerset East
Crewkerne	Somerset East	*†Taunton	Somerset West
Dulverton	Somerset West	Thornbury	South Gloucestershire
Filton	South Gloucestershire	*†Trinity Road	Bristol BCU
Fishponds	Bristol BCU	Wellington	Somerset West
Frome	Somerset East	Wells	Somerset East
Ilminster	Somerset East	*†Weston-super-Mare	North Somerset
Keynsham	Bath & North East Somerset	Williton	Somerset West
		Wincanton	Somerset East
†Minehead	Somerset West	*†Yeovil	Somerset East
Nailsea	North Somerset		

† Denotes stations designated under s35, P.A.C.E. Act 1984
* Denotes permanently staffed designated custody suites.

HM CORONERS
Avon: Ms M E Voisin. HM Coroner's Court, The Courthouse, Old Weston Road, Flax Bourton, Bristol BS48 1UL. Tel: 01275 461920. Fax: 01275 462749.
Eastern Somerset: Mr T Williams. Argyll House, Bath Street, Frome BA11 1DP. Tel: 01761 411030 Fax: 01761 416272. Email: info@hmcoroner.co.uk
Western Somerset: Mr Michael Rose. Blackbrook Gate, Blackbrook Park Avenue, Taunton TA1 2PG. Tel: 01823 445380. Fax: 01823 445825. Email: coroner@clarkewillmott.com

BEDFORDSHIRE POLICE

Woburn Road, Kempston, Bedford MK43 9AX.
Tel: 01234 841212. Fax: 01234 846450 (24 hrs); 01234 842133 (0830–1700).
The dialling code for all numbers is 01234, unless otherwise indicated.
X400: C = GB; A = CWMAIL; P = PNN40MS; O = BEDFORDSHIRE POLICE; S = POSTMASTER
Text messaging: 07786 200011.
Email: firstname.lastname@bedfordshire.pnn.police.uk
Website: www.bedfordshire.police.uk

The following places have a Bedfordshire postal address but are policed by the forces shown. Cambridgeshire Constabulary: Gamlingay, Great Gransden, Hatley St George, Little Gransden, Waresley. Hertfordshire Constabulary: Cockernhoe, Darley Hall, Lilley, Peters Green, Tea Green. Thames Valley Police: Cheddington, Cublington, Edlesborough, Ivinghoe, Ivinghoe Aston, Ledburn, Mentmore, Newton Blossomville, Northall, Pitstone, Slapton, Soulbury, Stewkley, Wing.

Lord Lieutenant: Mrs Helen Nellis.
Police & Crime Commissioner: Mr Olly Martins.
Chief Executive/Monitoring Officer: Mrs Stephanie McMenamy.
Office of Police & Crime Commissioner: Bridgebury House, Woburn Road, Kempston, Bedford MK43 9AX. Tel: 01234 842066. Email: pcc@bedfordshire.pnn.police.uk

Chief Constable: Alfred Hitchcock QPM BSc(Hons) MA(Econ) MBA.
Chief Constable's PA: Mrs Bridget Murphy. Tel: 846983.
Staff Officer: Insp Matt Thompson. Tel: 846990.
Deputy Chief Constable: John Fletcher BA(Hons). Tel: 846986.
Assistant Chief Constable (Crime & Operations): Andrew Richer BA(Hons) MA. Tel: 846984.
Assistant Chief Officer: Mr Vince Hislop PGDipPM Chtd FCIPD. Tel: 846997.

CORPORATE
Director: Mr Parjinder Basra. Tel: 842273.
Organisational Development: Supt Neil Wilson. Tel: 842370.
Senior Business Partner HR: Maureen Rose. Tel: 842844.
Business Partner Workforce Relations: Mrs Louise Bareford. Tel: 842545.
Business Partner Workforce Resourcing: Mrs Emily Alleyne. Tel: 842841.
Business Partner Workforce Health & Wellbeing: Ms Emma Vine. Tel: 842399.
Business Partner Training: Mrs Karen Dandridge. Tel: 842395.
Performance & Planning: Mr Pete Woolley. Tel: 842362.
Information Management: Mr Andy Gilks. Tel: 846947.

FINANCE & RESOURCES
Business Support Director: Mr Phil Wells. Tel: 846840.
Senior Accountant: Mr Stuart Goodwin. Tel: 842240.
Estates & Facilities Manager: Mr Nigel Achurch. Tel: 846923.

COMMUNICATIONS
Media Relations Manager: Ms Jo Hobbs. Tel: 842028.
E-Communications Manager: Mrs Andrea Briggs. Tel: 842341.
Internal Communications Manager: Mr Dave Cook. Tel: 842384.
Publicity Officer: Mr John Sheffield MIPR. Tel: 842179.

COLLABORATED/SHARED SERVICES
FLEET
Transport Fleet Support Officer: Mrs Mary Noah MICFM. Tel: 842478.
INFORMATION & COMMUNICATIONS TECHNOLOGY
Assistant Director (ICT): Mr Steve Taylor. Tel: 01707 354300.
LEGAL SERVICES
Head of Legal Services: Mr Afzal Chowdhury LLB(Hons) LLM. Tel: 01707 354530.
PROCUREMENT
Head of Procurement: Mr Simon Mulvey. Tel: 01480 422382.

STAFF ASSOCIATIONS/TRADE UNION
Superintendents' Association: Det Chief Supt Andy Street. Tel: 01438 757394.
Police Federation: *JBB Secretary:* Insp Ray Reed. Tel: 842429.
UNISON: Mrs Sarah Crowe. Tel: 842305.

CRIME
Head of Crime: Det Chief Supt Clare Simon. Tel: 842260.
Crime: Det Supt Bob Johnston. Tel: 842817. **North:** Det Chief Insp Ged McCarthy. Tel: 275320. **South:** Det Chief Insp Steve Vesztrocy. Tel: 844337.
Intelligence: T/Det Supt Kevin Conneely. Tel: 842198.
Serious & Organised Crime: Det Chief Insp David Cestaro. Tel: 842881.
Intelligence & Tasking: T/Det Chief Insp Nick Bellingham. Tel: 842321.
Specialist Intelligence & Operations: Det Chief Insp Jon Gilbert. Tel: 842321.
Principal Analyst: Vacant. Tel: 842333.
Public Protection: Det Supt Nigel Stone MBE. Tel: 842239. Chief Insp Karena Thomas. Tel: 842018.

LOCAL POLICING OPERATIONS
Head of Local Policing Operations: T/Chief Supt Mark Turner. Tel: 846856.
First Contact: Supt Jim Saunders. Tel: 842798.
Force Control Room: Mr Wayne Humberstone. Tel: 842314.
Project Athena: Supt Linda Kelly. Tel: 842801.
Local Policing Operations: Vacant. Tel: 275155.
Crime Reduction Partnerships: Supt Paul Schoon. Tel: 846846.
Community Safety: Chief Insp Neill Waring. Tel: 275124.

COMMUNITY & PARTNERSHIPS
BEDFORD
Chief Insp Mark Upex. Tel: 275315.
Greyfriars Police Station. Greyfriars, Bedford MK40 1HR. Tel: 271212. Fax: 275005.
Riseley Police Station. 37 High Street, Riseley MK44 1OX. Tel: 275175. Fax: 709373.
CENTRAL
Chief Insp Shane Roberts. Tel: 842680.
Ampthill Police Station. Woburn Street, Ampthill MK45 2HX. Tel: 842621. Fax: 842605.
Biggleswade Police Station. Station Road, Biggleswade SG18 8AL. Tel: 841212. Fax: 842505.
Dunstable Police Station. West Street, Dunstable LU6 1SJ. Tel: 01582 471212. Fax: 01582 865507.
Houghton Regis Police Station. Sundon Road, Houghton Regis LU5 5RN. Tel: 01582 473341.
Leighton Buzzard Police Station. Hockliffe Road, Leighton Buzzard LU7 3FI. Tel: 01582 401212. Fax: 01582 473405.
LUTON
Chief Insp Rob McCaffray. Tel: 01582 474212.
Luton Police Station. Buxton Road, Luton LU1 1SD. Tel: 01582 401212. Fax: 01582 394006.
Luton North Police Station. Leagrave High Street, Luton LU4 9LG. Tel: 01582 473473. Fax: 01582 473472.
Futures House, The Moakes, Luton LU3 3QB. Tel: 01582 473475. Fax: 01582 473472.
Police stations designated under s35 P.A.C.E. Act 1984: Bedford, Luton, Dunstable.

BEDFORDSHIRE, CAMBRIDGESHIRE AND HERTFORDSHIRE – JOINT PROTECTIVE SERVICES COMMAND
Please contact the host force (in brackets) or use email in order to speak to the collaborative leads. Add .pnn.police.uk to all email addresses below.
Head of Joint Protective Services Command: Assistant Chief Constable Jon Boutcher (Hertfordshire). Email: jon.boutcher@herts
Head of Uniform Operations: Chief Supt Mike Colbourne (Bedfordshire). Email: mike.colbourne@bedfordshire
Head of Crime: Chief Supt Nigel Trippett (Cambridgeshire). Email: nigel.trippett@cambs
Firearms, Dogs, Public Order & Civil Contingencies: Chief Insp Mark Canning (Hertfordshire). Email: mark.canning@herts
Roads Policing & ANPR: Chief Insp Richard Hann (Hertfordshire). Email: richard.hann@herts
Major Crime: Det Supt Jeff Hill (Cambridgeshire). Email: jeff.hill@cambs
Scientific Support: Richard Johnson OBE (Bedfordshire). Email: richard.johnson@bedfordshire
Professional Standards: Det Supt Mark Hodgson (Cambridgeshire). Email: mark.hodgson@cambs

HM CORONER AND OTHER OFFICIALS
Bedfordshire & Luton: Mr David S Morris. Coroner's Office, 8 Goldington Road, Bedford MK40 3NF. Tel: 0300 300 6557/8. Fax: 01234 273014.
NSPCC
North London & East of England Local Office: NSPCC, First Floor, Ash House, Woodlands Business Park, Milton Keynes MK14 6ET. Tel: 01908 328060.
Children & Young People's Trust – Luton Project: 110–112 Leagrave Road, Luton. Tel: 01582 436070. Fax: 01582 431972.

State Veterinary Service (Animal Health)
South East Region (including Bedford, Luton & Central Bedfordshire): AHVLA Reigate Field Services, Liberty House, 105 Bell Street, Reigate, Surrey RH2 7JB. Tel: 01284 778150. Fax: 01737 241189.

Trading Standards
Bedford: Bedford Borough Council, Town Hall, Bedford MK40 1SJ. Tel: 01234 227270.

Central Bedfordshire: Central Bedfordshire Council, Priory House, Monks Walk, Chicksands, Shefford, Bedfordshire SG17 5TQ. Tel: 0300 300 8064.

Luton: Luton Borough Council, Clemitson House, Gordon Street, Luton LU1 2QP. Tel: 01582 547262.

CAMBRIDGESHIRE CONSTABULARY
Police Headquarters, Hinchingbrooke Park, Huntingdon PE29 6NP.
Tel: 101. Fax: 01480 422447 (24 hrs).
Email: firstname.lastname@cambs.pnn.police.uk
Website: www.cambs.police.uk

Lord Lieutenant: A H Duberley CBE.
Police & Crime Commissioner: Sir Graham Bright.
Chief Finance Officer: J Hummersone.

Chief Constable: Simon Parr.
Deputy Chief Constable: John Feavyour.
Assistant Chief Constable: Mark Hopkins.

CORPORATE FUNCTIONS
FINANCE & RESOURCES
Chief Finance Officer ACPO: Nicola Howard CPFA.
A/Deputy to Director of Resources: Laura Gunn.
Head of Estates & Facilities Management: Colin Luscombe FRCIS IRRV.
Estates & Services Manager: Mark Hotchkin BSc MRICS.
Fleet Manager: John Robinson BSc(Hons) MCIT MILT.
Financial Systems Manager: Mel Pettit.
Insurance Services Manager: Mike Beales.

HUMAN RESOURCES
Head of HR: Linda McHale.
Head of Operational HR & Policy: Sarah Knight.
Heads of Recruitment, Resourcing & Resizing: Paula Waller; Paula Kirkpatrick.
Equality & Diversity Advisor: Angela Hayward.
Health, Safety & Wellbeing Services Manager: Hannah Crisford.
Locum Force Medical Advisor: Dr R Lewis.
Selected Medical Practitioners: Dr W Cheng; Dr D Baxendine.

CORPORATE DEVELOPMENT
Head of Corporate Development: T/Chief Supt Simon Megicks.
Deputy Head of Corporate Development: Supt Steve Welby.
Business/Risk Manager: Kate Moore.
Inspection & Audit Liaison Manager: Chief Insp Mat Newman.
Force Operational Planning Unit: Chief Insp Jane Weir.
Firearms & Explosives Licensing Manager: Ralph Barker.
Corporate Performance Department: *Performance Manager:* Neil Stacey.
Information Management: *Head of Information Management/Crime Registrar/Auditor:* Rachel Badcock.
Information Access Office/Freedom of Information/Data Protection/Subject Access: Kathleen Love.

CORPORATE COMMUNICATIONS
Head of Corporate Communications: Kate Tonge.
Internal Communications Manager: Erin Mitchell.
Marketing Manager: Sarah Cooper.
Senior Press Officer: Shelley Spratt.

INFORMATION COMMUNICATION TECHNOLOGY
Head of ICT: Ian Bell.
Head of ICT Service Delivery: Jonathan Black.

TERRITORIAL POLICING
Cambridgeshire is divided into territorial policing areas using existing local authority and community safety partnership (CSP) boundaries.

Head of Territorial Policing: Chief Supt Andy Hebb.
Head of Operational Support: Supt Mike Brown.
Operational Support (Custody): Chief Insp Laura Hunt.
Force Duty Managers (FDM) 1: Gordon Whyte; Malcolm Graham; Andy Sullivan; Richard Turner; Vic Galpin.
Force Duty Managers (FDM) 2: David Greenwood; James Sutherland; Matt Johnson; Jamie Rice; Nik Percival.
Community Safety Unit: Strategy & Governance: Insp Steve Kerridge. **Youth & ASB:** Insp Dick Lowings. **Specials/Police Support Volunteers:** Insp Sue Taylor.

CONTACT MANAGEMENT
Head of Contact Management: Det Supt Chris Mead.
Force Control Room Manager: Ed Essad.
Police Service Centre Manager: Tracy Blackwood.
SPECIAL CONSTABULARY
Special Constabulary Chief Officer: Philip Hill.
Special Constabulary Co-ordinator & Police Support Volunteers SPOC: Shahina Ahmed.
CSAS Co-ordinator: PC Karen Raine.
TERRITORIAL POLICING AREAS
PETERBOROUGH
Area Commander: Supt Dan Vazjovic.
Chief Inspectors: Nick Knight; Karen Newton.
Local Inspectors: Robert Hill; Dominic Glazebrook; Iain Clark; Andy Bartlett; Det Insp Gary Etherington; Det Insp Mike Branston.
CAMBRIDGE
Area Commander: Supt Vicky Skeels.
Chief Inspectors: Nick Church; Neil Sloan; Det Chief Insp Andy Gipp.
Local Inspectors: Ian Lyons; Steve Poppitt; Det Insp Billy Bremner; Det Insp Mark Newman.
HUNTINGDON
Area Commander: Det Chief Insp Melanie Dales.
Local Inspectors: Terri Griffin; Mark Greenhalgh; Det Insp Jon McAdam.
FENLAND
Area Commander: Chief Insp Mike Winters.
Local Inspectors: Robin Sissons; Det Insp David Murphy.
SOUTH CAMBRIDGESHIRE
Area Commander: Chief Insp Darren Alderson.
Local Inspectors: Chris Savage; Det Insp Ian Simmons.
EAST CAMBRIDGESHIRE
Area Commander: Chief Insp Russ Waterston.
Local Inspectors: Paul Ormerod; Det Insp Donna Wass.
CUSTODY BLOCKS
Custody Blocks designated under s35 P.A.C.E. Act 1984: Cambridge, Peterborough (Thorpe Wood), Huntingdon, Police Investigation Centre (Kings Lynn), March (only open when demand dictates), St Neots (only open when demand dictates).
INVESTIGATIONS
Head of Investigations: Chief Supt Karen Daber.
Investigations: Crime Policy: Det Supt Paul Fullwood.
Customer Relations Manager: Anthea Dodson.
Team Leaders: Mike McFadyzean; Paul Heath.
Authorising Officer: Det Supt Tom Mackinnon.
Head of Harm Reduction: Det Supt Gary Ridgway.
Head of Central Intelligence Bureau: Det Supt Tony Ixer.
BEDFORDSHIRE, CAMBRIDGESHIRE AND HERTFORDSHIRE – JOINT PROTECTIVE SERVICES COMMAND
Please contact the host force (in brackets) or use email in order to speak to the collaborative leads. Add .pnn.police.uk to all email addresses below.
Head of Joint Protective Services Command: Assistant Chief Constable Jon Boutcher (Hertfordshire). Email: jon.boutcher@herts
Head of Uniform Operations: Chief Supt Mike Colbourne (Bedfordshire). Email: mike.colbourne@bedfordshire
Deputy Head of Uniform Operations: Supt Simon Hawkins(Hertfordshire). Email: simon.hawkins@herts
Head of Crime: Chief Supt Nigel Trippett (Cambridgeshire). Email: nigel.trippett@cambs
Firearms, Dogs, Public Order & Civil Contingencies: Chief Insp Mark Canning (Hertfordshire). Email: mark.canning@herts
Roads Policing & ANPR: Chief Insp Richard Hann(Hertfordshire). Email: richard.hann@herts
Major Crime: Det Supt Jeff Hill (Cambridgeshire). Email: jeff.hill@cambs
Scientific Support: Richard Johnson (Bedfordshire). Email: richard.johnson@bedfordshire
Professional Standards: Det Supt Mark Hodgson (Cambridgeshire). Email: mark.hodgson@cambs

HM CORONERS

North & East Cambridgeshire: Mr William R Morris. HM Coroner's Office, Lawrence Court, Princes Street, Huntingdon PE29 3PA. Tel: 0345 045 1364. Fax: 01480 372777.

South & West Cambridgeshire: Mr David S Morris. HM Coroner's Office, Lawrence Court, Princes Street, Huntingdon PE29 3PA. Tel: 0345 045 1364. Fax: 01480 372777.

Peterborough: Mr David Heming. Peterborough Coroner's Office, Town Hall, Bridge Street, Peterborough PE1 1QT. Tel: 01733 452275. Fax: 01733 452515. Email: hmcoroner@peterborough.gov.uk

CHESHIRE CONSTABULARY

Clemonds Hey, Oakmere Road, Winsford CW7 2UA.
Tel: 101. Telex: 36261/2. Fax: 01606 362269 (24 hrs).
The dialling code for all numbers is 01606 unless otherwise indicated.
Operational email: force.control.room@cheshire.pnn.police.uk (24 hrs).
Email: firstname.lastname@cheshire.pnn.police.uk (due to duplicate names, some addresses may vary slightly).
Website: www.cheshire.police.uk

All members of the Cheshire Constabulary have email accounts enabling them to send/receive external mail. If you have difficulty sending a message to a member of the Cheshire Constabulary, contact the IT Help Desk. Tel: 01606 362248. Email: it.service.desk@cheshire.pnn.police.uk. Please note that to maintain data security, we continually monitor and block emails containing attachments with the potential to carry viruses.

Lord Lieutenant: Mr D Briggs. Dukenfield Hall, Knutsford Road, Mobberley.
Police & Crime Commissioner: Mr J Dwyer. Tel: 364000.
Deputy Police & Crime Commissioner: Mrs M Ollerenshaw.
Chief Executive of the Office of the Police & Crime Commissioner: Mr M Sellwood.
Chief Finance Officer: Ms E Lunn BA(Hons) CPFA.

CONSTABULARY HEADQUARTERS, WINSFORD

Chief Constable: D Whatton QPM.
Secretary. Tel: 362090.
Chief Constable's Staff Officer: Insp S Case. Tel: 362115.
Deputy Chief Constable: H King QPM MA(Oxon).
Secretary. Tel: 362940.
Assistant Chief Constable (Investigations): R Purdie.
Secretary. Tel: 362092.
Assistant Chief Constable (Neighbourhoods): J McCormick.
Secretary. Tel: 362969.
Assistant Staff Officer: PC P Mace. Tel: 362450.
Assistant Chief Officer: D Rattigan.
Secretary. Tel: 362940.
Special Constabulary: *Chief Officer, Special Constabulary:* Mr B Woodward. Tel: 364549.
Volunteers' Manager: Ms J Ford. Tel: 01606 364551.

LEGAL SERVICES

Force Solicitor: Ms S Pimlott. Tel: 364592.
Deputy Force Solicitor: Mr P Kenyon. Tel: 364510.
Principal Lawyers: Mrs J Rose. Tel: 364007. Mrs S Phillips. Tel: 365788.
Administration. Tel: 364168/4579. Fax: 364593.

PROFESSIONAL STANDARDS

Head of Professional Standards: Det Supt J Armstrong. Tel: 362050.
Deputy Head of Professional Standards: Det Chief Insp P Shaw. Tel: 362051.
Office Administration. Tel: 362055.
Information Security Manager: Mr N Regan. Tel: 364113.
Freedom of Information Officer: Mr J Gannon. Tel: 364176.
Data Protection Officer: Mrs P O'Brien. Tel: 362384.

MULTI-FORCE SHARED SERVICE (CHESHIRE & NORTHAMPTONSHIRE)

Head of MFSS: Ms S Copley-Hirst. Tel: 366849.
HR Service Manager: Mrs D Bullock. Tel: 365798.
Accounts & Purchasing: Ms P Rourke. Tel: 366825.
Service Delivery Manager: Mr S Schooler. Tel: 366820.

BUSINESS SERVICES

Director of Corporate Services: Mrs K Watkins MSc. Tel: 362202.
Head of Planning & Performance: Mr P Woods BA(Hons). Tel: 362103.
Corporate Research & Analysis Manager: Ms K Cain BSc. Tel: 362878.
Head of Business Improvement: Mrs S Clarke. Tel: 362467.
Head of Corporate Communications: Mrs B N Cowling. Tel: 362972.
Internal Communications Manager: Mrs J Hanson. Tel: 365782.
Public Information Manager: Ms J Gregory. Tel: 365152.
Technical Architect: Mr S Rogers. Tel: 362239.

Director of Human Resources: Chief Supt R Strachan. Tel: 362250.
Head of Employee Relations: Mrs J Fitzmaurice-Higgins. Tel: 364014.
Head of Organisation Development: Mrs N Bailey. Tel: 364123.
Director of Finance: Mr R Muirhead. Tel: 364500.
Transport Manager: Mr J Heussi. Tel: 362333.
Head of Procurement: Mrs A Gibbs MBA MCIPS. Tel: 362010.

BUSINESS SERVICE CENTRE
Service Assurance Manager: Mrs J Watts. Tel: 362291.
Change & Improvement Lead: Ms S Makinson. Tel: 362208.
Head of Estates & Facilities: Mrs E Marvell. Tel: 366526.
A/Head of IT & Business Systems: Mr R Alkunshalie. Tel: 365176.
Head of Distribution & Logistics: Mrs J Hulmston. Tel: 364155.
Service Desk Lead: Mrs K Marx. Tel: 365761.
Administration Services Manager: Ms P Francis. Tel: 362015.

FORCE OPERATIONS

All departments are located at Cheshire Constabulary Headquarters, Clemonds Hey, Oakmere Road, Winsford, Cheshire CW7 2UA, unless otherwise stated.
Head of Crime: Det Chief Supt G Hindle. Tel: 362104.

CRIME SUPPORT
Head of Department: Det Supt G Jones. Tel: 365262.
Level 2 Crime: Det Chief Insp K Bennett. Tel: 362410.
Technical Support Unit: Ms C Moon. Tel: 362446.
Covert Policing Unit: Det Insp G Pierce. Tel: 365032.
Dedicated Surveillance Unit: A/Det Insp M Horton. Tel: 365206.
Force Crime Operations Unit: Det Insp S Pengelly. Tel: 365049.

CRIME OPERATIONS
Force Major Investigation Team: A/Det Supt A Smith. Tel: 362441.
Counter Terrorism Branch: A/Det Chief Insp D Blood. Tel: 362120.
Director of Intelligence: Det Supt A Mitchell. Tel: 362106.
Force Intelligence Bureau: Det Insp P Merrill. Tel: 365056.
Civil Contingency & Resilience Unit: Insp A Hinze. Tel: 362287. Sgt K Robbins.
Head of Forensic Investigations: Mr H Owen DipCSE(Dunelm). Tel: 362442. Fax: 362417.
Local Resilience Forum Business Support Officer: Mrs S Hand. Tel: 364009.
Fingerprints: Mr N Davies. Tel: 362412.
Crime Scene Investigations: Mrs C Godwin. Tel: 365232.
Firearms Licensing: Mrs S Deighton. Tel: 362243.
Economic Crime Unit: A/Det Insp K Jaundrill. Tel: 365089.
Strategic PPU: Det Chief Insp N Wenham. Tel: 362108.
Dedicated Rape Unit: Det Insp D Dodd. Tel: 365452

UNIFORM OPERATIONS
Head of Uniform Operations. Det Chief Supt G Hindle. Tel: 362104. Supt P Wilson. Tel: 365178.
Force Control Centre: Chief Insp D Smethurst. Tel: 362264.
Joint Underwater Search Unit (based at Runcorn Police Station and covering Manchester, Merseyside, North Wales, Cumbria, Lancashire & Cheshire police areas): Insp D Corcoran. Tel: 363993. Sgt R Reid. Tel: 363994.
Custody: Chief Insp P Crowcroft. *Secretary.* Tel: 364043.

VECTOR UNIT
Road Policing, Traffic Management, Firearms, Air Support, Area Support Group, Dogs: Supt J Betts. Tel: 365178.
North West Motorway Police Group (NWMPG). North West Regional Control Room, Rob Lane, Newton-le-Willows WA12 0DR. Tel: 0151 777 6900 (police only) covering Cheshire, Lancashire & Merseyside police areas. Insp A Chandler (Cheshire Constabulary). Tel: 0151 7776912.
Tactical Training Unit: Vacant.
Firearms Tactical Training Team: Insp D Price. Tel: 364581.
Air Support Unit: based at Aviation Park, Saltney Ferry, Chester (0700–1900): Sgt J Griffiths. Tel: 362551.
Dog Co-ordination Unit: Insp I Gallagher. Tel: 362267.

DEPARTMENT OF CRIMINAL JUSTICE

Head of Department: Det Supt A Southcott. Tel: 364075.
Deputy Head of Department: Chief Insp P Crowcroft. Tel: 364043.
Inspector Criminal Justice: Det Insp P Lawless. Tel: 365729.
CRB Disclosures & Vetting: Mr B. Wilson. Tel: 364590.
Courts & Criminal Records Section: Mr P Davies. Tel: 362180.

Central Ticket Office: Mr P Brocklehurst. Tel: 365713.
Offender Management: Ms E Acton. Tel: 364549.
LCJB Support Officer: Ms A Hall. Tel: 364078.
Western Witness Care Unit: Sgt J Gorge. Tel: 363119.
Northern Witness Care Unit: Sgt S Hughes. Tel: 364867.
Eastern Witness Care Unit: Sgt P Burns. Tel: 363381.

COMMUNITIES UNIT

Manager: Mr J S Roberts. Tel: 362212.
Community Engagement: Ms J Ford. Tel: 364551.
Safer Schools & Young People: PC L Stanton. Tel: 364565.
PREVENT: Miss E Labeda. Tel: 365147.
Cheshire Crime-beat: Mr F Harding. Tel: 364559.
Diversity Advisory Unit: Mrs J Tinning Tel: 364520.
Licensing: Mrs K Makinson. Tel: 364557.

STAFF ASSOCIATIONS

Superintendents' Association: *Chairman:* Det Supt J Armstrong. Tel: 362050. *Treasurer:* Supt L McDonnell. Tel: 363378.
Police Federation: *JBB Chairman:* Insp S Roberts. Tel: 362350. *JBB Secretary:* Insp A Todd. Tel: 362350. Fax: 362351.
UNISON: *Secretary:* Mr D Trussell. Tel: 362297. *Assistant Secretary:* Ms C Hulse. Tel: 362184. Fax: 364132.

EASTERN AREA BCU
Tel: 101.
Civic Centre, Crewe CW1 2DQ. Fax: 01606 364377.
Brunswick Street, Macclesfield SK10 1HQ. Fax: 01606 363489.
Chief Supt M Garrihy. Tel: 01606 364379.
Supt L McDonnell. Tel: 01606 363378.

NORTHERN AREA BCU
Tel: 101.
Charles Stewart House, 55 Museum Street, Warrington WA1 1NE. Fax: 01606 363809.
Halton Lea, Runcorn WA7 2HG. Fax: 01606 363909.
Chief Supt S Boycott. Tel: 01606 363810.
Supt M Cleworth. Tel: 01606 364876.

WESTERN AREA BCU
Tel: 101.
Blacon Avenue, Blacon, Chester CHI 5BD. Fax: 01606 363109.
Chester Way, Northwich CW9 5EP. Fax: 01606 363209.
4 Stanney Lane, Whitby, Ellesmere Port CH65 9ER. Fax: 01606 363009.
Chief Supt P Jones. Tel: 01606 363110.
Supt N Bailey. Tel: 01606 363110.

CUSTODY SUITES
Tel: 101.
Eastern BCU: Pochin Way, Middlewich CW10 0GY.
Northern BCU: Manor Farm Road, Manor Park, Runcorn WA7 1TD.
Western BCU: Blacon Avenue, Blacon, Chester CH1 5BD.

Place	BCU	Place	BCU	Place	BCU
Acton (Crewe)	E	Arclid	E	Barrow	W
Acton (Vale Royal)	E	Ashley	E	Barthomley	E
		Ashton	W	Barton	W
Adlington	E	Aston	W	Basford	E
Agden	E	Aston-by-	E	Batherton	E
Alderley Edge	E	Budworth		Beeston	W
Aldersey	W	Aston Juxta	E	Betchton	E
Aldford	W	Mondrum		Bexton	E
Allostock	E	Audlem	E	Bickerton	E
Alpraham	E	Austerton	E	Bickley	W
Alsager	E	Bache	W	Blacon	W
Alvanley	E	Backford	W	Blakenhall	E
Anderton	W	Baddiley	E	Bollington	E
Antrobus	W	Baddington	E	Bosley	E
Appleton	N	Barnton	W	Bostock	W

Place	BCU	Place	BCU	Place	BCU
Bradley	W	Cuddington	W	High Legh	E
Bradwall	E	(Chester)		Hockenhull	W
Brereton	E	Cuddington	W	Holmes Chapel	E
Bridgemere	E	(Northwich)		Hoole Village	W
Bridge Trafford	W	Cuerdley	N	Horton-by-	W
Brindley	E	Culcheth	N	Malpas	
Broomhall	E	Daresbury	N	Horton-cum-Peel	W
Broxton	W	Darnhall	W	Hough	E
Bruen Stapleford	W	Davenham	W	Hulme Walfield	E
Buerton	E	Delamere	W	Hunsterson	E
Buglawton	E	Disley	E	Huntington	W
Bulkeley	E	Dodcott	E	Hurdsfield	E
Bunbury	E	Doddington	E	Hurleston	E
Burland	E	Dodleston	W	Huxley	W
Burton (Chester)	W	Duckington	W	Iddenshall	W
Burton (Ellesmere	W	Duddon	W	Kelsall	W
Port)		Dunham-on-the-	W	Kettleshulme	E
Burwardsley	W	Hill		Kings Marsh	W
Burtonwood	N	Dutton	N	Kingsley	W
Byley	W	Eaton (Chester)	W	Knutsford	E
Caldecott	W	Eaton	E	Lach Dennis	W
Calveley	E	(Macclesfield)		Langley	E
Capenhurst	W	Eccleston	W	Larkton	W
Carden	W	Edge	W	Lea-by-Backford	W
Caughall	W	Edgerley	W	Lea Newbold	W
Checkley	E	Edleston	E	Ledsham	W
Chelford	E	Egerton	E	Leighton	E
Chester	W*	Ellesmere Port	W	Little Budworth	W
Chidlow	W	Elton	W	Little Leigh	W
Cholmondeley	E	Faddiley	E	Little Warford	E
Chorley (Crewe)	E	Farndon	W	Littleton	W
Chorley	E	Foulk Stapleford	W	Lostock Gralam	W
(Macclesfield)		Frodsham	W	Lower Kinnerton	W
Chorlton	W	Gawsworth	E	Lymm	N
(Chester)		Glazebury	N	Macclesfield	E
Chorlton	E	Goostrey	E	Macclesfield	E
(Nantwich)		Grafton	W	Forest	
Chowley	W	Grappenhall	N	Macefen	W
Christleton	W	Great Boughton	W	Malpas	W
Church Hulme	W	Great Budworth	W	Manley	W
Church Lawton	E	Great Sankey	N	Marbury	W
Church Minshull	E	Great Warford	E	Marbury-cum-	E
Church Shocklach	W	Guilden Sutton	W	Quoisley	
Churton-by-	W	Hale	N	Marlston-cum-	
Farndon		Hampton	W	Lache	
Churton Heath	W	Handforth	E	Marston	W
Claverton	W	Handley	W	Marthall	E
Clotton	W	Hankelow	E	Marton	E
Clutton	W	Hapsford	W	(Macclesfield)	
Coddington	W	Hargrave	W	Marton (Vale	E
Comberbach	W	Hartford	W	Royal)	
Congleton	E	Harthill	W	Mere	E
Coole Pilate	E	Haslington	E	Mickle Trafford	W
Cotebrooke	W	Hassall	E	Middlewich	E
Cotton Abbots	W	Hatherton	E	Millington	E
Cotton Edmunds	W	Hatton (Chester)	W	Minshull Vernon	E
Cranage	E	Hatton	N	Mobberley	E
Crewe	E*	(Warrington)		Mollington	W
Crewe-by-Farndon	W	Haughton	E	Moore	N
Croft	N	Helsby	W	Moston	W
Croughton	W	Henbury	E	Moston Green	E
Crowton	W	Henhull	E		

Place	BCU	Place	BCU	Place	BCU
Mottram St Andrew	E	Rixton-with-Glazebrook	N	Threapwood	W
				Tilston	W
Mouldsworth	W	Rope	E	Tilstone Fearnall	W
Moulton	W	Rostherne	E	Tiverton	W
Nantwich	E	Rowton	W	Toft	E
Ness	W	Rudheath	W	Tushingham	W
Neston	W	Runcorn	N	Twemlow	E
Nether Alderley	E	Rushton	E	Upton	W
Nether Peover	E	Saighton	W	Utkinton	W
Newbold Astbury	E	Sandbach	E	Walgherton	E
Newhall	E	Sankey	N	Wardle	E
Newton-by-Malpas	W	Saughall	W	Warmingham	E
		Scholar Green	E	Warrington	N*
Newton-by-Tattenhall	W	Shavington	E	Waverton	W
		Shocklach	W	Weaverham	W
Norbury	E	Shotwick	W	Wervin	W
Norley	E	Shotwick Park	W	Weston	E
North Rode	E	Siddington	E	Wettenhall	E
Northwich	W	Smallwood	E	Whatcroft	W
Oakmere	W	Snelson	E	Whitley	N
Old Rode	W	Somerford	E	Widnes	N
Oldcastle	W	Somerford Booths	E	Wildboarclough	E
Ollerton	E	Sound	E	Willaston (Crewe)	E
Over Alderley	E	Sproston	E	Willaston (Ellesmere Port)	W
Overton	W	Spurstow	E		
Padgate	N	Stanthorne	W	Willington	W
Parkgate	W	Stapeley	E	Wilmslow	E
Peckforton	E	Stockton (Malpas)	W	Wimboldsley	W
Peover Inferior	E	Stockton Heath	N	Wimbolds Trafford	W
Peover Superior	E	Stoke (Chester)	W		
Penketh	N	Stoke (Crewe)	E	Wincham	W
Pickmere	E	Stretton (Chester)	W	Wincle	E
Picton	W	Stretton (Warrington)	N	Winsford	W
Plumley	E			Winwick	N
Poole	E	Sutton (Macclesfield)	E	Wirswall	E
Pott Shrigley	E			Wistaston	E
Poulton	W	Sutton (Vale Royal)	E	Withington	E
Poulton-with-Fearnhead	N			Woodbank	W
		Swettenham	E	Woodcott	E
Poynton	E	Tabley Inferior	E	Woolstanwood	E
Prestbury	E	Tabley Superior	E	Woolston	N
Preston Brook	N	Tarporley	W	Worleston	E
Prior's Heys	W	Tarvin	W	Wrenbury	E
Puddington	W	Tattenhall	W	Wybunbury	E
Pulford	W	Tatton	E	Wychough	W
Rainow	E	Thornton-le-Moors	W		
Ridley	E				

* Stations manned 24 hrs per day and designated under s35, P.A.C.E. Act 1984.

HM CORONER

County of Cheshire: Mr Nicholas L Rheinberg. The West Annexe, Town Hall, Sankey Street, Warrington WA1 1UH. Tel: 01925 444216. Fax: 01925 444219.
Email: nrheinberg@warrington.gov.uk

CLEVELAND POLICE

PO Box No 70, Ladgate Lane, Middlesbrough, TS8 9EH.
Tel: 01642 326326. Telex: 58516. Fax: 01642 301200. Out of hours fax: 01642 301115. DX: 68800 Middlesbrough 7. The dialling code for all numbers is 01642, unless otherwise indicated.
Email: firstname.lastname@cleveland.pnn.police.uk
Website: www.cleveland.police.uk

Lord Lieutenant (North): Sir Paul Nicholson.
Lord Lieutenant (South): The Lord Crathorne.
Police & Crime Commissioner: Barry Coppinger.
Chief of Staff: Ed Chicken.

Chief Constable: Jacqui Cheer QPM BA(Hons) MBA Dip(Cantab).
Deputy Chief Constable: Vacant.
Assistant Chief Constable (Crime): Dave Pickard BA(Hons).
Assistant Chief Constable (Operations): Sean White BA(Hons) MBA.
T/Assistant Chief Constable (Territorial): Adrian Roberts BSc(SocSci)(Hons) Dip (Cantab).
Assistant Chief Officer: Ann Hall LLB(Hons) ACA.

STAFF ASSOCIATIONS
Superintendents' Association: *Branch Secretary.* Tel: 301463.
Police Federation: *JBB Secretary.* Tel: 301286.
Unison: *Branch Secretary.* Tel: 301395.

FORCE SERVICE UNITS
EXECUTIVE
Chief Constable's Staff Officer. Tel: 301214. Fax: 301462.
Executive Staff Officer. Tel: 301229.
PA to Chief Constable. Tel: 301215. Fax: 301462.
PA to Deputy Chief Constable & Assistant Chief Constables (Crime & Territorial). Tel: 301216.
PA to Assistant Chief Constable (Operations) & Assistant Chief Officer. Tel: 301217.

PERFORMANCE REVIEW AND INSPECTORATE
Head of Performance Review & Inspectorate. Tel: 301221.
Corporate Planning & Development. Tel: 301488.
Research & Management Information. Tel: 301440.
Press Office. Tel: 301789.

OPERATIONAL PERFORMANCE TEAM
Chief Superintendent. Tel: 301478.
Superintendent. Tel: 301679.
General Office. Tel: 301311/301173.

BUSINESS SERVICES
(Steria UK employees working on behalf of Cleveland Police)
Head of Police Shared Business Services Delivery. Tel: 301234 option 2.
Lead Business Partner, Support Services. Tel: 301234 option 2.
Typing, PA Services. Tel: 301234 option 2.
Alarms Administration. Tel: 301241.
Digital Imaging Service. Tel: 301234 option 2.
Stores. Tel: 301234 option 2.

LEGAL SERVICES
Head of Legal Services. Tel: 301355. DX 68801 Middlesbrough 7. Fax: 301227.
Legal Advisor. Tel: 301231.
Legal Advisor (General Claims). Tel: 301225.
Legal Executive (General Claims). Tel: 301288.
General Office. Tel: 301305.

FINANCE
(Steria UK employees working on behalf of Cleveland Police)
Treasury Management. Tel: 301292/760/761.
Lead Business Partner, Finance. Tel: 301234 option 2.

PROCUREMENT & FLEET
(Steria UK employees working on behalf of Cleveland police)
Lead Business Partner. Tel: 301234 option 2.

CORPORATE ESTATES
Lead Business Partner. Tel: 301234 option 2.

INFORMATION AND COMMUNICATIONS TECHNOLOGY
(*Steria UK employees working on behalf of Cleveland Police*)
Head of ICT. Tel: 301706.
Telecommunications Manager. Tel: 301181.
Information Systems Manager. Tel: 301710.
Service Desk. Tel: 301234 option 1.

PEOPLE AND DIVERSITY
(*Steria UK employees working on behalf of Cleveland Police*)
Head of People & Development (*Client Side*). Tel: 301477.
Lead Business Partner People Services. Tel: 301234 option 2.
Lead Business Partner Learning & Development. Tel: 301296.
Occupational Health Manager. Tel: 302855.
HR Business Partners. Tel: 301234 option 2.
HR Business Partner Resourcing. Tel: 301234 option 2.
Force Chaplain: Vacant.
Special Constabulary Liaison. Tel: 301234 option 2.
Volunteer Management Team. Tel: 301234 option 2.

PROFESSIONAL STANDARDS
Head of Professional Standards. Tel: 306800.
General Office. Tel: 306834/5.
Data Compliance Manager. Tel: 306817.
Data Control Unit. Tel: 306818/9.
Freedom of Information. Tel: 306825/32.

COMMUNITY JUSTICE
Middlesbrough HQ, Bridge Street West, Middlesbrough TS2 1BH.
Head of Criminal Justice: (Steria UK employee working on behalf of Cleveland Police). Tel: 302032.
Inspector Prisoner Handling Teams. Tel: 302096.
Custody Management. Tel: 302088.
Court Resulting Team: (Steria UK employees working on behalf of Cleveland Police). Tel: 302011.
Witness Care Unit: (Steria UK employees working on behalf of Cleveland Police). Tel: 303383.
Central Ticket Office: (Steria UK employees working on behalf of Cleveland Police). Tel: 302094.

OPERATIONAL SUPPORT
Middlesbrough HQ, Bridge Street West, Middlesbrough TS2 1BH.
Head of Operational Support. Tel: 302000.
Chief Inspector Operational Support. Tel: 301487.
Chief Inspector Control Room. Tel: 301109.
Chief Inspector Custody. Tel: 302004.
Chief Inspector Communities. Tel: 302030.
Force Control Room
Control Room Inspector. Tel: 301101. Fax: 301115.
  Email: force.control@cleveland.pnn.police.uk
Road Policing Unit
Inspector. Tel: 301551. Fax: 301555.
Sergeants' Office. Tel: 301552.
Traffic Management. Tel: 301569.
Specialist Support
Inspector. Tel: 303500.
Dog Section. Tel: 303502.
Mounted Section. Tel: 303510.
Specialist Support Unit. Tel: 301457.
Air Support Unit
Tel: 01325 333524.
Firearms Operations
Inspector. Tel: 301293.
Main Office. Tel: 301799.
Risk, Resilience & Operational Planning
(*Steria UK employees working on behalf of Cleveland Police*)
Mr Dave Moir. Tel: 302850.
Main Office. Tel: 303256.

CRIME

Head of Crime. Tel: 301336.
Organised Crime Lead. Tel: 301430.
HOLMES Training. Tel: 301427/301282/301281.
Force Intelligence Bureau. Tel: 301409/301411
Chemist Inspection/Liaison. Tel: 301745.
Organised Crime Unit. Tel: 306931.
Economic Crime Unit. Tel: 306852. *Detective Inspector.* Tel: 306840.
Vulnerability Unit: North. Tel: 306775. **South.** Tel: 306789.
Public Protection Unit. Tel: 306725. *Detective Inspector.* Tel: 306720.
Scientific Support. Tel: 301341/301342.
Special Branch. Tel: 301326/301328/301329/301320.
Technical Surveillance Unit. Tel: 301581.
Director of Intelligence. Tel: 301429.
Covert Standards Unit & DOI Support Team. Tel: 301315/301738/ 301733/301720.

HARTLEPOOL DISTRICT

Avenue Road, Hartlepool TS24 8AB. Tel: 326326. Fax: 302163.
District Commander. Tel: 302100.
Neighbourhood Manager. Tel: 302102.
Operations Manager. Tel: 302101.
Crime Manager. Tel: 302104.
District Liaison Manager. (Steria UK employee). Tel: 302153.
District Resource Centre General Enquiries. Tel: 302110/302126/302127. Fax: 302163.

MIDDLESBROUGH DISTRICT

Middlesbrough HQ, Bridge Street West, Middlesbrough TS2 1AB. Tel: 248184. Fax: 303163.
District Commander. Tel: 303100.
District Liaison Manager. (Steria UK employee). Tel: 303109.
Chief Inspector (Operations). Tel: 303101.
Chief Inspector (Neighbourhood Policing). Tel: 303102.
Crime Manager. Tel: 303104.
District Resource Centre & General Enquiries (24 hrs). Tel: 303126. Fax: 303163.
Coulby Newham Police Station. Tel: 303410. Fax: 303463 (not 24 hrs).

REDCAR AND CLEVELAND DISTRICT

Redcar & Cleveland HQ, Troisdorf Way, Kirkleatham Business Park, Redcar TS10 5AP. Tel: 302626.
Fax: 302627.
District Commander. Tel: 302600.
District Liaison Manager. (Steria UK Employee). Tel: 302653.
Chief Inspector Operations. Tel: 302602.
Chief Inspector Neighbourhood Policing. Tel: 302603.
Crime Manager. Tel: 302604.
District Resource Centre & General Enquiries (24 hrs). Tel: 302626. Fax: 302627.
Loftus Police Station. Tel: 302800 (not 24 hrs). Fax: 302808.
South Bank Police Station. Tel: 302810 (not 24 hrs). Fax: 302818.
Redcar Police Station. Tel: 302826 (not 24 hrs). Fax: 302868.
Saltburn Police Station. Tel: 302860 (not 24 hrs). Fax: 302868.
Eston Police Station. Tel: 302840 (not 24 hrs). Fax: 302848.
Guisborough Police Station. Tel: 302880 (not 24 hrs). Fax: 302888.

STOCKTON DISTRICT

Thistle Green, Stockton-on-Tees TS18 1TZ. Tel: 607114. Fax: 302263.
District Commander. Tel: 302200.
Chief Inspector of Operations. Tel: 302202.
Chief Inspector Neighbourhoods. Tel: 302216.
Crime Manager. Tel: 302204.
District Liaison Manager. (Steria UK employee). Tel: 302253.
District Resource Centre & General Enquiries (24 hrs). Tel: 302226/302227. Fax: 302263.
Thornaby Police Station. Tel: 769819. Fax: 302464 (not 24 hrs).
Yarm Police Station. Tel: 789249 (not 24 hrs).
Billingham Police Station. Tel: 552107. Fax: 302463 (not 24 hrs).

Place	District	Place	District	Place	District
Acklam	M	Billingham	S	Boulby	L
Aislaby	S	Boosbeck	L	Brotton	L

Place	District	Place	District	Place	District
Carlin How	L	Kirkleatham	L	Redmarshall	S
Carlton	S	Kirklevington	S	Saltburn	L
Charltons	L	Lazenby	L	Scaling Dam	L
Coulby Newham	M	Lingdale	L	Seal Sands	S
Cowbar	L	Liverton	L	Seaton Carew	H
Cowpen Bewley	S	Liverton Mines	L	Skelton	L
Dalton Piercy	H	Loftus	L	Skinningrove	L
Dormanstown	L	Long Newton	S	South Bank	L
Dunsdale	L	Maltby	S	South Lackenby	L
Eaglescliffe	S	Marske	L	Stainton	M
Easington	L	Marton	M	Stanghow	L
Elton	S	*Middlesbrough	M	Stillington	S
Elwick	H	Moorsholm	L	*Stockton	S
Eston	L	Newton-under-	L	Teesville	L
Grangetown	L	Roseberry		Thornton	M
Graythorpe	H	Newton Bewley	H	Thorpe Larches	S
Greatham	H	New Marske	L	Thorpe Thewles	S
Grindon	S	Normanby	L	Upleatham	L
Guisborough	L	North Ormesby	M	Warrenby	L
Hart	H	Norton	S	Whitton	S
*Hartlepool	H	Nunthorpe	M	Wolviston	S
Haverton Hill	S	Ormesby	L	Worsall	S
Hemlington	M	Pinchinthorpe	L	Yarm	S
Hilton	S	Preston-on-Tees	S	Yearby	L
Ingleby Barwick	S	Port Clarence	S		
Kilton	L	*Redcar	L		

* Denotes designated Police Stations under s35, P.A.C.E. Act 1984, and manned 24 hours per day.

HM CORONERS

Teesside: Mr M J F Sheffield. Register Office, Corporation Road, Middlesbrough TS1 2DA. Tel: 01642 729350. Fax: 01642 729948.

Hartlepool: Mr C W M Donnelly. c/o Donnelly McArdle Adamson, Solicitors, 155 York Road, Hartlepool TS26 9EQ. Tel: 01429 274732. Fax: 01429 260199.

CUMBRIA CONSTABULARY

Police Headquarters, Carleton Hall, Penrith, Cumbria CA10 2AU.
Tel: 101. The dialling code for all numbers is 01768, unless otherwise indicated.
Fax: 01768 868283 (Communications Centre 24 hrs).
Email: comms@cumbria.pnn.police.uk
Website: www.cumbria.police.uk

Lord Lieutenant: Mrs Claire Hensman. Cumbria County Council, The Courts, Carlisle CA3 8NA.
Police & Crime Commissioner: Richard Rhodes. Tel: 217732.
Chief Executive: Stuart Edwards. Tel: 217732.
Treasurer: Ruth Hunter CPFA. Tel: 217631.

T/Chief Constable: Bernard Lawson QPM MSt (Cantab).
Staff Officer to Chief Constable. Tel: 217004.
T/Deputy Chief Constable: Michelle Skeer BA(Hons). Tel: 217765.
Staff Officer to Deputy Chief Constable. Tel: 217004.
Assistant Chief Constable (Specialist Operations): Jerry Graham BA(Hons) MA. Tel: 217007.
Assistant Chief Constable (Territorial Policing): Vacant.

STAFF ASSOCIATIONS
Police Federation: *JBB Secretary.* 1 The Green, Carleton Hall, Penrith. Tel: 217424.
Superintendents' Association: *Secretary.* Carleton Hall, Penrith. Tel: 217302.
UNISON: *Secretary.* Tel: 218002.

PROFESSIONAL STANDARDS DEPARTMENT
Director of Professional Standards. Tel: 217731.
Detective Inspector, Complaints & Misconduct. Tel: 217130.
Detective Inspector, Anti-Corruption. Tel: 217130.
Force Disclosure Manager. Tel: 217081.
Records & Information Security Officer. Tel: 217693
Data Protection/Freedom of Information. Tel: 217356.
Vetting Officer. Tel: 217121.

HUMAN RESOURCES
Head of Human Resources. Tel: 217691.
Occupational Health Manager. Tel: 213756.
Human Resources Business Partners. Tel: 217170/755.

LEARNING AND DEVELOPMENT
Head of Learning & Development. Tel: 217074.

INFORMATION & COMMUNICATIONS TECHNOLOGY
Director of ICT. Tel: 217010.
ICT Operations Manager. Tel: 217080.
ICT Service Support Manager. Tel: 217122.
ICT Business Development Manager. Tel: 217798.

MARKETING & COMMUNICATIONS
Marketing & PR Manager. Tel: 217786.
Press Office. Tel: 217748/447.
E-communications Manager. Tel: 217086.
Web & Multimedia Officer. Tel: 217682.

FINANCE & RESOURCES
Head of Financial Services. Tel: 217020.
Estates & Facilities Manager. Tel: 217034.
Fleet Manager. Tel: 217288.
Procurement Manager. Tel: 217050.
Payroll & Pensions Manager. Tel: 217011.
Accountancy Services Manager. Tel: 217021.

STRATEGIC DEVELOPMENT
Structures Review Team Director. Tel: 217155.
Structures Review Team Best Value Manager. Tel: 217494.
Information Management. Tel: 217028.

LEGAL SERVICES
Director of Legal Services. Tel: 217209.
Senior Legal Advisor. Tel: 217154.

CRIMINAL JUSTICE
Head of Criminal Justice. Tel: 217653.
Central Ticket Office. Tel: 217522.
Firearms Licensing. Tel: 217016.

COMMUNITY SAFETY
Head of Community Safety. Tel: 217294.
Alarms Unit Manager. Tel: 217296.

CRIME COMMAND
Head of CID Detective Chief Superintendent. Tel: 217302.
Detective Superintendent (Major Crime). Tel: 217251.
Detective Chief Inspector (Major Crime). Tel: 218203.
Detective Inspector (Major Crime). Tel: 217676.
Scientific Support Manager. Tel: 217350.
Principal Fingerprint Officer. Tel: 217621.
Detective Superintendent (Public Protection Unit). Tel: 217251.
Detective Chief Inspector (Public Protection Unit). Tel: 217662.
Detective Superintendent (Director of Intelligence & Specialist Support). Tel: 217662.
Detective Chief Inspector (Specialist Support/FIB/Surveillance). Tel: 213766.
Detective Inspector (Surveillance Unit). Tel: 217214.
Detective Chief Inspector (Specialist Support/Covert Policing). Tel: 218203.
Detective Inspector (Covert Intelligence). Tel: 213729.

TERRITORIAL POLICING
Commander of Territorial Policing. Tel: 217239.
Chief Inspector (Uniform Operations). Tel: 01900 844041.
RPU Inspectors: **West.** Tel: 01900 844079. **South.** Tel: 01539 818680. **North.** Tel: 01228 558401.
Tactical Support Group. Tel: 01228 558450.
Firearms Training Unit. Tel: 213713.
Collision Investigation Unit. Tel: 217235.
Chief Inspector (Civil Contingencies & Events Planning Unit). Tel: 217210.
Chief Inspector (Communications Centre). Tel: 217397.

NORTH CUMBRIA TPA POLICE HEADQUARTERS
Brunel Way, Durranhill, Carlisle CA1 3NQ. Tel: 101. Admin fax: 01228 558458 (office hours).
Superintendent Operations Manager. Tel: 01228 558201.
Chief Inspector – Area NPTs. Tel: 01228 558202.
Detective Chief Inspector – Crime Manager. Tel: 01228 558203.
Courts: Carlisle (Mon, Tues, Thurs & Fri; Youth: Wed).
Penrith Police Station: Hunter Lane, Penrith CA11 7UT. Tel: 01768 217546. Admin fax: 01768 217598 (office hours).

WEST CUMBRIA TPA POLICE HEADQUARTERS
Hall Brow, Workington CA14 4AP. Tel: 101.
West Communications Centre. Fax: 01900 844099 (24 hrs). Admin fax: 01900 844195 (office hours).
Superintendent. Tel: 01900 844139.
Chief Inspector. Tel: 01900 844041.
Detective Chief Inspector. Tel: 01900 844130.
Prison Liaison Officer. HM Prison, Haverigg, Whitehaven Police Station. Ext: 7844.
Court: West Cumbria Courthouse: Magistrates & County Court, Workington (every weekday).
Whitehaven Police Station: Scotch Street, Whitehaven CA28 7NN. Tel: 101. Admin fax: 01946 517899 (office hours).

SOUTH CUMBRIA TPA POLICE HEADQUARTERS
Busher Walk, Kendal LA9 4RJ. Tel: 101. Admin fax: 01539 818772.
Superintendent. Kendal. Tel: 01539 818610. Barrow. Tel: 01229 848810.
Chief Inspector. Kendal. Tel: 01539 818605. Barrow. Tel: 01229 848970.
Detective Chief Inspector. Tel: 01229 848976.
Courts: Kendal (Mon, Tues, Thurs; Youth: every other Wed); Furness (sitting at Barrow Mon, Tues, Wed & Thurs; Youth: Fri).
Barrow Police Station: Market Street, Barrow LA14 2LE. Tel: 0845 330 0247. Admin fax: 01229 848866.

HM CORONERS AND OTHER OFFICIALS
North & West Cumbria: Mr David Ll Roberts. Unit 5D/5E Lakeland Business Park, Lamplugh Road, Cockermouth, Cumbria CA13 0QT. Tel: 01900 706902. Fax: 01900 706915. Email: hmcoroner.northwest@cumbria.gov.uk

South & East Cumbria: Mr Ian Smith. Central Police Station, Market Street, Barrow-in-Furness, Cumbria LA14 2LE. Tel: 01229 848966. Fax: 01229 848953.

Department of Trading Standards
Trading Standards Service Manager: Angela Jones. County Offices, Stricklandgate, Kendal LA9 4RQ. Tel: 01539 713594. Email: trading.standards@cumbria.gov.uk

NSPCC Office
7 Chatsworth Square, Carlisle CA1 1HB. Tel: 01228 521829.

DERBYSHIRE CONSTABULARY
Butterley Hall, Ripley, Derbyshire DE5 3RS.
Tel: 101; if calling from outside the area 0345 123 3333. Fax: 01773 572225.
Email: pressoffice@derbyshire.pnn.police.uk General enquiries email:
foi@derbyshire.pnn.police.uk
Website: www.derbyshire.police.uk

Lord Lieutenant: Mr W Tucker.
Police & Crime Commissioner: Mr Alan Charles.
Chief Executive: Mrs H Boffy BSc CPFA.
Treasurer: Mr M Marples.

Chief Constable: M F Creedon QPM BA(Hons) MA.
Deputy Chief Constable: A J Goodwin QPM BA(Hons).
Assistant Chief Constable (*Operational Support*): D Collins BA(Hons).
Assistant Chief Constable (*Crime & Territorial Policing*): Steve Cotterill.
Director of Finance & Business Services: Mr Terry J Neaves CIPFA.
Chief Constable's PA: Mrs Helen Drummond.
Staff Officer: Det Chief Insp Jim Allen
Executive Suite. Fax: 01773 572146.
Email: acpo@derbyshire.pnn.police.uk

FINANCE AND BUSINESS SERVICES
Head of Strategic Finance: Mr Daniel Fern CPFA FMAAT.
Head of Assets: Mr D Vaughan.
Facilities Manager (Fleet): Mr T Hitchcock AMIRTE MICFM.
Head of Business Support: Mrs E Hickman CPFA.

CORPORATE SERVICES
Head of Corporate Services: Chief Supt R Foster MSc.
Service Improvement: Chief Insp A Palmer.
Corporate Communications: Mr J M Leach DipICM.
Media/Public Relations: Miss J Walden.
Equality & Diversity: Mrs T Reid FCIPD BSc(Hons).
Community Safety Partnerships: Chief Insp B McKeown.
Crime Reduction Manager: Insp S Fairbrother.
County Partnerships Lead Liaison Officer: Insp B Thacker.
Community Involvement Officer: Insp A Parkin.
Research Information Team: I Bates.

EAST MIDLANDS LEGAL SERVICES
Head of Legal Services, East Midlands Police Legal Services: Mr C W Sutherland LLB.
Deputy Head, East Midlands Police Legal Services: Mr M Turner LLB.
Senior Solicitor: Mr D Ring.

INFORMATION SERVICES
Director of Information Services (Derbyshire & Nottinghamshire): Mr R Cariss BSc(Hons).
Head of Information Services: Mrs D Hillifer.
Support Centre Services: Mr D Stone.
Programme/Projects Manager: Mr C Watson.

CRIMINAL JUSTICE
Supt S Gamblin.
Criminal Justice Manager: Mrs S A Webb.
Custody & Identification: Chief Insp J R Hargreaves.
Custody Managers: Insp M Coxhead (B & C Divisions); Insp A Gascoyne (D Division).
Force Identification Unit Manager: Mr D Turner.
Force Firearms & Explosives Manager: Mr N Jones.
Firearms Licensing: Mrs P Painter.
Wanted Persons Unit: Ms J Bradshaw.
Central Process Unit: Mrs B Ryan; Mrs M Poxon.
Central File Review Unit: Mr G A Butler; Mr L Marriott; Mr P Kaye.
NSPIS Custody & Case Preparation Administration: Mrs P Smets.
Crown Court &Witness Care Unit: Mrs S Cox.
CCTV Process Unit: Mrs G. Stafford.
Criminal Justice Area Managers: Mrs A Glossop (North); Mr J Rice (South).

PROFESSIONAL STANDARDS
Head of Professional Standards Department: Supt Rachel Walker.
Complaints: Det Chief Insp Nick Lamb; Insp Mark Gahagan. *Investigative Support Manager:* Mr A Bannister.
Anti-corruption Unit: Det Chief Insp A Sproson; Det Insp Matt Thompson.
Information Security Officer: Mr J R Smith.
Vetting Officer: Mr M J Shaw.
Criminal Records Unit: Mrs K Bowman.
Head of Information Management: Miss A Turner (Data Protection, Freedom of Information, Central Disclosure Unit, Records Management & CRB Services).

HUMAN RESOURCES
Head of HR: Mr P Mason.
Head of Manager Services: Mrs S Donscha MCIPD.
Employee Relations Manager: Mrs N J Smith FCIPD; BA(Hons).
Training Service Manager: Mr P Holmes.
Head of HR Service Centre: Denise Hill BSC(Hons) MSC MCIPD.
HQ HR Managers: Mrs S Mitchell MCIPD; Mrs D Harrington GradCIPD; Ms M Clarke MCIPD.
OSPRE Contact: Jack Skelton. HR Service Centre, Derbyshire Constabulary HQ, as above.

CRIME SUPPORT
Head of Department: Det Chief Supt D Platt QPM.
PA to Head of Department: Mrs Julie Naughton.
Director of Intelligence: Det Supt T Branson.
Crimestoppers: Mrs D Ryan.
Public Protection: Det Supt A Stokes; Det Chief Insp G Goacher; Det Chief Insp M Cooper.
Principal Crime Scene Investigator: Mr R Crowley MFSSOC FSSocDIP MCMI.
Economic Crime Unit: Det Insp R King.

CONTACT MANAGEMENT
Supt D Matthews; Chief Insp T Harrison.
Incident Control Inspectors: B Crane; W Smedley; N Gyte; J Saunders; A Sandeman. Tel: 01773 572203. Email: force.control@derbyshire.pnn.police.uk
Call Centre Manager: Mrs A D Nicholson.

OPERATIONAL SUPPORT
Head of Department: Chief Supt G M Sherwood.
PA to Divisional Commander: Miss L Housley.
Operations: Supt H Veigas.
Roads Policing & Collision Investigation: Insp R Goodman.
Roads Policing & Casualty Reduction: Chief Insp S Wilson.
Traffic Management: Mr A Knott.
CREST: Mr G Hall.
Operational Support: Chief Insp M Kean.
Operational Planning: Insp A Colledge.
Task Force & Dog Section: Insp A E Johnson.
Firearms: Insp S Skelton.
Helicopter Support: Mr J G Jameson.

STAFF ASSOCIATIONS
Superintendents' Association: *Secretary:* Supt H Veigas. Derbyshire Constabulary HQ, as above.
Police Federation: *Chair:* Mr M Pickard. *JBB Secretary:* Mr Ian Godfrey. 1 Windmill Rise, South Normanton, Alfreton DE55 2AZ. Tel: 0300 122 8533.
UNISON: *Chair:* Mr R Butler. *Secretary:* Mrs M Davey. Tel: 01773 572030.
Derbyshire Black Police Association: *Chair:* Sgt Baldev Bilan. Derbyshire Constabulary HQ, as above. Tel: 01773 573640. 24-hr helpline: 07736 572647.
Special Constabulary: Denise Hill.

EAST MIDLANDS POLICE COLLABORATION
Deputy Chief Constable East Midlands: Peter Goodman.
PA to DCC East Midlands. Tessa Callow. Tel: 01623 608402.

EAST MIDLANDS COUNTER TERRORISM INTELLIGENCE UNIT – SPECIAL BRANCH
Email: emctiu@derbyshire.pnn.police.uk
PA to Head of Unit & Senior Management Team. Tel: 01623 608304.
Human Resources. Tel: 01623 608403.
Office Manager. Tel: 01623 608411.
Special Branch: Det Insp Rob Routledge. Ext: 800 1030.

EAST MIDLANDS POLICE COLLABORATION PROGRAMME
Arrow Centre, Annesley Road, Hucknall, Nottingham NG15 8AY. Tel: 01623 608262.
Email: eastmidlandscpt@nottinghamshire.pnn.police.uk
Programme & Business Change Manager: Chief Supt Phillip Whiteley.

EAST MIDLANDS SPECIAL OPERATIONS UNIT
EMSOU, PO Box 9557, Nottingham NG15 5BU. Tel: 01623 608054.
Head of EMSOU-SOC: T/Det Chief Supt Jason Caunt.
 Email: jason.caunt@leicestershire.pnn.police.uk
Deputy Head of EMSOU-SOC: T/Det Supt Steve Craddock
 Email: steven.craddock@leicestershire.pnn.police.uk
Command Team PA: Sarah Dillon. Email: sarah.dillon@leicestershire.pnn.police.uk
Business & Finance Manager: Jon Peatling. Email: jonathan.peatling@leicestershire.pnn.police.uk
Senior HR Officer: Tracy Meakin. Email: tracy.meakin@leicestershire.pnn.police.uk
Head of Operations Support: Det Chief Insp Andy Haydon.
 Email: andrew.haydon@leicestershire.pnn.police.uk
Head of RART: Det Chief Insp Mick Beattie. Email: michael.beattie@leicestershire.pnn.police.uk
Head of Regional Review Unit: Kevin Flint. Email: kevin.flint@leicestershire.pnn.police.uk
EMSOU – SERIOUS AND ORGANISED CRIME
EMSOU-SOC North Command: Det Chief Insp Andy Dickin.
 Email: andy.dickin@leicestershire.pnn.police.uk
EMSOU-SOC East Command: T/Det Chief Insp Alan Mason.
 Email: alan.mason@leicestershire.pnn.police.uk
EMSOU-SOC South Command: T/Det Chief Insp Joe Elliott.
 Email: joseph.elliott@leicestershire.pnn.police.uk
EMSOU – MAJOR CRIME
Head of Major Crime Unit: Det Chief Supt Andrew Hough.
 Email: andrew.hough@leicestershire.pnn.police.uk
EMSOU-MC North Command: Vacant.
EMSOU-MC East Command: Det Supt Stuart Morrison. Email: stuart.morrison@lincs.pnn.police.uk
EMSOU-MC South Command: Vacant.
EMSOU – FORENSIC SERVICES
Regional Director of Forensic Services: Joanne Ashworth.
 Email: joanne.ashworth.16204@derbyshire.pnn.police.uk
EMSOU – SPECIAL BRANCH
EMSOU, PO Box 9557, Nottingham NG15 5BU. Tel: 01623 608304.
Det Supt Stephen Lowe. Email: stephen.lowe.314568@derbyshire.pnn.police.uk
PA to Senior Management Team: Sue Hogg. Email: susan.hogg.16244@derbyshire.pnn.police.uk

B DIVISION
Silverlands, Buxton SK17 6QJ. Tel: 101. Fax: 01298 762092 (weekdays 0830–1700).
Divisional Commander: Chief Supt G Knighton.
Operations: Supt G McLaughlin; Chief Insp T Frohwein.
Crime: Det Chief Insp G Meadows; Det Insp S McElheron; Det Insp J Allen.
Community Intelligence: Insp S Woodcock.
HR Manager: Mrs M Millar.
Section Inspectors: B Hall; J Clark; M Coey.

C DIVISION
Beetwell Street, Chesterfield S40 1QP. Tel: 101. Fax: 0300 122 8519 (weekdays 0830–1630) Fax 0300
122 8083 (C DHQ custody 24 hrs);
Divisional Commander: Chief Supt K Smethem.
Operations: Supt L Grewal; Chief Insp P Markham.
Crime: Det Chief Insp S Dawson; Det Insp J Roddis; K Mehmet; J Wilson; Det Insp M Huckerby.
HR Manager: Mrs A M Williams MCIPD.
Section Inspectors: S Ball; G Lamin; R Smith; G Hoggard.
Community Safety: Insp R Dakin.
Licensing Inspector: G Jones.
Reactive Inspectors: F Burns; J Turner; G Brown; G Rigby.
Divisional Business Manager: Mr J Fidler.

D DIVISION
St Mary's Wharf, Prime Parkway, Chester Green, Derby DE1 3AB. Tel: 101. Fax: 01332 613011
(control room 24 hrs); 01332 613087 (weekdays 0830–1630).
Divisional Commander: Chief Supt J Atwal.
Operations: Supt G Parkin; Chief Insp S Gamblin.

Community Safer Neighbourhoods: Chief Insp S Pont.
Crime: Det Chief Insp S Slack; Det Chief Insp M Bibbings; Det Insp A Brittan; Det Insp R Cuttell; Det Insp G Tomlinson; Det Insp G Prince; Det Insp D Naden; Det Insp E Richards.
Support: Insp J Munro.
HR Manager: Mr C Brooks.
Inspectors: P Cannon; D Roberts; R Keene; K Bria; P Laing; N Daines; I Mallard; K Andrews; N Lidsey; D Abbott; D Richardson; S Fairbrother.
The following villages have a Derby postal address but are within the Leicestershire Police area: Breedon-on-the-Hill, Castle Donington, Diseworth, Hemington, Kegworth, Lockington.

Place	Division	Place	Division	Place	Division
Abney	B	*Belper	C	Carsington	B
Aldercar	C	Belph	C	Castle Gresley	D
Alderwasley	C	Biggin	B	Castleton	B
Aldwark	B	Birchover	B	Catton	D
*Alfreton	C	Birch Vale	B	Cauldwell	D
Alkmonton	B	Blackwell	C	Chaddesden	D
Allenton	D	Blackwell-in-the-	B	Chapel-en-le-Frith	B
Allestree	D	Peak		Charlesworth	B
Alma Leisure	C	Bolehill	B	Chatsworth	B
Park		Bolehill	C	Chellaston	D
Alport	B	*Bolsover	C	Chelmorton	B
Alsop-en-le-Dale	B	(Mon–Fri		*†Chesterfield	C
Alton	C	0900–1330,		(Mon–Sat	
Alton	C	1400–1700)		0800–2200, Sun	
Alvaston	D	Bonsall	B	1000–2000,	
Ambergate	C	Borrowash	D	bank holidays	
Ankerbold	C	Boulton	D	1000–1600,	
Apperknowle	C	Bowden Head	B	closed	
Arkwright Town	C	Boylestone	B	Christmas Day)	
Arleston	D	Brackenfield	C	Chinley	B
Ash	D	Bradbourne	B	Chisworth	B
Ashbourne	B	Bradley	B	Chunal	B
(Mon–Fri		Bradwell	B	Church	D
1000–1400)		Brailsford	B	Broughton	
Ashford-in-the-	B	Bramley Vale	C	Church Gresley	D
Water		Brampton	C	Church Wilne	D
Ashgate	C	Brassington	B	*Clay Cross	C
Ashleyhay	C	Breadsall	D	Clifton	B
Ashover	C	Breaston	D	Clowne	C
Aston	B	Bretby	D	Coal Aston	C
Aston-on-Trent	D	Bridgemont	B	Codnor	C
Atlow	B	Brimington	C	Combs	B
Ault Hucknall	C	Brough & Shatton	B	Corbriggs	C
Bakewell	B	Brushfield	B	Cotmanhay	D
(Mon–Sat		Bubnell	B	Coton-in-the-Elms	D
0900–1300,		Burbage	B	Cowdale	B
closed		Burnaston	D	Coxbench	C
Christmas Day,		*†Buxton	B	Cressbrook	B
New Year's		(Mon–Fri		Creswell	C
Day)		0900–12300,		Crich	C
Bakestone Moor	C	1300–1700, Sat		Cromford	B
Ballidon	B	until 1600,		Crowdicote	B
Bamford	B	closed		Cubley	B
Barlborough	C	Christmas Day,		Curbar	B
Barlow	C	Boxing Day,		Cutthorpe	C
Barrow Hill	C	New Year's		Dalbury Lees	D
Barrow-on-Trent	D	Day)		Dale Abbey	D
Barton Blount	D	Buxworth	B	Danesmoor	C
Baslow	B	Calke	D	Darley Abbey	D
Batham Gate	B	Callow	B	Darley Dale	B
Beard	B	Calow	C	Denby	C
Bearwardcote	D	Calver	B		
Beeley	B	Carr Vale	C		

Place	Division
*†Derby (St Mary's Wharf Mon–Sat 0800–2200, Sun 1000–2000, bank hols 1000–1800, closed Christmas Day; City Centre Mon–Sat 0900–1700; *Cotton Lane Mon–Fri 0900–1300, 1330–1700; *Peartree Mon–Fri 0900–1700)	D
Derby Hills	D
Derwent	B
Dethick	C
Doe Lea	C
Dove Holes	B
Doveridge	B
Drakelow	D
Draycott	D
*Dronfield	C
Dronfield Woodhouse	C
Duckmanton	C
Duffield	C
Dunston	C
Earl Sterndale	B
Eastmoor	C
Eckington	C
Edale	B
Edensor	B
Edlaston	B
Ednaston	B
Egginton	D
Egstow	C
Elmton	C
Elton	B
Elvaston	D
Etwall	D
Eyam	B
Fairfield	B
Farley	B
Fenny Bentley	B
Fernilee	B
Findern	D
Flagg	B
Foolow	B
Foremark	D
Foston	D
Fritchley	C
Froggatt	B
Furness Vale	B
Gamesley	B
Gildwells	C
Glapwell	C

Place	Division
*†Glossop (Mon–Fri 0900–1330, 1400–1700)	B
Grangemill	B
Grangewood	C
Grassmoor	C
Gratton	B
Great Longstone	B
Green Fairfield	B
Grindleford	B
Grindlow	B
Haddon (Over & Nether)	B
Hadfield	B
Hady	C
Hadyhill	C
Hallam Fields	D
Handley	C
Hardstoft	C
Hardwick	C
Hardwick Hall	C
Harpur Hill	B
Harthill	B
Hartington	B
Hasland	C
Hassop	B
Hathersage	B
Hatton	D
Hayfield	B
Hazelwood	C
Hazlebadge	B
Heage	C
*Heanor	C
Heath	C
Higham	C
Highlow	B
Hilcote	C
Hillstown	C
Hilton	D
Hodthorpe	C
Hognaston	B
Holbrook	C
Hollington	B
Hollingwood	C
Holloway	C
Holme Hall	C
Holmesfield	C
Holmewood	C
Holymoorside	C
Hoon	D
Hope	B
Hope Woodlands	B
Hopton	B
Hopwell	D
Horsley	D
Horsley Woodhouse	C
Horwich End	B
Hucklow (Great & Little)	B
Hulland	B

Place	Division
Hulland Ward	B
Hundall	C
Hungry Bentley	B
Ible	B
Idridgehay	C
*Ilkeston (Mon–Fri 0900–1400, 1430–1700)	D
Ingleby	D
Inkersall	C
Inkersall Green	C
Ireton Wood	C
Ironville	C
Ivonbrook Grange	B
Kedleston	C
Kelstedge	C
Kilburn	C
*Killamarsh	C
King Sterndale	B
Kings Newton	D
Kirk Hallam	D
Kirk Ireton	B
Kirk Langley	C
Kniveton	B
Langley Mill	C
Langwith	C
Langwith Junction	C
Langwith Upper	C
Lea	C
Leabrooks	C
Lea Hall	B
Lees	B
Lightwood	C
Linton	D
Little Eaton	D
Little Hallam	D
Little Hucklow	B
Little Longstone	B
Littlemoor	C
Littleover	D
Litton	B
Long Duckmanton	C
*Long Eaton (Mon–Fri 0900–1300, 1330–1700)	D
Longford	B
Loscoe	C
Loundsley Green	C
Lowgates	C
Lullington	D
Mackworth	D
Mapleton	B
Mapperley	C
Marehay	C
Marlpool	C
Marsh Lane	C
Marston Montgomery	B
Marston-on-Dove	D

Place	Division	Place	Division	Place	Division
Mastin Moor	C	Pebley	C	Spondon	D
Matlock	B	Pentrich	C	Stainsby	C
(Mon–Fri		Pike Hall	B	Stanfree	C
0900–1330,		Pilsley	B	Stanhope Bretby	D
1400–1700)		Pilsley	C	Stanley	D
Matlock Bath	B	Pinxton	C	Stanton	D
Melbourne	D	Pleasley	C	Stanton-by-Bridge	D
Mercaston	B	Poolsbrook	C	Stanton-by-Dale	D
Meynell Langley	C	Postern	C	Stanton-in-the-	B
Mickleover	D	Priestcliffe	B	Peak	
Mickley	C	Quarndon	C	Starkholmes	B
Middlecroft	C	Radbourne	D	Staveley	C
Middleton	B	Radley	B	Steetley	C
Middleton-by-	B	Ramsley Moor	C	Stenson	D
Wirksworth		Ravensdale Park	C	Sterndale Moor	B
Midway	D	Renishaw	C	Stoke	B
Milford	C	Repton	D	Stone Edge	C
Millthorpe	C	Riddings	C	Stonebroom	C
Milltown	C	Ridgeway	C	Stonegravels	C
Milton	D	*Ripley (Mon–Fri	C	Stoney Houghton	C
Monsal Dale	B	0900–1230,		Stoney Middleton	B
Monyash	B	1300–1700)		Stretton	C
Morley	D	Risley	D	Stydd	B
Morton	C	Rodsley	B	Sudbury	B
Mugginton	C	Rosliston	D	Summerley	C
Nether Padley	B	Roston	B	Sutton-cum-	C
Netherseal	D	Rowarth	B	Duckmanton	
New Brampton	C	Rowland	B	Sutton-on-the-Hill	D
New Houghton	C	Rowsley	B	Sutton Scarsdale	C
New Mills	B	Rowthorne	C	Swadlincote	D
New Sawley	C	Rylah	C	(Mon–Fri	
New Tupton	C	Sandiacre	D	0900–1330,	
Newbold	C	Sawley	D	1400–1700)	
Newbridge	C	Scarcliffe	C	Swanwick	C
Newhall	D	Scropton	D	Swarkestone	D
Newhaven	B	Shardlow	D	Taddington	B
Newton	C	Shatton	B	Tansley	B
Newton Grange	B	Sheepbridge	C	Tapton	C
Newton Solney	D	Sheldon	B	Temple	C
Newtown	B	Shipley	C	Normanton	
Norbury	B	Shirebrook	C	Thornhill	B
Normanton	D	Shirland	C	Thornsett	B
North Wingfield	C	Shirley	B	Thorpe	B
Oakerthorpe	C	Shottle	C	Thurvaston	D
Ockbrook	D	Shuttlewood	C	Tibshelf	C
Offcote	B	Sinfin	D	Ticknall	D
Offerton	B	Sinfin Moor	D	Tideswell	B
Ogston	C	Slatepit Dale	C	Tintwistle	B
Old Brampton	C	Smalldale	B	Tissington	B
Old Tupton	C	Smalley	C	Toadhole Moor	C
Old Whittington	C	Smerrill	B	Totley Moor	C
Ollersett	B	Smisby	D	Troughbrook	C
Osleston	D	Smithy Moor	C	Troway	C
Osmaston	B	Snelston	B	Trusley	D
Over Haddon	B	Snitterton	B	Tunstead Milton	B
Overseal	D	Somercotes	C	Tupton	C
Oxcroft	C	Somersal Herbert	B	Turnditch	C
Padfield	B	Somersall	C	Twyford	D
Palterton	B	South Normanton	C	Unstone	C
Parwich	B	South Wingfield	C	Wadshelf	C
Peak Dale	B	Spinkhill	C	Waingroves	C
Peak Forest	B	Spitewinter	C	Walton	C

Place	Division	Place	Division	Place	Division
Walton-on-Trent	D	Whaley Thorns	C	Winsick	C
Wardlow	B	Whatstandwell	C	Winster	B
Waterloo	C	Wheeldon Mill	C	Wirksworth	B
Wensley	B	Wheston	B	Woodthorpe	C
Wessington	C	Whittington Moor	C	Woodville	D
West Hallam	C	Whitle	B	Woolley Moor	C
Westhouses	C	Whitwell	C	Wormhill	B
Weston-on-Trent	D	Wigley	C	Wyaston	B
Weston	C	Willington	D	Yeaveley	B
Underwood		Windley	C	Yeldersley	B
Whaley Bridge	B	Wingerworth	C	Youlgreave	B

* Denotes stations staffed 24 hrs per day (limited opening times to the public).

† Denotes stations designated under s35, P.A.C.E. Act 1984, namely B Divisional HQ (including Glossop), C Divisional HQ & D Divisional HQ.

HM CORONERS AND OTHER OFFICIALS

HM Coroners for the County of Derbyshire

Derby & South Derbyshire: Dr Robert Hunter. St Katherine's House, St Mary's Wharf, Mansfield Road, Derby DE1 3TQ. Tel: 01332 343225. Fax: 01332 294942. Email: derby.coroner@derbyshire.gov.uk

Scarsdale & High Peak: Dr Robert Hunter. Coroner's Court, Ground Floor, 5–6 Royal Court, Basil Close, Chesterfield S41 7SL. Tel: 01246 201391. Fax: 01246 273058.

Inspector under Food & Drugs & Diseases of Animals Acts

Mr R Taylour. Head of Trading Standards, Cultural & Community Service Department, Derbyshire County Council, Chatsworth Hall, Chesterfield Road, Matlock DE4 3FW. Tel: 01629 580000.

DEVON AND CORNWALL CONSTABULARY
Middlemoor, Exeter EX2 7HQ.
Tel: 101. The dialling code for all numbers is 01392, unless otherwise indicated.

Email: firstname.lastname@devonandcornwall.pnn.police.uk

Website: www.devon-cornwall.police.uk

Lords Lieutenant: Mr Eric Dancer CBE KStJ JP (Devon); Colonel Edward T Bolitho OBE DL(Cornwall).
Police & Crime Commissioner: Commodore Tony Hogg.

Chief Constable: Mr Shaun Sawyer. Tel: 452011.
Staff Officer: Insp Jeremy Capey. Tel: 452031.
Executive Assistant: Mrs Paula Faulkner. Tel: 452011.
ACPO Support: Mrs Clare Tucker. Tel: 452693. Email: acpo@devonandcornwall.pnn.police.uk
Deputy Chief Constable: Mr David Zinzan. Tel: 452022.
Executive Assistant: Ms Jackie Clements. Tel: 452022.
Assistant Chief Constable Local Policing & Partnerships (LP&P): Mrs Sharon Taylor. Tel: 452014.
Executive Assistant: Mrs Hazel Excell. Tel: 452014.
T/Assistant Chief Constable Crime & Justice (CJ): Mr Christopher Boarland. Tel: 452015.
Executive Assistant: Ms Sandra Densham. Tel: 452015.
Assistant Chief Constable Operations Support (OS): Mr Paul Netherton. Tel: 452944.
Executive Assistant: Mrs Sue Banks. Tel: 452944.
Director of People & Leadership: Mr Chris Haselden. Tel: 452016.
Executive Assistant: Ms Alison Dobson. Tel: 452016.
Director of Finance & Resources: Mrs Sandy Goscomb. Tel: 452665.
Executive Assistant: Miss Anna Drew. Tel: 452021.
Director of Legal Services: Mr Michael Stamp LLB. Tel: 452863.
Executive Assistants: Ms Belinda Taylor (Mon–Wed); Miss Sheryl Hopkin (Thurs–Fri). Tel: 452143.

PROFESSIONAL STANDARDS DEPARTMENT
Email: professional.standards@devonandcornwall.pnn.police.uk
Head of Professional Standards: Det Supt Emma Webber. Tel: 452138.
Head of PSD Operations: Det Chief Insp Alastair Cuthbert. Tel: 01752 751271.
Anti-corruption Intelligence Unit: *Unit Head:* Det Insp Ian Ringrose. Tel: 01752 751253.
Vetting Manager: Mr Philip Sincock. Tel: 452343.

LEGAL SERVICES
Senior Legal Advisors: Mrs Jill Gratwick CFILEX. Tel: 542008. Miss Caroline Denley LLB(Hons). Tel: 452646.
Force Legal Advisors: Miss Lucy Seymour LLB(Hons). Tel: 452307. Mr Christopher Rendell LLB PGDip. Tel: 452633. Miss Tara Tynan-Smith MA. Tel: 224041.
Paralegals: Mr Adam Cutler. Tel: 452345. Mr Christopher Richards Tel: 224180. Mrs Sarah Knight. Tel: 452714.

PERFORMANCE DEPARTMENT
Head of Performance & Analysis: Ms Alexis Poole. Tel: 452115.
Review & Inspection Manager: Det Chief Insp Sam de Reya. Tel: 452418.
Force Performance Manager: Dr Richard Bullock. Tel: 452812.
Force Strategic Analysis Manager: Ms Clare Gollop. Tel: 452274.
Force Consultation Manager: Ms Gill Sims. Tel: 452676.
Force Crime & Incident Registrar: Mr Tony Cook. Tel: 452859.
Lead for Risk Management: Mr Phil Rigg. Tel: 452110.

BUSINESS CHANGE
Strategy Delivery Director: Mr Simon Vry. Tel: 452264.
Blueprint Change Manager: Chief Supt Andy Boulting. Tel: 224101.
Programme & Executive Support Officer: Ms Shelly Gove. Tel: 452210.

CRIMINAL CASE REVIEW
Unit Head: Det Chief Insp Sam de Reya. Tel: 452418.

CORPORATE COMMUNICATIONS
Head of Corporate Communications: Ms Tanya Croft. Tel: 452571.
External Communications Manager: Ms Victoria Goodwin. Tel: 452061.
Internal Communications Manager: Mrs Tamsin Boyde. Tel: 01837 658414.
Public Relations & Events Officer: Miss Philippa Thompson. Tel: 452501.
Force Media Services Manager: Mr Dan Mountain. Tel: 452699.

Press Enquiries. Tel: 452200.
Heritage & Learning Resources: Ms Angela Sutton-Vane. Tel: 203025.
Reprographics Manager: Mr Roger Morley. Tel: 452046.

CALL MANAGEMENT
Call Management Department Head: Supt Craig Downham. Tel: 452305.
Geographic Contact Centre Manager East: Mrs Juliette Pryce. Tel: 452162.
Geographic Contact Centre Manager West: Lorna Boneham. Tel: 01752 751203.
Control Room Chief Inspector: Matthew Lawler. Tel: 452989.
Business Development Chief Inspector: Vacant. Tel: 452896.
Force Alarms Manager: Mr Anthony Marshall. Tel: 452779.

ICT SERVICE MANAGEMENT DEPARTMENT
Head of ICT Service Management: Mr Paul Lea. Tel: 452849.
IT Services Liaison Manager: Mrs Linda Lane. Tel: 452299.
Airwave Development & Services Manager: Mr Tim Bishop. Tel: 452348.
Data Network Systems Manager: Mr Jim Goodwin. Tel: 452298.
Corporate Systems Support Manager: Ms Liz Milne. Tel: 452104.
Telecoms Network Manager: Ms Denise Smith. Tel: 223195.
Change Transition Manager: Mr Simon James. Tel: 452065.
Customer Service Centre. Tel: 452747. Email: customerservice@devonandcornwall.pnn.police.uk

INFORMATION MANAGEMENT DEPARTMENT
Head of Information Management: Miss Louise Fenwick BA. Tel: 452903.
Force Information Assurance Manager, Force Accreditor: Mr Tim Moorey CITP MBCS CISSP, MSyl MInstISP. Tel: 452533.
Data Protection Officer: Mrs Tracey Furbear. Tel: 452916.
Freedom of Information Officer: Vacant. Tel: 452203.
Records Centre Manager: Mrs Pauline Rodea. Tel: 01752 343657.

CRIME AND JUSTICE DEPARTMENT
Commander: Det Chief Supt Russell Middleton. Tel: 01364 625863.
Secretariat. Tel: 01364 625863.

MAJOR INVESTIGATIONS AND SERIOUS, ORGANISED AND SPECIALIST CRIME BRANCH
Force & Senior Investigating Officer: Det Supt Paul Burgan. Tel: 453781.

CRIME SUPPORT BRANCH
Crime Support Branch Head: Det Insp Tanya Youngs. Tel: 452155.
Policy Officer: Miss Natalie Rowley. Tel: 452869.
Planning & Performance Managers: Mrs Samantha Bishop. Tel: 452236. Mr Mike Griffiths. Tel: 452498.

PUBLIC PROTECTION BRANCH
Public Protection Branch Head: Det Supt Paul Northcott. Tel: 01364 655061.

FORCE INTELLIGENCE CENTRE
Branch Head/Director of Intelligence: Det Supt Glen Mayhew. Tel: 452984.

SCIENTIFIC SUPPORT UNIT
Branch Head: Ms Julita Neale. Tel: 453114.
Head of Identification Conversion: Det Chief Insp Bob Harrison. Tel: 224119.

FORCE REGISTRAR AND COVERT POLICING AUTHORITIES
Branch Head: Det Supt Danny Caldwell. Tel: 452766.

CRIMINAL JUSTICE DEPARTMENT
Head of Criminal Justice: Supt David Sumner. Tel: 452976.
CJ Operations & Support: Chief Insp Donna Braund. Tel: 452580.
Custody & ID: Chief Insp Claire Armes. Tel: 452491.
Force Witness Care & Courts Manager: Mr Brian Tapley. Tel: 451598.
Collisions & Central Ticket Unit Manager: Miss Kelly Webber. Tel: 01752 751216.
Strategic Support Office Manager: Sam Slater. Tel: 452195.
Custody: Barnstaple. Tel: 01271 335274. Camborne. Tel: 01209 611297. Launceston. Tel: 01566 771450. Newquay. Tel: 01637 854550. Exeter. Tel: 451545. Plymouth. Tel: 01752 720440/441.
Force ID Manager: Insp Steve Rickard. Tel: 01566 771402.

OPERATIONS DEPARTMENT
Commander: T/Chief Supt Stuart Lander. Tel: 452674.
Head of Specialist Operations: Chief Insp Jane Taylor. Tel: 452366.
Driver Training: Sgt Glynn Currey. Tel: 224093.
Finance & Business Support Services: Mr Steve Fairburn. Tel: 452794.
Abnormal Loads. Tel: 452268. Fax: 452426.

Air Operations: Captain Ian Payne. Tel: 452292.
Operations Planning Unit (Events, Contingency Plans, Football Unit): Insp Richard Hooper-Bennett. Tel: 452590.
Firearms Operations & Training: Chief Insp Ian Dabbs. Tel: 452624.
Public Order: Insp Tanya Mackenzie-Clarke. Tel: 01837 658462.
Dog Section: Mr Tony Jordan. Tel: 452398.
Force Support Group: Insp John Maunder. Tel: 01752 283454.
Collision Investigations. Tel: 452718.
POLSA: Sgt Michael Rose. Tel: 452448.

PEOPLE MANAGEMENT & LEADERSHIP DIRECTORATE
PEOPLE MANAGEMENT & LEARNING
Head of People Management & Learning: Mr Graham Cooper. Tel: 451292.
Employee Relations Manager: Mr Trevor Dicks. Tel: 451254.
LEADERSHIP & ORGANISATIONAL DEVELOPMENT
Head of Leadership & Organisational Development: Mrs Carey Owen. Tel: 451133.
Organisational Development Manager: Ms Samantha Squance. Tel: 421135.
HR Business Partners: Ruth Mundy. Tel: 451225. Carol Grocott. Tel: 451226. Dawn Jenkins. Tel: 451228. Louise Tate. Tel: 01752 751204.
Leadership Development Unit: Insp Mick Glynn. Tel: 451219.
Force Wellness Manager: Mr David Mackenzie-Clarke. Tel: 451431.
EQUALITY AND DIVERSITY DEPARTMENT
Head of Equality & Diversity: Juliet Simmons. Tel: 452932.
Force Diversity Inspector: Insp John Jackson. Tel: 451236.
Equal Opportunities & Force Diversity Officer: Ms Teresa Berridge. Tel: 451222.
Equality & Diversity Training Manager: Ms Niema Burns. Tel: 451304.
OCCUPATIONAL HEALTH SUPPORT UNIT
Senior Medical Advisor: Dr Richard Johnston MBBS MRCP MFOM DavMed Royal Navy. Tel: 452850.
Practice Manager: Mrs Judith Bishop. Tel: 452958.
Senior Force Nursing Advisor: Mrs Freda Griffiths RGN OHDip. Tel: 452850.
Force Occupational Health & Welfare Advisor: Miss Rachel Ackland HGDipP MHGI. Tel: 452813.
Force Nursing Advisors: Mrs Tina Vogt RGN; Mr Aaron Piper OHDip. Tel: 452850.
HEALTH AND SAFETY
Health & Safety Manager: Mr Andy Cole. Tel: 452832.
Health & Safety Advisors: Mrs Becky Foxley. Tel: 01872 326039. Mr Martin Coombes. Tel: 01803 841283. Ms Judy Luker. Tel: 226061. Mr Shaun Doyle. Tel: 452234.
Exercise Facilities Manager: Mr Sammy Spall. Tel: 451128.
LEARNING AND DEVELOPMENT DIRECTORATE
Force Learning & Development Manager: Ms Rosalind Penny. Tel: 451246.
Operations Inspector: Vacant. Tel: 451206.
Services Delivery Manager: Vacant. Tel: 451264.
Operations & Custody Training: Sgt Michael Giarchi. Tel: 01752 751267.
Crime Training: Det Sgt Steve Selley. Tel: 451206.
IT Training Unit: Mr Charles Shwenn. Tel: 223226.
Dog Training: Sgt Andrew Thompson. Tel: 452398.
Quality Assurance & Development Unit Facilities & Projects Officer: Mr Ian Williams. Tel: 451302.

STAFF ASSOCIATIONS
Superintendents' Association: *Chair:* Det Supt Emma Webber. Tel: 452138. *Secretary:* Supt Chris Eastwood. Tel: 451506.
Police Federation: *JBB Chairman:* Sgt Nigel Rabbitts. Tel: 354770. *JBB Secretary:* PC David James. Tel: 354770.

TRADE UNIONS
UNISON: *Branch Secretary:* Neil Wooldridge. Tel: 452247. *Branch Chair:* Steve Ford. Tel: 452247.
GMB: *Convenor:* Mr Bill Stevens. Tel: 01752 720432.
T&G Unite: Mr Keith Symes. Tel: 452521.

FINANCE AND RESOURCES
PROCUREMENT DEPARTMENT
Head of Regional Procurement: Mr Stuart Jose MCIPS. Tel: 452867.
ESTATES DEPARTMENT
Head of Estates: Mr Andrew Morris. Tel: 452072.
Head of Programmes & Service Development (Estates): Mr Nick Grech-Cini. Tel: 452152.
Site Services Manager: Mrs Julia Wordley. Tel: 452280.

FINANCE AND BUSINESS SUPPORT SERVICES DEPARTMENT
Head of Finance: Mr Colin Papworth CPFA. Tel: 452668.
People Services Manager: Mrs Sandie Williams. Tel: 453986.
Head of Technical Accounting: Mrs Angela Daveney IPFA. Tel: 452361.
Head of Business Accounting: Mr Robin Wheeler ACMA. Tel: 452130.
ERP Systems Manager: Mr Adrian Logan. Tel: 224123.
Business Manager (Crime & Justice & Headquarters): Mr Barry Johns. Tel: 452133.
Finance Manager (Employee Relations): Mrs Lois Swarbrick. Tel: 452207.
Payroll Manager: Miss Diane Stephens. Tel: 452321.
People Services Centre Operations Manager: Miss Claire Ambrose. Tel: 453987.
People Services Centre Resourcing Manager: Mrs Maggie Simpson. Tel: 453980.

TRANSPORT DEPARTMENT
Transport Manager: Mr Richard Brimacombe. Tel: 452302.

LOCAL POLICING AND PARTNERSHIPS
Head of Local Policing & Partnerships: Supt Phil Kennedy. Tel: 452654.
Neighbourhood Policing: Insp Paul Morgan. Tel: 452221.
Community Safety: Insp Adam Cornish. Tel: 452771.
Youth Issues: Brent Davison. Tel: 452823.
Special Constabulary Co-ordinator: Miss Vicky Hollinshead. Tel: 224010.
Special Constabulary Commandant: Mr Richard Clatworthy (contact via Co-ordinator).
Firearms & Explosives Licensing Manager: Mr Thomas Sands MBE. Tel: 452297.
Contact Services Manager: Mrs Sandra Brooks. Tel: 452191.

CORNWALL AND THE ISLES OF SCILLY
Headquarters: Tollgate Road, Bodmin Police Hub, Cornwall PL31 2FJ.
Commander: Chief Supt Julie Fielding. Tel: 01872 326000.
Business Manager: Mr John Shepherd. Tel: 01872 326002.
LPA Commander West: Supt Jim Pearce. Tel: 01872 326236.
LPA Commander East: Supt Julie Whitmarsh. Tel: 01566 771390.

PLYMOUTH
Headquarters: Budshead Way, Crownhill, Plymouth, Devon PL6 5HT.
Commander: Chief Supt Andy Bickley. Tel: 01752 751200.
Business Manager: Mr John Shepherd. Tel: 01752 751210.
HR Business Partner: Mrs Louise Tate. Tel: 01752 751204.
LPA Commander: A/Supt Brendan Brookshaw. Tel: 01752 751207.
Local Investigation Commander: Det Supt Keith Perkin. Tel: 01752 751207.

DEVON
Headquarters: Cornwall House, Police HQ, Middlemoor, Exeter EX2 7HQ.
Commander: Chief Supt Paul Davies. Tel: 452720.
LPA Commander Exeter, Mid & East Devon: Supt Chris Eastwood. Tel: 451506.
LPA Commander North & West Devon: Supt Michele Slevin. Tel: 01837 658420.
LPA Commander South Devon: Supt Jim Nye. Tel: 01626 323714.
Business Manager: Mr Stephen Fairburn. Tel: 452794.
Communications Officer: Karen Mandefield. Tel: 452379.

POLICE STATIONS SHOWING GEOGRAPHICAL AREAS

Station	Area	Station	Area	Station	Area
Ashburton	D	Dartmouth	D	Looe	C
Axminster	D	*† Exeter	D	Lynton	D
† Barnstaple	D	Exminster	D	Moretonhamp-	D
Bideford	D	Exmouth	D	stead	
Bodmin	C	Falmouth	C	† Newquay	C
Bovey Tracey	D	Great Torrington	D	Newton Abbot	D
Braunton	D	Hayle	C	Okehampton	D
Brixham	D	Helston	C	Ottery St Mary	D
Bude	C	Holsworthy	D	Paignton	D
Budleigh Salterton	D	Honiton	D	Penzance	C
Callington	C	Ilfracombe	D	Perranporth	C
† Camborne	C	Isles of Scilly	C	*† Plymouth	P
Camelford	C	Ivybridge	D	(Charles Cross)	
Chudleigh	D	Kingsbridge	D	Plymouth	P
Crediton	D	Launceston	C	(Crownhill)	
Cullompton	D	Liskeard	C	Plympton	P

Station	Area	Station	Area	Station	Area
Plymstock	P	Saltash	C	Torpoint	C
Pool	C	Seaton	D	† Torquay	D
Redruth	C	Sidmouth	D	Totnes	D
St Austell	C	South Brent	D	Tregony	C
St Blazey	C	South Molton	D	Truro	C
St Columb	C	Tavistock	D	Wadebridge	C
St Ives	C	Teignmouth	D		
Salcombe	D	Tiverton	D		

C = Cornwall and the Isles of Scilly. D = Devon. P = Plymouth.
* Denotes stations open to the public 24 hours a day.
† Denotes stations designated under s35, P.A.C.E. Act 1984: Barnstaple (D); Camborne (C); Exeter (D); Newquay (C); Plymouth (Charles Cross) (P); Torquay (D).

HM CORONERS AND OTHER OFFICIALS

Cornwall: Dr E E Carlyon. 14 Barrack Lane, Truro, Cornwall TR1 2DW. Tel: 01872 261612. Fax: 01872 262738. Email: ecarlyon@cornwallcoroner.com

Exeter & Greater Devon: Dr Elizabeth A Earland. Room 226, Devon County Hall, Topsham Road, Exeter EX2 4QL. Tel: 01392 383636. Fax: 01392 383635. Email: coroner@exgd-coroner.co.uk

Isles of Scilly: Mr Ian M Arrow. Cary Chambers, 1 Palk Street, Torquay TQ2 5EL. Tel: 01803 380705. Fax: 01803 380704.

Plymouth & South West Devon: Mr Ian M Arrow. 3 The Crescent, Plymouth PL1 3AB. Tel: 01752 204636. Fax: 01752 313297.

Torbay & South Devon: Mr Ian M Arrow. Cary Chambers, 1 Palk Street, Torquay TQ2 5EL. Tel: 01803 380705. Fax: 01803 380704.

DORSET POLICE
Winfrith, Dorchester, Dorset DT2 8DZ.
Tel: 101. Fax: 01202 223987 (24 hrs).
The dialling code for all numbers is 01202, unless otherwise indicated.
Email: firstname.lastname@dorset.pnn.police.uk
Website: www.dorset.police.uk

HM Lord-Lieutenant of Dorset: Mrs Anthony Pitt-Rivers.
Police & Crime Commissioner: Martyn Underhill.

Chief Constable: Miss D Simpson.
Chief Constable's PA: Mrs R Ford. Tel: 223727.
Deputy Chief Constable: A J Whiting QPM.
Deputy Chief Constable's PA: Miss L Collins. Tel: 223705.
Assistant Chief Constable: J Vaughan.
Assistant Chief Constable's PA: Mrs H Laidler. Tel: 223501.
Assistant Chief Officer (Director of Finance): J B Jones BSc CPFA.
Assistant Chief Officer's PA: Miss J Taylor. Tel: 223710.
Assistant Chief Officer (Director of HR): G Smith FCIPD.
Director of HR's PA: Debbie Dalley. Tel: 223689.
ACPO Staff Office: Insp P Browning. Tel: 223717. Sgt R Chalkley. Tel: 223473. Sue Cox. Tel: 223684.
   ACPO Driver/Staff Officer: Steve Frier. Tel: 223802.

SPECIAL CONSTABULARY
Chief Officer: Mrs D Potter. Email: debi.potter@dorset.pnn.police.uk
Volunteer Support Team. Tel: 226842.

STAFF ASSOCIATIONS
Police Federation: *Chairman:* PC C Chamberlain. Tel: 223732. *Secretary:* Sgt T Eggleston. Tel: 223732.
   Federation Welfare Case Manager: Mr P Dashwood. Tel: 223732.
Superintendents' Association: *Chair:* Supt M Cooper. Tel: 223920. *Secretary:* Supt D Thorp. Tel: 223369.
UNISON: Mrs D Potter. Tel: 223691.

SUPPORT SERVICES
General Enquiries. Tel: 223456. Email: helpdesk@dorset.pnn.police.uk
Head of Estates: Mr M P Moysey BSc MRICS. Tel: 223811.
Head of Stores, Distribution & Administration Services: Mr B Hallett DMS MCIPS MCMI. Tel: 223785.
Head of Finance: Mr N Butterworth ACMA. Tel: 223932.
Head of Transport Services: Mr P Chick MBE. Tel: 223733.
Head of Governance (Audit, Insurance & Risk Management): Miss K Brownjohn MBA Chtd MCIPD RRP. Tel: 223429.
Force Solicitor: Mrs S Hounsell. Tel: 223543.
Force Solicitor's PA: Mrs A Hayes. Tel: 223706.

PROFESSIONAL STANDARDS
General Enquiries. Tel: 223881.
Head of Department: Supt Tim Whittle. Tel: 223768.
Department Analyst: Mrs K Mann. Tel: 223758.
Head of Complaints & Misconduct Unit: Mr Neil Redstone. Tel: 223769.
Inspectors' Office. Tel: 223770.
Anti-corruption Unit: Det Insp A Strong. Tel: 223524.
Force Vetting Officer: Mr R Smith. Tel: 223503.
Force Data Protection Officers: Mr S Lewis. Tel: 223716. Mr S Walbridge. Tel: 223810.
Force Disclosure Unit Manager: Mrs J Farquharson. Tel: 223659.
Freedom of Information Manager: Mr K Campbell. Tel: 223590.
Force Information Security Officer & Assurance Manager: Mr J Stephens. Tel: 223760.
Force Information Standards Manager: Mrs K Elliott. Tel: 223492.
Records Management Supervisor: Mrs J Twist. Tel: 223858.

SUPPORT SERVICES (INFORMATION SYSTEMS)
Head of Information Systems: Mr A Bennington. Tel: 223936.
Computer Manager: Mr A Stephenson. Tel: 223526.
Airwave Manager: Mr I Rowe. Tel: 223571.

Development Manager: Mr J Grindle. Tel: 223638.

SUPPORT SERVICES (HUMAN RESOURCES)
General Enquiries. Tel: 223764.
Director of Human Resources: Mr G Smith FCIPD. Tel: 223883.
Head of Personnel Services: Mr P Channon MCIPD. Tel: 223709.
Head of Organisational Development: Mrs N Anderson Grad CIPD. Tel: 223922.
A/Head of Business Change: Miss C Beasley. Tel: 223959.
Training & Governance: Mrs S Mayes. Tel: 223469.
Leadership & Postings: Insp C Phillips; Insp A Power. Tel: 223593.
Volunteer Team Leader: Insp M Darkin. Tel: 223842.
Senior Welfare Officer: Mr J Nickson BA(Hons). Tel: 223880.
Personnel Manager Business Support: Mr S Hounsell Grad CIPD. Tel: 223465.
Health & Safety Policy Strategy & Audit Officer: Mr R Aiston MIOSH. Tel: 223724.

SUPPORT SERVICES (CORPORATE DEVELOPMENT)
Head of Department: Ms J Yates. Tel: 223718.
Performance & Productivity Manager: Mr P Marsh. Tel: 223789.
Planning & Consultation Manager: Mr D Cregg. Tel: 223719.
Confidence & Equality Manager: Miss K Brown. Tel: 223755.
Policy Co-ordinator: Mrs K Berchem. Tel: 223722.

OPERATIONAL SUPPORT COMMAND
Commander: Chief Supt C Searle. Tel: 223890.
Deputy Commander: Supt D Thorp. Tel: 223363.
PA: Ms C Newell. Tel: 223890.

CONTACT SERVICES
Head of Contact Services: Ms J Jennings. Tel: 222909.
Operations Manager (Police Enquiry Centre): Ms D Place. Tel: 222084.
Operations Manager (Counter Services): Mr J Sharp. Tel: 222201.

FORCE CONTROL ROOM
Chief Inspector: C Naughton. Tel: 223960.
Force Incident Commanders. Tel: 227190.

MEDIA AND CORPORATE COMMUNICATION
Communications Manager: Ms G Lovelass. Tel: 220914.
Media Relations Manager: Mr A Harrold. Tel: 223859.
Web Co-ordinator: Mr C Redwood. Tel: 223730.

SAFETY EDUCATION ENFORCEMENT SERVICES
Head of Safety Education Enforcement Services: Mr M Garrett. Tel: 227501.
ANPR Manager: Mr R Storey. Tel: 223971.
Dorset Road Safe Freedom of Information: Mr B Austin. Tel: 227507.
Dorset Road Safe General Enquiries. Tel: 227600.
Central Ticket Office General Enquiries, Tel: 227549 (core hours 1000–1500).
Driver Awareness Scheme General Enquiries. Tel: 227670.
Firearms Licensing, Disposals & Data Protection: Mr B Austin. Tel: 227507.
Firearms Licensing: Ms J Welch. Tel: 227614.

SPECIALIST OPERATIONS SUPPORT
Head of Road Policing & Firearms: Chief Insp T Lumley. Tel: 223350.
Road Policing Unit Inspectors: M Butler. Tel: 223143. J Mallace. Tel: 223373.
Firearms Training & Tactical Firearms Unit: Insp A Allkins. Tel: 222943.
Head of Operational Planning: Chief Insp N Searle. Tel: 220947.
Operational & Contingency Planning Section: Insp D Osborne. Tel: 223159.
Enhanced Policing Team: Insp H Dixey. Tel: 222109.
Public Order Unit: Insp R Acaster; Sgt A Owen. Tel: 223833.
Licensing Unit: Bournemouth. Tel: 222591. **Ferndown.** Tel: 226083. **Weymouth.** Tel: 226418.
Dog Unit: Insp E Henley. Tel: 226283. Sgt G Batt; Sgt S White; Sgt C Fryer. Tel: 226282.
Marine Unit: Insp E Henley. Tel: 226869. Sgt M Haynes. Tel: 229830/223351.
Air Operations Support Unit: Sgt I Wood; Sgt N Cartwright. Tel: 223924.

CRIME AND CRIMINAL JUSTICE COMMAND
Crime & Criminal Justice Commander: Det Chief Supt C Stanger. Tel: 223712.
PA: Mrs S Taylor. Tel: 223752.
Director of Investigations: Det Supt A Clowser. Tel: 223872.
Det Chief Inspector Investigations West: B Hargreaves. Tel: 222453.
Det Chief Inspector Investigations East: J Gately. Tel: 222457.
Det Chief Inspector Public Protection: F Grant. Tel: 223293.

Director of Intelligence: T/Det Supt K Connolly. Tel: 223750.
Head of Force Intelligence Bureau: Det Chief Insp P Powley. Tel: 222222.
Force Intelligence Manager: Det Chief Insp P Trevillion. Tel: 223920.
Det Chief Inspector Special Branch: C Naughton. Tel: 229300.
Director of Specialist Support: Det Supt M Cooper. Tel: 223872.
Det Chief Inspector Major & Serious Organised Crime: P Trevillion. Tel: 222277.
Head of Technical Forensic Investigations: Mr I Jakeman. Tel: 223753.
Head of Forensic Investigations: Mr S Halls. Tel: 223992.
Head of Identification: Mr P Budd. Tel: 226110.
Head of Technical Investigations: E Bernasconi. Tel: 223857.
Director Criminal Justice: Det Supt G Smith. Tel: 220946.
Det Chief Inspector Criminal Justice (Crime Management): J Crossland. Tel: 226143.
Det Chief Inspector Criminal Justice (Custody): S Thorneycroft. Tel: 220601.
Criminal Justice Unit Manager: Ms J Steadman. Tel: 498789.
Disclosure Unit Manager: Ms J Farquhason. Tel: 223659.
Economic Crime Unit: Det Insp S Wynn. Tel: 223120.
Financial Investigation Unit: Det Sgt C Boyle. Tel: 223139.
Senior Coroner's Officer: J Jeneson. Tel: 789057.
Youth Justice. Tel: 223324.
Specified Offences. Tel: 223884.
Prosecution Files. Tel: 498834.
Witness Care Unit. Tel: 498817.
PNC Bureau. Tel: 222581.
Central Records. Tel: 222370.
Warrants Enquiries. Tel: 222372.

TERRITORIAL POLICING COMMAND
c/o Force Headquarters, Winfrith, Dorchester, Dorset DT2 8DZ.
Territorial Policing Commander: T/Chief Supt J Newall. Tel: 223523.
Territorial Policing Command Staff Office. Tel: 223523.
Territorial Policing Superintendent Bournemouth: C Eggar. Tel: 223358.
Territorial Policing Superintendent County: W Trickey. Tel: 223369.
Territorial Policing Superintendent Poole: M Rogers. Tel: 223362.
Neighbourhood Chief Inspectors
Poole: J Parkin. Tel: 223319.
County: G Morris. Tel: 226425. B Duffy. Tel: 226204.
Bournemouth: P Kessell. Tel: 220615. A Adams. Tel: 222349.
Neighbourhood Inspectors
Weymouth & Portland. Tel: 226475.
Christchurch. Tel: 222908.
East Dorset. Tel: 226008.
North Dorset. Tel: 223005.
Purbeck. Tel: 220405.
West Dorset. Tel: 226920.
Dorchester & Sherborne. Tel: 226820.
Poole North. Tel: 223234.
Poole South. Tel: 223250.
North Bournemouth (Winton/Kinson). Tel: 222730.
East Bournemouth (Boscombe). Tel: 222630.
Central Bournemouth. Tel: 220648.
Head of Community Safety: Mr J Ferguson. Tel: 223299.
Licensing Officer Weymouth: Mrs K O'Donnell. Tel: 226418.
Licensing Officer Ferndown: Mrs C Wateridge. Tel: 226083.
Licensing Office Bournemouth. Tel: 223352. Email: licensing@dorset.pnn.police.uk
Police stations designated under s35, P.A.C.E. Act 1984
Bournemouth; Blandford; Bridport; Christchurch; Poole; Shaftesbury; Sherborne; Swanage; Wareham; Weymouth.

HM CORONERS
Dorset, Bournemouth & Poole: Sheriff S Payne. The Coroner's Court, Stafford Road, Bournemouth BH1 1PA. Tel: 01202 310049. Fax: 01202 780423. Email: coroner@bournemouth.gov.uk

DURHAM CONSTABULARY
Aykley Heads, Durham DH1 5TT.
Tel: 0345 606 0365. Fax: 0191 375 2160/2190 (24 hrs). The dialling code for all
numbers is 0191 unless otherwise indicated.
Email: durham@pnn.police.uk
Website: www.durham.police.uk

Lord Lieutenant: Sir Paul Nicholson.
Police & Crime Commissioner (PCC): Mr R Hogg BA(Hons) Dip Crim.
PCC Chief Executive: Mrs L A Davies LLB.
PCC Chief Finance Officer: Mr K Thompson CPFA.

Chief Constable: M Barton LLB. Tel: 375 2208. Exec fax: 375 2210 (weekdays 0900–1700).
T/Deputy Chief Constable: M Banks BA(Hons). Tel: 375 2206.
T/Assistant Chief Constable: D Orford. Tel: 375 2207.
Assistant Chief Officer: Mr G Ridley. Tel: 375 2207.
Chief Constable's Legal Advisor: Mr C H Southey LLB.

CRIME & JUSTICE COMMAND
Head of Command: Det Chief Supt J Spraggon. Tel: 375 2251.
Serious Priority Crime & Justice Branch Head: Det Supt K Donnelly. Tel: 375 2224.
Witness Care Unit. Tel: 0345 606 0365.
Criminal Justice Unit (CJU). Police Headquarters, Aykley Heads, Durham DH1 5TT Tel: 0345 606 0365.
Central Ticket Office: *Managers:* Tel: 0345 606 0365 ext HQ 2370.
Specialist Crime Operations Branch Head: Det Supt A Green. Tel: 375 2128.
Specialist Crime Operations Unit: A/Det Chief Insp V Fuller. Tel: 375 2769.
Special Branch: Det Insp J Tray. Tel: 375 2233.
Fraud & Financial Investigation, Special Operations: Det Insp G Pallas. Tel: 375 2078.
Major Crime, Safeguarding & Scientific Support Branch Head: A/Det Supt P Goundry. Tel: 375 2253.
Vulnerability, Safeguarding & E-safety: A/Det Chief Insp T McNally. Tel: 375 2247.
Major Crime Team (including HOLMES): Det Insp M Callan. Tel: 375 2255.
Scientific Support Manager, including Cleveland & Durham Fingerprint Bureau: Mr A E Edgar. Tel: 375 2267.

PROFESSIONAL STANDARDS & LEGAL SERVICES
Head of Department: Supt D Ellis. Tel: 375 2291. Fax: 375 2290.
Deputy Head of Department: Det Chief Insp S Winship. Tel: 375 2292.
Integrity Unit Head: Insp B Maudling. Tel: 375 2295.
Office Manager: Mr P Garfoot. Tel: 375 2293.

TASKING & COORDINATION COMMAND
Head of Command: T/Chief Supt R Coulson. Tel: 375 2085.
Head of Intelligence & Authorisations: T/Det Supt K Weir. Tel: 375 2241.
Head of Performance & Analysis: Ms G Porter. Tel: 375 2777.
Head of Operational Planning & Change: T/Supt W Dutton. Tel: 375 2089.
Media & Corporate Communications Manager: Mrs B Brewis. Tel: 375 2789.

SUPPORT SERVICES COMMAND
FINANCIAL SERVICES
Head of Department: Mr C Oakley FCMA. Tel: 375 2212.
Head of Procurement: Mrs M Dale. Tel: 375 2018.
BUSINESS SERVICES
Business Services Manager: Mrs C Jackson. Tel: 375 2216.
ESTATES
Head of Estates: Mrs M March BA(Hons) MRICS. Tel: 375 2222.
Fleet Manager: Mr M Mastaglio. Tel: 375 2087.
INFORMATION AND COMMUNICATIONS TECHNOLOGY
Head of Service Operations & Support: Mr S Wright. Tel: 375 2281.
Head of Systems Development & Delivery: Mr S Grainger. Tel: 375 2074.
PERSONNEL AND DEVELOPMENT
Head of Personnel: Mrs J Clewlow FCIPD ACIS. Tel: 375 2121.
Resourcing Manager: Mrs S Keveney MCIPD. Tel: 375 2104.
Head of Learning & Development: Vacant. Tel: 375 2135.

OSPRE Contact: Mrs S Race. Tel: 375 2569.
Health Management Unit Manager: Miss D Thomas FRSH ACIS. Tel: 375 2775.
Health & Safety Officer: Mr J Dwyer CMIOSH. Tel: 375 2047.
Occupational Health Nurse: Ms J Reilly RGN DOHN BSc(Hons). Tel: 375 2889.
Welfare Manager: Mrs M Toward. Tel: 375 2000.
Chaplaincy: *Senior Force Chaplain:* Rev A Gatrill. Tel: 0345 6060 365.

SPECIAL CONSTABULARY
Chief Officer: G C Knupfer MBE BA(Hons) MSc. Tel: 07966 518135.
Co-ordinator: PC L Joyce. Tel: 375 2909.

STAFF ASSOCIATIONS
Superintendents' Association: *Chair:* Chief Supt J Bell. Tel: 375 2890.
Police Federation: *JBB Secretary:* PC A Metcalfe. Tel: 375 2131.
UNISON: *Secretary:* Mr A Dickinson. Tel: 375 2134.

RESPONSE & COMMUNICATIONS COMMAND
Head of Command: Chief Supt J Bell. Tel: 375 2757.
Head of Operations: Supt H McMillan. Tel: 375 2890.
Head of Locality Response: Supt G Hall. Tel: 375 2890.
Response Manager East/West: Chief Insp E Taylor. Tel: 375 2890.
Response Manager South Durham & Darlington: Chief Insp V Martin. Tel: 375 2890.
Communications Manager: Chief Insp S Exley. Tel: 375 2890.
Specialist Operations Unit Manager: Chief Insp A Huddleston. Tel: 375 2890.

NEIGHBOURHOODS & PARTNERSHIPS COMMAND
County Durham Neighbourhood Policing: Chief Supt I Wood. Tel: 3752100
Darlington Neighbourhood Policing & Force Strategic Partnership Lead: Chief Supt A Reddick. Tel: 01325 742500.
Partnerships: Chief Insp C McGillivray. Tel: 375 2357.
Neighbourhoods T/Superintendent: C Williamson. Tel: 375 2547.
Durham West Neighbourhood Policing Manager: Chief Insp I Butler. Tel: 375 2428.
Durham East Neighbourhood Policing Manager: T/Chief Insp K Naunton. Tel: 0345 606 0365 2911.
Darlington Neighbourhood Policing Manager: Chief Insp C Reeves. Tel: 01325 742507.
South Durham Neighbourhood Policing Manager: Chief Insp D Turner. Tel: 01325 742502.
Neighbourhood Support Services Managers: Mrs J Forster. Tel: 375 2509. Mr F Lewis-Bynoe. Tel: 01325 742010.

Place	Area	Place	Area
*Barnard Castle	South	*Newton Aycliffe	South
*Bishop Auckland	South	Pelton	North
Blackhall	North	*Peterlee	North
Bowburn	North	Sacriston	North
Catchgate	North	Seaham	North
*Chester-le-Street	North	Sedgefield	South
Cockerton	South	Sherburn Road, Durham	North
*Consett	North	Shildon	South
*Crook	South	Southmoor	North
*Darlington	South	*Spennymoor	South
*Durham City	North	Stanhope	South
Easington Colliery	North	*Stanley	North
Ferryhill	South	Staindrop	South
Framwellgate Moor	North	Wheatley Hill	North
Firthmoor	South		
Lanchester	North		

* Denotes stations manned 24 hrs per day.
The following police stations are designated under s35, P.A.C.E. Act 1984: Bishop Auckland, Darlington, Durham & Peterlee.

HM CORONERS
Darlington & South Durham: Mr Andrew Tweddle. 2nd Floor, Royal Corner, Crook, Co Durham DL15 9UA. Tel: 01388 761564. Fax: 01388 765430. Email: hmcoroner@durham.gov.uk
North Durham: Mr Andrew Tweddle. As above.

DYFED-POWYS POLICE

PO Box 99, Llangunnor, Carmarthen SA31 2PF.
Tel: 101. Fax: 01267 234262 (operations, 24 hrs); 01267 222185 (non-urgent, weekdays 0830–1700).
The dialling code for all numbers is 01267, unless otherwise indicated.
DX: 120325 Carmarthen 4.
Email: firstname.lastname@dyfed-powys.pnn.police.uk
Website: www.dyfed-powys.police.uk

Police & Crime Commissioner: Mr Christopher Salmon. Tel: 226440.
Chief Executive, Office for the Police & Crime Commissioner: Mr Keith B Reeves LLB(Hons) LLM. Tel: 226440.
Chief Finance Officer, Office for the Police & Crime Commissioner: Mr Andrew Bevan CPFA. Tel: 226317.

Chief Constable: Jackie Roberts QPM.
PA: Carol Price. Tel: 226308.
Staff Officer: Sgt Clark Jones-John. Tel: 226303.
Deputy Chief Constable: Nick Ingram.
PA: Nicola Squires. Tel: 226305.
Assistant Chief Constable: Carl Langley.
PA: Catherine Lewis. Tel: 226307.
Director of Finance & Resources: Mr A J Bevan CPFA.
PA: Menna Davies. Tel: 226317.

CORPORATE DEVELOPMENT
Head of Corporate Development: Mr P Morris BSc(Hons) MBA. Ext: 23900.
Strategy & Planning: Mrs L Davies. Ext: 23930.
Force Crime & Incident Registrar: Ms Helen Rea. Ext: 23880.
Performance Manager: Mr James Walford MSc(Econ) BA(Hons). Ext: 23905.
Risk Advisor (Risk Management & Health & Safety): Mr S Davis RRP. Ext: 23167.
Organisational Development Manager: Mr Ian Hoskison. Ext: 23685.
Senior Manager Corporate Communications: Rhian Davies-Moore MCIPR. Ext: 23663.

FINANCE AND RESOURCES DIRECTORATE
Head of Financial Management: Mr E Harries BA(Hons) CPFA. Ext: 23801.
Financial Controller: Ms D Jones ACCA. Ext: 23802.
Head of Facilities: Mr E P Jeremy Dip BA. Ext: 23140.
Business Support Manager: Ms S Harries-Williams BA(Hons). Ext: 23141.
Senior Manager Procurement & Contracts: Ms L Frizi BA(Hons) MCIPS. Ext: 23205.
Firearms Licensing Manager: Mrs H Rees. Ext: 23145.
Information Manager: Mr S Mears.
Estates Manager: Mr C Powell.
Fleet Manager: Mr M Marks AMIMI MICFM. Ext: 23855.
Joint ICT Manager: Dr S Havard. Ext: 23400.

LEGAL SERVICES
Head of Legal Services: Ms S Waters LLB. Tel: 226398.
Territorial Lawyers: Mr Paul Casey LLB. Ext: 23161. Ms Rachel James LLB. Ext: 23162.

HUMAN RESOURCES DEPARTMENT
Head of Human Resources: Mrs Tracy Hawthorne LLM MSc FCIPD. Ext: 23050.
Senior Manager Learning & Development Services: Linda Hutton FCIPD. Ext: 23500.
Senior Manager Employee Relations & IIR Business Centre: Mr Steve Cadenne de Lannoy BA(Hons) CMS FCIPD. Ext: 23057.
Senior Manager Change Management & Employee Resourcing: Mr Dylan Davies DMS. Ext: 23059.
Senior Manager Occupational Health: Mrs Maria Van Der Pas RGN DipOH CMIOSH MSc. Ext: 23675.

OPERATIONAL SUPPORT DEPARTMENT
Tel: 226274 (general office). Fax: 242810. Email: dppiid@dyfed-powys.pnn.police.uk
Head of Operational Support: Chief Supt H Rees. Ext: 23470.
Superintendent Operations: C Parmenter. Ext: 23460.
Chief Inspector Conflict Management: A Twigger. Ext: 23550.
Chief Inspector Roads Policing: I Thomas. Ext: 23461.

Chief Inspector Custody Services: Chief Insp Peter Roderick. Ext: 23324.
Planning Officer (Royal Visits/Events/Public Order): Mr I Miles. Ext: 23463.
Civil Contingencies Planning: Mr M Lloyd. Ext: 23464.
Air Support Unit/Dog Section: Insp I Richards. Ext: 23498.
Safety Camera Partnership: S Poston. Ext: 23480.
Collision Investigation: Sgt A King. Ext: 23471.
Road Safety Officer: Susan Storch. Ext: 23475.
Director of Intelligence: Det Supt A Davies. Ext: 23314.
Deputy Director of Intelligence: T/Chief Insp Gary Mills. Ext: 23328.
Detective Inspector Intelligence: Shirley Davies. Ext: 23360.
Intelligence Principal Analyst: Dafydd Llewellyn. Ext: 23365.
PROFESSIONAL STANDARDS DEPARTMENT
Det Supt D M Evans. Ext: 23560.
Complaints & Discipline: *Senior Manager:* Mr Gavin Lemon. Ext: 23561.
General Office. Ext: 23568/23569/23570.
Vetting Officer: I Griffiths. Ext: 23585.
Anti-corruption Unit: Det Insp N Thomas. Ext: 23581.
Office Manager: Mrs M Phillips. Ext: 23567.
CRIMINAL INVESTIGATION DEPARTMENT (CID)
Det Chief Supt Simon Powell. Ext: 23320.
Crime Management: Det Supt R Bevan. Ext: 23329. Det Supt A John. Ext: 23323. Det Chief Insp S Williams. Ext: 23325. Det Chief Insp A Williams. Ext: 23321. Det Chief Insp G Williams. Ext: 25315.
CID Admin. Tel: 101. Fax: 226239.
Force Intelligence Bureau: Det Insp S Davies. Ext: 23360.
Central Authorities Bureau: Colin Clarke. Ext: 23351.
Dedicated Source Handling Unit: Det Insp F Phillips. Ext: 23350.
Serious & Organised Crime Team: Det Insp H Davies. Ext: 23395.
Major Crime Team: Det Insp R Hopkin. Ext: 23730.
Public Protection Unit: Vacant. Ext: 23343.
Financial Crime Unit: Det Insp R Hopkins. Ext: 23350.
Hi-tech Crime: Mr M Ray. Ammanford Police Station.
Special Branch: Det Insp D Bizby. Ext: 23330.
Technical Support: Mr R Phillips. Ext: 23770.
Scientific Support & Fingerprint Bureau: *Scientific Support Manager:* Mr G Thomas. Ext: 23732. Fax: 231363.
Port Security: Det Insp L Harries. Fishguard Port Office. Tel: 01348 871968. Fax: 01348 874046. Pembroke Dock Port Unit. Tel: 01646 687288. Fax: 01646 621593.
CRIMINAL JUSTICE DEPARTMENT
Fax: 221620.
Senior Manager Criminal Justice: Mrs Irene Davies Jones MCIPD. Tel: 239100 ext 24700.
Case Progression Manager: Monica Lewis. Tel: 239105 ext 24707.
Traffic Process Manager: Jason Rudall. Tel: 239101 ext 24706.
PNC Manager: Judith Jenkins. Tel: 239103 ext 24701.
Witness Care Unit. Tel: 0845 330 00180.
JOINT BRANCH BOARD
Joint Branch Board. Tel: 220731. Fax: 242949 (operates but not manned 24 hrs). *Secretary:* Mr P Herdman.
TERRITORIAL POLICING
Head of Territorial Policing: Chief Supt Pam Kelly. Police HQ. Ext: 23601.
Deputy Head (Territorial Policing Pembrokeshire & Ceredigion): Supt Ian John. Haverfordwest Police Station, PO Box 31, Pembrokeshire SA61 1PF. Ext: 40603.
Local Policing Commander (Pembrokeshire): Chief Insp Chris Curtis. Haverfordwest Police Station, as above.
Local Policing Commander (Ceredigion): T/Chief Insp Nicola Carter. Aberystwyth Police Station, Boulevard Saint Brieuc, Aberystwyth, Ceredigion SY13 1PH.
West Partnerships Haverfordwest: Chief Insp Angela Reed.
Deputy Head (Territorial Policing Carmarthenshire & Powys): Supt Richard Lewis. Carmarthen Police Station, Friars Park, Carmarthen SA31 3AN. Ext: 25601.
Local Policing Commander (Carmarthenshire): Chief Insp Steve Matchett. Carmarthen Police Station, as above.

Local Policing Commander (Powys): Chief Insp Robyn Mason. Newtown Police Station, Park Lane, Newtown, Powys SY16 1EN.
East Partnerships: Chief Insp Peter Westlake.
Head of Contact & Incident Management: Supt Huw Meredith.
Deputy Head (Contact & Incident Management): Chief Insp Mark Bleasdale.
All correspondence on operational matters should be addressed to the Local Policing Commander.

Station	Division	Station	Division
Aberaeron	Ceredigion	Llandrindod Wells	Powys
†Aberystwyth	Ceredigion	†Llanelli	Carmarthenshire
†Ammanford	Carmarthenshire	Llanfyllin	Powys
†Brecon	Powys	Llanidloes	Powys
Builth Wells	Powys	Llwynhendy	Carmarthenshire
Burry Port	Carmarthenshire	Machynlleth	Ceredigion
†Cardigan	Ceredigion	Milford Haven	Pembrokeshire
Carmarthen	Carmarthenshire	Narberth	Pembrokeshire
Crickhowell	Powys	Newcastle Emlyn	Ceredigion
Cross Hands	Carmarthenshire	†Newtown	Powys
Crymych	Ceredigion	Pembroke Dock	Pembrokeshire
Fishguard	Ceredigion	Presteigne	Powys
†Haverfordwest	Pembrokeshire	Rhayader	Powys
Hay-on-Wye	Powys	St Clears	Carmarthenshire
Kidwelly	Carmarthenshire	St David's	Pembrokeshire
Knighton	Powys	Tenby	Pembrokeshire
Lampeter	Ceredigion	Welshpool	Powys
Llandeilo	Carmarthenshire	Whitland	Carmarthenshire
Llandovery	Carmarthenshire	Ystradgynlais	Powys

† **Denotes stations designated under s.35, P.A.C.E. Act 1984.**

HM CORONERS AND OTHER OFFICIALS

Carmarthenshire: Mr Mark Layton. Corner House, Llandeilo, Carmarthenshire SA19 6AG. Tel: 01646 698129. Fax: 01646 690607. Email: hmcpembs1@btconnect.com
Cardiganshire: Mr P L Brunton. 6 Upper Portland Street, Aberystwyth, Ceredigion SY23 2DU. Tel: 01970 612567. Fax: 01970 615572. Email: peter.brunton@bruntonandco.co.uk
Pembrokeshire: Mr Mark Layton. The Town Hall, Hamilton Terrace, Milford Haven, Pembrokeshire SA73 3JW. Tel: 01646 698129. Fax: 01646 690607. Email: hmcpembs1@btconnect.com
Powys: Louise Hunt. Coroner's Office, 1st Floor Rock Ground, Aberdare, Rhondda-Cynnon-taf CF44 7AE. Tel: 01685 885202. Fax: 01685 885250. Email: louise.hunt@rhondda-cynnon-taf.gov.uk
Carmarthenshire
Lord Lieutenant: Robin Lewis. The Cottage, Cresswell Quay, Kilgetty, Pembrokeshire SA68 0TE.
Chief Executive: Mr M James. Carmarthenshire County Council, County Hall, Carmarthen SA31 1JP. Tel: 01267 234567.
Trading Standards Manager: Mr Roger Edmunds. Ty Elwyn, Llanelli SA15 3AP. Tel: 234567.
Team Leader Fair Trading: Mr Huw Lloyd. Ty Elwyn, Llanelli SA15 3AP. Tel: 01267 234567.
Ceredigion
Lord Lieutenant: Robin Lewis, as above.
Chief Executive: Mrs Bronwen Morgan. Ceredigion County Council, Town Hall, Aberaeron, Ceredigion SY23 2EB. Tel: 01545 570881.
Consumer Service Manager: Mr Dafydd Roberts. Ceredigion County Hall, Penmorfa, Aberaeron SA46 0PA. Tel: 01545 572105
Pembrokeshire
Lord Lieutenant: Robin Lewis, as above.
Chief Executive: Mr D Bryn Parry-Jones. Pembrokeshire County Council, Cambria House, Winch Lane, Haverfordwest, Pembrokeshire SA61 1TP. Tel: 01437 764551.
Trading Standards, Animal Health & Welfare Manager: Mr Nigel Watts. Tourist Information Centre, 19 Old Bridge, Haverfordwest, Pembrokeshire SA61 2EZ. Tel: 01437 771354.
Powys
Lord Lieutenant: Mrs S Legge-Bourke. Penmyarth, Glan Usk Estate, Tre Tower, Crickhowell, Powys.
Chief Executive: Mr Jeremy Patterson. Powys County Council, County Hall, Llandrindod Wells, Powys LD1 5LG. Tel: 01597 826082
Trading Standards Manager: Mr Ken Yorston. The Gwalia, Ithon Road, Llandrindod Wells, Powys LD1 6AA. Tel: 01597 826032.

ESSEX POLICE

PO Box 2, Springfield, Chelmsford, Essex CM2 6DA.
Tel: 101. Telex: 99235. Fax: 01245 452259.
Individuals where extension number only is listed, tel: 101. The dialling code for all
other numbers is 01245, unless otherwise indicated.
**X400: c = GB; a = CWMAIL; p = PNN42MS; o = ESSEX POLICE;
s = POSTMASTER.**
Email: firstname.lastname@essex.pnn.police.uk
Website: www.essex.police.uk

The following places, although situated in Essex, are policed by the Metropolitan Police. All summonses and
enquiries should be addressed to the superintendents of the respective sub-divisions: Barkingside, Chadwell Heath,
Chingford, Claybury, Ilford, Leyton, Leytonstone, Walthamstow, Wanstead, Woodford, Barking, Collier Row,
Dagenham, East Ham, Forest Gate, Harold Hill, Hornchurch, Plaistow, Plough Corner, Rainham, Romford,
Upminster and West Ham.

Lord Lieutenant: The Rt Hon The Lord Petre JP.
Police & Crime Commissioner: Nicholas Alston.

Chief Constable: Mr Stephen Kavanagh. Tel: 452814.
Chief Constable's Staff Officer: Chief Insp Alan Cook. Tel: 452121.
PA: Mrs Tracey Hitching. Tel: 452814.
Deputy Chief Constable: Mr Derek Benson.
PA: Mrs Michelle Bradley. Tel: 452112.
Assistant Chief Constable (Operations): Mrs Sue Harrison.
PA: Mrs Maria Vieira. Tel: 452111.
T/Assistant Chief Constable: Julia Wortley.
PA: Mrs Tracey Hitching. Tel: 452814.
Assistant Chief Constable: Mr Maurice Mason.
Chief Officer Special Constabulary: Mr Leon Dias. Mob: 07715 771095.
Assistant Chief Officers: Mr Derek Hopkins. Mob: 07970 271397. Miss Lynette Flint. Mob: 07715
771093.
Chief Officers. Fax: 452123.
Chief Finance Officer: Debbie Martin BA(Hons) CPFA. Tel: 452615.
Force Solicitor: Mr Adam Hunt LLB. Tel: 452603.
Director of Joint Kent & Essex IT Directorate: Andrew Barker. Tel: 01622 652900.
Director of Joint Support Services: Mark Gilmartin. Tel: 01622 652501.

KENT AND ESSEX SERIOUS CRIME DIRECTORATE (SCD)
Headquarters: North Kent Police Station, Thames Way, Northfleet, Kent DA11 8BD. Tel: 01474
366126.
Head of Kent & Essex Serious Crime Directorate: Assistant Chief Constable Gary Beautridge. Tel:
01474 366325.
PA: Colleen McMonies. Tel: 01474 362126.
Deputy Head of Kent & Essex Serious Crime Directorate: Det Chief Supt Liam Osborne. Tel: 01474
366134.
PA: Kelly Ramsden. Tel: 01474 366134.
SCD Staff Officer: Det Sgt Richard Vickery. Tel: 01474 366131.
Head of Intelligence: A/Det Supt Mark Wheeler. Tel: 01474 366278.
Head of Major Crime: Det Supt Mick Judge. Tel: 01474 366284.
Head of Serious Organised Crime: Det Supt Tracy Hawkings. Tel: 01474 366281.
Head of Covert Support: Det Supt Steve Worron. Tel: 01474 366285.
Head of Covert Human Intelligence Sources: Det Supt Dan Murphy. Tel: 01474 366283.
Head of Forensics: Det Supt Martyn Cochrane. Tel: 01474 366133.
Business Manager: Christina Drewitt. Tel: 01474 366139.
Chief of Staff: Det Sgt Emma Lawry. Tel: 01474 366168.

KENT AND ESSEX IT DIRECTORATE
Director of Joint Kent & Essex IT Directorate: Andrew Barker. Tel: 01622 652900.
Head of IT Transformation: Robert Nelson. Tel: 01622 652800.
Senior Business Manager: Sally Manley. Tel: 01622 652902.
Head of IT Operations: Brian Jaggs. Tel: 01622 652801.
Head of Application Development: Conrad Crampton. Tel: 01622 652885.

Head of Programme Delivery: Fiona Brown. Tel: 01622 652920.
Chief Technical Architect: Mark Williams. Tel: 01622 652806.

SUPPORT SERVICES

Director of Joint Services: Mark Gilmartin. Tel: 01622 652501.
PA: Alison Ansell. Tel: 01622 652502.
Head of Business Services: Dave Marshall. Tel: 01474 366620.
Interim Head of Kent & Essex Estate Department: Simon Curling. Tel: 01622 652718.
Head of Human Resources Department: Ian Drysdale. Tel: 01622 653100.
Head of Procurement Services: Candace Bloomfield-Howe. Tel: 01474 366650.
Head of Transport Services: John Gorton. Tel: 01245 240641.

NEIGHBOURHOOD POLICING

BASILDON DISTRICT
Basildon Police Station, Great Oaks, Basildon SS14 1EJ. Tel: 101.
District Commander: Chief Insp Glen Pavelin.
Neighbourhood Policing Teams: Billericay East; Billericay West; Burstead; Crouch; Fryerns; Laindon Park; Langdon Hills; Lee Chapel North; Nethermayne; Pitsea North West; Pitsea South East; St Martin's; Vange; Wickford Castledon; Wickford North; Wickford Park.

BRAINTREE DISTRICT
Blyths Meadow, Braintree CM7 3DJ. Tel: 101.
District Commander: Chief Insp Nick Lee.
Neighbourhood Policing Teams: Bocking; Braintree South; Braintree Town; Cressing & Stisted; Halstead; Hatfield Peverel; Hedinghams; Kelvedon; Notley & Rayne; Three Colnes; Three Fields; Witham North; Witham South; Yeldham.

BRENTWOOD DISTRICT
Brentwood Police Station, London Road, Brentwood CM14 4QJ. Tel: 101.
District Commander: Chief Insp Ed Wells.
Neighbourhood Policing Teams: Brentwood North; Brentwood South; Brentwood Town Centre; Hutton & Shenfield.

CASTLE POINT DISTRICT
Canvey Island Police Station, Long Road, Canvey Island SS8 0JD. Tel: 101.
District Commander: Chief Insp Ian Cummings.
Neighbourhood Policing Teams: Benfleet; Canvey; Hadleigh; Thundersley.

CHELMSFORD DISTRICT
Chelmsford Police Station, New Street, Chelmsford CM1 1NF. Tel: 101.
District Commander: Chief Insp Steve Ditchburn.
Neighbourhood Policing Teams: Baddow & Galleywood; Boreham; Broomfield; Chelmsford Rural South; Chelmsford Rural West; Chelmsford Town; Goat Hall; Marconi; Moulsham; South Woodham Ferrers; Springfield; Waterhouse.

COLCHESTER DISTRICT
10 Southway, Colchester CO3 3BU. Tel: 101.
District Commander: Chief Insp Paul Wells.
Neighbourhood Policing Teams: Birch & Layer; Chappel; Christchurch New Town; Colchester Town; Copford; Dedham; Harbour Berechurch; Highwoods Mile End & St John's; Horkesley; Lexden Prettygate; Mersea Abberton Fingringhoe; Rowhedge; Shrub End; St Andrew's St Anne's; Stanway; Tiptree; Wivenhoe.

EPPING FOREST DISTRICT
Loughton Police Station, 158 High Road, Loughton IG10 4BE. Tel: 101.
District Commander: Chief Insp Ed Wells.
Neighbourhood Policing Teams: Buckhurst Hill; Chigwell; Debden; Epping South East; Epping Town; Epping West; Loughton; Ongar; Waltham Abbey.

MALDON DISTRICT
Maldon Police Station, West Square, Maldon CM9 5PA. Tel: 101.
District Commander: Chief Insp Steve Ditchburn.
Neighbourhood Policing Teams: Burnham; Great Totham; Heybridge; Maldon; Purleigh; Southminster.

HARLOW DISTRICT
The High, Harlow CM20 1HG. Tel: 101.
District Commander: Chief Insp Justin Smith.
Neighbourhood Policing Teams: Harlow Central; Harlow East; Harlow North; Harlow South; Harlow West.

ROCHFORD DISTRICT
Rayleigh Police Station, 119 High Street, Rayleigh SS6 7QB. Tel: 101.
District Commander: Chief Insp Ian Cummings.

Neighbourhood Policing Teams: Ashingdon & Canewdon; Hockley; Hullbridge; Rayleigh; Rochford; Wakering.

SOUTHEND DISTRICT
Victoria Avenue, Southend-on-Sea SS2 6ES. Tel: 101.
District Commander: Chief Supt David Colwell.
Neighbourhood Policing Teams: Blenheim; Leigh; Eastwood; Shoebury; Southchurch; Southend Central.

STANSTED AIRPORT
Enterprise House, Bassingbourn Road, Stansted Airport CM24 1PS. Tel: 101 or 01279 680298.
District Commander: Chief Insp Graham Stubbs.

TENDRING DISTRICT
Clacton Police Station, 8 Beatrice Road, Clacton-on-Sea CO15 1ET. Tel: 101.
District Commander: Chief Insp Mark Schofield.
Neighbourhood Policing Teams: Alresford; Ardleigh; Brightlingsea; Clacton Central; Clacton East; Clacton West; Elmstead Market; Frinton; Great Bentley; Harwich; Kirby Cross; Manningtree; Oakley; Ramsey & Parkeston; St Osyth; Thorpe Le Soken; Walton; Weeley.

THURROCK DISTRICT
Brooke Road, Grays RM17 5BX. Tel: 101.
District Commander: Chief Insp Ben Hodder.
Neighbourhood Policing Teams: Aveley; Belhus; Chadwell; Chafford; Corringham East; Corringham West; East Tilbury; Grays Central; Grays East; Grays North; Grays South; Ockendon; Orsett, Horndon, Bulphan; Stanford; South West Thurrock; Tilbury.

UTTLESFORD DISTRICT
Saffron Walden Police Station, East Street, Saffron Walden CB10 1LX. Tel: 101.
District Commander: Chief Insp Nick Lee.
Neighbourhood Policing Teams: Clavering; Dunmow Central; Felsted; Hatfield Heath; Saffron Walden Central; Stansted North; Thaxted.

HM CORONERS AND OTHER OFFICIALS

Essex & Thurrock: Mrs Caroline Beasley-Murray. New Bridge House, 60–68 New London Road, Chelmsford CM2 0PD. Tel: 01245 506837/763. Email: coroner@essex.gov.uk
Southend & South East Essex District: Dr Peter Dean. New Bridge House, 60 New London Road, Chelmsford CM2 0PD. Tel: 01245 506806. Fax: 01245 506839/40. Email: coroner@essex.gov.uk

GLOUCESTERSHIRE CONSTABULARY

Gloucestershire Constabulary Police Headquarters, No 1 Waterwells, Waterwells Drive, Quedgeley, Gloucester GL2 2AN.
Tel: 0845 090 1234.
Email: firstname.lastname@gloucestershire.pnn.police.uk
Website: www.gloucestershire.police.uk

Lord Lieutenant: Dame Janet Trotter. 1 Tivoli Court, Cheltenham GL50 2TD.
Police & Crime Commissioner: Martin Surl.

Chief Constable: Ms Suzette Davenport.
Executive Assistant: Jo Allsopp.
Deputy Chief Constable: Mr Kevin Lambert.
PA: Helen Dutton.
Assistant Chief Constable, Operations: Mr Richard Berry.
PA: Jayne Spiers.
Assistant Chief Constable, Organisation: Ms Sally Crook.
PA: Angela Hipwell.

FINANCE AND PROCUREMENT
Assistant Director of Finance: Peter Skelton.
Corporate Accountant: Chris Burgham.
Transport Services Manager: Duane Leach.

COMMUNITY ENGAGEMENT
Head of Community Engagement: Vacant.
Head of Corporate Communications: Vacant.

PROFESSIONAL STANDARDS
Head of Department: Chief Insp Charlie Laporte.
Office Manager: Vivienne House.

OPERATIONS
T/Chief Supt Jerry Foster-Turner.
Head of Intelligence: Det Supt Alex Drummond.
Head of Investigations: Det Supt Bernie Kinsella.
Head of Public Protection: Det Supt Paul Yeatman.
Head of Forensic Services: Nick McCoy.

CRIMINAL JUSTICE DEPARTMENT & CORPORATE INFORMATION MANAGEMENT BUREAU
Central Police Station, Bearland, Gloucester GL1 2JP.
Supt Simon Atkinson
Custody: Chief Insp Richard Smith.
Criminal Justice: Insp Mark Soderland.
Head of Crime Unit: Ann Green.
Head of Non-crime: David Hawker.
Head of Tasking & Co-ordinating: Bob Keeble.
Firearms & Explosives Licensing: Les Spice.

INFORMATION SYSTEMS DEPARTMENT
Head of IS: Jane Baker.
Service Support Manager: Brian Lewis.
Technical Services Manager: Mike Crompton.
Development Manager: Vacant.
Business Support Manager: Dawn Lane.

OPERATIONAL COMMUNICATIONS
Contact Management: T/Chief Supt Gary Thompson.

OPERATIONAL SERVICES
Bamfurlong Lane, Cheltenham GL51 6ST.
Supt Neil Mantle.

HUMAN RESOURCES DIRECTORATE
T/ Resourcing Manager: Caroline Hollister.
Diversity & HR Policy Manager: Tracey Webb.
Head of Learning & Development: Lynn Moore.
Occupational Health & Safety Manager: Pauline Gill RN RSCPHN-OH.

Employment Relations Manager: Kim Carter.
HR & Performance Systems Manager: Barrie Griffiths.
BUSINESS TRANSFORMATION
Head of Business Transformation: Jane Baker.
Continuous Improvement: Chief Insp Steve Radcliffe.
Crime Registrar: David Howe.
Performance Data: Vacant.
Police Federation: *JBB Secretary:* Graham Riley. Federation Office, 6A Kingscroft Road, Hucclecote GL3 3RF. *Chairman:* Ian Anderson. *Deputy Secretary:* Tracey de Young.

LOCAL POLICING AREAS
CHELTENHAM LPA
Commander: Supt Bridget Woodhall.
TEWKESBURY LPA
Commander: Supt Rob Priddy.
STROUD LPA
Stroud Police Station, Parliament Street, Stroud GL5 1QQ.
Commander: Supt Jim McCarthy.
COTSWOLD LPA
Commander: Supt Tony Godwin.
GLOUCESTER LPA
Central Police Station, Bearland, Gloucester GL1 2JP.
Commander: Supt Emma Ackland.
FOREST LPA
Commander: Supt Phil Haynes.

HM CORONER
Gloucestershire: The Coroner's Court, Corinium Avenue, Barnwood, Gloucester GL4 3DJ. Tel: 01452 305661. Fax: 01452 412618.

GREATER MANCHESTER POLICE

Central Park, Northampton Road, Manchester M40 5BP.
Tel: 0161 856 plus extension (all numbers), unless otherwise indicated.
Email: firstname.lastname@gmp.pnn.police.uk
Enquiries mailbox (for non-urgent external enquiries):
GMPOperational.Enquiries@gmp.pnn.police.uk
Website: www.gmp.police.uk

Lord Lieutenant: Warren J Smith JP DL.
Police & Crime Commissioner: Tony Lloyd.

Chief Constable: Sir Peter Fahy QPM MA.
PA: Tracie Carmody. Ext: 2010.
Staff Officer: Insp Steve Hall. Ext: 2020.
ACPO Staff Officer: Donna Hope. Ext: 2040.
Chief Constable's Driver: Paul Fisher. Ext: 2021.
Deputy Chief Constable: Ian Hopkins MBA FCMI. Ext: 2001.
PA: Rebecca Collins. Ext: 2011.
Assistant Chief Constable, Criminal Justice & Professional Standards: Dawn Copley. Ext: 2008.
PA: Louise Bostock. Ext: 2018.
Staff Officer: Sgt Sarah-Jane Speakman. Ext: 2030.
Assistant Chief Constable, Neighbourhood Policing & Confidence: Garry Shewan. Ext: 2006.
Executive Support Officer: Jayne Jones. Ext: 2022.
Assistant Chief Constable, Serious Crime: Steve Heywood. Ext: 2007.
PA: Alwyn Davidson. Ext: 2017.
Staff Officer: Sgt Amanda Lindblom. Ext: 2348.
Assistant Chief Constable, Protective Services: Ian Wiggett. Ext: 2003.
PA: Linda Clarke. Ext: 2013.
Staff Officer: Sgt Ben Cowcill. Ext: 1162.
Assistant Chief Officer Corporate Services: Lynne Potts BA ACA MBA. Ext: 2004.
Executive Support Officer: Amy Rutter. Ext: 2014.
Executive Support Assistant/Reception: Julie Rottier. Ext: 1035.

FINANCE BRANCH
Tel: 0161 856 plus extension, unless otherwise indicated. Fax: 0161 856 1206.
Head of Finance: Neville Norton ACMA. Ext: 1200.
PA: Janet Wood. Ext: 1605.
Financial Planning & Value for Money Manager: Michael Carson ACA. Ext: 1209.
Strategic Financial Advice & Reporting Manager: Kate Connolly ACA. Ext: 1209.

HR BRANCH
Tel: 0161 856 plus extension, unless otherwise indicated.
Interim Head of HR: Tim Way. Ext: 2353.
PA: Lesley Brian. Ext: 2904.
Recruitment Unit Manager: Carole Chesworth MCIPD. Ext: 2299.
Policy & People Relations Manager: Susan Harrison FCIPD. Ext: 2340.
Performance & Resource Management Manager: John Parry. Ext: 1171.
Health & Safety Unit: *Health & Safety Manager:* Marie Parkinson MIOSH RSP. Ext: 2424.
Occupational Health & Welfare Unit: *Unit Manager:* Damian Morley BA(Psych). Ext: 0554/0644.
Senior Occupational Health Physician: Dr James Boag MB ChB AFOM DDAM. Ext: 0554.
Finance & Business Section (finance, house management, income generation): *Finance & Business Manager:* Helen Zanni. Ext: 0403.

ORGANISATIONAL LEARNING & WORKFORCE DEVELOPMENT BRANCH
Tel: 0161 856 plus extension, unless otherwise indicated.
Branch Commander: Vacant.
PA: Cheryl Mann. Ext: 0405.
Health & Safety Unit: *Manager:* Marie Parkinson MIOSH RSP. Ext: 2424.
Occupational Health & Welfare Unit: *Manager:* Damian Morley BA(Psych). Ext: 0554/0644.
Senior Occupational Health Physician: Dr James Boag MB ChB AFOM DDAM. Ext: 0554.
Head of Crime & Uniform Training: Det Chief Insp Tony Hughes. Ext: 0495.
Head of Specialist Operational Training: Chief Insp Alec McMurchy. Ext: 6241.
Finance & Business Section (finance, house management, income generation): Michelle Millington. Ext: 1263.

Head of Learning Services & Admin Hub: Steve Butterworth. Ext: 0647.
Head of Workforce Development: Emma Bilsbury. Ext: 2322.

SERIOUS CRIME DIVISION
Tel: 0161 856 plus extension, unless otherwise indicated.
Branch Head: Det Chief Supt Darren Shenton. Ext: 2600.
PA: Irene Hall. Ext: 2505. Fax: 3195.
Head of Crime Policy: Det Sgt Roque Fernandes. Ext: 6434. Fax: 2607.
Major Incident Team: Det Supt Robert Tonge. Ext: 6712. Fax: 6722.
Serious & Organised Crime Group/Robbery & Xcalibre: Det Supt Tony Creely. Ext: 6401. Fax: 0161 855 2109.
Robbery Unit: Det Chief Insp Tony Creely. Ext: 6482. Fax: 6259.
Xcalibre Organised Crime Unit: Det Supt Tony Creely. Ext: 6402.
Xcalibre Task Force: Det Chief Insp Debbie Dooley. Ext: 6402.
Serious & Organised Crime Group: Det Supt Tony Creely. Ext: 6401. Fax: 6529.
Economic Crime & Drugs Units: Det Supt Tony Creely. Ext: 6660. Fax: 6529. Det Chief Insp Rick Jackson. Ext: 6470.
Operation Warrior: Det Supt Alex Millett. Ext: 6430. Fax: 6449.
Performance & Communication Team: David S Kelly. Ext: 2198. Fax: 2607.
Firearms Licensing: James Jones. Ext: 0832.
Covert/Witness Support: Det Supt Graeme Swan. Ext: 1118.
Investigative Review Unit: Mr Martin Bottomley. Ext: 8183.
Dedicated Surveillance Unit/Technical Surveillance: Det Chief Insp Gareth Davies. Ext: 0772.
Senior Financial Advisor: Bryan Jones. Ext: 2602. Fax: 2607.

FORCE INTELLIGENCE BRANCH
Tel: 0161 856 plus extension, unless otherwise indicated.
Branch Head: Det Chief Supt Darren Shenton. Ext: 2600. Fax: 6765.
PA: Irene Hall. Ext: 2505.
OVERT SECTION
Det Supt Mark Smith. Ext: 6745. Det Chief Insp Chris Allsop. Ext: 1755.
COVERT SECTION
Det Supt Alan Lyon. Ext: 2172. Det Chief Insp Geoff Amir. Ext: 2190.

PUBLIC PROTECTION DIVISION
Branch Head: Det Chief Supt Mary Doyle. Ext: 6810.
PA: Lorraine Butler. Ext: 0070.
Territorial PPIUs/Safeguarding: Det Supt Phil Owen. Ext: 1787.
Central Area Territorial PPIUs (A/E/F Divisions)/SVPU/SCR/CDOP/Protect/Case Work Review Team: Det Chief Insp Sharon Scotson. Ext: 6571.
West Area Territorial PPIUs (K/L/P/N Divisions)/Adult Safeguarding/Force Mental Health SPOC/Domestic Abuse/MARAC/MFH: Det Chief Insp Linda Reid. Ext: 3113.
East Area Territorial PPIUs (G/J/P/Q Divisions)/Hate Crime, Training & Witness Interview Units: Det Chief Insp Chris Bridge. Ext: 6801.
Serious Sexual Offences Unit (Rape)/Sex Offenders Management Unit/Sexual Crime Unit/MAPPA: Det Supt Jonathan Chadwick; Det Chief Insp Jill Clarke. Ext: 4472.
Sex Offender Management Unit: Det Insp Debbie Conlon-Houldershaw. Ext: 3618.
Sexual Crime Unit: Det Chief Insp David Warren. Ext: 1730.
SCR & CDOP Reviews: Det Insp Nicky Porter. Ext: 1733.

FORENSIC SERVICES BRANCH
Tel: 0161 856 plus extension, unless otherwise indicated.
Branch Head: Det Chief Supt Mary Doyle. Ext: 6810.
PA: Lorraine Butler. Ext: 0070. Fax: 0161 855 2294.
Head of Crime Scene Investigation Unit: Nigel Kelly BSc(Hons) DipCSI. Ext: 6420.
Scientific Support Manager: Emily Burton MBA BSc(Hons) DipCSE NEBSM. Ext: 6682.

COUNTER TERRORISM UNIT
Tel: 0161 856 plus extension, unless otherwise indicated.
Branch Head: Det Chief Supt T Mole. Ext: 2560.
Command Support: DC Alison Swift. Ext: 2565.
Deputy Head/Unit Head Regional Counter Terrorism Intelligence Unit: Mr Tony Brett QPM. Ext: 1056.
General Enquiries: Headquarters. Ext: 1040. **Airport.** Ext: 0270.
Superintendent Operational Support. Ext: 0938.
Superintendent Greater Manchester Counter Terrorist Branch. Ext: 7921.
Superintendent Investigations. Ext: 9926.
Co-ordination & Tasking Office. Ext: 7920.

Training & Development. Ext: 0984.
Performance & Communication. Ext: 2159.
Administration & Finance. Ext: 1099.
Human Resources. Ext: 2565.

EXTERNAL RELATIONS & PERFORMANCE BRANCH
Branch Head: Peter Langmead-Jones. Ext: 2402.
PA: Brenda Cottrill. Ext: 1182.
Planning & Policy Manager: George Burns. Ext: 2388.
Head of Performance: Supt Shirley Cullis-Wilding. Ext: 1224.

BUSINESS SUPPORT SERVICES BRANCH
Tel: 0161 856 plus extension, unless otherwise indicated.
Branch Head, Business Support Services: Sharon Kaberry BA(Hons) ACIS. Ext: 0751.
PA: Sandra Young. Ext: 0757.
Assistant Branch Head Business Support Services (Transport): Russell Brown. Ext: 0775.
Assistant Branch Head Business Support Services (Support Services). Chris Holt. Ext: 4656.
Assistant Branch Head Business Support Services (Customer Services): Ian Heaton. Ext: 0721.
Assistant Branch Head Business Support Services (Procurement): Jude Leadbeater. Ext: 2975.
Workshop Manager: Tony Clitheroe. Ext: 0762.
Engineering Manager: Tim Sykes. Ext: 0750.
Principal Facilities Manager: Peter Bannister. Ext: 4657.
Principal Technical Manager: Carol Laing. Ext: 1121.
Facilities Managers: Claire Holden. Tel: 07920 287874. Phil Marcroft. Tel: 07825 780075. Julie Worswick. Tel: 07917 613846. John Greaves. Tel: 07920 205773. Barry Lomax. Tel: 07825 063241.
Sustainability Manager: Rob Hayes. Tel: 07760 992034.
Catering and Hospitality Manager: Julie Martin. Ext: 1195.
Project Managers: Brian Ritchie. Tel: 07768 006101. Julian Marcroft. Tel: 07900 467171. Lee Crompton. Tel: 07917 613836. Rob Sankey. Tel: 07768 006105.
Logistics Manager: David Brown. Ext: 1999.
Fleet Account Managers: Brad Waterfall. Ext: 0715. Stephen Bradley. Ext: 0734. John Turner. Ext: 0786.
Customer Services Manager (including Design & Print, Central Administration Hub, Duty Office): David Wright. Ext: 0756.
Uniform Stores Manager: Julie Blezzard. Ext: 0821.
Quality & Performance Managers: Xavier Brierley. Ext: 0758. Hazel McQuaid. Ext: 0639.
Health & Safety Advisor: Elaine Eaves (HR Branch). Ext: 2260. Mob: 07824 499793.
Contracts Manager: Hilary Corr. Ext: 2312.
Contracts Manager (IT): Sarah Baker. Ext: 1204.
Contracts Manager (PFI): Dan Rowlands. Ext: 1112.

FACILITIES BRANCH
Tel: 0161 856 plus extension, unless otherwise indicated.
Principal Facilities Manager: Peter Bannister. Ext: 4657.
Principal Technical Manager: Carol Laing. Ext: 1121.
Facilities Managers: Claire Holden. Tel: 07920 287874. Phil Marcroft. Tel: 07825 780075. Julie Worswick. Tel: 07917 613846. Barry Lomax. Tel: 07825 063241. John Greaves. Tel: 07920 205773.
Helpdesk. Ext: 0504.

CHANGE BRANCH
Branch Head: Rebecca Murphy. Ext: 0923.
PA: Brenda Cottrill. Ext: 1182.

INFORMATION SERVICES BRANCH
Tel: 0161 856 plus extension, unless otherwise indicated.
Head of Branch: Mario Devargas. Ext: 1300.
PA: Juli Emanuel. Ext: 1305.
Assistant Head: William Naylor. Ext: 61120.
Assistant Head, Technical Operations Strategy & Governance: Colin Carey. Ext: 1321.
Assistant Head, Information Management: Michelle Hallion. Ext: 2832.
A/Assistant Head, Change & Development: Alison Harper. Ext: 61349.
Strategic Financial Advisor: Janet Moores. Ext: 1149.
HR Delivery Manager: Laura Lamptey. Ext: 0123.

CRIMINAL JUSTICE & CUSTODY BRANCH
Strategic Lead for Criminal Justice & Custody: Supt Catherine McKay. Ext: 62970.
PA: Juli Emanuel. Ext: 1305.

Operational Lead for Custody Delivery & Staff Officer to ACC Copley, Business Area Lead for Custody & Prisoner Escort: Supt Alan Greene. Tel: 07788 564907.
Staff Officer to ACC Copley, Business Area Lead for Custody & PACE: Insp Shane O'Neill. Tel: 07867 468428.
Strategic Financial Advisor: Helen Zanni. Ext: 0403.
HR Delivery Manager: Lisa Parry. Ext: 68070.

SPECIALIST OPERATIONS BRANCH
Tel: 0161 856 plus extension, unless otherwise indicated.
Branch Head: Chief Supt John O'Hare. Ext: 1700.
PA. Ext: 1605.
OPERATIONAL PLANNING SECTION
Supt Bryan Lawton. Ext: 61192.
Chief Insp Steve Howard. Ext: 61604.
Civil Contingencies & Resilience Unit: Insp June Roby. Ext: 2829.
Business Continuity: Mr Andrew Swapp. Ext: 2741.
Force Events Unit: Insp John Haywood. Ext: 1683.
Conference Planning Unit: Chief Insp Anthony Simpson. Ext: 3076.
SPECIALIST SUPPORT SECTION
Supt Leor Giladi. Ext: 6201. Fax: 6226. (Claytonbrook.)
Tactical Firearms Unit & Firearms Training Unit: Chief Insp Michael Lawler. Ext: 0881. Fax: 0799.
Tactical Aid Unit: Chief Insp Rob Tinsley. Ext: 6202. Fax: 6226.
Tactical Mounted & Dogs Units, Firearms Policy & Compliance Unit: Chief Insp Rob Tinsley. Ext: 6291/1776. Fax: 6279.
Underwater Search Unit. Tel: 0928 713457. Ext: 3993. Fax: 01244 613909.
TERRITORIAL SUPPORT SECTION
Supt Craig Thompson. Ext: 0087. Fax: 0161 856 6226.
TRAFFIC NETWORK SECTION
Administration. Ext: 4787/4785/4767/4786/4789. Fax: 7845.
Roads Policing
Chief Insp Rachel Buckle. Peel Green, Eccles. Ext: 4751. Fax: 7845.
RPU1: Insp Phil Bromley. Ext: 67202.
RPU2: Insp Adam Greenslade. Ext: 66030.
RPU3: Insp Martin O'Connor. Ext: 68802.
Serious Collision Investigation Unit
Insp Paul Rowe. Ext: 64744. Insp Matt Bailey-Smith. Ext: 69956.
Road Traffic Collision Investigation Unit Manager: Carmella Yaffa. Ext: 62062.
Specialist Enforcement: Chief Insp Mark Dexter. Peel Green, Eccles. Ext: 4794. Fax: 7845.
ANPR Intercept: Insp Susan Redfern. Ext: 67771.
Specialist Enforcement: Insp John Armfield. Ext: 64768.
Central Ticket Office: Karen Stringer. Ext: 63491.
Air Support Units
Rotary: Sgt David Kibblewhite. Barton Airport, Liverpool Road, Eccles. Ext: 4605. Fax: 0161 707 9151.
Fixed Wing: Sgt David Clarke. World Freight Terminal, Manchester Airport. Ext: 7984. Fax: 0161 707 9151.
MANCHESTER AIRPORT SECTION
Supt Bob Lomas. Ext: 0201. Fax: 0206.
Chief Insp Mike Miskell. Ext: 0202.
General Airport Enquiries. Ext: 0250.

OPERATIONAL COMMUNICATIONS BRANCH
Claytonbrook 2 Complex, Louisa Street.
T/Branch Commander: Chief Supt Zoe Sheard.
T/Call Handling: Supt Julie Ellison.
Command & Control: Supt Jacqui Pendlebury.
Business Lead (Call Handling): Diane Grandidge.
Business Lead (Command & Control): Andrew Massey.
Call Handling: Trafford OCR.
Crime Recording Unit: Claytonbrook 2.
Customer Enquiry Unit: Claytonbrook 2 & Trafford.
Command & Control: Claytonbrook & Tameside.

OPERATIONS COMMUNICATIONS ROOMS
Claytonbrook
Covers North Manchester (A); Metropolitan (B); South Manchester (C); Salford (F), Wigan (L), Trafford (M) & Force Duty Officers.
Business Lead: Andrew Massey. Ext: 6384. Fax: 0161 855 2111.
Tameside
Covers Tameside (G); Stockport (J); Oldham (Q). Bolton (K), Bury (N), Rochdale (P).
Business Lead: Andrew Massey. Ext: 6384. Fax: 0161 855 2111.

CALL HANDLING
Business Lead for Contact Management: Diane Grandidge. Ext: 1884. Fax: 0161 877 6720.

CRIMINAL JUSTICE & CUSTODY BRANCH
Supt Catherine McKay. Ext: 62970.
Chief Insp Gail Spruce. Ext: 61636.
Officer (& CJ & C Branch Admin): Vivian Zuball. Ext: 62692.

SAFEGUARDING VULNERABLE PERSONS UNIT
Det Supt Philip Owen. Ext: 7142.
Det Chief Insp David Riddick. Ext: 6571. Det Chief Insp Henry Harrison. Ext: 0040.
Missing from Home Section: *Manager:* John Barnes. Ext: 2234.

ARCHITECTURAL LIAISON UNIT
Principal Architectural Liaison Officer: Michael Hodge FRICS. Ext: 5913.

PROFESSIONAL STANDARDS BRANCH
Tel: 0161 856 plus extension, unless otherwise indicated.
Head of Professional Standards: T/Chief Supt Paul Rumney. Ext: 2900.
PA: Lesley Brian. Ext: 2904.
T/HR Manager. Ext: 1636.

COMPLAINT AND MISCONDUCT INVESTIGATIONS – OPERATIONS
Chief Insp Mike Dawson. Ext: 2951.
Det Chief Insp Jane Little. Ext: 7827.

COMPLAINT ASSESSMENT, MISCONDUCT AND POLICY UNIT
Det Supt Peter J Matthews. Ext: 2921.
Complaints Manager: Mike Thornton. Ext: 2955.
Police Staff Complaints & Misconduct Manager: Wendy Boardman. Ext: 1656.
Inspector: Cheryl Hughes. Ext: 2959.

EVALUATION AND SUPPORT UNIT
General Enquiries. Ext: 2910.

INTERNAL INVESTIGATION UNIT
Det Supt Paul Savill. Ext: 2541.
Det Chief Insp James Riley. Ext: 2542.

FORCE VETTING UNIT
Force Vetting Officer: John Dineen. Ext: 2839.
Senior Vetting Officer: William Oxley. Ext: 2527.
Integrity/Local Intelligence Requests. Email: forcevettingunit@gmp.pnn.police.uk

LEGAL SERVICES
Director of Legal Services: Sandra Pope LLM BA(Hons). Ext: 1608. Fax: 6718.
Deputy Director of Legal Services: Sian Williams LLB. Ext: 1689. Fax: 2733.
PA. Ext: 2719.

CORPORATE COMMUNICATIONS BRANCH
Tel: 0161 856 plus extension, unless otherwise indicated.
Head of Corporate Communications: Amanda Coleman. Ext: 2239. Fax: 2236.
Administration/Media Co-ordinator: Lorna Owen. Ext: 2224.
Press Office. Ext: 2220. Fax: 2236.
Press Office & Internal Communications Manager: Sarah Ford. Ext: 2230.
Public Relations. Ext: 2284. Fax: 2259.
Public Relations Manager: Lynn Marsh. Ext: 2221.
Internal Communications. Ext: 2238.
Corporate & Media Imaging: *Head of Unit:* Chris Oldham. Ext: 2777.
Web Unit. *Web Manager:* Kevin Hoy. Ext: 1166.
Force Band: Lynn Marsh. Ext: 2771. Mob: 07825 116727. Email: police.band@gmp.police.uk
Force Museum: *Museum Curator:* Duncan Broady. Ext: 3287. Newton Street, Manchester M1 1ES.
  Main Office. Ext: 2387/8. **Shop.** Ext: 3281. Fax: 3286.

GREATER MANCHESTER POLICE FEDERATION
JBB Chair: Ian Hanson. Tel: 0161 355 4415.
JBB Secretary: Jackie Bowen. Tel: 0161 355 4416.
JBB Treasurer: Russ Lee. Tel: 0161 355 4417.
JBB Deputy Secretary: Karl Thurogood. Tel: 0161 355 4418.

TERRITORIAL DIVISIONS
NORTH MANCHESTER DIVISION (A)
Divisional Headquarters, Central Park, Northampton Road, Manchester M40 5BQ. Tel: 0161 856 plus extension, unless otherwise indicated.
Divisional Commander: Chief Supt Russ Jackson.
PA. Ext: 3005. Fax: 3009.
Uniform Operations: Supt Neil Bhole. Ext: 3201.
Crime Operations: Supt Vanessa Jardine. Ext: 63807.
Uniform Operations City Centre: Supt Stuart Ellison. Ext: 3229.
Stations: Bootle Street; Harpurhey; Plant Hill, Gorton.

SOUTH MANCHESTER DIVISION (E)
Divisional Headquarters, 2 Grindlow Street, Longsight, Manchester M13 0LL. Tel: 0161 856 4229 (front counter enquiries). Individual numbers tel: 0161 856 plus extension, unless otherwise indicated.
Divisional Commander: Chief Supt Rob Potts. Ext: 4200.
PA: Shirlee Hodgkinson. Ext: 6005.
Strategic Financial Advisor: Carol McKinnon. Mob: 07775 226198.
HR Delivery Manager: Suzanne Barr. Ext: 9603.
Operations: Supt Sarah Jackson. Ext: 4201. Chief Insp Dave Gilbride. Ext: 4208.
Integrated Neighbourhood Policing Teams
INPT 1 Central (Longsight): Supt Wasim Chaudhry. Ext: 4275. Chief Insp Arif Nawaz. Ext: 4442. Det Chief Insp: Vacant.
INPT 2 & 3 South (Fallowfield & Didsbury): Supt Ian Palmer Ext: 6141.
INPT 2: Chief Insp Cheryl Chatterton. Ext: 4624.
INPT 3: Chief Insp John McNeil. Ext: 4846.
INPT 2 & 3: Det Chief Insp Dave Pester. Ext: 6042.
INPT 4 (Wythenshawe): Supt Hughie Hardiman. Ext: 6101. Chief Insp Derek Hewitt. Ext: 6102. Det Chief Insp Colin Larkin. Ext: 6170.
Stations: Longsight Divisional Headquarters & Central Custody Centre, Greenheys.

THE CITY OF SALFORD DIVISION (F)
*† Divisional Headquarters, Chorley Road, Swinton M27 6BA. Tel: 0161 856 5229 (enquiries). Individual numbers tel: 0161 856 plus extension, unless otherwise indicated.
Divisional Commander: Chief Supt Kevin Mulligan.
PA: Helen Keefe. Ext: 5405.
Operations: Supt Stuart Barton. Ext: 5201. Chief Insp Mark Kenny. Ext: 5245.
Criminal Justice & Partnerships: Supt Wayne Miller. Ext: 5001. Chief Insp Dave Henthorne. Ext: 5451.
Serious Crime: Det Chief Insp Dave Riddick. Ext: 5042.
Volume Crime: Det Chief Insp Ben Ewart. Ext: 5202.
Strategic Financial Advisor: Philip Goodier.
HR Business Partner: Sue Barr.
Main Police Station: Swinton, M27 6BA. Tel: 0161 856 5229.
Other Police Stations: †Eccles; Little Hulton; Pendleton.

TAMESIDE METROPOLITAN BOROUGH DIVISION (G)
† Divisional Headquarters, Manchester Road, Ashton-under-Lyne OL7 0BQ. Tel: 0161 856 9209 (admin); 0161 856 9329 (enquiries). Individuals tel: 0161 856 plus extension, unless otherwise indicated.
Divisional Commander: Chief Supt Nicholas Adderley.
PA: Pamela McCarten. Ext: 9201.
Operations: Supt Neil Evans. Ext: 9202. Chief Insp Delma Barr. Ext: 9207.
Support & Partnership: Supt Nicola Spragg. Ext: 4088. Chief Insp Stephen McFarlane. Ext: 9203.
Crime Operations: Det Chief Insp Mark Hussey. Ext: 9231.
Strategic Financial Advisor: Julie Chiltern. Ext: 1149.
HR Delivery Manager: Rebecca J Smith. Mob: 07833 239 310.
Stations: Ashton-under-Lyne; Hyde.

STOCKPORT METROPOLITAN BOROUGH DIVISION (J)
† Divisional Headquarters, Spectrum Way, Adswood, Stockport SK3 0SA. Tel: 0161 856 plus extension, unless otherwise indicated. Fax: 0161 856 9806.
Divisional Commander: Chief Supt Chris Sykes.
PA: Jean Hatton. Ext: 9605.

Public Enquiry Counter. Ext: 9829/9864.
Response/Hub Operations: Supt Nick Phillips. Ext: 9801. Chief Insp Brian Davies. Ext: 9802.
Neighbourhood Policing, CID & Partnership: Supt John Berry. Ext: 9702. Chief Insp Leon Jacobs. Ext: 9756. A/Det Chief Insp Sam Pickering. Ext: 9742.
Neighbourhood Policing Units: Stockport North. Ext: 9786. Stockport East. Ext: 9973. Stockport West. Ext: 9770.
Strategic Financial Advisor: Julie Warren. Ext: 9602.
Business Support Officer: Roz Crewdson. Ext: 9604.

BOLTON METROPOLITAN BOROUGH DIVISION (K)
*† Divisional Headquarters, Bolton Police Station, Scholey Street, Bolton BL2 1HX. Tel: 0161 856 5629/30 (enquiries). Individuals tel: 0161 856 plus extension, unless otherwise indicated. Fax: 0161 856 5512.
Divisional Commander: Chief Supt David Hull.
PA: Julia Wharmby. Ext: 5505.
Superintendent: Operations: Stephen Nibloe. Ext: 5701.
Superintendent: Criminal Justice & Partnerships: Phil Davies. Ext: 5601.
Crime Operations: Det Chief Insp Sarah Jackson. Ext: 5042.
Divisional Area Stations: Astley Bridge. Ext: 5729. Farnworth. Ext: 5829). Horwich. Ext: 7971.

WIGAN METROPOLITAN BOROUGH DIVISION (L)
Divisional Headquarters, Robin Park Road, Wigan WN5 0UP. Tel: 0161 856 7107 (admin); 0161 872 5050 (enquiries). Individuals tel: 0161 856 plus extension, unless otherwise indicated. Fax: 0161 856 7006.
Divisional Commander: Chief Supt Shaun Donnellan. Ext: 7000.
PA: Jacqueline Ibbetson. Ext: 7005.
Specialist Support: A/Supt Andrea Jones. Ext: 7101. Chief Insp Stuart Wrudd. Ext: 7433.
Territorial Policing: A/Supt Mark Kenny. Ext: 7399. Chief Insp Gareth Hughes. Ext: 7102. Det Chief Insp Howard Millington. Ext: 7142.
HR Delivery Manager: Gail Burgess Tel: 07824 868451.
Strategic Financial Advisor: Philip Goodier. Tel: 07920 504298.
Integrated Neighbourhood Policing Teams
Wigan West – INPT1: Det Insp Martin Reddington. Ext: 7279. Insp Glenn Jones. Ext: 7121.
Wigan East – INPT2: Det Insp Jonathan Keeley. Ext: 7243. Insp Liz Sanderson. Ext: 7301.

TRAFFORD METROPOLITAN BOROUGH OPERATIONAL COMMAND UNIT (M)
† Divisional BCU Headquarters, PO Box 6, Talbot Road, Stretford, Manchester M32 0XB. Tel: 0161 856 7715 (admin). Individuals tel: 0161 856 plus extension, unless otherwise indicated. Fax: 0161 856 7714.
Divisional OCU Commander: Chief Supt James Liggett.
PA: Anne Nicholas. Ext: 7705.
Operations: Supt Simon Retford. Ext: 7601. Chief Insp Dean Howard. Ext: 7602.
Partnership & Justice: Supt Bob Pell. Ext: 7501. Chief Insp Andy Sutcliffe. Ext: 7661.
Crime Operations & Support: Det Chief Insp Melani Linton. Ext: 7726.
Strategic Financial Advisor: Phil Goodier.
Neighbourhood Stations: *†Stretford. Ext: 7627/29. Fax: 7647. *Altrincham. Ext: 7529. Fax: 7506. Urmston. Ext: 7681. Fax: 0161 748 7776. Sale. Ext: 7850. Fax: 0161 973 7852.
Substation: Partington. Fax: 0161 775 1431.

BURY METROPOLITAN BOROUGH DIVISION (N)
† Divisional Headquarters, Dunster Road, Bury BL9 0RD. Tel: 0161 856 8004 (admin); 0161 856 8129 (enquiries). Individuals tel: 0161 856 plus extension, unless otherwise indicated. Fax: 0161 856 8056.
Divisional Commander: Chief Supt Caroline Ball.
PA: Sylvia Cartwright. Ext: 8005.
Uniform Operations: Supt Karan Lee. Ext: 8050. Chief Insp Sean Hogan. Ext: 4931.
Criminal Justice & Partnership: Supt Mark Granby. Ext: 8012. Chief Insp Jonathan Lowe. Ext: 8101.
Crime Operations: Det Chief Insp Sara Wallwork. Ext: 8142.
Substations: *†Whitefield. Ext: 8229. Fax: 0161 796 3746. Prestwich. Ext: 4532. Fax: 7499. Radcliffe. Ext: 8291. Fax: 0161 723 0264. Ramsbottom. Ext: 8181. Fax: 01706 821930.
Please note that Bury DHQ is the only station designated under s35, P.A.C.E. Act 1984.

ROCHDALE METROPOLITAN BOROUGH DIVISION (P)
Divisional Headquarters, The Holme, The Esplanade, Rochdale OL16 1AG. Individuals tel: 0161 856 plus extension, unless otherwise indicated.
Divisional Commander: Chief Supt Annette Anderson. Ext: 8400.
PA: Janette Stott. Ext: 8405.
Uniform Operations: Supt John Graves. Ext: 8501. Chief Insp Mark Bell. Ext: 8502.

Uniform Criminal Justice & Partnership: Supt Chris Hankinson. Ext: 8401. Chief Insp John Taylor. Ext: 8556.
Investigative Crime Services: Det Chief Insp Alistair Mallen. Ext: 8542.
Strategic Financial Advisor: Marilyn Smith. Ext: 8539.
Integrated Neighbourhood Policing Teams
INPT1. Ext: 9953.
INPT2. Ext: 8441.
INPT2. Ext: 8718.

OLDHAM METROPOLITAN BOROUGH DIVISION (Q)

Divisional Headquarters, PO Box 5, George Street, Oldham OL1 1LR. Individuals tel: 0161 856 plus extension, unless otherwise indicated. Fax: 0161 856 8904.
Divisional Commander: Chief Supt Catherine Hankinson. Ext: 9005.
Secretary/PA: Wendy Lees. Ext: 9005.
Criminal Justice & Partnership: Supt Nadeem Butt. Ext: 9090. Chief Insp Joanne Marshall. Ext: 8902.
Uniform Operations: Supt Denise Worth. Ext: 9044. Chief Insp Andy Harty. Ext: 1322.
Crime Manager: Det Chief Insp Mike Mangan. Ext: 8941.
Strategic Financial Advisor: Julie Warren. Mob: 07796 276305.
Integrated Neighbourhood Policing Teams
INPT1 Central: Insp A Humphries. Ext: 9092. Insp J Morris. Ext: 9072. Det Insp D Milovanovic. Ext: 8993. Det Insp A Buckley.
INPT2 Borough: Insp M Kernain. Tel: 0161 684 8921. Insp K Taylor. Ext: 9035. Det Insp T Alogba.
* Denotes stations staffed 24 hrs per day.
† Denotes stations designated under s35, P.A.C.E. Act 1984.

POLICE STATIONS DESIGNATED UNDER S35, P.A.C.E. ACT 1984

24 Hours Division	Station		
A	Bootle Street, Collyhurst, Grey Mare Lane	L	Wigan, Leigh
		M	Stretford, Altrincham, Airport
E	Longsight Central Custody Centre	N	Bury, Whitefield
F	Crescent	P	Rochdale (only Rochdale DHQ is 24 hrs operational), Middleton
G	Ashton-under-Lyne (not Stalybridge)	Q	Oldham, Chadderton
J	Stockport, Cheadle Heath	*6 Hours Division*	*Station*
K	Bolton, Farnworth, Astley Bridge	F	Swinton, Eccles

Location	Division	Location	Division	Location	Division
Abbey Hey	E	Ashworth Valley	P	Barton Grange	F
Abbey Lakes	L	Aspull	L	Barton Locks	F
Abraham's Chair	G	Aspull Common	L	Barton Moss	F
Abram	L	Aspull Moor	L	Barton-upon-Irwell	F
Adam Hill	K	Astley Bridge	K	Bedford	L
Adswood	J	Astley Green	L	Bedford Moss	L
Affetside	N	Atherleigh	L	Beech Hill	L
Agecroft	F	Atherton	L	Belfield	P
Ainsworth	N	Atherton Hall	L	Belle Vue	E
Airport	M	Audenshawe	G	Belmont	K
Alkrington Garden Village	P	Austerlands	Q	Benchill	E
		Backbower	G	Bent Lanes	M
Altrincham	M	Back O'th Moor	P	Besom Hill	Q
Amberswood Common	L	Bagslate Moor	P	Besses O'th Barn	N
		Baguley	E	Beswick	A
Ancoats	A	Balderstone	L	Bickershaw	L
Ardwick	E	Baldingstone	N	Billinge	L
Ashley Heath	M	Bamford	P	Birch	P
Ashton-in-Makerfield	L	Bamfurlong	L,	Birches	G
		Bank Top	K	Birtle	P
Ashton-on-Mersey	M	Bardsley	Q	Blackford Bridge	N
Ashton-under-Lyne	G	Barns Green	A	Blackley	A
		Barrow Bridge	K	Blackmoor	L
Ashway Gap	Q	Barton Aerodrome	F		

Location	Division	Location	Division	Location	Division
Broadhall	P	Cheetham Hill	A	Delph Hill	K
Broadheath	M	Cheetwood	A	Denshaw	Q
Broadoak Park	F	Chelburn Moor	P	Denton	G
Bromley Cross	K	Chequerbent	K	Didsbury	E
Brook Bottom	G	Chesham	N	Diggle	Q
Brookhouse	F	Chew Moor	K	Dimple	K
Brooklands	E	Chorlton Fold	F	Dobcross	Q
Brooks Bar	E	Chorlton-cum-	E	Doffcocker	K
Brooks Bottoms	N	Hardy		Dog Hill	Q
Broomfield	P	Chortlon-on-	E	Dooley Lane	J
Broomwood	M	Medlock		Dover Lock	L
Booths Bank	F	Chorltonville	E	Droylsden	G
Boothstown	L	Clarksfield	Q	Duchy Estate	F
Broughton Park	F	Claypools	K	Dukes Gate	F
Browns Low	L	Clayton	A	Duckinfield	G
Brushes	G	Clayton Bridge	A	Dumplungton	M
Bryn	L	Clayton Vale	A	Dunham Massey	M
Bryn Cross	L	Clegg Moor	P	Dunham Town	M
Bryn Gates	L	Cleggswood Hill	P	Dunham	M
Buckley	P	Clifton	F	Woodhouses	
Buckton Vale	G	Clifton Junction	F	Dunscar	K
Buersil	P	Clough	Q	Durn	P
Buersil Head	P	(Crompton)		Eagley	K
Buile Hill Park	F	Clough	P	East Didsbury	E
Bunkers Hill	J	(Littleborough)		Eccles	F
Burnage	E	Collyhurst	A	Edge Fold	K
Burnden	K	Compstall	J	Edge Green	L
Burnedge	Q	Coopers Turning	K	Egerton	K
Burrs	N	Copley	G	Egerton Park	F
Bury	N	Coppice	Q	Ellenbrook	F
Busk	Q	Copster Hill	Q	Ellesmere Park	F
Butler Green	Q	Cornbrook	M	Elton	N
Cadishead	F	Cowlishaw	Q	Exchange	F
Cadishead Moss	F	Crankwood	L	Failsworth	Q
Calderbrook	P	Crimble	P	Fairfield (Bury)	N
Caldermoor	P	Crofters	K	Fairfield	G
Captain Fold	P	Crofts Bank	M	(Droylsden)	
Carrbrook	G	Crompton Fold	Q	Fallowfield	E
Carrgreen	M	Crossacres	E	Far Moor	L
Carrington	M	Cross Bank	Q	Farnworth	K
Castle Hill (Astley	K	Cross Hillock	L	Ferngrove	N
Bridge)		Crumpsall	A	Fernhill (Bury)	N
Castle Hill	J	Culcheth	E	Fernhill	K
(Bredbury)		Cutgate	P	(Farnworth)	
Castle Hill	L	Daisy Hill	K	Fernhill Gate	K
(Hindley)		Daisy Nook	Q	Fielden Park	E
Castle Shaw	Q	Dale	Q	Fingerpost	L
Castleton	P	Dales Brow	F	Firgrove	P
Catley Lane Head	P	Dane Bank	G	Firs Lane	L
Chadderton	Q	Dangerous Corner	L	Firswood	M
Chadderton Fold	Q	Darcy Lever	K	Firwood	K
Chadderton	Q	Darnhill	P	Firwood Fold	K
Heights		Dawbhill	K	Fishpool	N
Chain Bar	A	Davenport	J	Fitton Hill	Q
Charlestown	F	Davenport Green	M	Flixton	M
Chat Moss	F	Davenport Park	J	Flowery Field	G
Chauntry Brow	K	Davyhulme	M	Foggbrook	J
Cheadle	J	Deane	K	Fold	G
Cheadle Heath	J	Deans	P	Four Lane Ends	K
Cheadle Hulme	J	Deanwater	J	(Farnworth)	
Cheesden	P	Dearnley	P	Four Lane Ends	N
Cheetham	A	Delph	Q	(Tottington)	

Location	Division	Location	Division	Location	Division
Fourgates	K	Hazel Grove	J	Holts	Q
Fox Platt	G	Hazelhurst	G	Hooley Bridge	P
Freehold	Q	(Ashton-under-		Hooley Brow	P
Fullwood	Q	Lyne)		Hooley Hill	G
Garton	L	Hazelhurst	F	Hope Carr	L
Garton Common	L	(Worsley)		Hopwood	P
Gathurst	L	Headyhill	P	Horrocks Fold	K
Gatley	J	Heald Green	J	Horwich	K
Gatley Hill	J	Healds Green	Q	Howarth Cross	P
Gaythorne	A	Healey	P	Hulme	E
Gee Cross	G	Heap Bridge	P	Hulton Lane Ends	K
Gidlow	L	Heaton	K	Hulton Park	K
Gilnow	K	Heaton Chapel	J	Humphrey Park	M
Gin Pit Village	L	Heaton Mersey	J	Hunger Hill	K
Glodwick	Q	Heaton Moor	J	Hurst	G
Godley	Gn	Heaton Norris	J	Hursthead	P
Golborne	L	Heaton Park	A	Hyde	G
Gorse Hill	M	Heaviley	J	Hyde Green	G
Gorton	A	Hebbers	P	Ince Bar	L
Grains Bar	Q	Hephzibah Farm	F	Ince-in-Makerfield	L
Grasscroft	Q	Heyheads	G	Ince Moss	L
Gravel Hole	Q	Heyrod	G	Irlam	F
Great Horrocks	A	Heyside	Q	Irlam Moss	F
Great Howarth	P	Heywood	P	Irlam O'th Heights	F
Great Lever	K	Higginshaw	Q	Jenny Cross	F
Great Moor	J	High Crompton	Q	Jericho	N
Great Moss	L	Higher Blackley	A	Johnson Fold	K
Great Woolden	F	Higher Broughton	F	Jubilee	Q
Moss		Higher Fold	L	Junction	Q
Greave	J	Higher Green	L	Kearsley	K
Greenacres	Q	Higher Hurst	G	Kenworthy	E
Greenfield	Q	Higher Ince	L	Kenyon	L
Greengate	P	Higher Irlam	F	Kersal	F
Greenheys	F	Higher Ogden	P	Kersal Dale	F
(L/Hulton)		Highfield	K	Kersal Moor	F
Greenheys	E	(Farnworth)		Kiln Green	Q
(Manchester)		Highfield	L	Kings Moss	L
Green Hill	K	(Swinley)		Kingston	G
Greenmount	N	Highfield Moss	L	Kirkholt	P
Greenside	G	High Lane	J	Kirklees	L
Grotton	Q	Hill Top	F	Kitt Green	L
Guide Bridge	G	Hillend	G	Knott Lanes	Q
Hag Fold	L	Hilton House	K	Knott Mill	A
Haigh	L	Hilton Park	N	Knowl Moor	P
Hale	M	Hindley	L	Knutsford Vale	E
Hale Barns	M	Hindley Green	L	Ladybarn	E
Hall i'th Wood	K	Hindsford	L	Ladybridge	K
Halliwell	K	Hobson Moor	G	Lady House	P
Hart Common	K	Hodgefold	G	Lamberhead	L
Hartshead Green	G	Holcombe	N	Green	
Harper Green	K	Holcombe Brook	N	Lancashire Hill	J
Harpurhey	A	Hollin	P	Landgate	L
Harrop Dale	Q	Hollingworth	G	Lane End	E
Harwood	K	Hollingworth Lake	P	(Manchester)	
Hatherlow	J	Hollins	K	Lane End	P
Hathershaw	Q	(Farnworth)		(Rochdale)	
Haugh	P	Hollins	N	Lane Ends	J
Haughton	G	(Whitefield)		Lane Head	L
Haughton Green	G	Hollinwood	Q	Langley	P
Haulgh	K	Holly Nook	L	Langtree	L
Hawk Green	J	Holt Lane End	Q	Langworthy Park	F
Hawkshaw	N	Holt Town	E	Lee Gate	K

Location	Division	Location	Division	Location	Division
Pocket Nook (Lowton)	L	Shawfield	P	The Cliff	F
		Shevington	L	The Grange	M
Pocket Nook (W/Houghton)	K	Shevington Moor	L	Thornbank	K
		Shevington Vale	L	Thornhill	L
Poolstock	L	Sholver	Q	Thorpe	Q
Pownall Green	J	Shore	P	Thurston Clough	Q
Prestolee	K	Shuttleworth	N	Timperley	M
Prestwich	N	Siddow Common	L	Tonge Fold	K
Princes Park	F	Side O'th Moor	K	Tonge Moor	K
Prospect Grange	F	Sidebottom Fold	G	Top Lock	L
Quick Edge	G	Simister	N	Top of Heben	P
Quickwood	G	Simpson Clough	P	Top of Pike	P
Radcliffe	N	Sinderland Green	M	Top O'th Meadows	Q
Raikes	K	Sindsley	F		
Rain Shore	P	Slackcote	Q	Top of Turton	K
Rainsough	N	Slattocks	P	Top O'th Brow	K
Rakewood	P	Smallbridge	P	Top O'th Gorses	K
Ramsbottom	N	Smedley	A	Top O'th Moss	K
Red Lumb	P	Smithfield	A	Toppings	K
Red Moss	K	Smithills	K	Tottington	N
Red Rock	L	Smithills Moor	K	Town Green	L
Reddish	J	Smithy Bridge	P	Town Lane	L
Reddish Vale	J	Smithy Green	J	Trafford Park	M
Redvales	N	South Reddish	J	Trinity	F
Redwood	L	Spotland Bridge	P	Tuckers Hill	K
Rhodes	P	Spring Gardens	F	Tunshall	P
Ridge Hill	G	Spring View	L	Tunstead	Q
Ringley	K	Springfield (Bolton)	K	Tyldesley	L
Ringley Brow	K			University	E
Ringway	M	Springfield (Wigan)	L	Unsworth	N
Rochdale	P			Uppermill	Q
Roe Cross	G	Springhead	Q	Urmston	M
Roe Green	F	Stakehill	P	Victoria Park	E
Roebuck Low	Q	Stalybridge	G	Victory	K
Romiley	J	Stand	N	Walkden	F
Rooley Moor	P	Standish	L	Walker Fold	K
Rose Hill	K	Standish Lower Ground	L	Wallgate	L
Royley Park	Q			Wallness	F
Royton	Q	Stanley Green	J	Wallsuches	K
Ruins	K	Starling	N	Walmersley	N
Rumworth	K	Stepping Hill	J	Walshaw	N
Rusholme	E	Stock Brook	Q	Warburton Green	M
Saddleworth	Q	Stockport	J	Wardle	P
Sale	M	Stoneclough	K	Wardley	F
Sale Moor	M	Stoneclough Brow	K	Wardley Moss	F
Salford	F	Stoneycliffe	P	Warhill	G
Scholes	L	Stoneyfield	P	Water Heyes	L
School Common	L	Strangeways	A	Waterhead	Q
Scott Lane End	K	Stretford	M	Waterloo (Ashton-under-Lyne)	G
Scouthead	Q	Strines	J		
Scowcroft	L	Stubshaw Cross	L		
Sedgley Park	N	Sudden	P	Waterloo (Bolton)	K
Seedfield	N	Summerseat	N	Waters Nook	K
Seedley	F	Sun Green	G	Watersheddings	Q
Shackcliffe Green	A	Sutton	K	Weaste	F
Shakerley	L	Swinley	L	Werneth Low	G
Sharples	K	Swinton	F	West Didsbury	E
Sharston	E	Swinton Park	F	West Gorton	E
Shaw	Q	Syke	P	West Timperley	M
Shaw Moor	G	Tamar Lane End	L	Westhoughton	K
Shaw Side	Q	Tandle Hill P/	Q	Westhulme	Q
Shawclough	P	Tandle Hill Park	Q	Westleigh	L

Location	Division	Location	Division	Location	Division
Westwood	Q	Willows	K	Woodhouses	Q
Westwood Park	F	Windlehurst	J	(Failsworth)	
Whalley Range	E	Wingates	K	Woodley	J
Whelley	L	Winstanley	L	Woods End	M
White Horse	K	Winton	F	Woods Moor	J
Whitegate	Q	Withington	E	Woodshaw Rook	L
Whitley	L	Withins	K	Woolfold	N
Whittaker	P	Wolstenholme	P	Worsley	F
Whittle	P	Wood End	Q	Worsley Fold	F
Whittle Brook	F	Woodbank Park	J	Worsley Hall	L
Wicken Lane	P	Woodford	J	Worsley Mesnes	L
Wigan	L	Woodhouse Park	E	Worsley Moss	F
Wilderswood	K	Woodhouses	M	Worthington	L
Willoughbys	L	(Altrincham)		Wythenshawe	E

HM CORONERS

Manchester: N S Meadows. HM Coroner's Office, Crown Square, Deansgate, Manchester M60 1PR. Tel: 0161 830 4222. Fax: 0161 830 4328. Email: coroners@manchester.gov.uk

Manchester North: Mr Simon R Nelson. Coroner's Office, Fourth Floor, Telegraph House, Baillie Street, Rochdale OL16 1QY. Tel: 01706 924815. Fax: 01706 640720. Email: 75.mail@rochdale.gov.uk

Manchester South: Mr J S Pollard. Mount Tabor, Mottram Street, Stockport SK1 8PA. Tel: 0161 474 3993. Fax: 0161 474 3994. Email: john.pollard@stockport.gov.uk

Manchester West: Mrs Jennifer Leeming. Paderborn House, Civic Centre, Howell Croft North, Bolton BL1 1JW. Tel: 01204 338799. Fax: 01204 338798. Email: jennifer.leeming@bolton.gov.uk

GWENT POLICE
Croesyceiliog, Cwmbran, Torfaen NP44 2XJ.
Tel: 01633 838111. Fax: 01633 865211 (24 hrs). The dialling code for all numbers is 01633, unless otherwise indicated.

X400: c = GB; a = CWMAIL; p = PNN61MS; o = GWENT CONSTABULARY; s = POSTMASTER.

Email: firstname.lastname@gwent.pnn.police.uk

Website: www.gwent.police.uk

Lord Lieutenant: Mr Simon Boyle.
Police & Crime Commissioner: Mr Ian Johnston.

Chief Constable: Mrs Carmel Napier QPM.
Staff Officer for ACPO Domestic Violence Portfolio: Denise Puckett.
PA: Mrs Alison Green.
Deputy Chief Constable: Mr Jeff Farrar BSc(Hons) MPA.
PA: Mrs Lorraine Van Der Meer.
Assistant Chief Constable: Mr Simon Prince.
PA: Ms Kate Evans.
Director of Resources: Mr Nigel Stephens.
Contracts/Procurement Officer: Ms Paula Corfield.
Standards Unit: *Head of Standards Unit:* Det Supt Mark Warrender. Tel: 01495 745372.

INFORMATION SECURITY & DATA PROTECTION
Head of Data Management: Helen Edwards. Tel: 643082.
Freedom of Information Officer: Mr Dylan Collins. Tel: 643014.

CORPORATE COMMUNICATIONS
Head: Stuart John. Tel: 642444. Fax: 642338.
Deputy Head: Ms Gail Foley. Tel: 647158.

SOUTH WALES & GWENT POLICE JOINT LEGAL SERVICES
Assistant Director, Head of Joint Legal Service: Mr R Leighton Hill LLB. Tel: 01656 869476.
Deputy Head of Joint Legal Service: Mrs Nia Brennan LLB. Tel: 01656 869476.
Gwent Senior Solicitor (Employment): Mr Dylan Rowlands LLB. Tel: 642500.
SWP Solicitor (Operational Policing): Mrs Louise Emmitt LLB. Tel: 01656 869476.
Gwent Solicitor (Operational Policing): Ms Ciaran Gould LLB. Tel: 642500.
SWP Solicitor (Corporate): Mrs Nicola White LLB. Tel: 01656 869476.
SWP Solicitor (Litigation): Ms Rachel Davies LLB. Tel: 01656 869476.
Gwent Solicitor (Litigation): Mr Bryn Thomas LLB. Tel: 642500.
SWP Solicitor (Employment): Mrs Helen Stevens LLB. Tel: 01656 869476.

OPERATIONAL SUPPORT
Head: Chief Supt Alun Thomas. Tel: 647153. Fax: 865211.
Management Team: Supt Nigel Russell. Tel: 642262. Chief Insp Glyn Fernquest. Tel: 647045.
Contingency Planning: Insp Wayne Yandle. Tel: 642420.
Roads Policing Unit: Insp Lee Ford. Tel: 642230.
Armed Response Unit: Insp Paul Jackson. Tel: 647020.
Communications Suite: Chief Insp Rod Grindlay. Tel: 642206.

NEIGHBOURHOOD POLICING & PARTNERSHIPS
Head: Chief Supt Paul Symes. Tel: 647155. Fax: 865211.
NEWPORT
Supt Dave Johnson. Tel: 245200. Fax: 245256.
CID: Det Insp Judith Roberts. Tel: 245201.
Neighbourhood Policing
Central Section: Insp Chris Watts. Tel: 245220.
Newport East (Maindee & Alway): Insp Martyn Smith. Tel: 245341.
Newport West (Bettws & Pill): Insp Neil Muirhead. Tel: 245219.
Neighbourhood Support: Insp Chris Hocking-Brown.
T/Partnership Inspector: Dave Jenkins. Tel: 245332.
BLAENAU GWENT
Chief Insp Marc Budden. Tel: 01495 238042.
CID: Det Insp Matthew Sedgebeer. Tel: 01495 232201.

Neighbourhood Policing
Abertillery & Brynmawr: Insp Gavin Clifton. Tel: 01495 232237.
Ebbw Vale: Insp David Morgan. Tel: 01495 232206.
Tredegar: Insp Russell Thomas.
Neighbourhood Support: Insp Russell Thomas.
Partnership Inspector: Andy O'Keefe. Tel: 01495 232246.
TORFAEN
Chief Insp Stephen Corcoran. Pontypool, Torfaen NP4 6YN. Tel: 01495 232272. Fax: 01495 232261.
CID: T/Det Insp Alun Davies. Tel: 01495 238047.
Neighbourhood Policing
Pontypool: T/Insp Micah Hassell. Tel: 01495 233363.
Cwmbran: Insp Richard Blakemore. Tel: 642355.
Neighbourhood Support: Insp Mark Sparrey. Tel: 642133.
T/Partnership Inspector: Nicholas McLain. Tel: 01495 238016.
CAERPHILLY
Supt Brandon Williams. Tel: 01495 223673. Fax: 01495 232859.
CID: Det Insp Richard Williams. Tel: 01495 232495.
Neighbourhood Policing
Bargoed/Rhymney Section: Insp Huw Jones. Tel: 029 2085 7348.
Blackwood/Ystrad Mynach Section: Insp Mark Smith. Tel: 01495 232320.
Caerphilly/Bedwas Section: T/Insp Gareth Jones. Tel: 029 2085 7316.
Risca Section: Insp Ian Muirhead. Tel: 01495 232230.
Neighbourhood Support: Insp Karen Evans. Tel: 01495 238048. Insp Gareth Lintern. Tel: 01495 238048.
Partnership Inspector: Kevin Childs.
MONMOUTHSHIRE
Chief Insp Joanne Bull. Tel: 01495 745555.
CID: T/Det Insp Lyndon Hawker. Tel: 01495 238281.
Neighbourhood Policing
Abergavenny: Insp Michael Boycott. Tel: 01495 232288.
Monmouth: Insp Michael Boycott. Tel: 01495 232288.
Chepstow: Insp Mark Pope. Tel: 642383.
Caldicot: Insp Mark Pope.
Neighbourhood Support: Insp Fran Richley.
Partnership Inspector: Geoff Smith.
CRIME INVESTIGATION
Head: T/Det Chief Supt Peter Keen. Tel: 642388.
Crime Operations: Det Supt Pete Jones. Tel: 642238.
Crime Intelligence: T/Det Supt Russ Tiley. Tel: 642241.
Public Protection Unit: Det Supt Ian Roberts. Tel: 01495 745470. Det Chief Insp Jeremy Rogers. Tel: 01495 768456.
Volume Crime: T/Supt Simon Jefferies. Tel: 642543.
CRIMINAL JUSTICE
Head of Criminal Justice: Kathy Ikin. Tel: 647103.
Deputy Head of Administration of Justice: Mr David Broadway. Tel: 245236.
Central Ticket Office. Tel: 245371.
Warrants. Tel: 245345.
Witness Care. Tel: 844502.
Police Trials Unit. 2nd Floor, Vantage Point, Ty Coch Way, Cwmbran NP44 7XX. *Manager:* Tel: 647061.
Custody Unit: Chief Insp Daniel Taylor. Tel: 01633 245234.
Custody Unit (North – Ystrad Mynach): Insp Jeff Smith; Insp Bob Thompson. Tel: 01443 865559.
Custody Unit (South – Newport Central): Insp Geraint Evans. Tel: 245314.
SERVICE DEVELOPMENT
Head: Chief Supt Julian Knight. Tel: 647154. Fax: 865211.
Head of Business Change & Planning: Dawn Jeffery ACCA. Tel: 642567.
Head of Information & Statistics: Mr Matthew Didcott. Tel: 642350.
Head of Service Improvement: Mr John Metcalfe. Tel: 642087.
People Services Head: Mr Robert V Parker BA MCIPD. Tel: 642001.
Human Resources Manager: Kathryn Thomas. Tel: 642019.
Professional Development Manager: Alisa Quartermaine. Tel: 642028.
Learning & Development Manager: Insp Stefan Williams. Tel: 642076.

Health & Safety Manager: Mr Glen Piper. Tel: 642135.
Welfare Officer: Mr Nigel Pocknell. Tel: 647044.
Occupational Health & Welfare Manager: Mrs Chris Price. Tel: 647042.
Occupational Health Advisor: Miss Nicola Williams. Tel: 647043.

HM CORONER AND OTHER OFFICIALS

Gwent: Mr David T Bowen. Victoria Chambers, 11 Clytha Park Road, Newport NP20 4PB. Tel: 01633 264194. Fax: 01633 841146.

Trading Standards
County Hall, Cwmbran NP44 2XH. Tel: 644102.

RSPCA
Control Centre (Police Only) Tel: 0300 123 8026. **Kennels:** Ringland Way, Newport, Gwent NP6 2LL. Tel: 01633 412049.

NSPCC
Diane Engelhardt House, Treglown Court, Dowlais Road, Cardiff CF24 5LQ. Tel: 0808 800 5000 (24 hrs).

HAMPSHIRE CONSTABULARY

West Hill, Winchester, Hampshire SO22 5DB
Tel: 101 (non-emergency number); 0845 045 4545 (all areas and departments).
Fax: 01962 874201 (24 hrs). The dialling code for all numbers is 01962, unless
otherwise indicated.
X400 Postmaster: c = GB; a = CWMAIL; p = PNN44; o = HAMPSHIRE
CONSTABULARY, s = POSTMASTER
Email: postmaster@hampshire.pnn.police.uk
Email individuals: firstname.lastname@hampshire.pnn.police.uk
Website: www.hampshire.police.uk

Lord Lieutenant: Dame Mary Fagan.
Police & Crime Commissioner: Mr Simon Hayes. Westgate Chambers, Staple Gardens, Winchester
SO23 8AW. Tel: 871595. Email: opcc@hampshire.pnn.police.uk
Chief Constable: Andy Marsh. Tel: 871002.
Deputy Chief Constable: Vacant. Tel: 871148.
Assistant Chief Constable Crime & Criminal Justice: Laura Nicholson. Tel: 871092.
Assistant Chief Constable Territorial Operations: David Pryde. Tel: 871003.
Director of Human Resources & Corporate Services: Ms Nicole Cornelius. Tel: 871003.
Chief Finance Officer: Richard Croucher. Tel: 871026.
Staff Officers to Chief Constable: Chief Insp Paul Bartolomeo; Det Sgt Fiona Bitters. Tel: 871015.
Staff Officer to Deputy Chief Constable: Sgt Peter Boakes. Tel: 875096.
Staff Officer to Assistant Chief Constable Territorial Operations: Vacant.
Staff Officer to Assistant Chief Constable Crime & Criminal Justice: Det Insp Sue Orr. Tel: 871017.
Email: acpo.secretariat@hampshire.pnn.police.uk

PROFESSIONAL STANDARDS
Email: professional.standards@hampshire.pnn.police.uk
Head of Professional Standards Department: Det Supt Colin Smith. Tel: 871164.
Deputy Head of Professional Standards Department: Det Chief Insp Peter Gallagher. Tel: 843665.
Force Solicitor: Mr Roger Trencher. Tel: 871135. Fax: 871226.
Email: force.solicitor@hampshire.pnn.police.uk
Licensing (Firearms, Shotguns & Explosives): *Manager:* Mr Mark Groothuis. Tel: 871061.
Central Vetting Unit Manager: Mrs Christine Dashwood.

FORCE CHANGE PROGRAMME
Email: force.change.team@hampshire.pnn.police.uk
Force Change Manager: Mrs Mairead Whiting. Tel: 814738.
Corporate Support Review Lead: Chief Supt Ann Wakefield. Tel: 871563.

TASKING AND CO ORDINATION DIRECTORATE
Head of Directorate: Chief Supt Richard Rowland. Tel: 814779.
Head of Intelligence: Supt Lucy Hutson.
Head of Performance & Consultation: Mrs Melanie Williams; Mrs Clare Simkin. Tel: 871671; 871656.
Principal Analyst: Mr Matt Stagg. Tel: 871399.
Head of Resource Management & Event Planning: Chief Insp Gavin McMillan.

PUBLIC SERVICE DIRECTORATE
Head of Directorate: Chief Supt Scott Chilton.
Partnerships & Neighbourhoods: Chief Insp Jerry Patterson. Tel: 871016.

CALL MANAGEMENT DEPARTMENT
Vickery Building, Hampshire Constabulary, Hamble Lane, Southampton SO31 4TS.
Tel: 023 8074 5438. Fax: 023 8074 5451.
Email (not 24 hrs): call.management.admin@hampshire.pnn.police.uk
Head of Department: Supt Julie Earle. Tel: 023 8074 5578.
Deputy Head of Department: Mrs Alison Craig. Tel: 023 8074 5439.
Force Enquiry Centre: Mrs Jill Webber. Tel: 875099.

CORPORATE COMMUNICATIONS
Email: corporate.comms@hampshire.pnn.police.uk
Head of Corporate Communications: Vacant. Tel: 871059.

JOINT OPERATIONS UNIT (HAMPSHIRE & THAMES VALLEY POLICE)
Email: strategic.operations@hampshire.pnn.police.uk
Chief Supt Chris Shead. Tel: 871093.

Supt Richard Burrows. Tel: 023 8074 5358.
Operational Support (Operational Policy): Chief Insp Jon Malley. Tel: 023 8074 5019.
Emergency Planning: Ms Jane Conway. Tel: 871598. Mr Greg Snelgrove. Tel: 023 8053 3285.
Dog Section: Insp John Ramsbottom. Tel: 01993 814082.
Tactical Firearms Support Unit: Supt Tony Ismay; Chief Insp Tim Ashman. Tel: 023 8060 4741.

ROADS POLICING UNIT
Email: rpu.command@hampshire.pnn.police.uk
Supt Chris Brown. Tel: 871645. Fax: 871130.
Chief Insp Andy Bottomley. Tel: 875041.
Road Policing Districts
Northern District (Farnborough, Whitchurch): Insp Jon Snook. Tel: 01256 406452. Fax: 01256 405170.
Eastern District (Fratton, Isle of Wight): Insp Martin Goodall. Tel: 023 9289 1593. Fax: 023 9289 3257.
Western District (Totton): Insp Kirsty Shannon. Tel: 023 8067 4308. Fax: 023 8074 5368.
RDIT (Road Death Investigation Team, Forensic Crash Investigation Unit): Insp Richard Parsons. Tel: 023 8067 4363. Fax: 023 8045 0861.

CRIME AND CRIMINAL JUSTICE PORTFOLIO
SERIOUS CRIME DIRECTORATE
Email: cid.hq@hampshire.pnn.police.uk
Head of Serious Crime Directorate: Det Chief Supt Sara Glen. Tel: 871404.
Head of Special Branch: Supt Rob Dexter. Tel: 023 8045 0834.
Public Protection Department (Child Abuse Investigation Teams, Vulnerable Adults, Paedophile Online Investigation Team (POLIT), Central Referral Unit, MAPPA): Det Supt Jason Hogg. Southern Support Headquarters, Hamble Lane, Hamble, Southampton SO31 4TS. Tel: 023 8074 5289. Fax: 023 8074 5289.
Scientific Services Department: Det Chief Insp Phil McTavish. Southern Support Headquarters, Hamble Lane, Hamble, Southampton SO31 4TS. Tel: 023 8074 5083.
Major Investigation Team: Det Supt Tony Harris. Southampton Central Police Station, Southern Road, Southampton SO15 1AN. Tel: 023 8053 3330. Fax: 023 8067 4712.
Head of Crime Standards & Serious Crime Review: Det Supt Rachel Farrell.

CUSTODY & CRIMINAL JUSTICE DEPARTMENT
Email: criminal.justice@hampshire.pnn.police.uk
Head of Department: Ms Jo Rowland. Tel: 871151.
Force Custody Lead: Chief Insp Jason Kenny. Tel: 871151.
Strategic PNC Lead & PND Business Change Manager: Mrs Clare Chamberlain. Tel: 834674.

FINANCIAL SERVICES DEPARTMENT
Email: finance.dept@hampshire.pnn.police.uk
Chief Finance Officer: Mr Richard Croucher. Tel: 871026.
Estate Manager: Mr David Elliott. Tel: 023 8059 9931.
Deputy Estate Manager: Mr Gary Sinfield. Tel: 814723.

FINANCIAL ACCOUNTING DEPARTMENT
Email: finance.dept@hampshire.pnn.police.uk
Head of Financial Accounting: Mr Craig Southin. Tel: 871471.

BUSINESS AND PROPERTY SERVICES
Email: baps.procurement@hampshire.pnn.police.uk
Principal Procurement Manager: Vacant. Tel: 814765. Fax: 871190.
Procurement Manager: Mr Steve Colville. Tel: 871041.

TRANSPORT
Fleet Manager: Mr Roy Mariner. Tel: 871316.

HUMAN RESOURCES DEPARTMENT
Email: human.resources@hampshire.pnn.police.uk
Director of Human Resources & Corporate Services: Ms Nicole Cornelius. Tel: 871003.
Deputy Head of Human Resources: Mr Graham Love. Tel: 871003.
Senior HR Manager: Mrs Gemma Gair.
HR Manager Organisational Support: Miss Louise Hudson. Tel: 023 8074 5178.

OCCUPATIONAL HEALTH, WELFARE & SAFETY TEAM
Southern Support Headquarters, Hamble Lane, Hamble, Southampton SO31 4TS.
Head of Occupational Health, Safety & Welfare: Ms Caroline Russell. Tel: 023 8074 5481.
Health & Safety Advisor: Mr Dave Leverett. Tel: 023 8074 5488.
Force Welfare Officer: Ms Quita Walker. Tel: 023 8074 5481.

LEARNING & DEVELOPMENT DEPARTMENT
Southern Support Headquarters as above. Fax: 023 8074 5001.
Email: training.management@hampshire.pnn.police.uk
Head of Training (including Public Order): Chief Insp Adi Kingswell. Tel: 023 8074 5609.
Training Project & Standards Manager: Mr Brian Seggie. Tel: 023 8074 5584.
Organisational Development
Head of Leadership & Professional Development Programmes Manager: Mr Chris Bishop.
Head of Recruitment: Mrs Valerie King. Tel: 023 8074 5231.
Email: recruiting@hampshire.pnn.police.uk
Training Business Administration Manager: Mr Stephen Harvey. Tel: 023 8074 5087.
OSPRE Contact: Mrs Caroline Paulls. Tel: 023 8074 5137.

INFORMATION COMMUNICATION TECHNOLOGY DEPARTMENT (HAMPSHIRE & THAMES VALLEY POLICE)
Email: it.services@hampshire.pnn.police.uk
Head of IT & Communications Services (Hampshire & Thames Valley Police): Steve Vercella. Tel: 01865 846603; 01962 875048.
Service Delivery Manager: Adrian Hudson. Tel: 875061.
ICT Programme Manager: Brian Gibbins. Tel: 814810.
Business Relationship Manager: Steve Bottom. Tel: 01865 846970.

JOINT INFORMATION MANAGEMENT DEPARTMENT (HAMPSHIRE & THAMES VALLEY POLICE)
Head of Information Management (Hampshire & Thames Valley Police): Ms Marion Peulevé. Tel: 01865 846140.
Public Access Manager (Hampshire & Thames Valley Police): Jason Russell. Tel: 871014.
Information Governance Manager (Hampshire & Thames Valley Police): Paul Church. Tel: 01865 846008.
Records Management (Hampshire & Thames Valley Police): Mark Gould. Tel: 01865 846179.

AREAS
Tel: 0845 045 4545.

NORTHERN AREA
Aldershot Police Station, Wellington Avenue, Aldershot GU11 1NZ. Fax: 01256 405103.
Email: northern.restricted@hampshire.pnn.police.uk
Area Commander: Chief Supt Jason Hogg.
Supt Dave Powell.
Principal Areas: Andover; Basingstoke; East Hampshire; Hart; Rushmoor; Winchester.

WESTERN AREA
Southampton Central Police Station, Southern Road, Southampton SO15 1AN. Fax: 023 8067 4201.
Email: western.restricted@hampshire.pnn.police.uk
Area Commander: Chief Supt Dave Thomas.
Supt Scott Chilton; Supt Steve France-Sargeant.
Principal Areas: Bitterne; Central Southampton; Eastleigh; Hedge End; New Forest; Portswood; Romsey; Shirley.

EASTERN AREA
Kingston Crescent, Portsmouth PO2 8BU. Fax: 023 9289 1504.
Email: portsmouth.management@hampshire.pnn.police.uk
Area Commander: Chief Supt Nigel Hindle.
Supt Paul Brooks; Supt Richard John; Supt Will Schofield.
Principal Areas: Central Portsmouth; Cosham; Fareham; Fratton; Gosport; Havant; Isle of Wight; Southsea; Waterlooville.

HM CORONERS AND OTHER OFFICIALS
Central Hampshire: Mr G A Short. c/o Blake Lapthorn, New King's Court, Chandlers Ford, Eastleigh SO53 3LG. Tel: 023 8085 7038 Fax: 023 8036 0634 Email: centralhants-coroner@bllaw.co.uk
North East Hampshire: Mr A M Bradley. Goldings, London Road, Basingstoke RG21 4AN. Tel: 01256 478119. Fax: 01256 814292.
Portsmouth & South East Hampshire: Mr David Clark Horsley. The Guildhall, Guildhall Square, Portsmouth PO1 2AJ. Tel: 023 9268 8326. Fax: 023 9268 8331.
Email: david.horsley@portsmouthcc.gov.uk
Southampton & New Forest: Mr K St J Wiseman. Coroner's Office, 12–18 Hulse Road, Southampton SO15 2JX Tel: 023 8071 0452. Fax: 023 8067 4479. Email: elaine.ridley@hants.gov.uk
Isle of Wight: Mrs Caroline Sumeray. The Coroner's Office, 3–9 Quay Street, Newport, Isle of Wight PO30 5BB. Tel: 01983 520697. Fax: 01983 520678. Email: coroners@iow.gov.uk

Hampshire County Council
Chief Executive: Mr A Smith, The Castle, Winchester SO23 8UJ. Tel: 01962 847323.

HERTFORDSHIRE CONSTABULARY

Constabulary Headquarters, Stanborough Road, Welwyn Garden City, Hertfordshire AL8 6XF.
Tel: 101. Telex: 8951769 Herts PG. Fax: 01707 354409 (24 hrs).
The dialling code for all numbers is 01707 unless otherwise indicated.
Email: firstname.lastname@herts.pnn.police.uk
Website: www.herts.police.uk

Lord Lieutenant: Lord Charles Cecil.
Police & Crime Commissioner: David Lloyd.

The following places are policed by the Metropolitan Police: Arkley, Barnet, Cockfoster, East Barnet and Totteridge. The following places have a Royston (Hertfordshire) postal address but are in Cambridgeshire, and are policed by Cambridgeshire Constabulary: Bassingbourn, Fowlmere, Great Chishall, Heydon, Litlington, Meldreth and Shepreth. The following places have a Tring (Hertfordshire) postal address but are in Buckinghamshire, and are policed by Thames Valley Police: Marsworth and St Leonards. The following places have a Bishop's Stortford (Hertfordshire) postal address but are policed by Essex Police: Birchanger, Clavering, Elsenham, Farnham, Great Hallingbury, Hatfield Broad Oak, Hatfield Heath, Henham, Little Hallingbury, Manuden, Quendon, Sheering, Stansted, Stansted Airport, Takeley and Ugley.

Chief Constable: Andy Bliss QPM.
Executive Assistant: Stephanie Harrison. Tel: 354511.
Senior Staff Officer: Vacant.
Deputy Chief Constable: Andy Adams.
Executive Assistant: Zoë Hitchcock. Tel: 354512.
Assistant Chief Constable (*Joint Protective Services*): Jon Boutcher.
Executive Assistant: Sue Wilmot. Tel: 354515.
Assistant Chief Constable (*Territorial Policing*): Alison Roome-Gifford LLB.
Executive Assistant: Sarah McGuinness. Tel: 354390.
Assistant Chief Constable (*Crime & Operational Support*): Vacant.
Executive Assistant: Donna Turner. Tel: 354513.
Staff Officer: Sgt Louisa Cox. Tel: 354086.
Director of Resources: James Hurley IPFA.
Executive Assistant: Kim Holmes. Tel: 354514.
Staff & Research Officer: Katrina Moss BSc. Tel: 354084.
Chief of Staff: Supt Shirley Sargent. Tel: 354783.

CRIME AND OPERATIONAL SUPPORT
Head of Crime & Operational Support: Det Chief Supt Mark Drew. Tel: 354524.
Head of Contact Management: Supt Trevor Rodenhurst. Tel: 354054.
Head of Community Safety: Supt Mick Hanlon. Tel: 354835.
Crime Reduction & Early Intervention: Det Chief Insp Clare Smith. Tel: 354695.
Head of Offender Management: Chief Insp Julie Wheatley. Tel: 01438 757404.
Head of Protecting Vulnerable People: Chief Insp Glen Channer. Tel: 355912.
Serious & Organised Crime: Det Chief Insp Neil Ballard. Tel: 638411.
Economic Crime Unit: Det Insp Steve Keating. Tel: 354676.
Covert Investigations Unit/Witness Protection: Det Insp Bryan Harwood; Det Insp Simon Williams. Tel: 354314.

COLLABORATED PROTECTIVE SERVICES
*Head of Collaborated Protective Services (*Crime*):* Chief Supt Andy Street. Tel: 01438 757394.
*Head of Collaborated Protective Services (*Uniform Operations*):* Chief Supt Nigel Trippett. Tel: 01438 757395.
Eastern Region Serious & Organised Crime: Det Chief Supt Mark Birch. Tel: 01438 757932.
Head of Beds & Herts Major Crime Unit: Det Supt Jeff Hill. Tel: 354790.
Head of Beds & Herts Scientific Services Unit: Richard Johnson. Tel: 354360.
Scenes of Crime: A/Head of Crime Scene Operations: Neil Jay. Tel: 354018.
Uniform Protective Services: Supt Simon Hawkins. Tel: 01992 533920.
Head of Road Policing Strategic Unit: Chief Insp Richard Hann. Tel: 757734.

COLLABORATION UNIT
Collaboration Director: Philip Wells. Tel: 01438 757200.
PA to Collaboration Director: Jo Hunter. Tel: 01438 757219.
Collaboration Programme Co-ordinator: Rebecca Turner. Tel: 01438 757247.

CORPORATE COMMUNICATION
Head of Corporate Communication: Colin Connolly BA MSc CIM(Dip). Tel: 354580. Fax: 354589.
Media Relations Manager: Rachel Hyde. Tel: 354586.
Public Relations Manager: Annabel Maghie. Tel: 354584.

CORPORATE SERVICES
Head of Corporate Services: Chief Supt Mick Campbell. Tel: 354531.
Director of Performance: Supt Shirley Sargent. Tel: 354082.
Head of Performance Information: Julie Lloyd. Tel: 354555.
Crime & Incident Registrar: Julie Mann. Tel: 354114.
Information Manager: Tanya Clark. Tel: 01438 757442
Performance Review Manager: Adrian Culleton. Tel: 354730.
Strategic Process Manager: Chris Pratt. Tel: 354554.
Business Manager: Sharon Bendall. Tel: 354607.
Head of Professional Standards: Det Supt Nat Briant. Tel: 01234 842501.
Vetting & Disclosure Manager: Ian Hunt. Tel: 01438 757550.
Special Branch: Det Insp Daniel Lawrence.

CRIMINAL JUSTICE
Head of Criminal Justice Unit: Det Supt Jane Swinburne. Tel: 354606.
Criminal Justice Manager: Carole Ward. Tel: 354841.
Criminal Justice & Custody Policy Manager: Chief Insp Mark Caldicott. Tel: 354035.
Hertfordshire Criminal Justice Board Manager: Marianne Vits. Tel: 354758.
PNC Manager: Louise Seabrook. Tel: 355895.
Central Ticket Office. Hatfield Police Station, Comet Way, Hatfield AL10 9SJ. Tel: 806289.

ESTATES & FACILITIES
Head of Estates & Facilities: Ian Potter ICIOB MBIFM. Tel: 354240.
Deputy Head of Estates & Facilities: Amanda Grosse. Tel: 354368.
Building Services Manager: Mike Carvell IEng MIET. Tel: 354266.
Assistant Building Services Manager: Liam Shine. Tel: 354174.
Estates Surveyor: Laurence Jones. Tel: 354353.
Facilities Manager: Sharon Dawson. Tel: 355654.

FINANCE
Head of Finance: Mike Jarvis. Tel: 354241.
Head of Management Accounting: Alison Sharkey 354259.
Financial Accountant: Iain Davie. Tel: 354245.
Project Accountant (Efficiencies & Collaboration): Luke La Plain. Tel: 01438 757232.
Project Accountant (Change Management): Nigel Williams. Tel: 354070.
Management Accountants: Tony Peduto. Tel: 354212. Kim Robinson. Tel: 354252.

FLEET
Fleet Consortium Manager: Sam Sloan. Tel: 354380.
Deputy Fleet Manager: Stephen Bradford. Tel: 354381.
Fleet Administration: Don Winning. Tel: 354382.
Workshop Team Leaders: Peter Purdue; Ian Tarbet. Tel: 354384.

HUMAN RESOURCES
Head of Human Resources: Pauline Lawrence BA(Hons) Chtd FCIPD. Tel: 354294.
HR Superintendent: Sue Jameson. Tel: 354238.
Head of Training: Lesley Pritchard BA(Hons) Assoc CIPD. Tel: 355450.
Training Manager: Amanda Sayers. Tel: 355447.
Resourcing Manager: Amanda Johnson. Tel: 355407.
Senior HR Managers: Holly Gore BA(Hons); Tamara Hanton. Tel: 354591.
Senior HR Projects Manager: Jane Klaassen. Tel: 354073.
Pay & Projects Manager: Karen Morgan GradCIPD. Tel: 354407.

BEDFORDSHIRE & HERTFORDSHIRE – INFORMATION & COMMUNICATION TECHNOLOGIES (ICT) DEPARTMENT
Director ICT: Steve Taylor. Tel: 354300.
Head of Operations: Tony Ollett. Tel: 01234 842270.
Head of Service Design: Emma Payne. Tel: 01234 842372.
Head of Strategy & Programmes: Diana Wyers. Tel: 354334.
Architecture Manager: Dave Marvell. Tel: 354423.
ICT Customer Services Manager: Keith Tume. Tel: 354339.
Services & Systems Manager: Pat Bygraves. Tel: 01234 842303.
Infrastructure Manager: Andrew Clifton. Tel: 354342.
ICT Desktop Services Manager: Doug Taylor. Tel: 354320.

Airwave Manager: Mike Dealhoy. Tel: 354786.

Development Manager: Paul Preston. Tel: 01224 842057.

BEDFORDSHIRE, CAMBRIDGESHIRE AND HERTFORDSHIRE – JOINT PROTECTIVE SERVICES COMMAND

Please contact the host force (in brackets) or use email in order to speak to the collaborative leads. Add .pnn.police.uk to all email addresses below.

Head of Joint Protective Services Command: Assistant Chief Constable Jon Boutcher (Hertfordshire). Email: jon.boutcher@herts

Head of Uniform Operations: Chief Supt Mike Colbourne (Bedfordshire). Email: mike.colbourne@bedfordshire

Head of Crime: Chief Supt Nigel Trippett (Cambridgeshire). Email: nigel.trippett@cambs

Firearms, Dogs, Public Order & Civil Contingencies: Chief Insp Mark Canning (Hertfordshire). Email: mark.canning@herts

Roads Policing & ANPR: Chief Insp Richard Hann (Hertfordshire). Email: richard.hann@herts

Major Crime: Det Supt Jeff Hill (Cambridgeshire). Email: jeff.hill@cambs

Scientific Support: Richard Johnson (Bedfordshire). Email: richard.johnson@bedfordshire

Professional Standards: Det Supt Mark Hodgson (Cambridgeshire). Email: mark.hodgson@cambs

LEGAL SERVICES

Head of Legal Services: Mr Afzal Chowdhury LLB(Hons) LLM. Tel: 354530. Fax: 354518.

BEDFORDSHIRE, CAMBRIDGESHIRE & HERTFORDSHIRE PROCUREMENT & SUPPLIES

Strategic Head of Procurement: Patrick Ruddy. Tel: 01480 422791.

Senior Contracts Manager: David Canham. Tel: 01234 842018.

Contracts Managers: Emma-Louise Savine. Tel: 354261. Vee Brown: Tel: 01234 842229.

Uniform & Stores Manager: Sarah Deal. Tel: 01480 422566.

Stores/Supply Chain Manager: Bob Cox. Tel: 01480 422227.

Procurement Officers: Lorraine Tatton. Tel: 01480 422203. Robert Clark. Tel: 01480 422402.

PROFESSIONAL STANDARDS

Head of Professional Standards: Det Supt Nat Briant. Tel: 01234 842501.

Chief Inspector Misconduct: Dave Green. Tel: 01234 842504.

Det Chief Inspector Complaints: Jason Gordon.

Det Chief Inspector Anti-Corruption: Dave Rhodes. Tel: 01234 842527.

Det Inspector Operational Security: Christine Burden. Tel: 01234 842591.

STAFF ASSOCIATIONS

Black & Asian Police Association: *Chair:* Gerard McDonald. Tel: 01992 533641.

Police Federation: *Chair:* Neal Alston. *Secretary:* Vojislav Mihailovic. *Treasurer/Deputy Secretary:* Stephen Hutchings. Welwyn Garden City Police Station. Tel: 638096.

Superintendents' Association: Supt Jeff Taylor. Tel: 01438 757160. Stevenage Police Station.

UNISON: *Branch Chair:* Steph Raddings. Tel: 638742. *Branch Secretary:* Liz Davidson. Tel: 638742.

Office Administration: Lauren Attfield. Tel: 638741. Hatfield Police Station. Fax: 638743.

SPECIAL CONSTABULARY

Chief Officer: David Tewkesbury. Tel: 07977 486222.

LOCAL POLICING COMMAND

Area Headquarters, Hatfield Police Station, Comet Way, Hatfield, Herts AL10 9SJ. Tel: 0845 330 0222.

LPC Commander (Local Policing Command): Chief Supt Mick Ball. Tel: 806900.

PA to Chief Supt Ball: Lydia Saunders. Tel: 806908.

Deputy LPC Commander (Crime Portfolio): Det Supt Bill Jephson. Tel: 806907.

PA to Det Supt Jephson: Frances Barnacle. Tel: 806911.

Tactical Resources: T/Det Chief Insp Tannis Perks. Tel: 806902.

Local Specialist Crime: Det Chief Insp Jon Humphries. Tel: 806901.

Case Investigation: Det Chief Insp Mike Marren. Tel: 806745.

Deputy LPC Commander: Supt Jeff Taylor. Tel: 01438 757160.

PA to Supt Taylor: Linzi Jolin. Tel: 01438 757161.

Responsible for the following Community Safety Partnerships:

Broxbourne: Chief Insp Dave Newsome. Tel: 01992 533280.

East Herts: Chief Insp Gerard McDonald. Tel: 01992 533641.

North Herts: Chief Insp Donna Pierce. Tel: 01438 757691.

St Albans: Chief Insp Simon Warwick. Tel: 01727 796081.

Stevenage: Chief Insp Richard Harbon. Tel: 01438 757166.

Deputy LPC Commander: Supt Matt Nicholls. Tel: 01923 472082.

PA to Supt Nicholls: Claire Boot. Tel: 01923 472083.
Responsible for the following Community Safety Partnerships:
Dacorum: Chief Insp Mike Pryce. Tel: 01442 271081.
Hertsmere: Chief Insp Dean Patient. Tel: 01727 796666.
Watford: Chief Insp Nick Caveney. Tel: 01923 472084.
Welwyn Hatfield: Chief Insp David Wheatley. Tel: 01707 806904.
Three Rivers: Det Chief Insp Catherine Akehurst. Tel: 01923 472250.

POLICE STATIONS
Tel: 0845 330 0222.

Abbots Langley: Manor Lodge, High Street, Abbots Langley WD5 0AP.
Berkhamsted: 187 High Street, Berkhamsted HP4 3HB. Fax: 01442 271109.
Bishop's Stortford: Basbow Lane, Bishop's Stortford CM23 2NA. Fax: 01992 503109.
Borehamwood: Elstree Way, Borehamwood WD6 1JP. Fax: 01727 796609.
Buntingford: Baldock Road, Buntingford SG9 9DB.
Cheshunt: 101 Turners Hill, Cheshunt EN8 9BD. Fax: 01992 533809.
Harpenden: 15 Vaughan Road, Harpenden AL5 4GZ. Fax: 01727 796109.
Hatfield: Comet Way, Hatfield AL10 9SJ.
Hemel Hempstead: Combe Street, Hemel Hempstead HP1 1HL. Fax: 01442 271009.
Hertford: Hale Road, Hertford SG13 8ED. Fax: 01992 533009.
Hitchin: College Road, Hitchin SG5 1JX. Fax: 01462 425009.
Hoddesdon: High Street, Hoddesdon EN11 8BJ. Fax: 01992 443209.
Letchworth: Nevilles Road, Letchworth SG6 4ER. Fax: 01462 425109.
North Watford: A405 North Orbital Road, Garston WD2 7AX. Fax: 01923 472309.
Oxhey: Oxhey Drive, Watford WD19 7SD. Fax: 01923 472209.
Police Headquarters: Stanborough Road, Welwyn Garden City AL8 6XF.
Rickmansworth: Three Rivers House, North Way, Rickmansworth WD3 IRL.
Royston: Melbourn Street, Royston SG8 7BZ. Fax: 01763 425209.
St Albans: Victoria Street, St Albans AL1 3JL. Fax: 01727 796009.
Stevenage: Lytton Way, Stevenage SG1 1HF. Fax: 01438 757009.
Tring: 63 High Street, Tring HP23 4AB. Fax: 01442 271209.
Watford: Shady Lane, Watford WD17 1DD. Fax: 01923 472309.
Welwyn Garden City: Rosanne House, Bridge Road, Welwyn Garden City AL8 6UB. Fax: 638009.

The following police stations are designated under s35, P.A.C.E. Act 1984: Hatfield (Welwyn Hatfield CSP), Hemel Hempstead (Dacorum CSP), Hertford (East Herts CSP), St Albans (St Albans CSP), Stevenage (Stevenage CSP) & Watford (Watford CSP).

Place	*Community Safety Partnership*	*Place*	*Community Safety Partnership*
Abbots Langley	Three Rivers	Benington	East Herts
Albury	East Herts	Berkhamsted	Dacorum
Aldbury	Dacorum	Birch Green	East Herts
Aldenham	Hertsmere	Bishop's Stortford	East Herts
Amwell	East Herts	Borehamwood	Hertsmere
Anstey	East Herts	Bourne End	Dacorum
Apsley End	Dacorum	Bovingdon	Dacorum
Ardeley	North Herts	Bowers Heath	St Albans
Ashwell	North Herts	Boxmoor	Dacorum
Aspenden	East Herts	Bramfield	East Herts
Aston End	East Herts	Braughing	East Herts
Ayot St Lawrence	Welwyn Hatfield	Breachwood Green	North Herts
		Brent Pelham	East Herts
Ayot St Peter	Welwyn Hatfield	Brickendon	East Herts
		Bricket Wood	St Albans
Baldock	North Herts	Bridens Camp	Dacorum
Barkway	North Herts	Brookmans Park	Welwyn Hatfield
Barley	North Herts		
Barwick	East Herts	Broxbourne	Broxbourne
Batchworth Heath	Three Rivers	Buckland	East Herts
Batford	St Albans	Bucks Hill	Dacorum
Bayford	East Herts	Bulls Green	East Herts
Bedmond & Primrose Hill	Three Rivers	Buntingford	East Herts
Bendish	North Herts	Burnham Green	East Herts
Bengeo	East Herts	Bury Green	Broxbourne

Place	Community Safety Partnership	Place	Community Safety Partnership
Bushey	Hertsmere	Hatfield	Welwyn
Bygrave	North Herts		Hatfield
Caldecote	North Herts	Hayling	Three Rivers
Callowland	Watford	Hemel Hempstead	Dacorum
Carpenders Park	Three Rivers	Heronsgate	Three Rivers
Chandlers Cross	Three Rivers	Hertford	East Herts
Chapmore End	East Herts	Hertford Heath	East Herts
Charlton	North Herts	Hertingfordbury	East Herts
Cheshunt	Broxbourne	Hexton	North Herts
Cheveralls Green	St Albans	High Cross	East Herts
Childwick Green	St Albans	High Wych	East Herts
Chipperfield	Dacorum	Hinxworth	North Herts
Chipping	East Herts	Hitchin	North Herts
Chiswell Green	St Albans	Hoddesdon	Broxbourne
Chorleywood	Three Rivers	Holwell	North Herts
Clothall	North Herts	Hormead	East Herts
Codicote	North Herts	How Green	East Herts
Cole Green	East Herts	Hudnall	Dacorum
Coleman Green	St Albans	Hunsdon	East Herts
Colliers End	East Herts	Hunton Bridge	Watford
Colney Heath	St Albans	Ickleford	North Herts
Colney Street	St Albans	Kelshall	North Herts
Cottered	East Herts	Kimpton	North Herts
Cromer	East Herts	Kings Langley	Dacorum
Croxley Green	Three Rivers	Kings Walden	North Herts
Cuffley	Welwyn	Kinsbourne Green	St Albans
	Hatfield	Knebworth	North Herts
Cumberlow Green	North Herts	Langleybury	Three Rivers
Cupid Green	Dacorum	Leavesden	Three Rivers
Dane End	East Herts	Lemsford	Welwyn
Datchworth	East Herts		Hatfield
Digswell	Welwyn	Letchworth	North Herts
	Hatfield	Leverstock Green	Dacorum
Dudswell	Dacorum	Ley Green	North Herts
East End Green	East Herts	Lilley	North Herts
Eastwick	East Herts	Little Amwell	St Albans
Elstree	Hertsmere	Little Berkhampstead	East Herts
Epping Green	East Herts	Little Gaddesden	Dacorum
Essendon	Welwyn	Little Hadham	East Herts
	Hatfield	Little Heath	Welwyn
Flamstead	Dacorum		Hatfield
Flaunden	Dacorum	Little Hormead	East Herts
Frithesden	Dacorum	Little Munden	East Herts
Furneaux Pelham	East Herts	Little Wymondley	North Herts
Gaddesden Row	Dacorum	London Colney	St Albans
Garston	Watford	Long Marston	Dacorum
Goffs Oak	Broxbourne	Luffenhall	Stevenage
Graveley	North Herts	Mackerye End	St Albans
Great Amwell	East Herts	Maple Cross	Three Rivers
Great Gaddesden	Dacorum	Mardley Heath	Welwyn
Great Hormead	East Herts		Hatfield
Great Munden	East Herts	Markyate	St Albans
Great Wymondley	North Herts	Meesden	East Herts
Green Tye	East Herts	Mill Green	Welwyn
Gustard Wood	St Albans		Hatfield
Hare Street	East Herts	Moor Park	Three Rivers
Harmer Green	Welwyn	Much Hadham	East Herts
	Hatfield	Nash Mills	Dacorum
Harpenden	St Albans	Nettleden	Dacorum

Place	Community Safety Partnership	Place	Community Safety Partnership
Newgate Street	Welwyn Hatfield	Stanstead Abbots	East Herts
Newnham	North Herts	Stapleford	East Herts
North Mymms	Welwyn Hatfield	Stevenage	Stevenage
		Stocking Pelham	East Herts
Northaw	Welwyn Hatfield	Tea Green	North Herts
		Tewin	Welwyn Hatfield
Northchurch	Dacorum	Therfield	North Herts
Norton	North Herts	Thorley	East Herts
Nuthampstead	North Herts	Throcking	East Herts
Oaklands	Welwyn Hatfield	Thundridge	East Herts
		Tonwell	East Herts
Offley	North Herts	Tring	Dacorum
Old Hall Green	East Herts	Trowley Bottom	Broxbourne
Oxhey	Three Rivers	Tyttenhanger Green	St Albans
Park Street	St Albans	Wadesmill	East Herts
Perry Green	East Herts	Walkern	East Herts
Piccots End	Dacorum	Wallington	North Herts
Pirton	North Herts	Walton-at-Stone	East Herts
Potten End	Dacorum	Ware	East Herts
Potters Bar	Hertsmere	Water End	Dacorum
Potters Heath	Welwyn Hatfield	Waterford	East Herts
		Watford	Watford
Preston North	North Herts	Watham Cross	Broxbourne
Puckeridge	East Herts	Welham Green	Welwyn Hatfield
Pudds Cross	North Herts		
Puttenham	Dacorum	Wellpond Green	East Herts
Rabley Heath	North Herts	Welwyn	Welwyn Hatfield
Radlett	St Albans		
Radwell	North Herts	Welwyn Garden City	Welwyn Hatfield
Redbourn	St Albans		
Reed	North Herts	West Hyde	Three Rivers
Rickmansworth	Three Rivers	Westland Green	East Herts
Ringshall	Dacorum	Westmill	East Herts
Roe Green	St Albans	Weston	North Herts
Royston	North Herts	Wheathampstead	St Albans
Rushden	East Herts	Whitwell	North Herts
Sacombe	East Herts	Widford	East Herts
St Albans	St Albans	Wigginton	Dacorum
St Ippolytts	North Herts	Wildhill	Welwyn Hatfield
St Pauls Walden	North Herts		
Sandon	East Herts	Willian	North Herts
Sandridge	St Albans	Wilstone	Dacorum
Sarratt	Three Rivers	Wood End	East Herts
Sawbridgeworth	East Herts	Woolmer Green	Welwyn Hatfield
Shenley	Hertsmere		
Smallford	St Albans	Wormley	Broxbourne
Standon	East Herts	Wyddiall	East Herts
Standon Green End	East Herts		

All correspondence relating to places named above should be addressed to the Divisional Commander except for matters relating to motorways, which should be addressed to the Chief Inspector of Road Policing.

HM CORONER & OTHER OFFICIALS

Hertfordshire: Mr Edward Thomas. The Old Courthouse, St Albans Road East, Hatfield AL10 OES. Tel: 01707 897409. Fax: 01707 897399.

State Veterinary Service: Chelmsford Divisional Office, Beeches Road, Chelmsford. Tel: 01245 358383. Southend and Stansted airports use Chelmsford office. Animal Health nightline tel: 01245 358383.

Trading Standards & Animal Health: 45 Grosvenor Road, St Albans AL1 3AW. Tel: 01727 813849.

HUMBERSIDE POLICE

Priory Road Police Station, Priory Road, Hull HU5 5SF.
Tel: 101; 01482 578461. The dialling code for all numbers is 01482, unless otherwise indicated.

Minicom: 01482 568352.

Email: firstname.lastname@humberside.pnn.police.uk

Website: www.humberside.police.uk

Police & Crime Commissioner: Matthew Grove. Tel: 220787.

Chief Constable: Ms Justine Curran.
PA. Tel: 578205.
Deputy Chief Constable: David Griffin QPM MA.
PA. Tel: 578226.
Assistant Chief Constable (Operations Support): Alan Leaver. Tel: 578238.
PA: Catherine Meade. Tel: 578238.
Assistant Chief Constable (Operations): Stuart Donald QPM MA.
PA. Tel: 578268.
Assistant Chief Officer (Support): Philip Goatley BA CPFA.
PA. Tel: 578268.
Assistant Chief Officer (HR): Ian Watson MBA MSc FCIPD.
PA: Catherine Meade. Tel: 578238
Chief Constable's Staff Officer. Tel: 578295.
Fax: 578260.
Force Medical Officer: Dr G Clayton. Tel: 808043.

OPERATIONS BRANCH
Hessle Police Station, Hessle High Road, Hull HU4 7BA. Tel: 101.
Branch Head: Chief Supt Brian Kelly. Tel: 578287. Fax: 578171.
PA. Tel: 578213
Incident Handling: Supt Mark Summer. Tel: 597783. Fax: 597759.
Operations: Supt Tracey Bradley. Tel: 220899. Fax: 220886.
Business Centre Manager: Miss Lynne Bentley. Tel: 597666.
Operations & Emergency Planning: Chief Insp David Hall. Tel: 220898. Fax: 220886.
Helicopter Support: Mr Kevin Limbert. Tel: 630176. Fax: 630116.
Traffic Management: Chief Insp Roger Mitchell. Tel: 220893.
ADMINISTRATION OF JUSTICE UNIT
Queens Gardens, Hull HU1 3DJ. Tel: 101. Fax: 220168.
Supt Steve Graham. Tel: 220655.
CJU Manager: Mr Colin Andrews. Tel: 220045. Insp Andy Maultby. Tel: 220542.
Central Ticket Office. Tel: 398200. Fax: 398201.
Fixed Penalty Clerk. The Magistrates' Court, PO Box 111, Market Place, Hull HU1 1EX. Tel: 610405. Fax: 329759.

CRIME MANAGEMENT BRANCH
Police HQ, Priory Road Police Station, Priory Road Hull HU5 5SF. Tel: 101. Fax: 01482 578171.
Branch Head: Det Chief Supt Philip Walker. Tel: 578289.
PA. Tel: 578176.
Intelligence Unit & Covert Standards Unit: Det Supt Jeremy Huyton. Tel: 597777.
Major Crime Unit: Det Supt Lauren Poultney. Tel: 597662.
Scientific Investigation Unit: Mr Peter Morriss. Tel: 220801.
Special Branch: Det Chief Insp Nicholas Jackson. Tel: 220742.
Major Incident Team: Det Supt Christine Wilson. Tel: 274257.
Business Centre Manager: Miss Lynne Bentley. Tel: 597666.

CORPORATE DEVELOPMENT BRANCH
Police HQ, as above. Tel: 101. Fax: 01482 578146.
Branch Manager: Mr Justin Partridge.
PA. Tel: 578297.
Performance Development Unit: Chief Insp Derek Shepherd. Tel: 578104. Fax: 578146.
Strategic Change Unit: *Force Business Manager:* Emma Ahern. Tel: 578212. Fax: 578146.
Community Safety Unit: *Community Safety Unit Head:* Supt Samantha Manning. Tel: 220704.
Business Change Unit: Chief Insp Alan Farrow. Tel: 578211. Fax: 578146.

Marketing & Communications: Mr James Cartwright. Tel: 578208. Fax: 578146.
  Email: pressoffice@humberside.pnn.police.uk. Tel: 0871 220 7789 (media lines for journalists).
Programme Management Section: *Programme Manager:* Mr Barry Edwards. Tel: 220997. Fax: 220941.
Legal Services Manager: Mr Stephen Hodgson LLB. Tel: 578162. Fax: 578166.
Information Compliance Unit: *Information Compliance Unit Head:* Mr Richard Heatley. Tel: 317088.
  Fax: 317090. **General Office.** Tel: 317094.
Information Security Officer: Mr David Ingham. Tel: 317098.
Vetting & Disclosure Manager: Mrs Lesley Gell. Tel: 317070.
Registrar: Mr Mike Richmond. Tel: 317114. Fax: 334851.
Assistant Registrar (Registry): Dawn Conroy. Tel: 220858. Fax: 334853.
Assistant Registrar (Tape Library): Mr Jonathan Blyth. Tel: 220843. Fax: 334855.
Assessment & Review Unit: *Assessment & Review Manager:* Mr John Ford. Tel: 578243.
Head of Business Support: Mrs Kim Redburn. Tel: 578269. Fax: 578146.
Support Unit: *Chief Officer.* Tel: 578295. Fax: 578260.
Youth & Community Cohesion Unit: *Unit Head:* Mr Adil Khan. Tel: 220710. **Admin Office:** Mrs Judith
  Cutts. Tel: 220706. Fax: 578146.

SUPPORT SERVICES BRANCH
Police HQ, as above. Tel: 101.
Director of Estate: Mr Martin Knapp. Tel: 307429.
Buildings Unit: *Buildings Manager:* Mr Chris Hatfield. Tel: 306046.

FINANCE UNIT
Head of Finance: Mr Mike Chappell MA MBA FCMA. Tel: 220372.
Assistant Finance Manager (Financial Planning): Mr Ian Porter ACMA. Tel: 220367. Fax: 220648.
Assistant Finance Manager (Financial Management): Mr Michael Horne MAAT. Tel: 220342. Fax:
  220627.

FLEET & SUPPLIES UNIT
Fleet & Supplies Manager: Mr William Lambert. Tel: 220950. Fax: 220996.
Assistant Fleet Manager: Mr Wayne Hedges. Tel: 220967.
Assistant Contracts Officer: Ms Hayley Cairns. Tel: 220955. Fax: 220954.

INFORMATION SERVICES BRANCH
Police HQ, as above. Tel: 101.
Head of Information Services: Mr Paul Thrustle.
PA. Tel: 578314. Fax: 578171.
Communications Manager: Mr Ian Maughan. Tel: 220430.
Computer Operations Manager: Mr Stephen Harding. Tel: 220800.

HUMAN RESOURCES DEVELOPMENT BRANCH
Humberside Police Training Centre, Courtland Road, Hull HU6 8AW.
Assistant Chief Officer (HR): Mr Ian Watson MBA MSc Chtd FCIPD.
PA. Tel: 578238.
Head of Operational HR Services: Mrs Sarah Wilson. Tel: 808065.

HR SHARED SERVICES
HR Shared Services Manager: Ms Emma Siddy. Tel: 808154.
HR Manager (Delivery): Katie Dunn. Tel: 808109.
HR Manager (Ill Health, Injury & Pensions): Paul Barker. Tel: 808007.

OCCUPATIONAL HEALTH & WELFARE SERVICES
Principal Manager Occupational Health (SYP). Tel: 0114 296 4780.

PEOPLE DEVELOPMENT UNIT
Head of People Employee Support: Mr Aleks Stojkovic. Tel: 808087.
Workforce Planning Manager: Ms Margaret Shillito. Tel: 808082.
Career Development Manager: Sandy Powdrell. Tel: 808088.

LEARNING AND DEVELOPMENT
Head of Learning & Development Humberside & South Yorkshire Police: Jo Buck. Tel: 01709 443693.

HR CHANGE UNIT
HR Change Manager: Tammy Naylor. Tel: 808073.

PROFESSIONAL STANDARDS BRANCH
Police HQ, as above. Tel: 101.
Branch Head: Det Supt Raymond Higgins. Tel: 578345.
Deputy: Det Insp Stewart Miller. Tel: 578333.
Professional Standards Officer (Support): Mrs Janice Connor. Tel: 578332. Fax: 305004.

STAFF ASSOCIATIONS
Superintendents' Association: *Chairman:* Chief Supt Richard Kerman. Police Headquarters, as above.
  Tel: 334866. Fax: 334866. *Secretary:* Chief Supt Anthony Forbes. Tel: 808060.

Police Federation: 1A Redland Drive, Kirkella, Hull HU10 7UE. Tel: 653480. Fax: 653478. *Chairman:* Mr S Garmston. *Secretary:* Mr K Rack. *Treasurer/Deputy Secretary/Discipline Liaison Officer:* Sgt Ian Springett.
UNISON: Courtland Road , Hull HU6 8AW. Tel: 808080. *Branch Secretary:* Mr Tadeusz Krawczyk. *Assistant Branch Secretary:* Mr Harry Berry.

SOUTH BANK DIVISION
Victoria Street, Grimsby DN31 1PE. Corporation Road, Scunthorpe DN15 6QB. Tel: 101. Fax: 01724 274209 (24 hrs).
Divisional Commander: Chief Supt Tony Forbes.
PA. Tel: 01472 721242/01724 274146.
Detective Superintendent: Judi Heaton. Tel: 01472 721276.
Superintendent (Operations – Grimsby): Darren Wildbore. Tel: 01472 721273.
Superintendent (Operations – Scunthorpe): Kevin Bowe. Tel: 01724 274170.
Detective Chief Inspectors: Robert Clark. Tel: 01724 274103. Gerry Darling. Tel: 01472 721277.
Chief Inspector Neighbourhoods: Deborah Johnstone. Tel: 01472 721274.
Chief Inspectors (Operations): Phillip Ward. Tel: 01472 275336. Olukayode Adegbembo. Tel: 01472 721272.
Business Centre Manager: Mrs Toni Wright. Tel: 01472 721230.
HR Manager: Mrs Katie Dunn. Tel: 01472 721275.

C DIVISION
Sessions House, New Walk, Beverley HU17 7AF. Tel: 101. Fax: 01482 597814 (Mon–Fri 0800–2000; weekends 0800–1800; bank holidays 0900–1700).
Divisional Commander: Chief Supt Richard Kerman.
PA. Tel: 597841.
Superintendent (Operations): Darren Downs. Tel: 597870.
Detective Chief Inspector: Carl Vessey-Baitson. Tel: 597886.
Chief Inspector (Operations): Andrew Foster. Tel: 597885.
Chief Inspector (Neighbourhoods): Alan Farrow. Tel: 597865.
Business Centre Manager: Mrs Rosemary Maughan. Tel: 220319.
HR Manager: Ms Sarah Page. Tel: 220117.

EAST (HULL) D DIVISION
Clough Road, Hull HU5 1SW. Tel: 101. Fax: TBC.
Divisional Commander: Chief Supt Rick Proctor.
PA. Tel: 578630.
Detective Superintendent (Crime): Scott Young. Tel: 578623.
Superintendent Operations: Mark Johansson. Tel: 578622.
Detective Chief Inspector (Risk Crime Management): Simon Walker. Tel: 578627.
Detective Chief Inspector (Volume Crime Management): Paul Cunningham. Tel: 578628.
Chief Inspector (Operations): Ed Cook. Tel: 578625.
Chief Inspector (Neighbourhood): Dave Houchin. Tel: 578626.
Chief Inspector (Support Operations): Rich Kirven. Tel: 578624.
Business Centre Manager: Mrs Rosemary Maughan BA. Tel: 220319.
HR Manager: Ms Sarah Page. Tel: 578629.

PT Area	Division	PT Area	Division
Beverley	C	North Carr (Hull)	D
Bridlington	C	Northern (Hull)	D
Brigg	B	Park (Hull)	D
Cleethorpes	A	Pocklington	C
Cottingham & Haltemprice	C	Riverside (Hull)	D
Driffield East	C	Scunthorpe North and	B
Goole	C	Epworth & Isle of	
Grimsby Central & Grimsby	A	Axholme	
South		Scunthorpe West &	B
Grimsby North	A	Scunthorpe East &	
Hedon	C	Messingham	
Hessle & Hunsley	C	West (Hull)	D
Hornsea	C	Withernsea	C
Howden	C	Wyke (Hull)	D

To contact a local policing team please ring the appropriate division as shown above.
Stations designated under s.35, P.A.C.E. Act 1984 and manned 24 hours a day: Grimsby, Central and Hull (Queens Gardens).

HM CORONERS

North Lincolnshire & Grimsby: Mr Paul Kelly. HM Coroner's Office, The Town Hall, Knoll Street, Cleethorpes DN35 8LN. Tel: 01472 324005. Fax: 01472 324007.

East Riding & Hull: Prof Paul Marks. Coroner's Office & Court, The Guildhall, Kingston-upon-Hull HU1 2AA. Tel: 01482 613009. Fax: 01482 613020.

KENT POLICE
Sutton Road, Maidstone, Kent ME15 9BZ.
Non-emergency tel: 101 (central switchboard). Tel: 01622 65 followed by extension number (except where stated).

If deaf or speech impaired text 'Police' and your message to 60066.

**Email for urgent operational incidents (24 hrs): general.fcr@kent.pnn.police.uk
Emails for non-urgent enquiries (not 24 hrs) are shown under each area.
Email for individuals: firstname.lastname@kent.pnn.police.uk**

Website: www.kent.police.uk

The following places have a Kent postal address but are policed by the Metropolitan Police: Beckenham, Belvedere, Bexley, Bexleyheath, Bromley, Chislehurst, Crayford, Erith, Farnborough, Orpington, Sidcup, Slade Green, St Mary Cray and Welling.

Lord Lieutenant: Viscount De L'Isle MBE.
Police & Crime Commissioner: Mrs Ann Barnes.

Chief Constable: Ian Learmonth.
Staff Officer to Chief Constable: Chief Insp David Pascoe. Ext: 2004.
Deputy Chief Constable: Alan Pughsley. Ext: 2007.
Assistant Chief Constable (Central Operations): Paul Brandon. Ext: 2500.
Assistant Chief Constable (Serious Crime Directorate): Gary Beautridge. Tel: 01474 366325.
T/Assistant Chief Constable (Local Policing & Partnerships): Matthew Nix. Ext: 2656.
Director of Joint Kent & Essex IT Directorate: Andrew Barker. Ext: 2900.
Director of Joint Support Services: Mark Gilmartin. Ext: 2501.
DEPUTY CHIEF CONSTABLE'S COMMAND
Deputy Chief Constable: Alan Pughsley. Ext: 2007.
Head of Corporate Services: Bev Ashton. Ext: 2660.
Head of Professional Services Department: Det Chief Supt John Molloy. Ext: 3007.
Head of Corporate Communications: Gavin McKinnon. Ext: 2044.
Deputy Head of Corporate Communications: Maria Porter. Ext: 2158.
Head of Press Office: Chris Herbert. Ext: 2153.
Press Office: 2150.
Head of Legal Services: Bev Newman. Ext: 2023.
CENTRAL OPERATIONS
Assistant Chief Constable (Central Operations): Paul Brandon. Ext: 2500.
CENTRAL INVESTIGATIONS COMMAND
Head of Central Investigations Command: Det Chief Supt Chris Hogben. Ext: 2227.
Head of Strategic Criminal Justice: Det Supt Adrian Futers. Ext: 2032.
Head of Public Protection Unit: Det Supt Tim Smith. Ext: 4560.
Head of Frontier Operations: Det Supt Martin Very. Tel: 01303 297383.
Kent Ports (including Eurotunnel Terminal in Coquelles, France): Ports Co-ordination Centre, Longport Police Station, Ashford Road, Newington, Folkestone, Kent CT18 8AP. Tel: 01303 297320 (24 hours). Fax: 01303 289269.
Frontier Joint Intelligence Unit (Special Branch): Folkestone Police Station, Bouverie House.
CENTRAL RESPONSE COMMAND
Head of Central Response Command: Chief Supt Mark Nottage. Ext: 6101.
Head of Force Control Room: Carol Drake. Ext: 6105.
Head of Central Response: Supt Claire Nix. Ext: 6103.
TACTICAL OPERATIONS COMMAND
Head of Tactical Operations Command: Chief Supt Alison Roden. Tel: 01622 798511.
Head of Firearms & Public Order: Supt Peter Wedlake. Ext: 4880.
Head of Strategic Operations: Supt Stuart Kehily. Tel: 01622 798562.
Head of Tactical Operations: Supt Andrea Bishop. 01622 798575.
KENT AND ESSEX SERIOUS CRIME DIRECTORATE (SCD)
Headquarters: North Kent Police Station, Thames Way, Northfleet DA11 8BD. Tel: 01474 366126.
Head of Kent & Essex Serious Crime Directorate: Assistant Chief Constable Gary Beautridge. Tel: 01474 366325.
PA: Colleen McMonies. Tel: 01474 362126.
Deputy Head of Kent & Essex Serious Crime Directorate: Det Chief Supt Liam Osborne. Tel: 01474 366134.

PA: Kelly Ramsden. Tel: 01474 366134.
SCD Staff Officer: Det Sgt Richard Vickery. Tel: 01474 366131.
Head of Intelligence: A/Det Supt Mark Wheeler. Tel: 01474 366278.
Head of Major Crime: Det Supt Mick Judge. Tel: 01474 366284.
Head of Serious Organised Crime: Det Supt Tracy Hawkings. Tel: 01474 366281.
Head of Covert Support: Det Supt Steve Worron. Tel: 01474 366285.
Head of Covert Human Intelligence Sources: Det Supt Dan Murphy. Tel: 01474 366283.
Head of Forensics: Det Supt Martyn Cochrane. Tel: 01474 366133.
Business Manager: Christina Drewitt. Tel: 01474 366139.
Chief of Staff: Det Sgt Emma Lawry. Tel: 01474 366168.

LOCAL POLICING AND PARTNERSHIPS

T/Assistant Chief Constable (Local Policing & Partnerships): Matthew Nix. Ext: 2656.
Head of Partnerships & Communities Command: Chief Supt Steve Corbishley. Ext: 4525.
North Division Commander: Chief Supt Neil Jerome. Tel: 01634 792100.
East Division Commander: Chief Supt Alan Horton. Tel: 01303 289110.
West Division Commander: Chief Supt Andy Rabey. Tel: 01622 604110.

KENT AND ESSEX IT DIRECTORATE

Director of Joint Kent & Essex IT Directorate: Andrew Barker. Ext: 2900.
Head of IT Transformation: Robert Nelson. Ext: 2800.
Senior Business Manager: Sally Manley. Ext: 2902.
Head of IT Operations: Brian Jaggs. Ext: 2801.
Head of Application Development: Conrad Crampton. Ext: 2885.
Head of Programme Delivery: Fiona Brown. Ext: 2920.
Chief Technical Architect: Mark Williams. Ext: 2806.

SUPPORT SERVICES

Director of Joint Services: Mark Gilmartin. Ext: 2501.
PA: Alison Ansell. Ext: 2502.
Head of Business Services: Dave Marshall. Tel: 01474 366620.
Interim Head of Kent & Essex Estate Department: Simon Curling. Ext: 2718.
Head of Finance Department: Ann Caldwell. Ext: 2761.
Head of Human Resources Department: Ian Drysdale. Ext: 3100.
Head of Procurement Services: Candace Bloomfield-Howe. Tel: 01474 366650.
Head of Transport Services: John Gorton. Tel: 01245 240641.

DISTRICTS
Tel: 101.
For a full list of police stations in each division and the relevant opening times see website: www. kent.police.uk

NORTH DIVISION

North Division Commander: Chief Supt Neil Jerome. Tel: 01634 792100.
North Division Deputy Commander: Supt Nicky Kiell. Tel: 01474 366110.
Medway Police Station. Purser Way, Gillingham ME7 1NE.

DARTFORD DISTRICT
Dartford District Commander: Chief Insp Roscoe Walford. Tel: 01474 366111.
North Kent Police Station. Thames Way, Northfleet, Gravesend DA11 8BD.

GRAVESHAM DISTRICT
Gravesham District Commander: Chief Insp Philip Painter. Tel: 01474 366113.
North Kent Police Station.

SWALE DISTRICT
Swale District Commander: Chief Insp Tony Henley. Tel: 01795 419111.
Sittingbourne Police Station. Central Avenue, Sittingbourne ME10 4NR

MEDWAY UA DISTRICT
Medway UA District Commander: T/Supt Julia Chapman. Tel: 01634 792112.
Medway Police Station.

REACTIVE INVESTIGATION
Head of Reactive Investigation: Det Chief Insp Trevor Lawry. Ext: 01622 2396.
Medway Police Station.

PROACTIVE INVESTIGATION
Head of Proactive Investigation: Det Chief Insp John Coull. Tel: 01474 366200.
North Kent Police Station.

EAST DIVISION

East Division Commander: Chief Supt Alan Horton. Tel: 01303 289110.
East Division Deputy Commander: Supt Sean Beautridge. Tel: 01303 289111.
Folkestone Police Station. Bouverie House, Bouverie Road West, Folkestone CT20 2SG.

ASHFORD DISTRICT
Ashford District Commander: Chief Insp Hayley Spedding. Tel: 01233 896110.
Ashford Police Station. Tufton Street, Ashford TN23 1BT.

CANTERBURY DISTRICT
Canterbury District Commander: Chief Insp Steve Barlow. Tel: 01227 868100.
Canterbury Police Station. Old Dover Road, Canterbury CT1 3JQ.

DOVER DISTRICT
Dover District Commander: Chief Insp Darren Mullins. Tel: 01304 218111.
Dover Police Station. Ladywell, Dover CT16 1DJ.

SHEPWAY DISTRICT
Shepway District Commander: Chief Insp Martin Bradley. Tel: 01303 289118.
Folkestone Police Station.

THANET DISTRICT
Thanet District Commander: Chief Insp Rob Fordham. Tel: 01843 222200.
Margate Police Station. Odell House, Fort Hill, Margate CT9 1HL.

REACTIVE INVESTIGATION
Head of Reactive Investigation: Det Chief Insp Nick Gossett. Tel: 01843 222111.
Folkestone Police Station.

PROACTIVE INVESTIGATION
Head of Proactive Investigation: Det Chief Insp Luke Dodson. Tel: 01303 289200.
Folkestone Police Station.

WEST DIVISION

West Division Commander: Chief Supt Andy Rabey. Tel: 01622 604110.
West Division Deputy Commander: Supt Des Keers. Tel: 01622 604112.
Maidstone Police Station. Palace Avenue, Maidstone ME15 6NF.

MAIDSTONE DISTRICT
Maidstone District Commander: Chief Insp Jon Bumpus. Tel: 01622 604111.
Maidstone Police Station.

SEVENOAKS DISTRICT
Sevenoaks District Commander: Chief Insp Peter Steenhuis. Tel: 01322 422511.
Sevenoaks Front Counter. Argyle Road, Sevenoaks TN13 1HG.

TONBRIDGE AND MALLING DISTRICT
Tonbridge and Malling District Commander: Chief Insp Jon Kirby. Tel: 01732 379111.
Tonbridge Police Station. 1 Pembury Road, Tonbridge TN9 2HS.

TUNBRIDGE WELLS DISTRICT
Tunbridge Wells District Commander: Chief Insp Nicola Faulconbridge. Tel: 01892 502022.
Tunbridge Wells Police Station. Crescent Road, Tunbridge Well, TN1 2LU.

REACTIVE INVESTIGATION
Head of Reactive Investigation: A/Det Chief Insp Chris Benson. Tel: 01622 604468.
Maidstone Police Station.

PROACTIVE INVESTIGATION
Head of Proactive Investigation: Det Chief Insp Simon Wilson. Tel: 01622 604200.
Maidstone Police Station.

POLICE FEDERATION
JBB Secretary: Mr Peter Harman. 67 Queen Elizabeth Square, Maidstone ME15 9DJ. Ext: 2250.

KENT POLICE MUSEUM
The Historic Dockyard, Chatham ME4 4TZ. Tel: 01634 403260.
Email: info@kent-police-museum.co.uk
Website: www.kent-police-museum.co.uk

Curator: Mrs Anna Derham.

Listed below are towns and parishes in Kent together with the name of the appropriate police area. Correspondence should normally be directed to the District Commander at the principal station.

Town/parish	District/(division)		
Abbey	Swale (N)	Chalkwell	Swale (N)
Borden	Swale (N)	Davington Priory	Swale (N)
Boughton &	Swale (N)	East Downs	Swale (N)
Courtenay		Grove	Swale (N)

Hartlip, Newington & Upchurch	Swale (N)
Iwade & Lower Halstow	Swale (N)
Kemsley	Swale (N)
Leysdown & Warden	Swale (N)
Milton Regis	Swale (N)
Minster Cliffs	Swale (N)
Murston	Swale (N)
Queenborough & Halfway	Swale (N)
Roman	Swale (N)
St Ann's	Swale (N)
St Michael's	Swale (N)
Sheerness East	Swale (N)
Sheerness West	Swale (N)
Sheppey Central	Swale (N)
Teynham & Lynsted	Swale (N)
Watling	Swale (N)
West Downs	Swale (N)
Chalk	Gravesham (N)
Coldharbour	Gravesham (N)
Higham	Gravesham (N)
Istead Rise	Gravesham (N)
Meopham North	Gravesham (N)
Meopham South & Vigo	Gravesham (N)
Northfleet North	Gravesham (N)
Northfleet South	Gravesham (N)
Painters Ash	Gravesham (N)
Pelham	Gravesham (N)
Riverside	Gravesham (N)
Riverview	Gravesham (N)
Shorne, Cobham & Luddesdown	Gravesham (N)
Singlewell	Gravesham (N)
Westcourt	Gravesham (N)
Whitehill	Gravesham (N)
Woodlands	Gravesham (N)
Chatham Central	Medway UA (N)
Cuxton & Halling	Medway UA (N)
Gillingham North	Medway UA (N)
Gillingham South	Medway UA (N)
Hempstead & Wigmore	Medway UA (N)
Lordswood & Capstone	Medway UA (N)
Luton & Wayfield	Medway UA (N)
Peninsula	Medway UA (N)
Rainham Central	Medway UA (N)
Rainham North	Medway UA (N)
Rainham South	Medway UA (N)
River	Medway UA (N)
Rochester East	Medway UA (N)
Rochester South & Horsted	Medway UA (N)
Rochester West	Medway UA (N)
Strood North	Medway UA (N)
Strood Rural	Medway UA (N)
Strood South	Medway UA (N)
Twydall	Medway UA (N)
Walderslade	Medway UA (N)
Watling	Medway UA (N)
Bean & Darenth	Dartford (N)
Brent	Dartford (N)
Castle	Dartford (N)
Greenhithe	Dartford (N)
Heath	Dartford (N)
Joyce Green	Dartford (N)
Joydens Wood	Dartford (N)
Littlebrook	Dartford (N)
Longfield, New Barn & Southfleet	Dartford (N)
Newtown	Dartford (N)
Princes	Dartford (N)
Stone	Dartford (N)
Sutton-at-Hone & Hawley	Dartford (N)
Swanscombe	Dartford (N)
Town	Dartford (N)
West Hill	Dartford (N)
Wilmington	Dartford (N)
Ash	Sevenoaks (W)
Brasted, Chevening & Sundridge	Sevenoaks (W)
Cowden & Hever	Sevenoaks (W)
Crockenhill & West Hill	Sevenoaks (W)
Dunton Green & Riverhead	Sevenoaks (W)
Edenbridge North & East	Sevenoaks (W)
Edenbridge South & West	Sevenoaks (W)
Eynsford	Sevenoaks (W)
Farningham, Horton Kirby & South Darenth	Sevenoaks (W)
Fawkham & West Kingsdown	Sevenoaks (W)
Halstead, Knockholt & Badgers Mount	Sevenoaks (W)
Hartley & Hodsall Street	Sevenoaks (W)
Hextable	Sevenoaks (W)
Kemsing	Sevenoaks (W)
Leigh & Chiddingstone Causeway	Sevenoaks (W)
Otford & Shoreham	Sevenoaks (W)
Penshurst, Fordcombe & Chiddingstone	Sevenoaks (W)
Seal & Weald	Sevenoaks (W)
Sevenoaks Eastern	Sevenoaks (W)
Sevenoaks Kippington	Sevenoaks (W)
Sevenoaks Northern	Sevenoaks (W)
Sevenoaks Town & St John's	Sevenoaks (W)
Swanley Christchurch & Swanley Village	Sevenoaks (W)
Swanley St Mary's	Sevenoaks (W)
Swanley Whiteoak	Sevenoaks (W)
Allington	Maidstone (W)
Barming	Maidstone (W)
Bearsted	Maidstone (W)
Boughton Monchelsea & Chart	Maidstone (W)
Boxley	Maidstone (W)
Bridge	Maidstone (W)

Coxheath & Hunton	Maidstone (W)	Kings Hill	Tonbridge & Malling (W)
Detling & Thurnham	Maidstone (W)		
Downswood & Otham	Maidstone (W)	Larkfield North	Tonbridge & Malling (W)
Fant	Maidstone (W)		
Harrietsham & Lenham	Maidstone (W)	Larkfield South	Tonbridge & Malling (W)
Headcorn	Maidstone (W)	Medway	Tonbridge & Malling (W)
Heath	Maidstone (W)		
High Street	Maidstone (W)	Paddock Wood East	Tonbridge & Malling (W)
Leeds	Maidstone (W)		
Loose	Maidstone (W)	Paddock Wood West	Tonbridge & Malling (W)
Marden & Yalding	Maidstone (W)		
North Downs	Maidstone (W)	Pantiles & St Mark's	Tonbridge & Malling (W)
Parkwood	Maidstone (W)		
Shepway North	Maidstone (W)	Park	Tonbridge & Malling (W)
Shepway South	Maidstone (W)		
Staplehurst	Maidstone (W)	Pembury	Tonbridge & Malling (W)
Sutton	Maidstone (W)		
Sutton Valance & Langley	Maidstone (W)	Rusthall	Tonbridge & Malling (W)
Aylesford	Tonbridge & Malling (W)	St James'	Tonbridge & Malling (W)
Bluebell Hill & Walderslade	Tonbridge & Malling (W)	St John's	Tonbridge & Malling (W)
Borough Green & Long Mill	Tonbridge & Malling (W)	Sherwood	Tonbridge & Malling (W)
Brenchley & Horsmonden	Tonbridge & Malling (W)	Snodland East	Tonbridge & Malling (W)
Broadwater	Tonbridge & Malling (W)	Snodland West	Tonbridge & Malling (W)
Burham, Eccles & Wouldham	Tonbridge & Malling (W)	Southborough & High Brooms	Tonbridge & Malling (W)
Cage Green	Tonbridge & Malling (W)	Southborough North	Tonbridge & Malling (W)
Capel	Tonbridge & Malling (W)	Speldhurst & Bidborough	Tonbridge & Malling (W)
Castle	Tonbridge & Malling (W)	Tench	Tonbridge & Malling (W)
Culverden	Tonbridge & Malling (W)	Vauxhall	Tonbridge & Malling (W)
Ditton	Tonbridge & Malling (W)	Wateringbury	Tonbridge & Malling (W)
Downs	Tonbridge & Malling (W)	West Malling & Leybourne	Tonbridge & Malling (W)
East Malling	Tonbridge & Malling (W)	Wrotham	Tonbridge & Malling (W)
East Peckham & Golden Green	Tonbridge & Malling (W)	Aylesford Green	Ashford (E)
		Beaver	Ashford (E)
Frittenden & Sissinghurst	Tonbridge & Malling (W)	Biddenden	Ashford (E)
		Bockhanger	Ashford (E)
Goudhurst & Lamberhurst	Tonbridge & Malling (W)	Boughton Aluph & Eastwell	Ashford (E)
Hadlow, Mereworth & West Peckham	Tonbridge & Malling (W)	Bybrook	Ashford (E)
		Charing	Ashford (E)
Hawkhurst & Sandhurst	Tonbridge & Malling (W)	Downs North	Ashford (E)
		Downs West	Ashford (E)
Higham	Tonbridge & Malling (W)	Godington	Ashford (E)
		Great Chart with Singleton North	Ashford (E)
Hildenborough	Tonbridge & Malling (W)	Highfield	Ashford (E)
Ightham	Tonbridge & Malling (W)	Isle of Oxney	Ashford (E)
		Kennington	Ashford (E)
Judd	Tonbridge & Malling (W)	Little Burton Farm	Ashford (E)
		Norman	Ashford (E)

North Willesborough	Ashford (E)
Park Farm North	Ashford (E)
Park Farm South	Ashford (E)
Rolvenden & Tenterden West	Ashford (E)
St Michaels	Ashford (E)
Saxon Shore	Ashford (E)
Singleton South	Ashford (E)
South Willesborough	Ashford (E)
Stanhope	Ashford (E)
Stour	Ashford (E)
Tenterden North	Ashford (E)
Tenterden South	Ashford (E)
Victoria	Ashford (E)
Washford	Ashford (E)
Weald Central	Ashford (E)
Weald East	Ashford (E)
Weald North	Ashford (E)
Weald South	Ashford (E)
Wye	Ashford (E)
Dymchurch & St Mary's Bay	Shepway (E)
Elham & Stelling Minnis	Shepway (E)
Folkestone Cheriton	Shepway (E)
Folkestone East	Shepway (E)
Folkestone Foord	Shepway (E)
Folkestone Harbour	Shepway (E)
Folkestone Harvey Central	Shepway (E)
Folkestone Morehall	Shepway (E)
Folkestone Park	Shepway (E)
Folkestone Sandgate	Shepway (E)
Hythe Central	Shepway (E)
Hythe West	Shepway (E)
Lydd	Shepway (E)
Lympne & Stanford	Shepway (E)
New Romney Coast	Shepway (E)
New Romney Town	Shepway (E)
North Downs East	Shepway (E)
North Downs West	Shepway (E)
Romney Marsh	Shepway (E)
Tolsford	Shepway (E)
Aylesham	Dover (E)
Buckland	Dover (E)
Capel-Le-Ferne	Dover (E)
Castle	Dover (E)
Eastry	Dover (E)
Eythorne & Shepherdswell	Dover (E)
Little Stour & Ashstone	Dover (E)
Lydden & Temple Ewell	Dover (E)
Maxton, Elms Vale & Priory	Dover (E)
Middle Deal & Sholden	Dover (E)

Mill Hill	Dover (E)
North Deal	Dover (E)
Ringwould	Dover (E)
River	Dover (E)
St Margaret's-at-Cliffe	Dover (E)
St Radigunds	Dover (E)
Sandwich	Dover (E)
Tower Hamlets	Dover (E)
Town & Pier	Dover (E)
Walmer	Dover (E)
Whitfield	Dover (E)
Beacon	Thanet (E)
Birchington North	Thanet (E)
Bradstowe	Thanet (E)
Central Harbour	Thanet (E)
Cliffsend & Pegwell	Thanet (E)
Cliftonville East	Thanet (E)
Cliftonville West	Thanet (E)
Dane Valley	Thanet (E)
Eastcliff	Thanet (E)
Garlinge	Thanet (E)
Kinggate	Thanet (E)
Margate Central	Thanet (E)
Nethercourt	Thanet (E)
Newington	Thanet (E)
Northwood	Thanet (E)
St Peter's	Thanet (E)
Salmestone	Thanet (E)
Sir Moses Montefiore	Thanet (E)
Thanet Villages	Thanet (E)
Viking	Thanet (E)
Westbrook	Thanet (E)
Westgate-on-Sea	Thanet (E)
Barham Downs	Canterbury (E)
Barton	Canterbury (E)
Blean Forest	Canterbury (E)
Chartham & Stone Street	Canterbury (E)
Chestfield & Swalecliffe	Canterbury (E)
Gorrell	Canterbury (E)
Greenhill & Eddington	Canterbury (E)
Harbledown	Canterbury (E)
Harbour	Canterbury (E)
Herne & Broomfield	Canterbury (E)
Heron	Canterbury (E)
Little Stour	Canterbury (E)
Marshside	Canterbury (E)
North Nailbourne	Canterbury (E)
Northgate	Canterbury (E)
Reculver	Canterbury (E)
St Stephens	Canterbury (E)
Seasalter	Canterbury (E)
Sturry North	Canterbury (E)
Tankerton	Canterbury (E)
West Bay	Canterbury (E)
Westgate	Canterbury (E)
Wincheap	Canterbury (E)

HM CORONERS AND OTHER OFFICIALS

Central & South East Kent: Helen Rachel Redman. Elphicks Farmhouse, Hunton, Maidstone, Kent ME15 0SB. Tel: 01622 820412. Fax: 01622 820800.

Mid Kent & Medway: Patricia Harding. The Archbishop's Palace, Mill Street, Maidstone, Kent ME15 6YE. Tel: 01622 701927. Fax: 01622 693690.

North East Kent: Ms R M Cobb. 5 Lloyd Road, Broadstairs, Kent CT10 1HX. Tel: 01843 863260. Fax: 01843 603927.

North West Kent: Roger L Hatch. The White House, Melliker Lane, Hook Green, Meopham, Kent DA13 0JB. Tel: 01474 815747. Fax: 01474 815356.

Trading Standards
Head of Trading Standards: Trading Standards, Invicta House, County Hall, Maidstone ME14 IXX. Tel: 08458 247247. Email: countyhall@kent.gov.uk

RSPCA
RSPCA HQ, Wilberforce Way, Southwater, Horsham, West Sussex RH13 9RS. Tel: 0300 1234999 (24 hrs).

NSPCC
Kent & Medway, Pear Tree House, 68 West Street, Gillingham, Kent ME7 1EF. Tel: 01634 308200. Helpline: freephone 0808 800 5000 (24 hrs).

LANCASHIRE CONSTABULARY

PO Box 77, Hutton, Nr Preston, Lancashire PR4 5SB.
Tel: 01772 614444 (switchboard); 101 (non-emergency enquiries). Fax: 01772 410732. The dialling code for all numbers is 01772, unless otherwise indicated.
Email: postmaster@lancashire.pnn.police.uk (for operational & general enquiries and messages to staff whose email address is not known); firstname.lastname@lancashire.pnn.police.uk (for known staff addressees).
Website: www.lancashire.police.uk

Lord Lieutenant: The Rt Hon the Lord Shuttleworth JP.
Police & Crime Commissioner: Clive Grunshaw.

Chief Constable: Stephen J Finnigan CBE QPM BA(Open) MA(Cantab) Diploma AC & PS(Cantab). Tel: 412221.
Staff Officer to Chief Constable. Tel: 412218.
Deputy Chief Constable (Corporate Development): Chris Weigh. Tel: 412206.
Assistant Chief Constable (Territorial Operations & Criminal Justice): Mark Bates. Tel: 412280.
Assistant Chief Constable (Specialist Operations): Andrew Rhodes BA(Hons). Tel: 412215.
Assistant Chief Constable (People Portfolio): Peter White. Tel: 412250.
Director of Resources: Ian Cosh MA CIPFA. Tel: 412348.

PROFESSIONAL STANDARDS
Head of Professional Standards: Det Supt Simon Giles. Tel: 412765.
Secretary: Christina Ibrams. Tel: 412681. Fax: 412504.
Principal Vetting Officer. Carol Benton. Tel: 412430.
Support Services Manager: Julie Yates. Tel: 412501. Fax: 412397.
Information Compliance & Disclosure Manager. Jayne Thompson. Tel: 412867.
Data Protection & Information Manager. Carl Melling. Tel: 413327.
CRB Disclosure Unit Manager: Sandra Kay. Tel: 413312.
PNC Manager. Richard Allan. Tel: 416560.

STAFF ASSOCIATIONS
Police Federation: *JBB Secretary:* Rachel Baines. Tel: 412520. Fax: 616712.
UNISON: Mrs Maureen Le Marinel. Tel: 412779. Fax: 412229.
Black Police Association: PC M Ahmed. Tel: 412441.
Superintendents' Association: Chief Supt Clive Tattum. Tel: 412851.
Disability Support Group: *Vice-Chair:* Martin Fishwick. Tel: 410038.
Women's Network: *Chairperson:* Supt Jennifer Gomery. Tel: 415804.
LGBT Support Group: *Chairperson:* PC Ian Ashton. Tel: 412626.

CORPORATE DEVELOPMENT DEPARTMENT
Head of Corporate Development: Supt Paul Wilson. Tel: 410891.
SMT Secretary: Jeni Hulme. Tel: 412388. Fax: 412024.
Policy & Planning Officer. Leah Watson. Tel: 412336.
Head of Monitoring & Analysis: Larry Weir. Tel: 412930.
Local Policing Unit: Chief Insp Ralph Copley. Tel: 413406.
Meeting Support: Jane Grant. Tel: 412009.
Legal Department: Supt Paul Wilson. Tel: 412790.

SUSTAINING EXCELLENCE
Head of Sustaining Excellence: Chief Supt James Lee. Tel: 412312/88.
Programme Manager. Supt Terry Woods. Tel: 412613.

CORPORATE COMMUNICATIONS
Head of Corporate Communications: Jane Astle. Tel: 412262.
Deputy Head of Corporate Communications: Elizabeth Riding. Tel: 412658.
Press Officer Manager. Nick Evans. Tel: 413446.
Internal Communications Manager. Sarah Airey. Tel: 412973.
PR & Digital Media Manager. Paula Duxbury-Lowe. Tel: 412799.
Newsline. Tel: 0871 550 8022.

CENTRAL PROCESS UNIT
PO Box 1329, Preston PR2 0SX. Tel: 0845 146 3030 (1000–1400) (members of the public).
Manager. Tel: 415003. Fax: 415072.
Deputy Manager/Camera Team Leader. Tel: 415001. Fax: 415072.
Team Leader Camera. Tel: 415001.

Team Leader Collision & Offence Processing. Tel: 415031. Fax: 415072.
Team Leader Customer Service & Case Builders. Tel: 415012. Fax: 415071.

BUSINESS SUPPORT SERVICES

Head of Business Support: Tim Ewen. Tel: 412136. Fax: 412552.
Responsible for: Criminal Justice; Custody (Policy); Central Process Unit; Estates; Finance; Fleet Services/Transport; Procurement; Services (Administration).

CRIMINAL JUSTICE

Western & Northern Divisions Justice Manager: Therese Clark. Tel: 01253 604034. Fax: 01253 604198.
Central & Southern Divisions Justice Manager: Deborah Birtles. Tel: 209940. Fax: 209956.
Eastern & Pennine Divisions Justice Manager: David Woodcock. Tel: 01282 472510.
Centralised Functions Unit Justice Manager: Lesley Miller. Tel: 01257 246310. Fax: 01257 246316.
Custody Policy: Chief Insp Steve Sansbury. Tel: 413866. Fax: 412881.

ESTATES

Head of Facilities Management: Robert Kay. Tel: 412785.
Asset & Strategy Manager: Tim Ellams. Tel: 413601.
Capital Projects Manager: Robert Sherwood. Tel: 413851.
Estates Administration. Tel: 413606/18/412387.

FINANCE

Management Accounts: Alan Brown CPFA. Tel: 412131.

FLEET SERVICES

Maintenance Manager: Colin Burns MSOE MIRTE. Tel: 412498. Fax: 412926.
Fleet Transport Manager: Christopher J Malkin MILDM. Tel: 412495.

PROCUREMENT

Purchasing & Contracts Manager: Peter Higson MCIPS. Tel: 412889.

SERVICES

Administration Services Manager: Philip Ridsdale. Tel: 412317.
Clothing & Stores Services. Tel: 412362.

INFORMATION AND COMMUNICATIONS TECHNOLOGY

Head of ICT: Supt Richard Robertshaw. Tel: 412314. Fax: 412762.
Business Managers: George Duckett IEng MIET. Tel: 412529. Bob Burns MBE. Tel: 410801. Jan Booth BSc(Hons). Tel: 410860. Fax: 412762.
Administration Office. Tel: 412235/410805/6; 412234/5. Fax: 412762.
Airwave Service Manager: Derek Wignall IEng MIET. Tel: 410889. Fax: 412762.

CONTACT MANAGEMENT

Head of Contact Management: Chief Supt Sarah Oldham. Tel: 416370.
Operations Manager: T/Supt Nicola Evans. Tel: 410786.
Contact Centre Managers: **Blackpool & Lancaster:** Kelly Thornton. Tel: 07943 315512 or 101. **Preston & Hutton:** Karen Greenwood Tel: 07525 409751 or 101. **Blackburn & Burnley:** Ann Holmes. Tel: 07508 036726 or 101.
Non-urgent enquiries, Tel: 101. Email: lancashirepolice@lancashire.pnn.police.uk

TRAINING CENTRE

Tel: 412350. Fax: 12821. (Mon–Thurs 0800–1700; Fri 0800–1600).
Head of Learning & Development: Victor Robinson FCIPD. Tel: 412291.
Learning Support & Standards Manager: Vacant.
Operational Training: Insp Andy Moore. Tel: 412475.
Leadership & Professional Development: Insp Andy Leck Cert Ed. Tel: 412482.
Criminal Investigation Training: Det Insp Daryl Turner. Tel: 413616.
Firearms Training: Insp Mark Baines. Tel: 412654.
Business Services Manager: Peter Cuerden BA. Tel: 412755.

HUMAN RESOURCES AND PAYROLL

Head of Human Resources & Payroll: Ashley Judd FCIPD. Tel: 410362.
Strategic HR Manager, Resourcing: Joanne Kane MCIPD. Tel: 410325.
Strategic HR Manager, Operations: Ann-Marie Bull FCIPD. Tel: 410394.
Payroll Services Manager: Diane Walmsley. Tel: 410341.
Recruitment & Selection Manager: Louise Miller MCIPD. Tel: 410301.
Force Health & Safety Advisor: Tony Boswell GradIOSH. Tel: 413656.
Transactional & Resourcing Manager: Matthew Dennis MCIPD. Tel: 410337.
Force Attendance Manager: Fiona Atherton PGCM. Tel: 412180.
Force Welfare Advisors: Kathleen Aherne MBACP(Acc). Tel: 412449. Ann Abbott AdvDip in Counselling, Member of BACP, Dip Supervision. Tel: 412344.
Force Medical Advisor: Dr Jerry Evans MB BCh DAvMed AFOM. Tel: 412550.

CRIME (G) DIVISION

Command: Det Chief Supt Clive Tattum.
Secretary: Cheryl Sutcliffe. Tel: 412851. Fax: 412852.
Projects & Planning Officer. Tel: 413850.
Finance & Administration Manager. Elaine Norris. Tel: 412628.
HR Business Partner: Brett Biscomb. Tel: 410321.

FORCE INTELLIGENCE DEPARTMENT

Head of Intelligence: T/Det Supt Pauline Lambert. Tel: 412251. Fax: 412687.
Force Intelligence Unit: T/Det Chief Insp Stuart Dixon. Tel: 412978.
Development, High Risk Sex Offenders & Prisons: Det Insp Simon Brooksbank. Tel: 412202.
Intelligence Co-ordinator/Analysis Head of Profession: Ian Billsborough. Tel: 412454.
Intelligence & Security: Det Insp Andy Cribbin. Tel: 413830.
Proceeds of Crime Unit: T/Det Insp Andy Ellis. Tel: 413665.
FID General Enquiries. Tel: 412465. Fax: 412744. Email: forceintelligence@lancashire.pnn.police.uk or fid-admin@lancashire.pnn.police.uk

COUNTER TERRORISM BRANCH

Head of Counter Terrorism Branch: Det Supt Martin Kay. Tel: 412341. Fax: 412780.
Counter Terrorism Branch: Det Chief Insp Gary Brooks. Tel: 413669. Fax: 412780.
Ports & Airport Unit: Det Insp Paul Phillpott. Tel: 404166.
SPOE (Single Point of Entry). Tel: 412742.
General Enquiries. Tel: 413355.

SERIOUS AND ORGANISED CRIME UNIT

Head of Department: Det Supt Lee Halstead.
Secretary. Tel: 416104.
Deputy Head: Det Chief Insp Tim Leeson. Tel: 416103.
General Enquiries. Tel: 416148.
Stolen Vehicle Syndicate. Tel: 416172.
Economic Crime Unit. Tel: 416142.
High Tech Crime Unit. Tel: 416203.
Financial Investigation Unit. Tel: 416220.
Drugs Support. Tel: 416153/184.

COVERT POLICING DEPARTMENT

Head of Covert Policing Department/Authorising Officer. Det Supt Martyn Leveridge.
Secretary. Tel: 413676.
Deputy Head: Det Supt Marc Vincent.
Secretary. Tel: 413676.
Responsible for: Covert Management Unit; Communications Data Investigation Unit; Operation Nimrod; Specialist Operations; Covert Protection Unit; Force Surveillance Unit; Technical Support Unit; Dedicated Source Unit.

FORCE MAJOR INVESTIGATION TEAM

SIO Team
A/B/D Div Cluster: Det Supt Andrew Murphy. Tel: 01253 407352.
E/F/C Div Cluster: Det Supt Paul Withers. Tel: 01254 353601.
G/H Div Cluster & Head of Public Protection Development & Compliance Unit: Det Supt Ian Critchley. Tel: 412868.
General Enquiries. Tel: 412618. Fax: 412607.
HOLMES Manager: Jackie Roach. Tel: 412321/412732/412587. Fax: 412607.

SCIENTIFIC SUPPORT

Scientific Support Manager. Dr Kathryn Mashiter MBE. Tel: 416001. Fax: 416006.
Crime Scene Investigation. Tel: 416082. Fax: 416089.
Digital Forensics. Tel: 416060.
CCTV & Imaging Unit. Tel: 416068.
Mobile Phone Examination. Tel: 416073.
DNA Submissions. Tel: 416093. Fax: 416089.
Fingerprints. Tel: 416021. Fax: 416046.
Forensic Submissions. Tel: 416085. Fax: 416089.

OPERATIONS (H) DIVISION

Command: T/Chief Supt William McMahon MBA BA(Hons). Tel: 413201.
Secretary: Emma Wignall. Tel: 412288. Fax: 412712.
Finance & Administration Manager. Elaine Norris. Tel: 412628.
Operations Services: Supt Richard Morgan. Tel: 412572. T/Chief Insp Gary Crowe. Tel: 412342. (**Road Policing**) Chief Insp Debbie Howard. Tel: 412231.

Air Support Unit: T/Insp Kim Sturgess. Tel: 410559. Fax: 855581.
Motorway: Insp Wendy Bower. Tel: 410460. Fax: 410469.
Accident Investigation Unit: Sgt Tracey Ward. Tel: 410459 Fax: 415785.
Mounted: Sgt Neil Persechino. Tel: 412468.
Operations Support Services Team: T/Insp Kim Sturgess. Tel: 410559.
Civil Contingencies Unit: T/Chief Insp Gary Crowe. Tel: 412342.
Force Search Co-ordinator: Insp Neil Sherry. Tel: 412679.
Force CBRN Co-ordinator: PC Alison Suffield. Tel: 412679. Fax: 412830.

NORTH WEST MOTORWAY POLICE GROUP (NWMPG)
North West Regional Control Room, Rob Lane, Newton-le-Willows WA12 0DR. Tel: 0151 777 6900. (Police only) covering Cheshire, Lancashire & Merseyside police areas.
Cheshire Contact: Insp E Cunningham. Tel: 01244 615260. Fax: 01244 612456.
Lancashire Contact: Insp Wendy Bower. Tel: 410460.
Merseyside Contact: Insp Dave Corcoran. Tel: 0151 777 3703.

NORTH WEST POLICE UNDERWATER SEARCH AND MARINE UNIT
Based at Runcorn Police Station; covering Cheshire, Cumbria, Lancashire, Manchester, Merseyside & North Wales police areas.
Insp J Milligan. Tel: 01244 613993. Sgt R Reid. Tel: 01244 613994.

WESTERN (A) DIVISION
Divisional Headquarters, Bonny Street, Blackpool FY1 5RL. Tel: 01253 293933 or 101 Fax: 01253 607232 (communications room); 01253 604062 (admin).
Command: Chief Supt Richard Debicki BSc(Hons). Tel: 01253 604021.
Operations Manager: Supt Stuart Noble. Tel: 01253 604102.
Secretary. Tel: 01253 604021.
Management Support. Tel: 01253 607320/604050.
Fylde Borough Commander/Operations: T/Chief Insp Laura Lawler. Tel: 01253 604708.
Geographic Policing: Chief Insp Ian Mills. Tel: 01253 607341.
Partnerships/Community Safety: Chief Insp Gary Dunnagan. Tel: 01253 604072.
Crime Reduction Manager: Det Chief Insp Sam Mackenzie. Tel: 01253 604106.
HR Business Partner (A & B Divisions): Helen Davies ChtdMCIPD. Tel: 01253 604039 (A Division); 01524 596652 (B Division).
Strategic Business Manager (A & B Divisions): Stuart Railton CPFA (Cert CDP) MCMI (IMDip). Tel: 01253 604045 (A Division); 01524 596717 (B Division).
Blackpool Custody Office. Tel: 01253 604114.
MAIN POLICE STATIONS
North: Red Bank Road, Bispham FY2 0HJ. Tel: 01253 604549.
St Annes: St Andrew's Road North, St Annes-on-Sea FY8 2JF. Tel: 01253 604697. Fax: 01253 604632.
Lytham: 23 Clifton Street, Lytham FY8 5EP. Tel: 01253 604834. Fax: 01253 604832.
South Shore: Montague Street, Blackpool FY4 1AT. Tel: 01253 604201. Fax: 01253 604200.
Kirkham: Freckleton Street, Kirkham PR4 2CN. Tel: 01253 604730. Fax: 01253 604732.

NORTHERN (B) DIVISION
Divisional Headquarters, Thurnham Street, Lancaster LA1 1YB. Tel: 01524 63333 or 101. Fax: 01524 596832 (communications room, 24 hrs); 01524 596703 (admin).
Command: Chief Supt Richard Bayly Tel: 01524 596600.
Secretary. Tel: 01524 596602.
Operations Manager: Supt Andrew Webster. Tel: 01524 596601.
Operations: Chief Insp Eddie Newton. Tel: 01524 596714.
Crime: Det Chief Insp Vickie Evans. Tel: 01524 596620.
Partnerships: Chief Insp Ian Sewart. Tel: 01524 596733.
HR Business Partner (A & B Divisions): Helen Davies. Tel: 01253 604039 (A Division); 01524 596652 (B Division).
Strategic Business Manager (A & B Divisions): Stuart Railton CPFA (CertCPD) MCMI (IM Dip). Tel: 01253 604045 (A Division). 01524 596717 (B Division).
Management Support. Tel: 01524 596604.
MAIN POLICE STATIONS
Wyre Operating Centre: North Church Street, Fleetwood FY7 6HN. Tel: 01253 604371. Fax: 01253 604436. Fax: 01253 604433 (admin).
Morecambe: 21 Poulton Square, Morecambe LA4 5PZ. Tel: 01524 596933. Fax: 01524 596919 (admin).
Carnforth: Grosvenor Road, Carnforth LA5 5DQ. Tel: 01524 596688. Fax: 01524 596402. (Not 24 hrs; Lancaster is the administrative and deployment centre for this station.)

SOUTHERN (C) DIVISION

Divisional Headquarters, Lancastergate, Leyland, Preston PR25 2EX. Tel: 01772 415834 or 101. Fax: 01772 415832.
Command: Chief Supt Stuart Williams. Tel: 415802. Fax: 415941.
Secretary: Sue Helm. Tel: 415801. Fax: 415941.
Operations Manager. Supt Jenny Gomery Tel: 415804. Fax: 415941.
Chorley & South Ribble Borough: Chief Insp Nikki Evans. Tel: 415850. Fax: 415941.
Crime Reduction: Det Chief Insp Andy Gilbert. Tel: 415974. Fax: 415941.
West Lancs Borough: Chief Insp Kevin Boyce. Tel: 01695 566000 Fax: 415941.
HR Business Partner C & D Divisions: Louise Fairclough. Tel: 415805. Fax: 415941. (Central tel: 209820. Fax: 209610.)
Strategic Business Manager C & D Divisions: Sally Falconer. Tel: 415803. Fax: 415941. (Central tel: 209608. Fax: 209610.)
Intelligence Unit Manager: Det Insp Graham Coates. Tel: 01257 246305. Fax: 01257 246349.
MAIN POLICE STATIONS
Leyland: Lancastergate, Leyland PR25 2EX. Tel: 415834 Fax: 415832.
Chorley: St Thomas's Road, Chorley PR7 1DR. Tel: 01257 269021. Fax: 01257 246232.
Skelmersdale: Southway, Skelmersdale WN8 6NH. Tel: 01695 566134. Fax: 01695 566132.

CENTRAL (D) DIVISION

Preston Divisional Headquarters, Lancaster Road North, Preston PR1 2SA. Tel: 01772 209600 or 101. Fax: 01772 209610 (admin weekdays 0900–1700). Fax: 01772 209332 (communications 24 hrs).
Command: Chief Supt Tim Jacques.
Secretary. Tel: 209600. Fax: 209610.
Operations Manager: Supt Eddie Thistlethwaite. Tel: 209602. Fax: 209610.
HR Business Partner: Louise Fairclough. Tel: 209820. Fax: 209610. (Southern tel: 415805. Fax: 415941.)
Strategic Business Manager: Sally Falconer. Tel: 209608. Fax: 209610. (Southern tel: 415803. Fax: 415941.)
Geographic Operations: Chief Insp June Chessell. Tel: 209603. Fax: 209610.
Crime/Support: Det Chief Insp Ian Dawson. Tel: 209605. Fax: 209610.
Community Safety/Partnerships: Chief Insp Tracie O'Gara. Tel: 209604. Fax: 209610.
Public Protection Unit: Det Insp Jo Edwards. Tel: 209900.
CJS Manager: Deborah Birtles DMS. Tel: 209040. Fax: 209097.
MAIN POLICE STATIONS
Preston: Lancaster Road North, Preston PR1 2SA. Tel: 08451 253545.
Lea: 785 Blackpool Road, Preston PR2 1QQ. Tel: 209434. Fax: 209420.

EASTERN (E) DIVISION

Divisional Headquarters, Greenbank Business Park, Whitebirk Drive, Blackburn BB1 3HT. Tel: 01254 51212; or 101. Fax: 01254 353515; 01254 353432 (24-hr emergency use only).
Command: Chief Supt Robert Eastwood. Tel: 01254 353500.
Secretary. Tel: 01254 353501.
Operations: Supt Jonathon Puttock. Tel: 01254 353502.
Chief Inspector Blackburn with Darwen: Julian Platt. Tel: 01254 353527.
Chief Inspector Hyndburn & Ribble Valley: Joanne McHugh. Tel: 01254 353973.
Det Chief Inspector Crime Co-ordinator: Dean Holden. Tel: 01254 353535.
Chief Inspector Operations Support: Justin Srivastava. Tel: 01254 353505.
Intelligence Unit Manager: Det Insp Robert Winstanley. Tel: 01254 353976.
HR Business Partner: Vacant. Tel: 01254 353634.
Strategic Business Manager: Carolyn Ewen. Tel: 01254 353602.
MAIN POLICE STATIONS
Accrington: Manchester Road, Accrington BB5 2BJ. Tel: 01254 353749. Fax: 01254 353729.
Blackburn (Town Centre): Blackburn Boulevard, Railway Road BB1 1EX. Tel: 01254 353590. Fax: 01254 353684.
Clitheroe: King Street, Clitheroe BB7 2EC. Tel: 01200 458734. Fax: 01200 458732.
Darwen: Union Street, Darwen BB3 0DA. Tel: 01254 353830. Fax: 01254 353832.
Great Harwood: Blackburn Road, Great Harwood BB6 7DZ. Tel: 01254 353334. Fax: 01254 353332.
Longridge: 71–73 Derby Road, Longridge PR3 3EE. Tel: 209581. Fax: 783174.

PENNINE (F) DIVISION

Divisional Headquarters, Parker Lane, Burnley BB11 2BT. Tel: 01282 425001 or 101. Fax: 01282 472132 (24 hours).
Command: Chief Supt Christopher Bithell. Tel: 01282 472100.
Secretary. Tel: 01282 472100.

Operations Manager: Supt Stephen Pemberton. Tel: 01282 472105.
Crime Reduction: Det Chief Insp Sion Hall. Tel: 01282 472102.
HR Manager. Tel: 01282 472208.
Intelligence Inspector: Derry Crorken. Tel: 01282 472416.
CJS Manager: Dave Woodcock. Tel: 01282 472510.
GEOGRAPHIC COMMAND
Burnley: Chief Insp Jon Bullas. Tel: 01282 472202.
Pendle: Chief Insp Jeff Brown. Tel: 01282 472400.
MAIN POLICE STATIONS
Colne: Craddock Road, Colne BB8 0JU. Tel: 01282 863161. Fax: 01282 472532.
Rossendale: Bacup Road, Rossendale BB4 9AA. Tel: 01706 237434. Fax: 01706 237432.

STATIONS IN THE CONSTABULARY AREA

Station	Sub-Division	Station	Sub-Division	Station	Sub-Division
†Accrington	E	†Clitheroe	E	Nelson	F
Aughton	C	†Colne	F	†Ormskirk	C
†Bamber Bridge	C	Coppull	C	†Padiham	F
Barnoldswick	F	Coupe Green	C	Poulton-le-Fylde	B
Bispham	A	†Darwen	E	†Preston	D
†Blackburn	E	Edgeworth	E	operating centre	
Blackburn Central	E	Garstang	B	* Rossendale	F
†Blackpool	A	Great Harwood	E	operating centre	
Central*		Kirkham	A	St Annes	A
Blackpool South	A	†Lancaster	B	Samlesbury	H(M/
Brierfield	F	Lea	D		way)
Broughton	D	†Leyland	C	†Skelmersdale	C
†Burnley	F	Longridge	E	Tarleton	C
Carnforth	B	Lytham	A	† Wyre Operating	B
†Chorley	C	†Morecambe	B	Centre	

† Denotes stations designated under s35, P.A.C.E. Act 1984.
*Denotes stations staffed 24 hours per day.

HM CORONERS

Blackburn, Hyndburn & Ribble Valley: Mr M J H Singleton. King George's Hall, Northgate, Blackburn BB2 1AA. Tel: 01254 588680. Fax: 01254 588681. Email: michael.singleton@blackburn.gov.uk
Blackpool/Fylde: Mrs Anne V Hind. 283 Church Street, Blackpool FY1 3PG. Tel: 01253 625731. Fax: 01253 291915.
East Lancashire: Mr Richard G Taylor. 6a Hargreaves Street, Burnley BB11 1ES. Tel: 01282 438446. Fax: 01282 446525.
Preston & West Lancashire: Dr James Adeley. 2 Faraday Court, Faraday Drive, Fulwood, Preston PR2 9NB. Tel: 01772 703700. Fax: 01772 704422.

LEICESTERSHIRE POLICE

St John's, Enderby, Leicester LE19 2BX.
Tel: 101. Fax: 0116 248 2227 (Force Headquarters Registry). Fax: 0116 2482427
(Force Operations Room; Mon–Fri 0800–1700).
Email: firstname.lastname@leicestershire.pnn.police.uk
Website: www.leics.police.uk

Lord Lieutenants: Lady Gretton (Leicestershire); Dr L Howard DL JP (Rutland).
Police & Crime Commissioner: Sir Clive Loader.
Chief Executive: Mr Paul Stock CPFA.
Chief Finance Officer: Mr Peter Lewis.
Email: police.commissioner@leics.pcc.pnn.gov.uk

Chief Constable: Mr Simon Cole BA(Hons)(Dunelm) MA(Worcester) DipCrim(Cantab).
Deputy Chief Constable: Mr Simon Edens.
Assistant Chief Constable: Ms Stephanie Morgan BA(Hons) MSc.
T/Assistant Chief Constable: Mr Chris Thomas.
Finance Director: Mr Paul Dawkins MBA CPFA DMS MAAT.
Human Resources Director: Mrs Alison Naylor FCIPD.

EXECUTIVE SUPPORT
Chief Constable's & Deputy Chief Constable's Secretary: Ms Jill Sharpe.
Chief Constable's National Mental Health Portfolio Staff Officer: Insp Siobhan Barber.
Chief Constable's & Deputy Chief Constable's Staff Officer: Sgt Tracey Willetts.
Assistant Chief Constables' Staff Officer: Mrs Kathy Astbury.
Assistant Chief Constables' Secretary: Mrs Jennifer Weston.
Support Officer to Finance & Human Resources Directors: Mrs Wendy Campion.

HUMAN RESOURCES
Head of HR Operations & Occupational Health: Miss Carol Hever DMS MCIPD.
Occupational Health Nurse Manager: Mrs Julie A Pitts DOHN RGN.
Head of Learning & Development: Mrs Sarah Pinner.

CORPORATE FINANCE
Head of Finance: Mrs Ruth Gilbert CPFA.
Head of Procurement & Support Services: Mr Ian Fraser MCIPS.

STAFF ASSOCIATIONS/TRADE UNIONS
Superintendents' Association: *Secretary:* Supt Phil Whiteley.
Police Federation: *JBB Chairman:* Sgt Ivan Stafford.
UNISON: *Branch Secretary:* Mr Christopher Hanrahan.
General Municipal Boilermakers' Union: Mr Stephen Alexander.

ESTATES MANAGER
Head of Estates: Mr Andrew Wroe BSc(Hons) MRICS.

IT DEPARTMENT
Head of IT: Mr Tim Glover.

TRANSPORT
Head of Transport: Mr Robert Pope.

CORPORATE SERVICES DEPARTMENT
Head of Corporate Services Department: Chief Supt Chris Haward.
Chief Inspectors: Sally Chivers; Neil Newell.
Service Improvement: Mr Glenn Brown LLB(Hons).
Force Health & Safety Manager: Mr Peter Coogan.
Force Diversity Manager: Ms Lynne Woodward.

PROFESSIONAL STANDARDS DEPARTMENT
Head of Department & Civil Claims: Det Supt Colin Stott.
Complaints & Misconduct: Det Chief Insp Roseanna Burton.
Anti-corruption Unit: Det Chief Insp Mick Graham.
Vetting & Disclosure: Ms Sara Berry; Mrs Gemma Crane.
Information Manager: Ms Anne C Chafer BA(Hons).

DELIVERING JUSTICE DIRECTORATE
Head of Delivering Justice Directorate: T/Det Chief Supt Stuart Prior.
Support Manager: Miss Emma Corns.
Human Resources Officer: Mrs Teresa Keegan.

CRIMINAL JUSTICE DEPARTMENT
Head of Criminal Justice: T/Supt Matt Hewson.
Chief Inspector: Peter Jackson.
Senior Manager – Case Preparation: Mrs Joanna Compton.
Road Safety Unit: Mr Stefan Szmega.

INVESTIGATIONS DEPARTMENT
City BCU Investigation Unit: Det Chief Insp Siobhan Ashford.
Counties BCU Investigation Unit: Det Chief Insp Rich Ward.

SAFEGUARDING & SPECIALIST CRIME DEPARTMENT
Head of Safeguarding & Specialist Crime Department: T/Det Supt David Sandall.
Safeguarding: Det Chief Insp Andy Sharp; Det Chief Insp Phil Brighouse; T/Det Chief Insp Jon Brown.
Special Operations Unit: T/Det Chief Insp Joe Elliott.
Force Targeting Team/ECU: Det Chief Insp Chris Baker.
Nationality/Special Branch HQ. Tel: 101.
Special Branch East Midlands Airport (EMA). Tel: 101.

FORENSIC SERVICES
Head of Forensic Services: Det Chief Insp Sarah Cox.
T/Forensic Services Manager: Mr Robert Gregory.
Hi-tech Crime Unit: Mr Martin Walker.

TASKING DIRECTORATE
Head of Tasking Directorate: T/Chief Supt Rachel Swann.
Management Support Officer: Mrs Jane Timms.
Special Constabulary: Special Chief Officer Paul R Smith.

OPERATIONS
Head of Operations: T/Supt Jim Holyoak.
Operations Chief Inspectors: Chris Brown; Stephen Potter MSc PGDL.

FORCE INTELLIGENCE BUREAU
Head of Department: Supt Steph Pandit.
T/Intelligence Manager: Miss Suzanne Houlihan.
Det Chief Inspector: Simon Hurst.
City BCU Intelligence Bureau: T/Det Insp Antony Dales.
Counties BCU Intelligence Bureau: Det Insp Rob Vivian.
Intelligence Research Centre Manager: Det Insp Helena Bhakta.

CONTACT MANAGEMENT DEPARTMENT
Head of Department: T/Supt Adam Streets.
Chief Inspectors: Dan Pedley (Temporary); Alistair Roe. East Midlands Police Collaboration

EAST MIDLANDS POLICE COLLABORATION
Deputy Chief Constable East Midlands: Peter Goodman.
PA to DCC East Midlands. Tessa Callow. Tel: 01623 608402.

EAST MIDLANDS COUNTER TERRORISM INTELLIGENCE UNIT
Email: emctiu@derbyshire.pnn.police.uk
PA to Head of Unit & Senior Management Team. Tel: 01623 608304.
Human Resources. Tel: 01623 608403.
Office Manager. Tel: 01623 608411.
Special Branch: Det Insp Rob Routledge. Tel: 0115 967 0999 ext 800 1030.

EAST MIDLANDS POLICE COLLABORATION PROGRAMME
Arrow Centre, Annesley Road, Hucknall, Nottingham NGG15 8AY. Tel: 01623 608262. Email: eastmidlandscpt@nottinghamshire.pnn.police.uk
Programme Manager: Chief Supt Phil Whiteley.

EAST MIDLANDS SPECIAL OPERATIONS UNIT
EMSOU, PO Box 9557, Nottingham NG15 5BU. Tel: 01623 608054.
Head of EMSOU-SOC: T/Det Chief Supt Jason Caunt.
Deputy Head of EMSOU-SOC: T/Det Supt Steve Craddock.
Command Team PA: Sarah Dillon.
Business & Finance Manager: Jon Peatling. Email: jonathan.peatling@leicestershire.pnn.police.uk
Senior Human Resources Officer: Tracy Meakin.
Head of Operations Support: Det Chief Insp Andy Haydon.
Head of RART: Det Chief Insp Mick Beattie. Email: michael.beattie@leicestershire.pnn.police.uk
Head of Regional Review Unit: Kevin Flint.

EMSOU – SERIOUS & ORGANISED CRIME
EMSOU-SOC North Command: Det Chief Insp Andy Dickin.
EMSOU-SOC East Command: T/Det Chief Insp Alan Mason.
EMSOU-SOC South Command: T/Det Chief Insp Joe Elliott.
    Email: joseph.elliott@leicestershire.pnn.police.uk

EMSOU – MAJOR CRIME
Head of Major Crime Unit: Det Chief Supt Andrew Hough.
EMSOU-MC North Command: Vacant.
EMSOU-MC East Command: Det Supt Stuart Morrison. Email: stuart.morrison@lincs.pnn.police.uk
EMSOU-MC South Command: Vacant.

EMSOU – FORENSIC SERVICES
Regional Director of Forensic Services: Joanne Ashworth.
    Email: joanne.ashworth.16204@derbyshire.pnn.police.uk

EMSOU – SPECIAL BRANCH
EMSOU, PO Box 9557, Nottingham NG15 5BU. Tel: 01623 608304.
Det Supt Stephen Lowe. Email: stephen.lowe.314568@derbyshire.pnn.police.uk
PA to Senior Management Team: Sue Hogg. Email: susan.hogg.16244@derbyshire.pnn.police.uk

CITY BCU
Mansfield House, 74 Belgrave Gate, Leicester LE1 3GG. Fax: 0116 248 4657.
Commander: Chief Supt Robert Nixon.
Superintendents: Andy Lee; Mark Newcombe.
Chief Inspector (Local Policing): Martyn Ball.
Chief Inspector (Operations): Donna Thomson.
Management Support Officer: Mr Jeremy O'Dwyer.
HR Officer: Mr Roman Nykolyszyn.

COUNTIES BCU
Southfields Road, Loughborough LE11 2XF. Fax: 0116 248 4127.
Commander: T/Chief Supt Sally Healy.
Superintendents: Jez Cottrill; Neil Castle.
Chief Inspector (Local Policing): Mark Thomson.
Chief Inspector (Operations): Duncan Cullen.
Management Support Officer: Mrs Anita Panchal.
HR Officer: Miss Louisa De Souza.

POLICE STATIONS

Station	*Area*	
Beaumont Leys	City	CB
Charnwood (Syston)	Counties	LC
City Centre	City	CM
Harborough	Counties	LA
Hinckley	Counties	LH
Hinckley Road	City	CH
Keyham Lane	City	CK
Loughborough	Counties	LO
Melton Mowbray	Counties	LM
NW Leicestershire (Coalville)	Counties	LN
Oadby & Wigston	Counties	LW
Rutland	Counties	LR
Spinney Hill	City	CN
Welford Road	City	CW

Stations staffed 24 hrs per day and designated under s35 P.A.C.E. Act 1984: Beaumont Leys, Loughborough, and Euston Street.

HM CORONERS AND OTHER OFFICIALS
Leicester City & South Leicestershire: Mrs Catherine E Mason. The Town Hall, Leicester LE1 9BG. Tel: 0116 225 2534. Fax: 0116 225 2537. Email: leicester.coroner@leicester.gov.uk
Rutland & North Leicestershire: Mr T H Kirkman. 34 Woodgate, Loughborough LE11 2TY. Tel: 0116 305 7732. Fax: 01509 210744.

LINCOLNSHIRE POLICE
PO Box 999, Lincoln LN5 7PH. Headquarters: Deepdale Lane,
Nettleham, Lincoln LN2 2LT.
Tel: 101. Textphone: 01522 558263. Fax: 01522 558686 (24 hrs).
The dialling code for all numbers is 01522, unless otherwise indicated.
Email: forcehq@lincs.pnn.police.uk.
Email individuals: firstname.lastname@lincs.pnn.police.uk, unless otherwise
indicated.
Website: www.lincs.police.uk

Lord Lieutenant: Mr A J L Worth. Old White House, Holbeach Hurn, Spalding PE12 8JP.
Police & Crime Commissioner: Alan Hardwick.

Chief Constable: Mr N Rhodes LLB(Hons).
Deputy Chief Constable: Mr A Wood.
Assistant Chief Constable (Protective Services): Mr R Bannister.
Assistant Chief Constable (Safer Neighbourhoods): Mr K Smy BSc MBA PgDip PM FInstLM.
Chief Financial Officer: Mr T Tomlinson. Tel: 558187.
Chief Constable's PA: Mrs M Freeman. Tel: 558007.
Deputy Chief Constable's PA: Mrs P Nicholson. Tel: 558006.
Assistant Chief Constables' PA: Mrs V Ashby. Tel: 558347.
Chief Constable's Staff Officer: Insp G Rooney. Tel: 558270.
Deputy & Assistant Chief Constables' Staff Officer: Sgt S Bromiley. Tel: 558114.
Executive Administration Assistant: Mrs N Turner. Tel: 558126.

LEGAL SERVICES DEPARTMENT
Force Solicitor: Mrs M J Blakey LLB. Tel: 558057. Fax: 558338.
Assistant Solicitor: Vacant. Tel: 558485.
Legal Executive: Miss G L Harris FInstLEx. Tel: 558021.
Claims Investigator: Mr D Canton. Tel: 558891.
Legal Secretary: Mrs S Curtis. Tel: 558334.

PROFESSIONAL STANDARDS DEPARTMENT
Supt M Staniland. Tel: 558010.
Office Manager: Mrs A Foster. Tel: 558013. Fax: 558041.
Anti-corruption Unit: Sgt M Vincent. Tel: 558011.

STRATEGIC DEVELOPMENT
Head of Strategic Development: Mrs Julie Hogan. Tel: 558243.
Force Programme, Planning & Performance Manager: Ms Nicola Prutton. Tel: 947187.
Service Development Manager: Ms Kathy Judge. Tel: 558711.
Crime Registrar: Mr Peter Bray. Tel: 558331.

CORPORATE COMMUNICATIONS
Head of Corporate Communications: Mr Tony Diggins BA(Hons) MCIPR. Tel: 07879 604001.
Press Officers: Mr Dick Holmes. Tel: 558026. Ms Debra Tinsley. Tel: 558026. Ms Jemma Peacock. Tel: 558026.
Press Office. Email: media@lincs.pnn.police.uk
Communications Officer (Website & Intranet): Mr Dominic Wilkinson. Tel: 558408.
Graphics & Publications: Ms Sandra Mason. Tel: 558163. Ms Julia Walford. Tel: 558655.
Television & Audio-visual: Mr David Buckley. Tel: 558215.
West Operations Communications Officer: Mr James Newall. Tel: 07768 615853.
East Operations Communications Officer: Ms Nerys McGarry. Tel: 07789 920683.
Operational Communications Support Officer & Marketing: Ms A Burge. Tel: 558026.

WEST AREA
Lincoln Police Station, West Parade, Lincoln LN1 1YP. Tel: 885300.
Chief Superintendent: Lee Freeman. Tel: 885300.
Superintendent: Paul Gibson. Tel: 885200.
PA to Chief Superintendent: Sharon Baker. Tel: 885201.
DISTRICT OFFICES
Lincoln & West Lindsey: Chief Insp Lee Pache. Lincoln Police Station, as above. Tel: 885340.
North & South Kesteven: Chief Insp Mark Housley. Grantham Police Station, Swingbridge Road, Grantham NG31 7XT. Tel: 01476 403206.

EAST AREA
Boston Police Station, Lincoln Lane, Boston PE21 8QS. Tel: 01205 312200.
A/Chief Superintendent: Paula Wood. Tel: 01205 312200.
A/Superintendent: Kieran English. Tel: 01205 312374.
DISTRICT OFFICES
Boston & South Holland: Chief Insp Paul Timmins. Boston Police Station, as above. Tel: 01205 312333.
East Lindsey: Chief Insp Daryl Pearce. Skegness Police Station, Park Avenue, Skegness PE25 1BJ. Tel: 01754 614203.

OPERATIONS SUPPORT
Head of Operations Support: Chief Supt R Hardy. Tel: 558059.
Superintendent Operations Support: S West. Tel: 558111.
Chief Inspector Operations: K English. Tel: 558110.
Chief Inspector Criminal Justice & Custody: S Brinn. Tel: 558799.
Secretary to Head of Operations Support: Ruth Fox. Tel: 558821.
OPERATIONS
Dog School, PSU & Under Water Search Unit: Insp A Ham. Tel: 521786.
Roads Policing: Insp R Gowler. Tel: 01205 312252. Insp N Key. Tel: 885338.
Lincolnshire Road Safety Partnership: Det Insp R Grace. 2nd Floor, Witham House, The Pelham Centre, Canwick Road, Lincoln LN5 8HE. Tel: 805800.
Casualty Reduction & Collision Investigation: 2nd Floor, Witham House, as above. Tel: 805815.
Firearms Co-ordinator: Mr N Duff. Tel: 558083.
Force Wildlife Crime Officer: PC N Willey. Tel: 551787.
Emergency Planning Officer: Mr I Watkins. Tel: 558137.
Central Ticket Office Manager: Mr D Picker. Tel: 558094.
Firearms Licensing & Explosives Manager: Mrs H Wilkie. Tel: 558081.
Criminal Justice Unit: Mrs K Bennett. Tel: 555250.
Collisions Unit: Mrs S Burdass. Tel: 01205 312261.
Crime Management Board: Mrs A Driver. Tel: 558288.

CRIMINAL INVESTIGATION DEPARTMENT
Det Chief Supt H Roach. Tel: 558030.
Operations: Det Supt K Hilton. Tel: 558248.
Director of Intelligence: Det Supt K Owen. Tel: 558545.
Public Protection Unit: Det Supt R Hatton. Tel: 558055.
Major Crime Unit: Det Supt S Morrison.
Head of Crime Scene Investigation Department: Miss J Mason Tel: 558061.
Intelligence Manager: Det Insp C Bennett. Tel: 885478.
Special Branch: Det Insp S Kent. Tel: 558620.
Multi-agency Public Protection Panel Manager: Ms N Hilton. Tel: 558668.
Economic Crime Unit. Tel: 47213.

INFORMATION MANAGEMENT UNIT
Information Manager: Mr R Burge. Tel: 947100.
RRD/Disclosure Manager: Mrs S Wood. Tel: 947101.
Data Protection & Freedom of Information Manager: Miss J Chapman. Tel: 947102.
CRB Disclosure Unit Supervisors: Mrs L Davies. Tel: 947106. Mr D Gale. Tel: 947107.
RRD Supervisors: Mr R Ward. Tel: 947110. Miss S Larder. Tel: 947109.
Force Vetting Officer: Mr J Day. Tel: 947111.
Data Protection: Miss N Timings. Tel: 947120.
Information Security Officer: Mrs L Hughes. Tel: 947115.
Auditors: Mr J Schopp. Tel: 947117. Ms I Watson. Tel: 947118.
Information Sharing Officer: Ms L Chapman. Tel: 947116.
ICT Security Officer: Mr P Ryan. Tel: 947117.

G4S STRATEGIC PARTNERSHIP
Service Delivery Director: Mr D Owen. Tel: 558400.
Project Manager: Ms B Rylatt. Tel: 947164
Head of Assets & Facilities Management: Mr N Rothwell. Tel: 558490.
Head of Learning & Development: Mrs D Cooper. Tel: 558195.
Director of Information & Communications Technology: Mr I McCorriston MBA BSc MIEE. Tel: 558321. Fax: 558281.
Crime Management Bureau Manager: Ms A Driver. Tel: 558288.
FCR Manager: Mr A Jolley. Tel: 947060.
Finance Director of PSS: Mr M Draisey. Tel: 558750.
Director of HR: Mr C Wilcockson. Tel: 558149.

EAST MIDLANDS POLICE COLLABORATION
Deputy Chief Constable East Midlands: Peter Goodman.
PA to DCC East Midlands: Tessa Callow. Tel: 01623 608402. Email: tessa.callow@nottinghamshire.pnn.police.uk

EAST MIDLANDS POLICE COLLABORATION PROGRAMME
Arrow Centre, Annesley Road, Hucknall, Nottingham NG15 8AY. Tel: 01623 608262. Email: eastmidlandscpt@nottinghamshire.pnn.police.uk
Programme Manager: Chief Supt Phil Whiteley.

EAST MIDLANDS SPECIAL OPERATIONS UNIT
EMSOU, PO Box 9557, Nottingham NG15 5BU. Tel: 01623 608054.
Head of EMSOU-SOC: T/Det Chief Supt Jason Caunt. Email: jason.caunt@leicestershire.pnn.police.uk
Deputy Head of EMSOU-SOC: T/Det Supt Steve Craddock. Email: steven.craddock@leicestershire.pnn.police.uk
Command Team PA: Sarah Dillon. Email: sarah.dillon@leicestershire.pnn.police.uk
Business & Finance Manager: Jon Peatling. Email: jonathan.peatling@leicestershire.pnn.police.uk
Senior Human Resources Officer: Tracy Meakin. Email: tracy.meakin@leicestershire.pnn.police.uk
Head of Operations Support: Det Chief Insp Andy Haydon. Email: andrew.haydon@leicestershire.pnn.police.uk
Head of RART: Det Chief Insp Mick Beattie. Email: michael.beattie@leicestershire.pnn.police.uk
Head of Regional Review Unit: Kevin Flint. Email: kevin.flint@leicestershire.pnn.police.uk

EMSOU – SERIOUS & ORGANISED CRIME
EMSOU-SOC North Command: Det Chief Insp Andy Dickin. Email: andy.dickin@leicestershire.pnn.police.uk
EMSOU-SOC East Command: T/Det Chief Insp Alan Mason. Email: alan.mason@leicestershire.pnn.police.uk
EMSOU-SOC South Command: T/Det Chief Insp Joe Elliott. Email: joseph.elliott@leicestershire.pnn.police.uk

EMSOU – MAJOR CRIME
Head of Major Crime Unit: Det Chief Supt Andrew Hough. Email: andrew.hough@leicestershire.pnn.police.uk
EMSOU-MC North Command: Vacant.
EMSOU-MC East Command: Det Supt Stuart Morrison. Email: stuart.morrison@lincs.pnn.police.uk
EMSOU-MC South Command: Vacant.

EMSOU – FORENSIC SERVICES
Regional Director of Forensic Services: Joanne Ashworth. Email: joanne.ashworth.16204@derbyshire.pnn.police.uk

EMSOU – SPECIAL BRANCH
EMSOU, PO Box 9557, Nottingham NG15 5BU. Tel: 01623 608304.
Det Supt Stephen Lowe. Email: stephen.lowe.314568@derbyshire.pnn.police.uk
PA to Senior Management Team: Sue Hogg. Email: susan.hogg.16244@derbyshire.pnn.police.uk

STAFF ASSOCIATIONS
Superintendents' Association: *Chairman:* Chief Supt R Hardy. Tel: 558059.
Superintendents' Association: *Secretary:* Supt P Wood. Tel: 558645.
Police Federation: *JBB Chairman:* PC S Hamilton. Tel: 558238. *JBB Secretary:* Insp J Kwee. Tel: 558357. Fax: 530382.
UNISON: *Chairman:* Mr J Gooding. Tel: 558375. *Secretary:* Mrs D Parker. Tel: 558375.

HM CORONERS AND OTHER OFFICIALS
South Lincolnshire: Professor A R W Forrest. Unit 1 Gilbert Drive, Endeavour Park, Boston PE21 7TQ. Tel: 01522 552064. Fax: 01522 516717. Email: robert.forrest@lincolnshire.gov.uk
North Lincolnshire & Grimsby: Mr Paul Kelly. Coroner's Office, The Town Hall, Knoll Street, Cleethorpes DN35 8LN. Tel: 01472 324005. Fax: 01472 324007.
Central Lincolnshire: Mr S P G Fisher. Coroner's Office, Lindum House, 10 Queen Street, Spilsby, Lincolnshire PE23 5JE. Tel: 01522 552500. Fax: 01522 516055. Email: lincscoroner@lincolnshire.gov.uk

Inspectors, Animal Health Act 1981
Mr I Newall. County Offices, Newland, Lincoln. Tel: 01522 552490.

RSPCA
Trinity Centre, Spilsby Road, Horncastle, Lincolnshire. Tel: 0990 555999 or 01733 555480.

NSPCC, Lincolnshire Children and Family Service
111 Nettleham Road, Lincoln. Tel: 01522 545225 (24 hrs).

Trading Standards
County Trading Standards Officer: P J Heafield. *Assistant County Trading Standards Officers:* G Seymour; A Bukavs. *Manager, Advice & Information:* M Keal. Tel: 01522 554949. Out of hours tel: 01522 552406.

MERSEYSIDE POLICE

PO Box 59, Liverpool L69 1JD.
Tel: 0151 777 8878. Fax: 0151 777 8999 (24 hrs).
Email: firstname.lastname@merseyside.pnn.police.uk
Website: www.merseyside.police.uk
Metropolitan County of Merseyside comprising the districts of Knowsley, Liverpool, St Helens, Sefton and Wirral.

Lord Lieutenant: Dame Lorna Muirhead.
Police & Crime Commissioner: Jane Kennedy.

Police Headquarters: Canning Place, Liverpool L69 1JD.
Chief Constable: J Murphy QPM LLB(Hons).
Chief Constable's Staff Officer: Chief Insp C Green.
PA: Mrs H Fothergill.
Deputy Chief Constable: B Lawson BSc DipAppCrim (seconded to Cumbria Constabulary).
T/Deputy Chief Constable: A Ward.
PA: Ms J Cassidy.
Assistant Chief Constable (Area Operations): A Cooke BA(Hons).
PA: Mrs L Baines.
T/Assistant Chief Constable (Personnel): C Armitt MBA Dip App Crim.
PA: Mrs M Kelly.
T/Assistant Chief Constable (Organisational Support & Development): I Pilling MSc.
PA: Ms L Massam.
Assistant Chief Constable (Protective Services): A Ward.
PA: Ms H Tanzey.
Director of Resources: G Broadhead CPFA.
PA: Mrs M Kelly.

STRATEGIC DEVELOPMENT DEPARTMENT

Head: Chief Supt S Richards.
Secretary: Ms J Lee.
Head of Audit & Inspection: Supt C Richards; T/Supt J Armstrong.
Head of Business Consultancy: Mrs K Seaman.
Force Risk Manager & Head of Corporate Governance: Mrs S Jones.
Head of Corporate Analysis: Ms H Selby.
Strategic Planning Manager: Mr E Williams.
Corporate Communications: Ms J Pugh.
Head of Information: Mr J Hampson MA.
Corporate Criminal Justice: *Head:* Chief Supt C Krueger.
Legal Services: Miss C Ashcroft.
Professional Standards Department: *Head:* Chief Supt J Young.
Professional Standards Unit: *Head:* T/Det Supt A James.
Anti-corruption Unit: *Head:* T/Det Chief Insp J McKeon.
Head of Finance: Ms H Stafford ACA.
Head of Facilities Management: Ms M Donnellan.
Head of Vehicle Fleet: Mr S Fletcher. Smithdown Lane, Liverpool L7 3PR.
Special Constabulary: *Chief Officer:* Mr D Burgess-Joyce.

PERSONNEL

T/Head of HR Operation: Mrs J McCreanney.
Head of HR Services: Mrs S Barker.
Health & Safety: Mr R Aspey.
Head of Academy: T/Supt C Howarth.
Training Centre. 222 Mather Avenue, Liverpool L18 9TG.
Occupational Health Manager: Ms C Foster.

CONTACT CENTRE

Head of Force Contact Centre: Mrs S Dooley.
Contact Centre Manager: Mr T Jackson.

FORCE OPERATIONS

Operational Support Unit: Smithdown Lane, Liverpool L7 3PR.
Force Operations Manager: T/Chief Supt P Costello.
Firearms: Supt P White.

Mounted: Insp M Farrows.
Operational Planning: Chief Insp M Woosey.
Serious Crime Review Unit: Mr P Currie QPM.
Force Crime Operations Unit: Det Chief Supt S Naylor.
Force Intelligence Bureau (FIB): Det Chief Supt A Barr.
Scientific Support Manager: Mr D Smith.

NORTH WEST MOTORWAY POLICE GROUP (NWMPG)
North West Regional Control Room, Rob Lane, Newton-le-Willows WA12 0DR.
Tel: 0151 777 6900.
(Covering Cheshire, Lancashire & Merseyside police areas.)
Contact: Insp Dave Corcoran. Tel: 0151 777 3701.

JOINT UNDERWATER SEARCH UNIT
(Covering Manchester, Merseyside, North Wales, Cumbria, Lancashire & Cheshire police areas.)
Tel: 01606 363993.

STAFF ASSOCIATIONS
Superintendents' Association: *Secretary:* Chief Supt C Krueger. Tel: 0151 777 1951.
Police Federation: *JBB Secretary:* I Leyland. Tel: 0151 259 2535.
UNISON Police Branch: *Secretary:* Mr W Burton. Tel: 0151 777 8147.
GMB/MPO: *Secretary:* Mr P Dow. Tel: 0151 777 4483.

WIRRAL AREA
Area Commander: Chief Supt J Martin.
Operations: Supt J Roy.
Area: *Wallasey Police Station, Manor Road, Wallasey CH44 1DA. Fax: 0151 777 2099.
OTHER POLICE STATIONS
*†Queens Road, Hoylake, Wirral CH47 2AG.
†Chadwick Street, Moreton CH46 7TE.
Mortimer Street, Birkenhead CH41 5EU.
*Village Road, Bromborough CH62 7ER.
†Laird Street, Birkenhead CH41 7AJ.
†Well Lane, Rock Ferry, Birkenhead CH42 4OG.
†Arrowe Park Road, Upton CH49 0UE.
†Telegraph Road, Heswall CH60 0AH.

SEFTON AREA
Area Commander: Chief Supt N Holland.
Operations: Supt K Johnson.
Area: *Alexandra Road, Waterloo, Liverpool L22 1RX. Fax: 0151 777 2399.
OTHER POLICE STATIONS
*Albert Road Police Station, Southport PR9 0LL.
Marsh Lane, Bootle L20 5BW.
†Copy Lane, Netherton L30 7PR.
†Westway, Maghull L31 0AA.
†Segars Lane, Ainsdale PR8 3HT.
†Church Road, Formby L37 3NA.

KNOWSLEY AREA
Area Commander: T/Chief Supt M Cloherty.
Operations: Supt M Harrison.
Area: *Huyton Police Station, Lathom Road, Huyton, Liverpool L36 9XU. Fax: 0151 777 6299.
OTHER POLICE STATIONS
*St Chad's Drive, Kirkby, Liverpool L32 8RF.
Derby Street, Prescot L34 3LG.
* Leathers Lane, Halewood L26 1XG.

ST HELENS AREA
Area Commander: Chief Supt R Carden.
Operations: Supt D Fox.
Area: *St Helens Police Station, College Street, St Helens WA10 1TD. Fax: 0151 777 6099.
OTHER POLICE STATIONS
*†Market Street, Newton-le-Willows WA12 9BW.
†Main Street, Billinge WN5 7PA.
†Burrows Lane, Eccleston WA10 5AE.
†Church Road, Rainford WA11 8QJ.
†Thatto Heath Road, Thatto Heath WA9 5PG.

†Robins Lane, Sutton WA9 3NU.

LIVERPOOL NORTH AREA

Area Commander: Chief Supt J Ward.
Operations: Supt S Irving; T/Supt M Wiggins.
Operations Support: Det Supt R Davies.
Area: *St Anne Street Police Station, Liverpool L3 3HJ. Fax: 0151 777 4099.
OTHER POLICE STATIONS
Stanley Road, Liverpool L5 7QQ.
Walton Lane, Liverpool L4 5XF.
Lower Lane Police Station, Liverpool L9 6DS.
Eaton Road, Liverpool L12 3HF.
West Derby Road, Tuebrook, Liverpool L6 4BR.

LIVERPOOL SOUTH AREA

Area Commander: Chief Supt N Waine.
Operations: Supt G Hilton.
Area: *Rose Lane, Allerton, Liverpool L18 6JE.
OTHER POLICE STATIONS
*Belle Vale, Childwall Valley Road, Liverpool L15 2PL.
Admiral Street, Liverpool L8 8JN.
*Wavertree Road, Liverpool L7 1RJ.
†Police Shop, Granby Street, Liverpool L8 2US.
Ganworth Road, Speke, Liverpool L24 2XQ.
Heald Street, Garston, Liverpool L19 2LY.

The police stations marked* are designated under s35, P.A.C.E. Act 1984.
All police stations are open 24 hours except those marked †.

HM CORONERS

Sefton, Knowsley & St Helens: Christopher Kent Sumner. Southport Town Hall, Lord Street, Southport PR8 1DA. Tel: 0151 934 2746/9. Fax: 01704 534321.
Email: ambra.warmbold@legal.sefton.gov.uk
Liverpool: Mr A J A Rebello OBE. HM Coroner's Court, St George's Hall, St George's Place, Liverpool L1 1JJ. Tel: 0151 225 5770. Fax: 0151 703 6838.
Wirral: Mr C W Johnson. Midland Bank Building, Grange Road, West Kirkby, Wirral CH48 4EB. Tel: 0151 625 6538. Fax: 0151 625 7757. Email: westkirbycoroner@btconnect.com

NORFOLK CONSTABULARY
Operations and Communications Centre, Jubilee House, Falconers Chase,
Wymondham, Norfolk NR18 0WW.
Tel: 101. Fax: 0845 345 4567.
Email: lastnameinitial@norfolk.pnn.police.uk
Website: www.norfolk.police.uk

HM Lord-Lieutenant: Mr R Jewson JP.
Police & Crime Commissioner: Mr S Bett.
Deputy Police & Crime Commissioner: Ms J McKibben.
Head of Staff (Chief Executive): Mr C Harding MBE LLB.
Chief Finance Officer: Mr R Summers IPFA FCCA.

Chief Constable: Mr P Gormley QPM BA DipAppCrim.
Deputy Chief Constable: Mr S Bailey.
Assistant Chief Constable (Local Policing): Mr G Wilson.
Assistant Chief Constable (Norfolk & Suffolk Joint Protective Services): Mr C Hall.
T/Assistant Chief Constable (Strategic Change & Collaboration): Ms S Hamlin.
Assistant Chief Officer (Resources): Mr R Birtles MA MCIPD FCMI FInstAM.
Staff Officers: Supt J Doyle; Insp H Olby; Sgt D Woodage; Ms M Harlow.

COUNTY POLICING COMMAND
Commander: T/Chief Supt N Dean.
District 1 King's Lynn & West Norfolk: Supt D Marshall. Police Station, St James' Road, Kings Lynn PE30 5DE.
District 2 Breckland: Chief Insp P Durham. Police Station, Norwich Road, Thetford IP24 2HU.
District 3 North Norfolk & Broadland: T/Supt C Edwards. Police Station, Yarmouth Road, North Walsham NR28 9AW.
District 4 Norwich: Supt P Sanford. Bethel Street, Norwich NR2 1NN.
District 5 South Norfolk: Chief Insp T Little. OCC, Falconers Chase, Wymondham, Norfolk NR18 0WW.
District 6 Great Yarmouth: Supt N Davison. Howard Street North, Great Yarmouth NR30 1PH.
Head of Contact & Control Room & Response: Supt M Fawcett.
Head of Community Safety: Supt S Gunn.
Royalty & VIP Protection Norfolk & Suffolk: T/Supt K Clarke.

CORPORATE COMMUNICATIONS NORFOLK & SUFFOLK
Interim Head of Corporate Communications Norfolk & Suffolk Constabularies: Supt M Cooke.

PROFESSIONAL STANDARDS NORFOLK & SUFFOLK
Norfolk & Suffolk Head of Professional Standards: Supt L Pepper.

PERFORMANCE AND ANALYSIS
Head of Performance & Analysis (Norfolk & Suffolk): Mrs G Stannard.

STRATEGIC CHANGE AND COLLABORATION
Strategic Change & Collaboration (Norfolk & Suffolk): T/Assistant Chief Constable S Hamlin.

HUMAN RESOURCES DEPARTMENT
Management team for HR – Norfolk & Suffolk
Director of HR (Norfolk & Suffolk): Mrs R Wilkinson MCIPD.
Head of HR Operations (Norfolk & Suffolk): T/Chief Insp L Hooper.
Head of HR Service Delivery (Norfolk & Suffolk): Mrs M Graveling LLM FCIPD.

LEGAL SERVICES
Head of Legal Services: Mrs A Ings LLB(Hons) Solicitor.

FINANCIAL SERVICES
Head of Joint Finance (Norfolk & Suffolk): Mr P Jasper ACMA.
Head of Accounting Services: Mrs L J Savory CPFA DMS.
Head of Payroll & Exchequer: Mr M Clenshaw.
Head of Systems Development: Mrs E J Brighton.

PROCUREMENT AND SUPPLIES NORFOLK & SUFFOLK
Head of Procurement & Supplies (Norfolk & Suffolk): Mr L Matthews.

ESTATES AND FACILITIES NORFOLK & SUFFOLK
Head of Estates & Facilities (Norfolk & Suffolk): Mr T Byam MIIM MBIFM.
Estates Manager (Norfolk & Suffolk): Mr D Potter BSc(Hons) MBA MRICS.

Facilities Manager (Norfolk & Suffolk): Mr N Critchley MBIFM.
PFI Contracts Manager (Norfolk & Suffolk): Mr J Henry MBIFM.

TRANSPORT SERVICES NORFOLK & SUFFOLK
Head of Transport Services (Norfolk & Suffolk): Mr M Davy MIMI.

INFORMATION SYSTEMS AND COMMUNICATIONS
Director of ICT (Norfolk & Suffolk): Mr J Close.
Technical Resource Coordinator & Planning Manager: Mr M Girling.

POLICE FEDERATION OFFICE
JBB General Secretary: Chief Insp D Benfield. Tel: 01953 606911.

SPECIAL CONSTABULARY
Manager: Sue Goode. Tel: 01953 425699 ext 2373.
Special Chief Officer: Mr M Pearson MBE.

PROTECTIVE SERVICES COMMAND NORFOLK & SUFFOLK
Head of Protective Services Command (Crime) Norfolk & Suffolk: Det Chief Supt D Skevington. Tel: 01953 424853.
Head of Protective Services Command (Operations) Norfolk & Suffolk: Chief Supt R Scully. Tel: 01953 424746.
Management Accountant Protective Services (Crime) Norfolk & Suffolk: Mr M Spratt. Tel: 01953 422858.
Management Accountant Protective Services (Operations) Norfolk & Suffolk: Ms J Hockley. Tel: 01473 613836.

CRIME
Head of Forensic Services Norfolk & Suffolk: Mr A Gilbert. Tel: 01953 424245.
Forensic Operations Managers Norfolk & Suffolk: (Wymondham): Mr M House. Tel: 01953 424244.
Forensic Operations Manager Norfolk & Suffolk (Halesworth): Mr P Stafford. Tel: 01986 835051.
Forensic Support Manager Norfolk & Suffolk: Mr J Revitt-Smith. Tel: 01953 424246.
Head of Intelligence Level 1 Norfolk & Suffolk (Local & Central Intelligence): T/Det Supt P Hornby. Tel: 01953 424013.
Detective Chief Inspector Level 1 Intelligence Norfolk & Suffolk: A Quantrell. Tel: 01473 782631.
Head of Intelligence Level 2 Norfolk & Suffolk (Special Branch, CONFI Unit, CHIS): A/Det Supt David Cutler. Tel: 01473 613802.
Detective Chief Inspector Level 2 Intelligence Norfolk & Suffolk: M Afford. Tel: 01953 424306.
Head of Major Investigation Team Norfolk & Suffolk: Det Supt J Brocklebank. Tel: 01473 613707.
Detective Chief Inspector Major Investigation Team Norfolk & Suffolk: N Luckett. Tel: 01473 782025.
T/ Detective Chief Inspectors Major Investigation Team Norfolk & Suffolk: A Guy. Tel: 01953 424544. A Smith. Tel: 01473 782044.
Head of Serious & Organised Crime Norfolk & Suffolk: Det Supt A McCullough. Tel: 01953 423682.
Operations Manager Serious & Organised Crime Norfolk & Suffolk: Det Chief Insp S Mattin. Tel: 01473 613833.
High Tech Crime Unit Norfolk & Economic Crime Unit Suffolk: Det Insp S Coyne. Tel: 01953 423892.
Serious & Organised Crime Unit Norfolk & Suffolk: Det Insp K Thacker. Tel: 01953 424120.
Technical Support Unit Norfolk & Suffolk: Mr A Osborne. Tel: 01473 613856.
Head of Vulnerable People Directorate Norfolk: Det Supt K Elliott. Tel: 01603 276306.
Detective Chief Inspector Vulnerable People Directorate Norfolk: J Wvendth. Tel: 01603 276001.
Head of Public Protection Directorate Suffolk: Det Supt A Caton OBE. Tel: 01473 613701.
Detective Chief Inspector Public Protection Directorate Suffolk: S McCallum. Tel: 01473 613899.

SPECIALIST OPERATIONS
Roads Policing & Firearms Operations: Chief Insp C Spinks. Tel: 01953 424872.
Operations Support: Chief Insp A Dawson. Tel: 01473 613702.
Operations Planning: Mr C Eldridge. Tel: 01953 424894.
Firearms Licensing Services: Mr R Kennett. Tel: 01473 613608.

JUSTICE COMMAND NORFOLK & SUFFOLK
Norfolk & Suffolk Justice Commander: Chief Supt L Parrett.
Norfolk & Suffolk Head of Criminal Justice Services: Mr K Wilkins.
Norfolk & Suffolk Head of Custody Services: Chief Insp R Wiltshire.
Norfolk & Suffolk Head of Custody Investigations Unit: Det Chief Insp K Cutler.
Norfolk Operational Business Manager: Mr R Wilkins.
Suffolk Operational Business Manager: Ms J Evans.
Norwich: CJS, Carmelite House, St James' Court, Whitefriars, Norwich NR3 1SS. Tel: 01603 276952. Fax: 01603 276957.
King's Lynn: CJS, St James' Road, King's Lynn, Norfolk PE30 5DE. Tel: 01553 665052. Fax: 01553 665148.

NSPIS Team: *Business Systems Administrator.* Carmelite House, as above. Tel: 01603 276281/276279. Fax: 01603 276841.

Streamline Processing Unit (based in Norwich): *Team Leader:* A Ellis.

Central Ticket Office & Safety Camera Team (based in Norwich): c/o PO Box 3293, Norwich NR7 7ET. *CTO & Safety Camera Team Manager:* P Anderson. Tel: 01603 276929. *Team Leader:* A Wells. Tel: 01603 276402. Fax: 01603 276841.

Case Assessment Support: *Team Leader:* M Palmer. Tel: 01603 276875/276893. Fax: 01603 276906.

Case Assessment Team: *Team Leader:* B Mason. Tel: 01603 276275/276893. Fax: 01603 276859.

Victim & Witness Services (based in Norwich): *Team Leader:* S Beaumont. Tel: 01603 276889. Fax: 01603 276261.

Traffic Justice Unit (based in Lowestoft): *Team Leader:* M Eaton. Tel: 01986 835162.

HM CORONER AND OTHER OFFICIALS

Norfolk Coroner's Service: Mr William J Armstrong, 69–75 Thorpe Road, Norwich NR1 1UA. Tel: 01603 663302. Fax: 01603 665511. Email: norwich@coroner.norfolk.gov.uk.

Force Medical Advisor
Occupational Health, OCC. Tel: 01953 423871.

Trading Standards
County Trading Standards Officer: Mr D Collinson, Assistant Director of Public Protection, County Hall, Martineau Lane, Norwich NR1 2UD. Tel: 0344 800 8013. Fax: 01603 222999. Email: tradingstandards@norfolk.gov.uk

NORTH WALES POLICE
Glan-y-Don, Colwyn Bay LL29 8AW.
Tel: 101 or 0300 330 0101.
Fax: 01745 535777 (24 hrs).
Email: northwalespolice@north-wales.police.uk (24 hrs).
The dialling code for all numbers is 01492, unless otherwise indicated.
DX: 20777 Old Colwyn. X400: c = GB; a = CWMAIL; p = PNN60;
o = NORTH WALES POLICE; s = POSTMASTER
Website: www.north-wales.police.uk
(Counties of Anglesey, Conwy, Denbighshire, Flintshire, Gwynedd and Wrexham)

Police & Crime Commissioner: Winston Roddick.

Chief Constable: Mr M Polin MBA QPM. Tel: 804080.
Deputy Chief Constable: Mr I Shannon BA(Hons) MA. Tel: 804081.
Assistant Chief Constable: Mr H G Pritchard MA. Tel: 804082.
Director of Finance & Resources: Mr M Parkin BA(Hons) ACMA. Tel: 804083.
Chief Constable's Staff Officer: Rebecca Jones Tel: 805318.
Deputy Chief Constable's Staff Officer: Sgt Colm McNelis. Tel: 805351.
PA to Chief Constable: Stephanie Arton. Tel: 804080.
PA to Deputy Chief Constable: Rachel Chan. Tel: 804081.
PA to Assistant Chief Constable: Katy Hopkins. Tel: 804082.
PA to Director of Finance & Resources: Gemma Jennings. Tel: 804083.
LEGAL SERVICES
Force Solicitors: Ann Warman. Tel: 804027. Diane Kaiser. Tel: 805020.
Assistant Solicitors: Karen Kinsey; Gill Jones.
CORPORATE SERVICES
Head of Corporate Services: Chief Supt Frazer Jones. Tel: 01978 348617.
PA Support: Sian Wyn Jones. Tel: 805440.
HR Business Partner: Diane Pierce. Tel: 805389.
Finance Business Partner: Stephen Hughes. Tel: 805283.
CORPORATE SERVICES – CHANGE
Head of Change: Ian Davies. Tel: 804030.
Head of In-life Services RMS: Victoria Lewin. Tel: 804016.
Head of Information Standards & Compliance: Judith Roberts. Tel: 804050.
Head of Freedom of Information: Sharon Dean. Tel: 805433.
CORPORATE SERVICES – PLANNING & GOVERNANCE
Head of Planning & Governance: Supt Sacha Hatchett. Tel: 01286 670877.
Risk Management: Sharon Pritchard. Tel: 804751.
Inspections & Improvement: Insp Catherine Pritchard. Tel: 01978 348992.
Force Crime Registrar: Insp Steve Pickering. Tel: 01407 724260.
CORPORATE SERVICES – TRUST & CONFIDENCE
Head of Diversity: Greg George. Tel: 01745 588483.
Head of Welsh Language: Meic Raymant. Tel: 01286 670810.
CORPORATE SERVICES – CORPORATE COMMUNICATIONS
Head of Corporate Communications: Sue Appleton. Tel: 805079.
Press Office: Kevin Evans. Tel: 805292. Claire Jones Rowe. Tel: 804159. Sian Brennan. Tel: 804158. Michael McGivern. Tel: 805362.
Press Office Helpdesk: Tel: 804666.
Marketing Officer: Delyth Thomas Jones. Tel: 804157.
Web Office: Shaun Barritt. Tel: 804939.
CORPORATE SERVICES – CORPORATE PROGRAMME OFFICE
Head of Programme Office: Supt Wayne Jones. Tel: 01745 588448.
ADMINISTRATION OF JUSTICE DEPARTMENT
Head of Administration of Justice Department: Julie Foster.
Operations Manager: Mr Simon Noton LLB(Hons) MA ChtdFCIPD. Tel: 804168.
Camera Safety Process: Mrs J Harrup. Tel: 01745 539408.
Collisions & Ticket Process (AJD Transactional Unit): Mrs Gemma Roberts. Tel: 01745 539399.

Disclosures & Vetting Manager: Miss T Davies. Tel: 01745 539374.
Firearms Registry: Mr A Davies. Tel: 01745 539360.

BUSINESS SERVICES
Director of Business Services: Mr G N Bradley BEng(Hons) MIET. Tel: 804900.
PA to Director of Business Services: Jennifer Lewis. Tel: 805133.

HR AND TRAINING
Head of HR & Training: Supt Rob Kirman. Tel: 01745 588600.

FACILITIES AND LOGISTICS
Head of Facilities & Logistics: Mr R S Roberts BSc ICIOB. PFI Building, St Asaph. Tel: 01745 588430.

ICT AND PROCUREMENT
Head of ICT & Procurement: Mr Keith Williams. Alexandra House. Tel: 804149.

MANAGEMENT INFORMATION
Head of Management Information: Mr J A Sutton BSc(Hons). Alexandra House. Tel: 804170.

PROGRAMME AND CUSTOMER SERVICES
Head of Programme & Customer Services: Ms H Wynne-Williams BSc(Hons) MSc. Alexandra House. Tel: 804698.

FLEET
Transport Manager: Mr T Duffy BSc AMICFM AMCIPS. Tel: 804084.

FINANCE
Head of Finance: Mr G L Edwards BA CPFA. Alexandra House. Tel: 804831.
Head of Shared Service Facility: Mr J Clegg BA(Hons). Tel: 01745 588685.

LOCAL POLICING SERVICES
LPS Headquarters: Ffordd William Morgan, St Asaph Business Park, St Asaph, Denbighshire LL17 0HQ.
LPS Commander: Chief Supt S Shaw. Tel: 804269.
Western Local Policing Services: Supt Pete Newton. Tel: 01286 670877.
Central Local Policing Services: Supt Andrew Jenks Gilbert. Tel: 01286 670688.
Eastern Local Policing Services: Supt Jeremy Vaughan. Tel: 01745 588448.
County Management Team
Ynys Mon: Chief Insp N Harrison. Tel: 01407 724440.
Gwynedd: Chief Insp P Gaffey. Tel: 01286 670802.
Conwy: Chief Insp J Banham. Tel: 804301.
Denbighshire: Chief Insp I R Jones. Tel: 01745 539638.
Flintshire: Chief Insp D Wareing. Tel: 01352 708301.
Wrexham: Chief Insp M Pierce. Tel: 804814.

Response Hubs	Corwen	Mold	St Asaph
Caernarfon	Dolgellau	Porthmadog	Wrexham
Colwyn Bay	Llangefni		

OPERATIONAL SUPPORT SERVICES
Force Communications Centre: Crud y Dderwen, Ffordd William Morgan, St Asaph Business Park, St Asaph, Denbighshire LL17 OJG.
Area Commander: Chief Supt S Humphreys. Tel: 01978 348594.
Call Handling Manager: Mr P Shea. Tel: 01745 539648.

CRIME SERVICES
St Asaph SSU Building, unless otherwise indicated.
Head of Crime Services: Chief Supt Neill Anderson.
Major Crime Team: Det Supt John Chapman. T/Det Chief Insp Gerwyn Lloyd.
Intelligence: Det Supt John Hanson.
Public Protection Unit: T/Det Chief Insp Mark Chesters.
Special Branch/WECTU: Det Chief Insp Paul Cuddihy. Force HQ, Colwyn Bay.
T/Scientific Support Manager: Lisa Morgan.
Finance Business Partner: Karen Norman. Alexandra House, Colwyn Bay.
HR Business Partner: Annalee Morris. Alexandra House, Colwyn Bay.
PA to Chief Superintendent: Kendal Goode.

STAFF ASSOCIATIONS
Police Superintendents' Association: *Chair:* Chief Supt Simon Humphreys. Tel: 805130.
Police Federation: *Chair:* Mr R Llewellyn-Jones. Tel: 805041. *Secretary:* Mr R W Eccles. Tel: 805403. *Assistant Secretary:* Mr D M Jones. Tel: 805404. *PAs:* Mrs N Williams; Mrs S Bray. Tel: 805400. Fax: 510773. *Policy, Consultation & Marketing Manager:* Mr C Warner. Tel: 805402.
UNISON: *Chair:* Mr Gary Leighton-Jones. Force Headquarters, Colwyn Bay. Tel: 804166. *Secretary:* Eileen Price. HQ, Colwyn Bay.

HM CORONERS AND OTHER OFFICIALS

North Wales (East and Central): John Gittins. Marbel House, Overton Arcade, High Street, Wrexham LL13 8LL. Tel: 01978 357775. Fax: 01978 358000.

North West Wales: Mr D Pritchard Jones. 37 Castle Square, Caernarfon, Gwynedd LL55 2NN. Tel: 01286 672804. Fax: 01286 675217.

NSPCC

NSPCC Cymru/Wales, North East Wales Centre, Unit A, Yale Business Village, Ellice Way, Wrexham LL13 7YL. Tel: 01978 362383.

RSPCA

Control Room, Llandudno. Tel: 01492 860260.

NORTH YORKSHIRE POLICE

Newby Wiske Hall, Northallerton, North Yorkshire DL7 9HA.
Tel: 101. The dialling code for all numbers is 01609, unless otherwise indicated.
Customers with hearing or speech impairments can contact North Yorkshire Police via the RNID Typetalk service by calling 18001 0845 606 0247.
Email: firstname.lastname@northyorkshire.pnn.police.uk
Website: www.northyorkshire.police.uk

Police & Crime Commissioner: Julia Mulligan.
Office of Police & Crime Commissioner. Tel: 01765 641063.

CHIEF OFFICE TEAM AND SECRETARIAT
T/Chief Constable: Tim Madgwick.
T/Deputy Chief Constable: Sue Cross.
Assistant Chief Constable: Iain Spittal.
Chief Officer Resource: Joanna Carter.
Chief of Staff: Chief Supt Ken Mckintosh.
Staff Officer to Chief Constable. Tel: 789027. Fax: 789025.
Staff Officer to Deputy Chief Constable. Tel: 789700.
PA to T/Chief Constable. Tel: 789000.
PA to T/Deputy Chief Constable. Tel: 789015.
PA to Assistant Chief Constable. Tel: 789953.
PA to Chief Officer Resource. Tel: 789030.

CRIME
Director of Crime: Det Chief Supt Karnail Dulk. Tel: 789015. Fax: 789169.
Head of Intelligence & Organised Crime: Det Supt Amanda Oliver. Tel: 789063. Fax: 789169.
Head of Investigations & Volume Crime Management: Det Supt Steve Smith. Tel: 789162.
Head of Major Crime & Specialist Investigations: Det Supt Simon Mason. Tel: 789682. Fax: 01904 669381.

SPECIALIST OPERATIONS
Director of Specialist Operations: Chief Supt Alison Higgins. Tel: 789030. Fax: 789169.
Head of Administration of Justice: Ms Leanne McConnell. Tel: 01904 731878.
Head of Specialist Operations: Supt Dave Foster. Tel: 768374.

RESPONSE AND REASSURANCE DIRECTORATE
Head of Force Control Room: Supt Richard Anderson. Tel: 789090. Fax: 768019.

HAMBLETON & RICHMONDSHIRE
Safer Neighbourhood Commander: Supt Andrew McMillan. Tel: 0845 6060 247.
Police Stations: †Northallerton; Bedale; Catterick Garrison; Easingwold; Leyburn; Richmond; Stokesley; Thirsk.

SCARBOROUGH & RYEDALE
Safer Neighbourhood Commander: Supt Glynn Payne. Tel: 0845 6060 247.
Police Stations: *†Scarborough; Filey; Helmsley; Malton; Pickering; Whitby.

YORK
Safer Neighbourhood Commander: Supt Lisa Winward. Tel: 01904 669301.
Police Station: *†York.

HARROGATE
Safer Neighbourhood Commander: Supt Aubrey Smith. Tel: 0845 6060 247.
Police Stations: *†Harrogate; Knaresborough; Ripon.

SELBY
Safer Neighbourhood Commander: Chief Insp Mark Iveson. Tel: 0845 6060 247.
Police Stations: Selby; Sherburn-in-Elmet; Strensall; Tadcaster; Whitley Bridge.

CRAVEN
Safer Neighbourhood Commander: Chief Insp Simon Lovell. Tel: 0845 6060 247.
Police Stations: † Skipton; Crosshills; Grassington; Ingleton; Settle.

† Denotes station designated under P.A.C.E. Act 1984. *Denotes station manned 24 hours.

HUMAN RESOURCES
Director: Karen Taylor. Tel: 789925.
Head of HR Operations: Rosie Holmes. Tel: 789267.
Head of Training: Richard Staines. Tel: 789934.
Health, Safety & Welfare Dept. Tel: 01423 539471 (health & welfare); 789009 (health & safety).

STAFF ASSOCIATIONS

Superintendents' Association: *Secretary:* Supt Glynn Payne. Tel: 789090. Fax: 768019.
Police Federation: *Secretary:* Mark Botham. Police Station, Castlegate, Knaresborough. Tel: 01423 866342. Fax: 01423 539567 (24 hrs).
UNISON: *Branch Secretary:* John Mackfall. Police Station, Fulford Road, York YO10 4BY. Tel: 01904 669368.

HEADQUARTERS FINANCE

Director of Financial Services: Gary MacDonald. Tel: 789990.

SUPPORT SERVICES

Director: Julie McMurray. Tel: 789119.
Head of Property & Facilities: Jonathan Garrett. Tel: 789699.
Head of Transport: Richard Flint. Tel: 01904 618843.

PROFESSIONAL STANDARDS

Director of Professional Standards: Mr Steven Read. Tel: 789125.
Investigation Manager: Ian Lemon. Tel: 789359.
Service Review Manager: Mrs Lesley Whitehouse. Tel: 789381.

LEGAL AND COMPLIANCE SERVICES

Director: Mr Simon Dennis.
Head of Risk Management: Mr Donald Stone. Tel: 789907.
Solicitors: Mr Len Miller. Tel: 768357. Ms J Wintermeyer. Tel: 789210.

FUTURES DIRECTORATE

Director: Liz Byrne. Tel: 769910.

INFORMATION SYSTEMS

Client Services Manager: Catherine Wilson. Tel: 789281.

COMMUNICATIONS AND MARKETING

Director: Chief Supt Ken McIntosh. Tel: 789122.
Media & Public Relations Manager: Mr G Tindall. Tel: 789711.
Internal Communications Planning Manager: Ms Niki Burgham. Tel: 789886.
New Media Officer: Tom Stirling. Tel: 789256.

HM CORONERS AND OTHER OFFICIALS

Eastern District: Mr M D Oakley. Forsyth House, Market Place, Malton YO17 7LR. Tel: 01653 600070. Fax: 01653 600049.
Western: R Turnbull. 21 Grammar School Lane, Northallerton DL6 1DF. Tel: 01609 533805. Fax: 01609 780793.
York: Mr W D F Coverdale. Sentinel House, Peasholme Green, York YO1 7PP. Tel: 01904 716000. Fax: 01904 716100.
NSPCC
65 Osbaldwick Lane, York YO10 3AY. Tel: 01904 430455. Tel: 0844 892 0226.

NORTHAMPTONSHIRE POLICE

Wootton Hall, Northampton NN4 0JQ.
Tel: 101. All numbers can be obtained by dialling 03000 111222, plus extension number shown, unless otherwise stated. Fax: 01604 703028.
Email: firstname.lastname@northants.pnn.police.uk
Website: www.northants.police.uk

Police & Crime Commissioner: Adam Simmonds.

CHIEF OFFICER GROUP
Chief Constable: Adrian Lee. Ext: 2005. Fax: 01604 888589.
Deputy Chief Constable: Vacant. Ext: 2007.
Assistant Chief Constable (Territorial Policing): Andy Frost. Ext: 2006.
Assistant Chief Constable (Crime & Justice): Martin Jelley. Ext: 8410.
Staff Officer to Assistant Chief Officer (Resources): Mr John Chatley. Ext: 2047.
Chief Constable's Staff Officer: Vacant. Ext: 2010.
Fax: 01604 888594.

CORPORATE COMMUNICATIONS
Head of Corporate Communications: Mr Tim Prince. Ext: 2183.
Strategic Marketing Manager: Mrs Kirsty Neeson. Ext: 2161.
Senior Media & Marketing Officer: Miss Kate Barrett. Ext: 2238.
Senior Marketing Officer: Mrs Denise Langford. Ext: 8094.
E-communications Manager: Vacant. Ext: 8095.

CORPORATE SERVICES
Head of Corporate Services: Ms Fiona Davies. Ext: 2040.
PA to Head of Corporate Services: Ms Sally Nichols. Ext: 3771.
Head of Operational Delivery: Supt Dave Hill. Ext: 4280.
PA to Head of Operational Delivery: Ms Christine Hill. Ext: 2147.
Head of Finance & Asset Management: Mr Gary Jones.
Head of Service Transformation: Vacant.
PA to Head of Finance & Asset Management & Head of Service Transformation: Ms Sally Nichols. Ext: 3771.

FORENSIC INVESTIGATION TEAM
Head of Forensic Investigation: Mr Ian Bailey Ext: 2201.
Business Support Officer: Mrs Trudy Loe. Ext: 2287.

JUSTICE DEPARTMENT
Crown Court Liaison. Tel: 01604 638880.
A/Head of Justice Department: Supt Sean Bell. Ext: 2600.
PA: Mrs Kim Billingham. Ext: 2707.
Force Custody Manager: Chief Insp Jim Turnell. Ext: 776567.
Justice Crime Manager: Mrs Kelly Wayman. Ext: 7516.
Deputy Head of Justice Department: Mrs Vicky French. Ext: 7069.
Firearms Licensing Manager: Mrs Bridget Hodgson. Ext: 2286.
Case & Traffic Manager: Mrs Rachel Hughes-Rowlands. Ext: 5492.
Case & Restorative Justice Manager: Miss Michelle Chapman. Ext: 7369.
Case & Disclosure Manager: Mr Simon Barnes.
Justice Programme Manager: Mr Gerry Bernard. Ext: 2089.
Justice Partnership & Policy Officer: Miss Mandy Rowlatt. Ext: 2607.

ESTATES & FACILITIES
Estates & Facilities Manager: Mr Stuart Bonner. Ext: 2060. Fax: 01604 703063.
Facilities Manager (Operations): Mr Robert Judd. Ext: 8790.
Facilities Manager (Compliance): Mr David Mcinally. Ext: 4134.
Facilities Manager Building Services & Maintenance: Mr Terry Anderson. Ext: 8251.
Force Registry Information Officer: Ms Alana Miller. Ext: 2135.

FORCE COMMUNICATIONS CENTRE
Head of Force Communications Centre: Supt Michael Stamper. Ext: 8214.
PA: Ms Bernadette Capon. Ext: 8169.
Strategic Business Partner: Ms Caroline Oppido. Ext: 7226.

HUMAN RESOURCES
Head of Human Resources: Mr David Williams. Ext: 2090.
Force Learning & Development Manager: Ms Caroline Oppido. Ext: 2110.

INFORMATION SERVICES DEPARTMENT
Head of ISD: Mr Chris Wright. Ext: 2193. Fax: 01604 888102.
Assistant Head of ISD: Ms Jenny Clarke. Ext: 2155.
ISD Business Manager: Mrs Clare Taylor. Ext: 2177.

COMMERCIAL PROCUREMENT DEPARTMENT
Head of Purchasing & Procurement: Barbara Cairney. Ext: 7440.
Procurement Office Manager: Maura Wallace Nichols. Ext: 7432.
Buyers: Mrs Hassina Hardwick. Ext: 7430. Mrs Kay Lee. Ext: 3796. Mrs Caroline Hall. Ext: 3798.

PROFESSIONAL STANDARDS
Head of Professional Standards: Supt Jan Meagher. Ext: 344967.
Deputy Head of Professional Standards Integrity Unit: Chief Insp Mark Taylor. Ext: 345805.
Civil Litigation Officer: Mr Geoff Harding. Ext: 346577.
Information Assurance Manager: Mrs Yvonne Mason. Ext: 4234.
Criminal Records Bureau Manager: Mrs Karen Brown. Ext: 2350.
Information Security Officer: Mr Tim Driver. Ext: 343838.
Business Manager: Mrs Sarah Peart. Ext: 345288. Fax: 01604 633757.

TRANSPORT MANAGEMENT
Head of Transport & Travel: Mr Graham Crow. Ext: 2050. Fax: 01604 703082.
Office & Administration Manager: Mrs Theresa Cheney. Ext: 8131. Fax: 01604 888083.

STAFF ASSOCIATIONS
Superintendents' Association: *Chair:* Det Chief Supt Simon Blatchly. Tel: 01604 703600. *Vice Chair:* Chief Supt Paul Phillips. *T/Secretary:* Det Supt Jan Meagher. *Treasurer:* T/Chief Supt Richard James.

Police Federation: *Secretary:* Sgt Neil Goosey. Federation Office, The Lodge, Wootton Hall Park, Northampton NN4 0JA. Tel: 01604 767377. Fax: 01604 767164.
Email: federation@northants.pnn.police.uk

UNISON: *Secretary:* Mr Peter Lake. Ext: 2149. Fax: 01604 703143.
Email: unison@northants.pnn.police.uk

CRIME AND JUSTICE COMMAND
Head of Crime & Justice Command: Det Chief Supt Simon Blatchly. Ext: 3652.
PA: Mrs Tanya Goulding. Ext: 3655.
Head of Crime Investigation Department: Det Supt Ivan Balhatchet. Ext: 77667.
PA: Mrs Susan Husk. Ext: 5566.
Head of Crime Support: Supt Pete Windridge. Ext: 346143.
PA: Mrs Annette Moffat. Ext: 345018.

EAST MIDLANDS POLICE COLLABORATION
Deputy Chief Constable East Midlands: Peter Goodman.
PA to DCC East Midlands. Tessa Callow. Tel: 01623 608402.

EAST MIDLANDS COUNTER TERRORISM INTELLIGENCE UNIT
Email: emctiu@derbyshire.pnn.police.uk
PA to Head of Unit & Senior Management Team. Tel: 01623 608304.
Human Resources. Tel: 01623 608403.
Office Manager. Tel: 01623 608411.
Special Branch: Det Insp Rob Routledge. Tel: 0115 967 0999 ext 800 1030.

EAST MIDLANDS POLICE COLLABORATION PROGRAMME
Arrow Centre, Annesley Road, Hucknall, Nottingham NG15 8AY. Tel: 01623 608262. Email: eastmidlandscpt@nottinghamshire.pnn.police.uk
Programme Manager: Chief Supt Phil Whiteley.

EAST MIDLANDS SPECIAL OPERATIONS UNIT
EMSOU, PO Box 9557, Nottingham NG15 5BU. Tel: 01623 608054.
Head of EMSOU-SOC: T/Det Chief Supt Jason Caunt.
Email: jason.caunt@leicestershire.pnn.police.uk
Deputy Head of EMSOU-SOC: T/Det Supt Steve Craddock.
Email: steven.craddock@leicestershire.pnn.police.uk
Command Team PA: Sarah Dillon. Email: sarah.dillon@leicestershire.pnn.police.uk
Business & Finance Manager: Jon Peatling. Email: jonathan.peatling@leicestershire.pnn.police.uk
Senior Human Resources Officer: Tracy Meakin. Email: tracy.meakin@leicestershire.pnn.police.uk

Head of Operations Support: Det Chief Insp Andy Haydon.
Email: andrew.haydon@leicestershire.pnn.police.uk
Head of RART: Det Chief Insp Mick Beattie. Email: michael.beattie@leicestershire.pnn.police.uk
Head of Regional Review Unit: Kevin Flint. kevin.flint@leicestershire.pnn.police.uk

EMSOU – SERIOUS & ORGANISED CRIME
EMSOU-SOC North Command: Det Chief Insp Andy Dickin.
Email: andy.dickin@leicestershire.pnn.police.uk
EMSOU-SOC East Command: T/Det Chief Insp Alan Mason.
Email: alan.mason@leicestershire.pnn.police.uk
EMSOU-SOC South Command: T/Det Chief Insp Joe Elliott.
Email: joseph.elliott@leicestershire.pnn.police.uk

EMSOU – MAJOR CRIME
Head of Major Crime Unit: Det Chief Supt Andrew Hough.
Email: andrew.hough@leicestershire.pnn.police.uk
EMSOU-MC North Command: Vacant.
EMSOU-MC East Command: Det Supt Stuart Morrison. Email: stuart.morrison@lincs.pnn.police.uk
EMSOU-MC South Command: Vacant.

EMSOU – FORENSIC SERVICES
Regional Director of Forensic Services: Joanne Ashworth.
Email: joanne.ashworth.16204@derbyshire.pnn.police.uk

EMSOU – SPECIAL BRANCH
EMSOU, PO Box 9557, Nottingham NG15 5BU. Tel: 01623 608304.
Det Supt Stephen Lowe. Email: stephen.lowe.314568@derbyshire.pnn.police.uk
PA to Senior Management Team: Sue Hogg. Email: susan.hogg.16244@derbyshire.pnn.police.uk

TERRITORIAL POLICING COMMAND
Tel: 101.
Territorial Commander: Chief Supt Paul Fell. Ext: 2100.
PA: Ms Debbie Farrow. Ext: 2102.
District Superintendent: Richard James. Ext: 344499.
PA: Ms Vanessa Jennings. Ext: 344521.
Specialist Operations Superintendent: Andy Cox. Ext: 2400.
PA: Carol Morgan. Ext: 2402.
Area HQ: *London Road Police Station: Kettering NN15 7QP. Fax: 01604 888802.
***Midland Road Police Station:** Wellingborough NN8 1HF. Fax: 01604 888650.
***Elizabeth Street Police Station:** Corby NN17 1SH. Fax: 01604 888673.
Area HQ: *Campbell Square Police Station: Upper Mounts, Northampton NN1 3EL. Fax: 01604 888619.
Area HQ: *New Street Police Station: Daventry NN11 4BS. Fax: 01604 888778.
***Weston Favell Police Station:** Pyramid Close, Weston Favell, Northampton NN3 8NZ. Fax: 01604 888549.
Denotes stations designated under s35, P.A.C.E. Act 1984.

Ward	District	Ward	District
Abbey North	Daventry	Brampton	Daventry
Abbey South	Daventry	Braunston	Daventry
Abington	Northampton	Brayfield & Yardley	South Northants
All Saints	Kettering	Brickhill	Wellingborough
Astwell	South Northants	Brixworth	Daventry
Avondale Grange	Kettering	Burton Latimer	Kettering
Badby	Daventry	Byfield	Daventry
Barnwell	East Northants	Castle	Northampton
Barsby & Kilsby	Daventry	Castle	Wellingborough
Barton	Kettering	Central	Corby
Beanfield	Corby	Clipston	Daventry
Billing	Northampton	Cosgrove & Grafton	South Northants
Blakesley & Cote	South Northants	Crick	Daventry
Blisworth & Roade	South Northants	Crispin	Northampton
Boughton & Pitsford	Daventry	Croyland	Wellingborough
Boughton Green	Northampton	Danvers & Wardoun	South Northants
Brackley East	South Northants	Deanshanger	South Northants
Brackley South	South Northants	Deansholme	Corby
Brackley West	South Northants	Delapre	Northampton
Brambleside	Kettering	Desborough St Gile's	Kettering

Ward	District	Ward	District
Desborough Loatland	Kettering	Queensway	Wellingborough
Drayton	Daventry	Raunds Saxon	East Northants
Earls Barton	Wellingborough	Raunds Windmill	East Northants
East	Corby	Ravensthorpe	Daventry
East Hunsbury	Northampton	Redwell East	Wellingborough
Eastfield	Northampton	Redwell West	Wellingborough
Ecton Brook	Northampton	Rothwell	Kettering
Exeter	Corby	Rowlett	Corby
Finedon	Wellingborough	Rural West	Corby
Fineshade	East Northants	Rushden Bates	East Northants
Flore	Daventry	Rushden Hayden	East Northants
Grange Park	South Northants	Rushden Pemberton	East Northants
Great Doddington &	Wellingborough	Rushden Sartoris	East Northants
Wilby		Rushden Spencer	East Northants
Great Oakley	Corby	St David's	Northampton
Hackleton	South Northants	St James'	Northampton
Harpole & Grange	South Northants	St Michael's & Wicksteed	Kettering
Headlands	Northampton	St Peter's	Kettering
Hemmingwell	Wellingborough	Salcey	South Northants
Heyfords & Bugbrooke	South Northants	Silverstone	South Northants
Higham Ferrers Chichele	East Northants	Slade	Kettering
Higham Ferrers Lancaster	East Northants	South	Wellingborough
Hill	Daventry	Spencer	Northampton
Irchester	Wellingborough	Spratton	Daventry
Irthlingborough John Pyel	East Northants	Stanion & Corby Village	Corby
Irthlingborough Waterloo	East Northants	Stanwick	East Northants
Ise Lodge	Kettering	Steane	South Northants
Kings Forest	East Northants	Swanspool	Wellingborough
Kings Sutton	South Northants	Thorplands	Northampton
Kingsley	Northampton	Thrapston Lakes	East Northants
Kingsthorpe	Northampton	Thrapston Market	East Northants
Kingswood	Corby	Tove	South Northants
Kingthorn	South Northants	Towcester Brook	South Northants
Little Brook	South Northants	Towcester Mill	South Northants
Lodge Park	Corby	Walgrave	Daventry
Long Buckby	Daventry	Washington	South Northants
Lower Nene	East Northants	Weedon	Daventry
Lumbertubs	Northampton	Weldon & Gretton	Corby
Lyveden	East Northants	Welford	Daventry
Middleton Cheney	South Northants	Welland	Kettering
Moulton	Daventry	West	Wellingborough
Nene Valley	Northampton	West Haddon &	Daventry
New Duston	Northampton	Guilsborough	
North	Wellingborough	West Hunsbury	Northampton
Northfield	Kettering	Weston	Northampton
Oakley Vale	Corby	Whittlewood	South Northants
Old Duston	Northampton	William Knibb	Kettering
Old Stratford	South Northants	Wollaston	Wellingborough
Oundle	East Northants	Woodford	East Northants
Parklands	Northampton	Woodford Halse	Daventry
Pipers Hill	Kettering	Yelvertoft	Daventry
Prebendal	East Northants		
Queen Eleanor &	Kettering		
Buccleuch			

HM CORONER AND OTHER OFFICIALS

County of Northamptonshire: Mrs Anne Pember. 300 Wellingborough Road, Northampton NN1 4EP. Tel: 01604 624732. Fax: 01604 232282.

Force Medical Advisor
Dr Peter Gordon.

NORTHUMBRIA POLICE
Ponteland, Newcastle-upon-Tyne NE20 0BL.
Tel: 01661 872555. All numbers can be obtained by dialling 01661 872555, plus
extension number shown, unless otherwise stated. Fax: 01661 869788.
Email: chief.constable@northumbria.pnn.police.uk
Website: www.northumbria.police.uk

The Northumbria Police area consists of the County of Northumberland and the metropolitan districts of Newcastle-upon-Tyne, Gateshead, North Tyneside, South Tyneside, and Sunderland.

Police & Crime Commissioner: Vera Baird. c/o Gateshead Metropolitan Borough Council, Civic Centre, Gateshead NE8 1HH.

Chief Constable: S Sim BA(Hons) MBA FCMI DipAppCrim(Cantab) QPM.
Deputy Chief Constable: Vacant.
Assistant Chief Constable, Crime & Intelligence: J Campbell.
Assistant Chief Constable, Area Operations: S Ashman.
Assistant Chief Constable, Central Support: G Vant.
Assistant Chief Officer (Corporate Services): B McCardle.
Staff Officer: Supt J Simmons. Ext: 68006.
Executive Support Co-ordinator: Ext: 69556.

HUMAN RESOURCES AND LEARNING & DEVELOPMENT
Head of Human Resources: Mrs J Lawson. Ext: 60250.
Head of Strategic Business Support: Mr Mike Mullen. Ext: 68903.
Recruitment & Workforce Planning Manager: Miss C Farnell. Ext: 60253.
HR Policy Manager: Vacant. Ext: 60252.
Employee Relations Manager: Vacant. Ext: 60251.
Learning & Development Manager People Development: Mrs G Dickinson. Ext: 60358.
Learning & Development Manager Planning & Evaluation: Ms T Smyth. Ext: 60342.
Occupational Health Team Leader: Ms L Moore. Ext: 68826.
Health & Safety Advisors: Mr T Norton. Ext: 60315. Mr A Lumsden Dip Shem MIOSH. Ext: 60313.

CRIME DEPARTMENT
Det Chief Supt W Keenen. Ext: 60383.
PPU, Reach, RIT: Det Supt Steve Wade. Ext: 60373.
MIT, Major Crime Review Team: Det Supt Roger Ford. Ext: 60391/66392.
Intelligence: Det Supt Steve Howes. Ext: 65241. Det Supt Sharon Stavers. Ext: 60676. Det Supt Mike Jones. Ext: 68046. Det Supt Steve Howes.
Scientific Support including Fingerprint Bureau: Chief Insp Fred Elrick. Ext: 68640.
Special Branch: Chief Insp Dave Anderson. Ext: 68250.

CORPORATE DEVELOPMENT DEPARTMENT
Head of Corporate Development: Mr Mike Mullen. Ext: 60200.
Corporate Development Manager: Mr P Godden. Ext: 60201.
Corporate Performance Manager: Mr P Dunbar. Ext: 60204.
Head of Corporate Communications: Mrs M Berne. Ext: 68920.
Force Statistician: Ext: 68320.

CRIMINAL JUSTICE
Chief Supt G Milward. Ext: 68310. Supt N Minto. Ext: 68581.
Chief Insp D Harris. Ext: 68431.
CIB Manager: Mrs T Watson. Ext: 61878.
A/Fixed Penalty Unit Manager: Ms P Oliver. Ext: 68552.
CJU Regional Manager: Mr D Heslop. Ext: 68783.
Force ID Unit: Chief Insp D Harris. Ext: 68431.

PROFESSIONAL STANDARDS
Chief Supt C Thomson. Ext: 68901.
Administration Office. Ext: 68353. Email: professionalstandards@northumbria.pnn.police.uk

FINANCE & CENTRAL SERVICES
Financial Services Manager: Mr M Tait IPFA. Ext: 60102.
Principal Accountant: Vacant. Ext: 60124.
Payroll & Pensions Manager: Vacant. Ext: 60146.
Exchequer Services Manager: Mrs E Hawkins. Ext: 60154.

Fleet Manager: Mr K Wilson. Fleet Management, Arrow Close, Killingworth, Newcastle-upon-Tyne NE12 6QN. Ext: 63406.
Estates Manager: Mr J Leslie MRICS. Ext: 60211.
Procurement & Supplies Manager: Mr D Veitch. Block 70, Headquarters. Ext: 69219.

LEGAL SERVICES
Head of Department: Miss D Aubrey LLB. Ext: 68030.
Force Solicitor: Mr R Heron LLB. Ext: 68040.

OPERATIONS DEPARTMENT
Chief Supt D Pryer. Ext: 68501.
Superintendent (Policy & Planning): C Sharman. Ext: 68543.
Superintendent (Operations): A McDyer. Ext: 68523.
Business Co-ordinator: Helen Ferguson. Ext: 68353.
Air Support Unit (NEASU). Tel: 0191 214 0365. Email: neasu@northumbria.pnn.police.uk
Marine Unit. International Diving & Marine School Administration, Viking Park, Jarrow, Tyne & Wear NE32 3DS. Tel: 0191 454 7555 ext 65333.
Wildlife Liaison Officer: PC P Henery. Ext: 68514.

COMMUNICATION CENTRES
Chief Supt L Young. Ext: 68050.
Northern: Force Headquarters, as above. Chief Insp S Patsalos. Ext: 69724.
Southern: Millbank, Station Road, South Shields, Tyne & Wear NE33 1RR. Tel: 0191 454 7555. Chief Insp M Anastasi. Ext: 65724.

INFORMATION SYSTEMS & TELECOMMUNICATIONS
Director of ICT: Paul Armatage. Ext: 69858.
IS Manager: Mr J R Taylor. Ext: 69800. Email: jon.taylor.9661@northumbria.pnn.police.uk
IT Manager: Mr I Woodward MEng BA. Ext: 69910.
Email: ian.woodward.4518@northumbria.pnn. police.uk

STAFF ASSOCIATIONS
Police Federation: *JBB Chairman:* Mr R Watson. Tel: 01661 863490.
Email: email@norpolfed.co.uk

AREA COMMANDS
AA SUNDERLAND
Area Command Headquarters: Gillbridge Avenue Police Station, Gillbridge Avenue, Sunderland SR1 3AW. Tel: 0191 454 7555.
Commander: Chief Supt K Blyth.
Superintendent (Inner): T Walker.
T/Superintendent (Outer): J Napier.

BB SOUTH TYNESIDE
Area Command Headquarters: Millbank, Station Road, South Shields NE33 1RR. Tel: 0191 454 7555.
Commander: Chief Supt I Dawes.
Superintendent (Neighbourhood): A Henderson.

CC GATESHEAD
Area Command Headquarters: High West Street, Gateshead NE8 1BN. Tel: 0191 454 7555.
Commander: Chief Supt N Adamson.
Superintendent: T Smith.
T/Business Manager: Mrs E Walter.

DD NORTH TYNESIDE
Area Command Headquarters: Middle Engine Lae, Wallsend, Tyne and Wear NE28 9NT. Tel: 0191 214 6555.
Commander: Chief Supt S Neill.
Superintendent: P Farrell.
A/Business Manager: R Fenwick.

EE NEWCASTLE
Area Command Headquarters: Etal Lane, Westerhope, Newcastle-upon-Tyne NE5 4AN. Tel: 0191 214 6555.
Commander: Chief Supt G Calvert.
Superintendent: D Bryne.
Superintendent: P Orchard.

FF NORTHUMBERLAND
Area Command Headquarters: Schalksmuhle Way, Bedlington NE22 7LA. Tel: 0161 872555.
Commander: Chief Supt J Farrell.

Superintendent (Operations & Criminal Justice): D Winship.
Superintendent: M Pearson.

All telephone enquiries to stations should initially be made to the appropriate Area Command.

Area	Area Command	Area	Area Command
Alnwick*	FF	Morpeth*	FF
Amble	FF	Newbiggin	FF
Ashington*	FF	Newcastle Central*	EE
Bedlington	FF	Newcastle East*	EE
Bellingham	FF	Newcastle West*	EE
Berwick*	FF	North Shields*	DD
Blanchland	FF	Otterburn	FF
Blyth*	FF	Ponteland	FF
Boldon	BB	Prudhoe	FF
Broomhill	FF	Rothbury	FF
Corbridge	FF	Seahouses	FF
Cramlington*	FF	South Shields*	BB
Etal Lane	EE	Southwick	AA
Felling	CC	Sunderland City*	AA
Gateshead East*	CC	Sunderland West*	AA
Haltwhistle	FF	Wallsend*	DD
Haydon Bridge	FF	Washington*	AA
Hebburn	EE	Whickham*	CC
Hexham*	FF	Whitley Bay*	DD
Houghton-le-Spring*	AA	Wooler	FF
Jarrow*	BB		

* Denotes stations designated under s35, P.A.C.E. Act 1984.

HM CORONERS AND OTHER OFFICIALS

City of Sunderland: Mr Derek Winter. Civic Centre, Burdon Road, Sunderland SR2 7DN. Tel: 0191 561 7843. Fax: 0191 533 7803. Email: derek.winter@sunderland.gov.uk

Gateshead & South Tyneside: Mrs T Carney. 35 Station Road, Hevvurn NE31 1LA. Tel: 0191 483 8771. Fax: 0191 428 6699.

Newcastle-upon-Tyne: Karen Dilks. Coroner's Department, Civic Centre, Barras Bridge, Newcastle-upon-Tyne NE1 8PS. Tel: 0191 277 7280. Fax: 0191 261 2952.
Email: karen.dilks@newcastle.gov.uk

North Northumberland: Tony Brown. 17 Church Street, Berwick-upon-Tweed TD15 1EE. Tel: 01289 304318. Fax: 01289 303591. Email: jane.tait@northumberland.gov.uk

North Tyneside: Mr E Armstrong. 3 Stanley Street, Blyth NE24 2BS. Tel: 01670 354777. Fax: 01670 797891.

South Northumberland: Mr E Armstrong. As above.

Police Surgeons

Dr H A Armstrong, Rothbury; Dr D S Blades, Bellingham; Dr P H Burnham, Haltwhistle; Dr C Dean, Wooler; Dr R J Curtis, South Shields; Dr G C D'Silva, Wideopen; Dr M J Dodd, Alnwick; Dr R P Duggal, Winlaton; Dr P V Gardner, Wallsend; Dr C S Hargreaves, South Shields; Dr B D Harte, Hexham; Dr C A Henderson, Blyth; Dr A I Jones, Houghton-le-Spring; Dr D M Kerr, Seaton Delaval; Dr T B G Lowe, Berwick-upon-Tweed; Dr M T Marashi, Houghton-le-Spring; Dr C May, Wideopen; Dr D E Mayes, North Shields; Dr K Megson, Felling; Dr P Moffitt, Sunderland; Dr I G Muir, North Shields; Dr I J Mungall, Bellingham; Dr R Murphy, Blyth; Dr H F Patton, Bedlington; Dr M Patton, Cramlington; Dr R H Pawson, Belford; Dr M R Preston, Killingworth; Dr N K Ray, Washington; Dr J B Roberts, North Shields; Dr E A Spagnoli, Pallion, Dr G K Taylor, Washington; Dr P Willis, Hexham; Dr T W Yellowley, Ryton.

NOTTINGHAMSHIRE POLICE
Sherwood Lodge, Arnold, Nottingham NG5 8PP.
Tel: 101; outside Nottinghamshire 0115 967 0999. Telex: 37/622.
Fax: 0115 967 0900 (24 hrs); 0115 967 2329 (0800–1600).
Email: firstname.lastname@nottinghamshire.pnn.police.uk (some email addresses may contain digits, please contact switchboard for details).

Lord Lieutenant: Sir Andrew Buchanan Bt.
Police & Crime Commissioner: Paddy Tipping.

Chief Constable: Mr C Eyre QPM. Ext: 800 2006.
Deputy Chief Constable: Mr P Scarrott. Ext: 800 2006.
T/Assistant Chief Constable (Crime): Mr I Waterfield. Ext: 800 2007.
Assistant Chief Constable (Territorial): Mrs S Fish OBE. Ext: 800 2007.
Assistant Chief Officer (Resources): Margaret Monckton. Ext: 800 2011.
Staff Officer to CC & DCC: Mrs L Spinks. Ext: 800 2014.
PA to CC & DCC: Mrs R Clement. Ext: 800 2006.
Staff Officer to ACCs: Mrs J Burrows. Ext: 800 2017.
PA to ACCs: Ms R Hammond. Ext: 800 2007.
PA to ACO: Mrs L Whiting. Ext: 800 2011.
Assistant Staff Officer/Driver: Mr P Godber. Ext: 800 2012.

HEADQUARTERS DEPARTMENTS
PROCUREMENT, ESTATES & FACILITIES
Commercial Director (Commercial area including Nottinghamshire, Derbyshire, Northamptonshire): Ronnie Adams. Tel: 07702 141531.
Head of Procurement Services: Barbara Cairney. Tel: 0300 011 1222.
Head of Supplier Services: Jayne Christer. Ext: 800 2306.
Head of Customer Services: James Trotter.
PA to Commercial Director: Ms J Clayton. Ext: 800 2314.
Procurement Manager: Graeme Unwin. Ext: 800 2311.
Transport Manager: Nigel Coupe. Ext: 800 2380.
Supplies Manager (Printing): Stephen Blanchard. Ext: 800 2365.
Supplies Manager (Supplies): Ms Sue Patterson. Ext: 800 2350.
Head of Estates & Facilities Management: Tim Wendels. Ext: 800 2370.
Estates Manager: Phil Ellis. Ext: 800 2374.
Facilities Managers: Ms Tracey Blincow; Louise Goodman. Ext: 800 2330.
Building Surveyor: David Heason. Ext: 800 2373.
Maintenance Surveyors: Darren Edwards. Ext: 800 3371. Paul Whittley. Ext: 800 2377.
Force Environmental Officer: Ainsley Peters. Ext: 800 2372.

HUMAN RESOURCES
Head of Human Resources & Organisational Development: Mrs Sharon Ault. Ext: 800 2400.
HR Departmental Secretary: Joanne Walker. Ext: 800 2423.
Senior HR Partner (Regional HR Shared Service Centre Project): Ms Elaine Herod. Ext: 800 3492.
Senior HR Partner (People Services): Mrs Claire Salter. Ext: 800 2413.
Senior HR Partner (Strategy & Performance): James Lunn. Ext: 800 2916.
Senior HR Partner (Business & People Wellbeing): Steve Mitchel. Ext: 800 3480.
Senior HR Partner (Performance Development): Ian Hebb. Ext: 800 2411.
Senior HR Partner (Organisational Change): Mrs Jacky Lloyd. Ext: 800 2917.
HR Business Partners: Ms Jill Samuels. Ext: 800 2421. Mrs Sandra Conway. Ext: 800 3406. Ms Lindsay Stillings. Ext: 800 3405.
HR Partner (Resourcing & Operations): Ms Katherine Player. Ext: 800 2464.
HR Partner (Systems): Ms Pauline Burgin. Ext: 800 3460.
HR Partner (Case Management): Ms Linda Nelson. Ext: 800 2464.
HR Partner (Performance): Mrs Nikkisha Hindocha-Gohil. Ext: 800 2451.
HR Partner (Senior Management Team). Ms Natasha Cook. Ext: 800 2450.
Health & Safety Manager: Carl Taylor-Walster. Ext: 800 2280.
Occupational Health Force Medical Advisor: Dr Andrew Booth. Ext: 800 2286.

LEARNING & DEVELOPMENT
Employed by Leicestershire
Interim Senior Business Partner: Phil Maddison. Ext: 804 4935.
Interim Business Partner: Helen Purcell. Ext: 804 4802.

Team Leaders, Business Development: Graham Martin. Ext: 804 4706. John Blundy. Ext: 804 4880.
Team Leader, Business Support: Roberta Heald. Ext: 804 4937.
Team Leader, Training Delivery: Sandra Wenborne. Ext: 804 4925.
T/Interim Team Leader, Local Policing: Kev Priest. Ext: 804 4743.
Employed by Nottinghamshire
Team Leader, Operational Support & Driver Training: Sgt Andy Diggle. Ext: 853 4181.
Team Leader, Crime & Intelligence: Det Sgt Nick Sawdon. Ext: 804 4924.

CRIME AND JUSTICE
Head of Crime & Justice: Det Chief Supt Helen Jebb. Ext: 817 1000.
Head of Public Protection: Supt Helen Chamberlain. Ext: 817 1012.
Head of Fraud & Financial Investigation: Det Insp Andy Baguley. Ext: 817 1340.
Child Abuse Unit: Det Insp Yvonne Dales. Ext: 810 1230/ 817 1020.
Head of Scientific Support: Phil Cotton. Ext: 800 1110.
ACPO Business Resilience: T/Insp Richard Stones. Tel: 07899 063801.
Substance Misuse & Integrated Offender Management County: Chief Insp Kim Molloy. Ext: 811 1009.
Integrated Offender Management City: Insp Zoe Hallam. Tel: 0115 915 1456.
Head of Intelligence Analysts: Mr David Hill. Ext: 817 1013.
Head of Intelligence: Det Supt Mark Pollock. Ext: 817 1028.
Deputy Head of Intelligence: Det Chief Insp Sue Inger. Ext: 817 1014.
Nottingham Immigration Crime Team: Det Sgt Jan Rusdale. Ext: 816 4501.

CRIMINAL JUSTICE
Head of Criminal Justice: Mrs Jane Dean MA GIPD MInstAM(Dip). Ext: 813 3800.
Prosecutions Manager: Ms Janet Carlin. Ext: 813 3801.
Custody Manager: Paul Saint. Ext: 813 3803.
Archive & Exhibits Manager: Maria Fox. Ext: 813 3821.
Operational Business Support Unit Manager: Leah Johnson. Ext: 813 3817.

PROFESSIONAL STANDARDS DIRECTORATE
Head of Professional Standards: Det Supt Jackie Alexander. Ext: 800 2550.
PA to Head of Department: Nicky Kamionko. Ext: 800 2556.
Head of Complaints & Misconduct Unit & Counter Corruption Unit: Det Chief Insp Mick Windmill-Jones. Ext: 800 2551.
Complaints Administration Manager: Nicky Thomas. Ext: 800 2561.
Head of Vetting & Information Security: John Hammond. Ext: 800 2553.
Vetting Officer: Donna Kendall. Ext: 800 2662.
Information Security Manager: Pat Stocker. Ext: 800 2632.

OPERATIONAL SUPPORT DEPARTMENT
Head of Operational Support: T/Chief Supt Ian Howick. Ext: 800 2200.
Deputy Head of Operational Support: T/Supt Ian Barrowcliff. Ext: 800 2201.
Head of Tactical Operations & Road Crime: T/Det Chief Insp Andrew Hall. Ext: 800 2245.
Road Safety & Partnerships: Chief Insp Andy Charlton. Ext: 800 2206.
Emergency & Operational Planning: Insp Rob Taylor. Ext: 800 2157.
Emergency Planning Officers: Ian Townsend. Ext: 800 2154. Sandie Higginbotham. Ext: 800 2152.
Underwater Search Unit: PC Paul Easter. Ext: 816 2237.

CONTACT MANAGEMENT
Head of Contact Management: Pauline Smith. Ext: 800 2100.
Deputy Head: Supt Paul Pollard. Ext: 800 2102.
Chief Inspectors: Ted Antil. Ext: 800 2101. Ross Cooke. Ext: 800 2116.
Business Systems Developer: Jo Miller. Ext: 800 2123.
Front Counter Manager: Sophie Barker. Ext: 800 2104.
Switchboard: Insp Tracey Lovegrove. Ext: 800 2105.

BUSINESS & FINANCE
Head of Business & Finance: Simon Tovey. Ext: 800 2501.
PA to Head of Business & Finance: Wendy Walker. Ext: 800 2512.
Head of Programme Management: Vacant. Ext: 800 2500.
Committee Administrator: Carol Parfrement. Ext: 800 2506.
Performance & Insight Manager: Chief Insp Craig Nolan. Ext: 800 2069.
Market Research: Bindy Kaur. Ext: 800 2638.
Performance Information: Sarah Morgan. Ext: 800 2533.
Performance & Partnership: Mike Swanwick. Ext: 800 2542.
GIS (Mapping): Alys Dillon. Ext: 800 2835.
Head of Business Partnering: Vacant. Ext: 800 2031.
Business Marketing Advisors: Fleur Winters. Ext: 800 3025. Paula King. Ext: 800 3025.

Financial Controller: John Gordon. Ext: 800 2046.
Financial Accounting: Pam Taylor. Ext: 800 2035.
Payroll & Payments: Julie Read. Ext: 800 2050.
Head of Organisation Development: Julie Mair. Ext: 800 2651.
Planning & Policy: Read Hibbert. Ext: 800 2646.
Programme & Research: Keiley Freeman. Ext: 800 2504.
Information Management: Glen Langford. Ext: 800 2515.

CORPORATE COMMUNICATIONS
Head of Corporate Communications: Matt Tapp. Ext: 800 2070.
Deputy Head of Corporate Communication & Internal Communications Manager: Paul Coffey. Ext: 800 2073.
Media Relations Manager: Donna Jordan. Ext: 800 2082.
Public Engagement Manager: Katie Ethelstone (maternity leave until October 2013).
T/Public Engagement Manager: Joanne Hall. Ext: 800 2084.

INFORMATION SERVICES
Head of Information Services: Christi Carson. Ext: 800 2802.
Secretary: Janet Hind. Ext: 800 2804.
Infrastructure & Service Delivery Manager: Julie Mansfield. Ext: 800 2805.
Solutions Manager: Richard Hitch. Ext: 800 2847.
Information Services Support Team Manager: Sue Jackson. Ext: 800 2807.
Airwave Infrastructure Manager: Phill Charlton. Ext: 800 2820.
Network Infrastructure Manager: Keith Morris. Ext: 800 2843.
Telephony Infrastructure Manager: Jim Donaghie. Ext: 800 2810.
Service Desk Manager: Toni Manning. Ext: 800 2870.
Operations Management Team Manager: Martin Rogers. Ext: 800 2876.
Solutions Architect Team Manager: Craig Mullen. Ext: 800 2884.
Mobile Data Project Manager: PC Andy Jackson. Ext: 800 2692.

STAFF ASSOCIATIONS
Police Superintendents' Association: *Chair:* T/Chief Supt Ian Howick. Ext: 800 2200. *Secretary:* Supt Paul Burrows. Ext: 801 5681. *Treasurer:* Det Supt Jackie Alexander. Ext: 800 2550.
Police Federation: *JBB Secretary:* PC Michael Taylor. Ext: 800 2572. *JBB Chair:* Sgt Philip Matthews. Ext: 800 2570. *JBB Treasurer:* Sgt Philip Read. Ext: 800 2571. Email: police.federation@nottinghamshire.pnn.police.uk
UNISON: *Joint Branch Secretary:* Rachel Thackray. Ext: 800 2578. *T/:* Sharon Brown. Ext: 800 2579. *T/Chair:* Chris Berry. Ext: 800 2578. *Treasurer:* Yvonne Davidson. Ext: 800 2060. Email: unison@nottinghamshire.pnn.police.uk

EAST MIDLANDS POLICE COLLABORATION
Deputy Chief Constable East Midlands: Peter Goodman.
PA to DCC East Midlands: Tessa Callow. Tel: 01623 608402.

EAST MIDLANDS COUNTER TERRORISM INTELLIGENCE UNIT
Email: emctiu@derbyshire.pnn.police.uk
PA to Head of Unit & Senior Management Team. Tel: 01623 608304.
Human Resources. Tel: 01623 608403.
Office Manager. Tel: 01623 608411
Special Branch: Det Insp Rob Routledge. Ext: 800 1030.

EAST MIDLANDS POLICE COLLABORATION PROGRAMME
Arrow Centre, Annesley Road, Hucknall, Nottingham NG15 8AY. Tel: 01623 608262. Email: eastmidlandscpt@nottinghamshire.pnn.police.uk.
Programme Manager: Chief Supt Phil Whiteley.

EAST MIDLANDS SPECIAL OPERATIONS UNIT
EMSOU, PO Box 9557, Nottingham NG15 5BU. Tel: 01623 608054.
Head of EMSOU-SOC: T/Det Chief Supt Jason Caunt.
Email: jason.caunt@leicestershire.pnn.police.uk
Deputy Head of EMSOU-SOC: T/Det Supt Steve Craddock.
Email: steven.craddock@leicestershire.pnn.police.uk
Command Team PA: Sarah Dillon. Email: sarah.dillon@leicestershire.pnn.police.uk
Business & Finance Manager: Jon Peatling. Email: jonathan.peatling@leicestershire.pnn.police.uk
Senior Human Resources Officer: Tracy Meakin. Email: tracy.meakin@leicestershire.pnn.police.uk
Head of Operations Support: Det Chief Insp Andy Haydon.
Email: andrew.haydon@leicestershire.pnn.police.uk
Head of RART: Det Chief Insp Mick Beattie. Email: michael.beattie@leicestershire.pnn.police.uk
Head of Regional Review Unit: Kevin Flint. Email: kevin.flint@leicestershire.pnn.police.uk

EMSOU – SERIOUS & ORGANISED CRIME
EMSOU-SOC North Command: Det Chief Insp Andy Dickin.
  Email: andy.dickin@leicestershire.pnn.police.uk
EMSOU-SOC East Command: T/Det Chief Insp Alan Mason.
  Email: alan.mason@leicestershire.pnn.police.uk
EMSOU-SOC South Command: T/Det Chief Insp Joe Elliott.
  Email: joseph.elliott@leicestershire.pnn.police.uk
EMSOU – MAJOR CRIME
Head of Major Crime Unit: Det Chief Supt Andrew Hough.
  Email: andrew.hough@leicestershire.pnn.police.uk
EMSOU-MC North Command: Vacant.
EMSOU-MC East Command: Det Supt Stuart Morrison. Email: stuart.morrison@lincs.pnn.police.uk
EMSOU-MC South Command: Vacant.
EMSOU – FORENSIC SERVICES
Regional Director of Forensic Services: Joanne Ashworth.
  Email: joanne.ashworth.16204@derbyshire.pnn.police.uk
EMSOU – SPECIAL BRANCH
EMSOU, PO Box 9557, Nottingham NG15 5BU. Tel: 01623 608304.
Det Supt Stephen Lowe. Email: stephen.lowe.314568@derbyshire.pnn.police.uk
PA to Senior Management Team: Sue Hogg. Email: susan.hogg.16244@derbyshire.pnn.police.uk

EAST MIDLANDS LEGAL SERVICES UNIT
Head of Legal Services, East Midlands Police Legal Services: Craig Sutherland LLB. Tel: 01773 572839/40.
Deputy Head, East Midlands Police Legal Services: Malcolm Turner LLB. Tel: 01773 572839/40.

COUNTY DIVISION
Headquarters: Mansfield Police Station, Great Central Road, Mansfield, Nottinghamshire NG18 2HQ. Tel: 01623 420999. Fax: 01623 483004.
Divisional Commander: Chief Supt Ak Khan.
Deputy Divisional Commander/Superintendent Performance, Business & Partnerships: Paul Anderson.
Operations (Gedling, Broxtowe & Rushcliffe): Supt Mark Holland.
Neighbourhoods (Mansfield/Ashfield): Supt Richard Fretwell.
Crime (Bassetlaw, Newark & Sherwood): Supt Mike Manley.

CITY DIVISION
North Church Street, Nottingham NG1 4BH. Tel: 0115 948 2999. Fax: 0115 844 5019.
City Commander: Chief Supt Simon Nickless.
Performance & Partnerships: Supt Steve Cooper.
Head of Crime: Supt Brian Beasley.
Operational Policing: T/Supt Linda McCarthy.
Neighbourhood Policing: Supt Paul Burrows.
City Centre: Chief Insp Shaun Ostle.
Canning: Chief Insp Andy Burton.
City North: Chief Insp Matthew McFarlane.
City South: T/Chief Insp Mark Stanley.
Response/Demand Management: T/Chief Insp James West.
Performance, Partnerships & Business Development Manager: Ms Erica Doran.

OPERATIONAL SUPPORT
Sherwood Lodge Drive, Arnold, Nottingham NG5 8PP. Tel: 0115 967 2216.
The following location/stations are designated under s35, P.A.C.E. Act. 1984. Bridwell, Carrington Street, Nottingham NG1 2EE; Mansfield Police Station, Great Central Road, Mansfield NG18 2HQ; Newark Police Station, Appleton Gate, Newark NG24 1JZ;

Place	Division	Place	Division	Place	Division
Abbey	City	Beechdale	City	Bingham	County
Abbey	County	Beeston Central	County	Birklands	County
Ash Lea	County	Beeston	County	Bishop	County
Aspley	City	North-East		Blidworth	County
Attenborough	County	Beeston Rylands	County	Blyth	County
Awsworth &	County	Berry Hill	County	Bonington	County
Cossall		Bestwood Park	County	Boughton	County
Basford	City	Bestwood Park	City	Bramcote	County
Beacon	County	Bilborough	City	Bridge	County
Beckingham	County	Bilsthorpe	County	Bridge	City

Place	Division	Place	Division	Place	Division
Brinsley	County	Kingswell	County	Retford East	County
Broomhill	County	Kirby-in-Ashfield	County	Retford North	County
Bullpit-Pinfold	County	Central		Retford West	County
Bulwell East	City	Kirby-in-Ashfield	County	Robin Hood	City
Bulwell West	City	East		Rufford	County
Burton Joyce &	County	Kirby-in-Ashfield	County	Selston	County
Stoke Bardolph		West		Sherwood	County
Byron	City	Lady Bay	County	Sherwood	City
Calverton	County	Lady Brook	County	Soar Valley	County
Carlton	County	Lambley	County	Southwell East	County
Carlton-in-	County	Lamcote	County	Southwell West	County
Lindrick		Leake	County	St Ann's	City
Carlton Hill	County	Leeming	County	St James'	County
Castle	County	Lenton	City	St Mary's	County
Caunton	County	Leys	County	Stanford	County
Cavendish	County	Lindhurst	County	Stapleford East	County
Chilwell East	County	Lowdham	County	Stapleford North	County
Chilwell West	County	Lutterell	County	Stapleford West	County
Clayworth	County	Magnus	County	Strelley	City
Clifton East	City	Malkin	County	Strelley & Trowell	County
Clifton West	City	Manor	County	Sturton	County
Clipstone	County	Manor	County	Sutton	County
Collingham	County	Manvers	City	Sutton-in-Ashfield	County
Conway	County	Mapperley	City	Central	
Cranmer	County	Mapperley Plains	County	Sutton-in-Ashfield	County
Cumberlands	County	Meden	County	East	
Dayncourt	County	Meering	County	Sutton-in-Ashfield	County
Devon	County	Melton	County	North	
Dover Beck	County	Milton-Lowfield	County	Sutton-in-Ashfield	County
Eakring	County	Misterton	County	West	
East Markham	County	Muskham	County	Sutton-on-Trent	County
Eastwood	County	Musters	County	Thoroton	County
Eastwood North	County	Netherfield	County	Titchfield	County
Edwalton	County	Nevile	County	Tollerton	County
Edwinstowe	County	Newstead	County	Toton	County
Elkesley	County	Northfield	County	Trent	County
Elston	County	North-West	County	Trent	City
Everton	County	Nuthall	County	Tuxford	County
Farndon	County	Oak Tree	County	Underwood	County
Farnsfield	County	Oakham	County	Welbeck	County
Forest	City	Ollerton North	County	Wilford	City
Forest Town	County	Ollerton South	County	Winthorpe	County
Gedling	County	Oxclose	County	Wiverton	County
Gotham	County	Packman	County	Wolds	County
Greasley	County	Park	City	Wollaton	City
Greenwood	City	Phoenix	County	Woodborough	County
Harworth East	County	Pleasleyhill	County	Woodhouse	County
Hodsock	County	Porchester	County	Woodthorpe	County
Hucknall Central	County	Portland	City	Worksop East	County
Hucknall East	County	Priory	County	Worksop North	County
Hucknall North	County	Radford	City	Worksop North	County
Hucknall West	County	Rainworth	County	East	
Jacksdale	County	Rampton	County	Worksop North	County
Keyworth North	County	Rancliffe	County	West	
Keyworth South	County	Ranskill	County	Worksop South	County
Killisick	County	Ravensdale	County	Worksop South	County
Kimberley	County	Ravenshead	County	East	

HM CORONER AND OTHER OFFICIALS

Nottinghamshire: Ms Mairin Casey. The Council House, Old Market Square, Nottingham NG1 2DT.
Tel: 0115 841 5553. Fax: 0115 876 5689. Email: coroners@nottinghamcity.gov.uk

RSPCA
Branch Office & Welfare Centre, 137 Radford Road, Nottingham. Tel: 0115 978 4965. Tel: 0300
  1234999.
NSPCC
Young Persons' Centre & Schools Service, 1 Cranmer Street, Nottingham NG3 4GH. Tel: 0115 960
  5481.
Community Safety, Regeneration and Protection
Mr Paul McKay. Service Director, Community Safety, Regeneration & Protection, 4th Floor, County
  Hall, West Bridgford, Nottingham NG2 7QP. Tel: 0115 977 3909.
  Email: paul.mckay@nottscc.gov.uk

SOUTH WALES POLICE

Cowbridge Road, Bridgend CF31 3SU.
Tel: 01656 655555. Fax: 01656 869399 (24 hrs). The dialling code for all numbers is 01656, unless otherwise indicated.
X400: c = GB; a = CWMAIL; p = PNN62; o = SOUTH WALES POLICE; s = POSTMASTER.
Email: firstname.lastname@south-wales.pnn.police.uk, unless otherwise indicated.
Website: www.south-wales.police.uk

(Unitary Authorities of Merthyr Tydfil, Rhondda Cynon Taff, Cardiff, Vale of Glamorgan, Bridgend, Neath & Port Talbot, Swansea)

Lords Lieutenant: South Glamorgan: Dr P Beck. Mid Glamorgan: Mrs K Thomas CVO JP. West Glamorgan: Mr B Lewis.
Police & Crime Commissioner: Rt Hon Alun Michael JP FRSA.

Chief Constable: Mr Peter Vaughan QPM CCMI BSc(Hons) DipAppCrim. Tel: 869200.
Deputy Chief Constable: Ms Colette Paul BA(Hons). Tel: 869201.
Assistant Chief Constable (Territorial Policing): Mr Julian Kirby BSc(Hons). Tel: 869202.
Assistant Chief Constable (Specialist Crime): Mr Matt Jukes MA(Oxon) MSc. Tel: 869539.
A/Assistant Chief Constable (Specialist Operations): Mr Richard Lewis MEd. Tel: 869367.
Director of Human Resources: Mr Mark Milton MCIPD. Tel: 869203.
Director of Finance: Mr Umar Hussain BA(Hons) FCCA. Tel: 869204.
Director of Corporate & Legal Services: Mr Gareth Madge LLB. Tel: 869367.
Chief Constable's Staff Officer: Chief Insp Jim Dyson. Tel: 869353.
Chief Constable's Secretary: Mrs Jayne Powney. Tel: 869200.
Email: acpo.staff.office@south-wales.pnn.police.uk

SOUTH WALES & GWENT POLICE JOINT LEGAL SERVICES
Assistant Director, Head of Joint Legal Service: Mr R Leighton Hill LLB. Tel: 869476.
Deputy Head of Joint Legal Service: Mrs Nia Brennan LLB. Tel: 869476.
Gwent Senior Solicitor (Employment): Mr Dylan Rowlands LLB. Tel: 01633 642500.
SWP Solicitor (Operational Policing): Mrs Louise Emmitt LLB. Tel: 869476.
Gwent Solicitor (Operational Policing): Ms Ciaran Gould LLB. Tel: 01633 642500.
SWP Solicitor (Corporate): Mrs Nicola White LLB. Tel: 869476.
SWP Solicitor (Litigation): Ms Rachel Davies LLB. Tel: 869476.
Gwent Solicitor (Litigation): Mr Bryn Thomas LLB. Tel: 01633 642500.
SWP Solicitor (Employment): Mrs Helen Stevens LLB. Tel: 869476.

CORPORATE GOVERNANCE
Assistant Director, Head of Corporate Governance: Mr M Huw Cogbill MSc MBA DMS(Dist) MMS (Dip) MIMgt. Tel: 302192.
Corporate Secretariat Business Area Manager: Mrs Carol Woodward AMInstLM. Tel: 869555.
Policy & Development Business Area Manager: Mr Stephen Routledge BA(Hons) MSc PgD. Tel: 306092.
Executive Support Business Area: Chief Insp Jim Dyson.

ORGANISATIONAL REVIEW & DEVELOPMENT
Head of Department: Supt Martin Jones LLB(Hons). Tel: 869382.
Deputy Head of Department: Mr Carl Walters BSc(Hons). Ext: 20957.

COLLABORATION AND STRATEGIC LEAD AND PERFORMANCE
Head of Collaboration: Chief Supt Josh Jones BA(Hons). Tel: 869234.
Head of Performance & Inspection: Vacant.
Force Inspection Team & Telephone Research Unit: Insp Simon Merrick. Ext: 20968.

HUMAN RESOURCES
Assistant Director, Human Resources: Mrs A M Davies FCIPD. Tel: 869220.
Health Care & Safety Manager: Mrs J L Wainwright BSc(Hons) Chtd MCIPD MCIOSH MICSC. Tel: 869229.
General Manager: Mrs J Evans. Ext: 20240.
Head of Shared Services: Mrs K Chadd BA FCIPD. Tel: 869557.
Head of Service Delivery: Mrs E Mills MCIPD. Tel: 305817.
Employee Resources Manager: Mrs J Jones LLM MBA FCIPD. Tel: 869537.

LEARNING DEVELOPMENT SERVICES
Assistant Director, Learning Development Services: Mr Phill Pyke QPM MSc(Econ). Tel: 869551.
Head of Operational Training Directorate: Chief Insp Stuart Parfitt. Tel: 869523.
Head of Organisational Training Directorate: Mrs Wendy Derrick BA(Hons). Tel: 869583.
PDU & Operational Training Manager: A/Insp Mark Jones CertEd. Tel: 07967 185879.
Driver Training Standards Manager: Mr Gareth Morgan MSc. Tel: 029 2052 7327.
Joint Firearms Training Unit: Insp David Manetta-Jones. Tel: 302194.
Head of Initial Police Learning & Assessment Unit: Insp Lisa Gore LLB(Hons). Tel: 303500.
Head of Investigative Training Unit: Det Insp Andy Paddison CertEd. Tel: 303501.
Head of Leadership, Equality & Diversity: Dr Charlotte Morgans. Tel: 07976 634006.
Head of Administration Unit: Mrs Karen Turner. Tel: 303516.
Head of IT Training: Sian Youlden BA(Hons). Tel: 07824 597645.
Support & Development Unit Head: Mr Nick Joyner BSc(Hons). Tel: 305804.

CORPORATE FINANCE
Assistant Director: Mr Gwyn Williams CPFA ACIS. Tel: 869299.
Head of Accountancy Services: Ms Beverley Peatling CPFA. Tel: 303412.
Head of Exchequer Services: Mr Steve Lewis MCIPP. Tel: 305859.

FORCE BUSINESS CENTRE
Head of Force Business Centre: Mrs Susan Watkins ACIB. Tel: 303413.
Head of Force Business Centre (Budgets): Mrs Karen Campbell-Ace.
General Manager (FBC Support): Mrs Susan Williams. Tel: 762910.
General Manager (FBC Budgets): Mr Ryan Collins. Tel: 305862.
Service Group Manager (FBC Ordering Team): Mrs Sian Newey. Tel: 305953.
Service Group Manager (FBC Customer Services): Mrs Helen Hayman. Tel: 306016.
Service Group Manager (FBC Sickness): Mrs Kate Perkins. Tel: 869349.
Service Group Manager (FBC Budgets): Miss Sharon Pritchard. Tel: 305946.
Vehicle Recovery Manager: Allison Palmer. Tel: 306072.

EQUALITY AND DIVERSITY UNIT
Head of Equality & Diversity Unit: Ms Jacqui Davies MCIPD. Tel: 302170.

PROFESSIONAL STANDARDS DEPARTMENT
Email: professional.standards@south-wales.pnn.police.uk
Head of Professional Standards: Det Chief Supt Tim Jones. Tel: 869406.
Deputy Head of Professional Standards: Det Supt Mark Lynch. Tel: 869406.
Chief Inspector PSD: Richie Jones. Tel: 869406.
Senior Manager/Decision Maker: Mr Dale Ponting. Tel: 302131.
Professional Standards, Anti-corruption Unit: Det Insp G Heatley. Tel: 302127.
    Email: pro.active@south-wales.pnn.police.uk
Force Vetting Unit: *Force Vetting Manager:* Colin Jenkins. Ext: 70643.

INFORMATION SERVICES
Assistant Director: Mr Martin H Smedley BSc(Hons) MBCS CITP. Tel: 305918.
Head of Information Systems: Mr Sheldon Cooper. Tel: 869357 ext 20500.
Head of Information Management: Mr Stephen Fryzer BA(Hons). Ext: 70955.
Customer Services Manager: Mr Clive J Richards BA(Hons). Tel: 869456 ext 20508.
Communications Manager: Mr Paul Dierden. Tel: 302186 ext 20505.
Systems Manager: Mr Andrew James BSc(Hons). Tel: 302186.
Database Manager: Mr Justin Hostettler-Davies BA(Hons). Tel: 869526.
Force Data Management & Disclosure Manager: Mr Jeff Newman. Tel: 305996.
Systems Maintenance & Security Manager: Mrs Sian Richards. Ext: 70947.
Business Intelligence Manager: Mr Simon Kinsey. Ext: 70965.
Vetting Disclosure Officer: Mr Colin Jenkins.
Data Protection Disclosure Officer: Miss Eloise Rosser. Tel: 306163. Email: foi@south-wales.pnn.police.uk
Force Information Security Officer: Mr David Jenkins. Tel: 306162.
Email: infosec@south-wales.pnn.police.uk
Firearms & Explosives Licensing Manager: Mrs Sara Williams. Tel: 869244.

JUSTICE & PARTNERSHIPS
Head of Justice & Partnerships: Assistant Director: Barbara Ranger LLB(Hons). Tel: 869215.
Deputy: Supt Liane Bartlett MPA. Tel: 01639 889183.
Strategy & Operations Unit: *Head of Strategy & Operations:* Mr Jeff Cooksley BA(Hons) MA. Tel: 869215.
Custody Services: Chief Insp Paul Murphy. Tel: 869215.
Central Ticket Office: *Manager:* Mrs Gloria Wort. Tel: 01443 660400.

Crime Registry: *Force Crime & Incident Registrar:* Mr Ceri Williams. Tel: 01443 660420.
Partnerships: Chief Insp Roger Whitcombe. Tel: 01639 889176.

SPECIALIST CRIME
Head of Division: Det Chief Supt Sally Burke. Tel: 305926.
Intelligence Directorate: Det Supt Huw Lewis. Tel: 029 2052 7340.
Specialist Crime Investigation Team: Det Supt Paul Hurley. Tel: 303461.
HOLMES Manager: Mr Paul James.
Public Protection Department (Sex & Dangerous Offenders, Child Protection, Domestic Abuse, Adult Protection, Missing Persons): Det Supt Lorraine Davies. Tel: 869434.
Senior Review Officer: Head of Department: Mr Martyn Lloyd-Evans. Tel: 306078.
Senior Review Officer: Review Manager: Mr Paul Bethell. Tel: 306079.
Covert Operations Management Unit: Det Supt Chris Parsons. Tel: 305971.

JOINT SCIENTIFIC INVESTIGATION UNIT (GWENT POLICE AND SOUTH WALES POLICE)
Head of Joint Scientific Investigation Unit: Mr Ian Brewster. Tel: 869425.
Forensic Operations Manager: Mr David Thomas. Tel: 869352.
Forensic Support Manager: Mr Paul Roberts. Tel: 305977.
Head of Forensic Technical Services: Mrs Kate Lantzos. Tel: 029 2077 4291.

SPECIALIST OPERATIONS DIVISION (INCLUDING FORCE PLANNING UNIT)
Operations: Chief Supt Cliff Filer. Tel: 761880. Supt Steve Furnham. Tel: 302190. Chief Insp Simon Belcher. Tel: 655555 ext 20320.
Airport Policing Group: Insp Steve Morris. Tel: 306111.
South & East Wales Air Support Unit: Insp Gary Smart. Tel: 01446 751391.
Dog Section, Mounted Section, Specialist Search & Rescue Team: Insp Mark Hobrough. Tel: 869340.
Roads Policing Unit: Insp Carwyn Evans. Tel: 869593.
Civil Contingencies & Resilience Unit: Chief Insp Jay Dave. Ext: 20340.
Force Planning Unit: Insp Joe Jones. Ext: 20821.
Territorial Support Teams & Continuous Improvement Team: Chief Insp Steve Clark. Ext: 70603.
Senior Performance Analyst: Mr Brett Davis BSc(Hons) MBA. Tel: 867011.

COMMUNICATIONS – PUBLIC SERVICE CENTRE
Chief Supt Cliff Filer. Tel: 761880.
Deputy: Supt Tony Smith. Tel: 761870.
Support: Chief Insp Alun Morgan. Tel: 869579.

FLEET MANAGEMENT
Head of Fleet Management: Mr Ray Forsey MCIPS. Tel: 869250.
Assistant Fleet Manager: Adrian Jay. Tel: 869253.

PROCUREMENT & LOGISTICS
Head of Procurement & Logistics: Mrs Siân Freeman MCIPS. Tel: 869260.
Procurement Manager: Mrs Adriel Roach MCIPS. Tel: 869394.
Contracts Manager: Mr Neil Watkins MCIPS. Tel: 303418.
Stores & Logistics Manager: Mrs Linda Webb. Tel: 869268.

ESTATES & FACILITIES
Head of Estates & Facilities: Mr Chris Shattock MSc MBA MMS(Dip). Tel: 869210.
Estates & Facilities Managers: **Delivery:** Mrs Clare Jones BSc(Hons) ICIOB. Tel: 869270. **Facilities:** Mr Dan Ferris. Tel: 869276.

CORPORATE COMMUNICATIONS DEPARTMENT
Assistant Director of Corporate Communications: Mr James Pritchard.
Secretary. Tel: 303449.
Head of Corporate Communications: Mrs Catherine Llewellyn.
Press Officer. Tel: 869291.

STAFF ASSOCIATIONS
Superintendents' Association: *Secretary:* Supt Tony Smith. *Chair:* Chief Supt Alun Thomas. South Wales Police HQ. *Treasurer:* Supt Julian Williams.
Police Federation: *Federation Office:* 155 Neath Road, Briton Ferry, Neath SA11 2BX. Tel: 01639 813569/820222. *Chair:* Mr Steve Trigg. *JBB Secretary:* Mr Del Hastings. *Deputy Secretary:* Mr Danny Aherne.
UNISON: *Branch Secretary:* Alyson Thomas. Unison Office, Port Talbot Police Station, Station Road, Port Talbot SA13 1JB. Tel: 762977. *Assistant Branch Secretary:* Mary Halligan.

NORTHERN BCU
Divisional Headquarters: Berw Road, Pontypridd CF37 2TR. Tel: 01443 485351. Fax: 01443 743639.
Divisional Commander: Chief Supt K O'Neill BA(Hons).

Deputy Divisional Commander, Northern District: Supt Simon Clarke.
Deputy Divisional Commander, Southern District: Supt Dawn Hubbard.
General Managers: Mr Emlyn Huish ACIB; Mrs Tessa Long.

EASTERN BCU CARDIFF
Divisional Headquarters: Cardiff Bay Police Station, James Street, Cardiff Bay, Cardiff CF10 5EW.
Tel: 029 2022 2111. Fax: 029 2052 7280.
Divisional Commander: Chief Supt Alun Thomas. Tel: 029 2052 7366.
Deputy Divisional Commanders: Supt Belinda Davies. Tel: 029 2052 7200.
General Managers: Mrs Sharon Lambert. Tel: 029 2052 7212. Mrs Vanessa Laity. Tel: 029 2033 8512.

CENTRAL BCU
Divisional Headquarters East: Gladstone Road, Barry CF63 1TD. Tel: 01446 734451.
Fax: 01446 731616.
Divisional Headquarters West: Brackla Street, Bridgend CF31 1BZ. Tel: 01656 655555. Fax: 01656
679551.
Divisional Commander: Chief Supt Liane James. Ext: 21200/32200.
Deputy Divisional Commander: Supt Paul E James. Ext: 21201/32201.
Chief Inspector (Operations) East: Gary Osborne. Ext: 32202.
Chief Inspector (Operations) West: Andy Morgan. Ext: 21202.
Chief Inspector Justice & Intelligence: Jason James. Ext: 21203/32203.
Detective Chief Inspector Investigations: Marc Lamerton. Ext: 32037.
General Manager: Maria Spence. Tel: 01446 731612.
General Manager (HUB): Megan Hughes. Tel: 679510.

WESTERN BCU
Divisional Headquarters: Western Division, Swansea Central Police Station, Grove Place, Swansea
SA1 5EA. Tel: 01792 456999.
Fax: 01792 562734.
Divisional Commander: Chief Supt Julian Williams. Ext: 50200.
Deputy Divisional Commander (Crime & Disorder): Supt Jonathan Edwards. Ext: 52201.
Deputy Divisional Commander (Operational): Supt Phil Davies. Ext: 50201.
Chief Inspectors: Phillip Ashby. Ext: 50203. Keith Jones. Ext: 50202. Darren Phillips. Ext: 51400. Det
Chief Insp Jane Mackay. Ext: 52409.
General Managers: Fiona Lewis. Ext: 50211. Craig Hargreaves. Ext: 54210.

Police Station	BCU	Police Station	BCU
Abercynon	Northern	Dunvant	Western
*†Aberdare	Northern	Ely	Eastern
Aberfan	Northern	*Fairwater	Eastern
Aberkenfig	Central	Ferndale	Northern
Baglan	Western	Gendros	Western
*Barry	Central	Gilfach Goch	Northern
Beddau	Northern	Glais	Western
Bishopston	Western	Glynneath	Western
Blaenymaes	Western	°Gorseinon	Western
Bonymaen	Western	Gower	Western
*†Bridgend	Central	Gowerton	Western
Briton Ferry	Western	Graigllwyd	Western
Cadoxton (Neath)	Western	Grangetown	Eastern
Caerau	Central	Gurnos	Northern
Cardiff Bay	Eastern	Gwaun-cae-Gurwen	Western
*Cardiff Central	Eastern	Hirwaun	Northern
Cathays	Eastern	Jersey Marine	Western
Church Village	Northern	Killay	Western
Cimla	Western	Landore	Western
Clase	Western	Llanedeyrn	Eastern
*†Cockett	Western	Llangyfelach	Western
Cowbridge	Central	Llanharan	Northern
Coychurch	Central	*Llanishen	Eastern
Crynant	Western	Llanrhidian	Western
Cwmavon	Western	Llansamlet	Western
Cwmbach	Northern	Llantwit Major	Central
Cymmer (Port Talbot)	Western	Loughor	Western
Cymmer (Porth)	Northern	*Maesteg	Central
Dowlais	Northern	Marina-Swansea	Western

Police Station	BCU	Police Station	BCU
*†Merthyr Tydfil	Northern	Roath (Clifton Street)	Eastern
Miskin	Northern	Rumney	Eastern
°Morriston	Western	St Mellons	Eastern
Mountain Ash	Northern	St Thomas	Western
Mumbles	Western	Sandfields	Western
*†Neath	Western	Seven Sisters	Western
Neath Abbey	Western	Sketty	Western
Parkmill	Western	Skewen	Western
Penarth	Central	*†Swansea	Western
Penclawdd	Western	Taffs Well	Northern
Pencoed	Central	Talbot Green	Northern
Penllergaer	Western	*†Ton Pentre	Northern
*Pontardawe	Western	Tonna	Western
Pontardulais	Western	Tonypandy	Northern
Pontycymmer	Central	Tonyrefail	Northern
*†Pontypridd	Northern	Treforest	Northern
Port Eynon	Western	Treharris	Northern
*†Port Talbot	Western	Troedyrhiw	Northern
Porth	Northern	Uplands	Western
*Porthcawl	Central	Waunarllwyd	Western
Pyle	Central	West Cross	Western
Resolven	Western	Ynysybwl	Northern
Reynoldston	Western	Ystalyfera	Western
Rhydyfelin	Northern		

* Denotes stations manned 24 hours per day.
° Denotes stations manned 16 hours per day.
† Denotes stations designated under s35, P.A.C.E. Act 1984.

HM CORONERS

Bridgend & Glamorgan Valleys: Louise Hunt. The Coroner's Office, Rock Grounds, Aberdare CF44 7AE. Tel: 01685 885202. Fax: 01685 885250. Email: louise.a.hunt@rhondda-cynon-taff.gov.uk

Cardiff & the Vale of Glamorgan: Mary Elizabeth Hassell. Coroner's Court and Offices, Central Police Station, Cathays Park, Cardiff CF10 3NN. Tel: 029 2022 2111 ext 30697/8/9. Fax: 029 2023 3886.

Neath & Port Talbot: Mr Phillip Rogers. The Coroner's Office, The Civic Centre, Oystermouth Road, Swansea SA1 3SN. Tel: 01792 636237. Fax: 01792 636603.

City & County of Swansea: Mr Phillip Rogers. As above.

SOUTH YORKSHIRE POLICE
Snig Hill, Sheffield S3 8LY.
Tel: 0114 220 2020. Fax: 0114 252 3888.
Email: firstname.lastname@southyorks.pnn.police.uk, unless otherwise indicated.
Website: www.southyorks.police.uk

Lord Lieutenant: Mr David Moody.
Police & Crime Commissioner: Shaun Wright.

Chief Constable: David Crompton QPM. Email: chief@southyorks.pnn.police.uk
T/Deputy Chief Constable: Max Sahota.
Assistant Chief Constable: Andy Holt.
T/Assistant Chief Constable: Simon Torr.
Staff Officer to the Chief Constable: Insp Richard Lambert.
Staff Officer to the Deputy Chief Constable: Sgt Clive Collings.
Director of Finance & Administration: Mr Nigel J Hiller CPFA FCCA.
Assistant Chief Officer (HR): Mr Ian Watson MBA MSc FCIPD.
Force Solicitor: Dr T Searl LLB MA PhD.

ADMINISTRATIVE SERVICES
Suite 3, Albion House, Savile Street, East, Sheffield S4 7UQ.
Head of Vehicle Fleet Management: Mrs Sarah Gilding. Unit 17 Churchill Way, Sheffield 35a Business Park, Chapeltown, Sheffield S35 2PY.
Head of Supply Chain Management: Mr Paul Whallet. Tel: 0114 296 3811.
Head of Facilities Management: Mr David Livingstone. Tel: 0114 296 3827.
Property Services Manager: Mr Paul Garner. Tel: 0114 296 3846.
Facilities Manager: Mr Keith Jones MBiSc. Tel: 0114 296 3856.
Facilities & Supply Chain Business Manager: Helen Willey. Tel: 0114 296 3885.
Head of Corporate Communications: Mr Mark Thompson BA(Hons) DipPR(CAM) MCIPR.

FINANCE
Head of Finance: Geoff Berrett BSc CPFA.
Exchequer Services Accountant: Robert Fennessy BSc CPFA.
Financial Accountant: Natalie Beal ACMA.
Insurance Manager: Jean Cookson BA(Hons) ACII.
Management Accountant: Debbie Carrington FCCA.
Systems Accountant: David Laughton ACMA.
Senior Payroll Officer: Mr A Marsden FMAAT MCIPP.

BUSINESS CHANGE DIRECTORATE
Head of Business Change Directorate: T/Supt Scott Green.
Information Manager: Mrs Lorraine Rogers MBA.
T/Diamond Programme Manager: Mrs Lorraine Rogers MBA.
Performance & Governance Unit: T/Chief Insp Mark Payling.
Business Manager: Mrs Jane Walker.

HR SERVICES
Deputy to ACO (HR): Supt Tim Innes.
Head of Training: Mrs Joanne Buck.
Head of Strategy & Change: Mrs Lorraine Booth.
HR Services Business Manager: Mrs Jane Walker.
Head of Shared Services: Miss Emma Siddy.
Conduct Manager: Ms Lorna Smith.
Diversity Manager: T/Chief Insp Simon Mellors.
Principal Health & Safety Advisor: Andy Helowicz BSc CMIOSH CertEd.
OCCUPATIONAL HEALTH UNIT
Senior Occupational Health Advisor: Sharon Nolan. Ext: 71 4780/81. Tel: 0114 296 4780. Email: occupationalhealth@southyorks.pnn.police.uk

STAFF ASSOCIATIONS
Police Federation: Joint Branch Board: *Secretary:* Clive McCready. Tel: 01709 832610. *Chairman:* Bob Pitt. Tel: 01709 832609.
UNISON: Glyn Boyington. Tel: 0114 252 3610.

TRAINING DEPARTMENT
South Yorkshire Police Training Centre, Robert Dyson House, Unit 5, Callflex Business Park, Wath-upon-Dearne, Rotherham S63 7EF9WL. Tel: 01709 723693. Fax: 01709 443706.

Head of Training: Joanne Buck MBA MCIPD PGCE.
  Email: jo.buck@southyorks.pnn.police.uk
OSPRE Contact: Julie Sherburn. Robert Dyson House, as above. Tel: 01709 443581. Fax: 01709 443706.

IS SHARED SERVICE – SOUTH YORKSHIRE & HUMBERSIDE
Head of IS: Mr Paul Thrustle.
ISD Administration: *Office Manager:* Mrs Julie Kyte.
Projects/Programme Delivery Manager: Jacqueline Bland.
Solutions Managers: Debbie Hillary; Kevin Priday.
Infrastructure & Communications Manager: Ian Maughan.
Infrastructure Managers: Andrew Stubbs; James Williams.
Service Delivery Manager: Mr Steve Harding.

CRIMINAL JUSTICE ADMINISTRATION DEPARTMENT
Chief Supt Rob Odell.
Superintendent (Integrated Offender Management & Restorative Justice): Nick Whitehouse.
Business Manager: Jane Wild.
Custody Suites, ID, Firearms Licensing: Chief Insp Jon Ekwubiri.
Firearms Licensing: Insp Tim Wright.
Explosive Liaison: FEO Russell Batty.
Warrants: Mrs Judith France.
Criminal Justice Manager: Mrs Anne-Marie Dempsey.

OPERATIONAL SUPPORT SERVICES
Chief Supt Rachel Barber.
Communications & Support: Supt Adrian Moran.
Call Centre Manager: Tracy Potter.
Operations/Support: Supt Simon Verrall.
Road Policing Group: Chief Insp Stuart Walne.
Firearms Support Group: Chief Insp Caroline Rollitt.
Tactical Support Group: Chief Insp Iain Chorlton.
Operational & Contingency Planning: Chief Insp Mark James.
Phoenix Bureau: Mrs Elizabeth Ellison.
Central Ticket Office: Ms Linda Kotke; Mrs Lynne Harrison.
Business Manager: Deborah Davis.
Administration Support Officer: Michelle Mottram.
COMMUNITY SAFETY
Community Safety Department: A/Supt Paul Varley.
Lifewise Centre Manager: Mrs Margaret Lawson.

SPECIALIST CRIME SERVICES
Force Crime Manager: Det Chief Supt Martyn Bates.
Director of Intelligence & Crime Operations: Det Supt James Abdy.
Major Crime: Det Supt Richard Fewkes.
Force Intelligence Bureau: Det Chief Insp Mark Foster.
Covert Operations: Det Supt Adrian Teague.
Economic Crime Unit: Graham Wragg.
Scientific Support: K Morton.
Public Protection Unit: Mr Pete Horner.
Business Manager: Mrs Joanna Fewkes.

PROFESSIONAL STANDARDS
Unit 20, Sheffield 35A Business Park, Churchill Way, Sheffield S35 2PY. Tel: 0114 292 1874. Fax: 0114 292 1885.
Head of Department: Chief Supt Neil Jessop.
Business Manager: Vacant.
Head of Information Compliance: Ms Gillian Bower-Lissaman.
Record Manager: Ms Nicola Hardy.
Vetting: Miss Kerry Walton.
Complaints & Discipline: Supt Vacant.

DONCASTER DISTRICT
1954 Barnsley Road, Scawsby, Doncaster DN5 8QE. Tel: 0114 220 2020.
District Commander: Chief Supt Richard Tweed.
Operations Superintendent: Eddie Murphy.
Chief Inspector (Response): Gwyn Thomas.
Support Superintendent: Peter Norman.

Chief Inspector (Safer Neighbourhoods): Neil Thomas.
Chief Inspector (Partnerships): Andy Kent.
Personnel Manager: Mrs Karen Lilley.
Business Manager: Mrs Helen Haigh.
Crime Manager: Det Chief Insp Craig Robinson.
Det Chief Inspector Public Protection: Chris Singleton.
Senior Investigating Officer: Vacant.
Custody Suite: Insp Richard Scholey.
CJU Manager: Mrs Karen Calladine.

BARNSLEY DISTRICT
Churchfields, Barnsley S70 2DL. Tel: 0114 220 2020. Fax: 01226 736373 (24 hrs).
District Commander: Chief Supt Andy Brooke.
Superintendent Operations: Liz Watson.
Chief Inspector: Andy Hodgkinson.
District Business Manager: Mrs Mary Verity.
Crime Manager: Det Chief Insp Mark Wilkie.
Personnel Manager: Heather Askwith.
Custody Suite: Insp Adrian Smith.
CJU: Cheryl Wynn; Kathryn Whittington.

ROTHERHAM DISTRICT
Main Street, Rotherham S60 1QY. Tel: 0114 220 2020. Fax: 01709 832252.
District Commander: Chief Supt Jason Harwin.
Chief Inspector (NPG): Ian Womersley.
Superintendent Operations: Andrew Parker.
Safer Neighbourhoods: Chief Insp Colin McFarlane.
Crime Manager: Det Chief Insp Dave Stopford.
Personnel Manager: Heather Askwith.
Business Manager: Mrs Mary Verity.
Custody Suite: Insp Karen Newton.
CJU: Mrs L Walker.

SHEFFIELD DISTRICT
60 Attercliffe Common, Sheffield S9 2AD. Tel: 0114 220 2020. Fax: 0114 296 3088.
District Commander: Chief Supt David Hartley.
Business Manager: Rachael Hayes.
HR Operational Partner: Catherine Parker.
Organisation Management Accountant: Sheryl Hawley.
Superintendent East Sector: Shaun Morley.
Superintendent West Sector: Martin Hemingway.
Operational Support & Crime: Supt Colin McFarlane.
Chief Inspector Partnerships: Paul McCurry.
Det Chief Inspector Crime Support: Bob Chapman.

Station	Division	Station	Division
Adwick	Doncaster	Main Street	Rotherham
Armthorpe	Doncaster	Maltby	Rotherham
Bentley	Doncaster	Mexborough	Doncaster
Brinsworth	Rotherham	Penistone	Barnsley
Cudworth	Barnsley	Rawmarsh	Rotherham
Deepcar	Sheffield	Rossington	Doncaster
Dinnington	Rotherham	Royston	Barnsley
Dodworth	Barnsley	Stainforth	Doncaster
Edlington	Doncaster	Thorne	Doncaster
Goldthorpe	Barnsley	Wath-upon-Dearne	Rotherham
Hammerton Road	Sheffield	Wharncliffe Flats	Rotherham
Hoyland	Barnsley	Woodseats	Sheffield

The following are designated police stations in accordance with s35, P.A.C.E. Act 1984: Doncaster (A); Barnsley (D); Wombwell (E); Rotherham (F); Moss Way (Sheffield) (H); West Bar (Sheffield) (I); Central Charge Office; Bridge Street (Sheffield) (I); Ecclesfield (Sheffield) (J); Attercliffe (Sheffield) (K).

HM CORONERS

East: Ms N J Mundy. Coroner's Court & Office, 5 Union Street, Off St Sepulchre Gate West, Doncaster DN1 3AE. Tel: 01302 320844. Fax: 01302 364833. Email: hmc.doncaster@doncaster.gov.uk

West: Mr C P Dorries OBE. Medico-Legal Centre, Watery Street, Sheffield S3 7ET. Tel: 0114 273 8721. Fax: 0114 272 6247.

STAFFORDSHIRE POLICE

Police Headquarters, Weston Road, Stafford ST18 0YY.
Tel: 101. Fax: 01785 232412 (09:00–17:00).
The dialling code for all numbers is 01785 unless otherwise indicated.
X400: c = GB; a = CWMAIL; p = PNN21MS; o = STAFFORDSHIRE
POLICE; s = POSTMASTER
Email: firstname.lastname@staffordshire.pnn.police.uk
Website: www.staffordshire.police.uk

Lord Lieutenant: Ian Dudson CBE.
Police & Crime Commissioner: Matthew Ellis. Police HQ, as above. Tel: 232400.

Chief Constable: Mike Cunningham QPM.
PA to Chief Constable: Mrs Jean Bristo. Tel: 232219.
Staff Officer to Chief Constable: Ms Deborah Wilne. Tel: 232383.
Deputy Chief Constable: Douglas Paxton.
Assistant Chief Constable (Investigative Services): Jane Sawyers.
Assistant Chief Constable (Local Policing & Operational Services): Julian Blazeby.
Director of Resources: Mr Graham Liddiard BSc CPFA.
Chief Officer of Special Constabulary: Michael Lane. Tel: 232221.
PA to DCC & Director of Resources: Mrs Janet Fellows. Tel: 232217.
PA to ACC Investigative Services, Local Policing & Operational Services: Ms Sarah Hands. Tel: 232120.

RESOURCES DIRECTORATE
Head of Business Development: Miss Christine Kelly. Tel: 232575.
FORCE BUSINESS SERVICES
Head of Force Business Services: Mrs Suzanne Birchall CPFA. Tel: 232196.
Head of Procurement: Miss Samantha Willetts. Tel: 232224.
Head of Payroll & Pensions: Mr Kevin Taplin. Tel: 232454.
Technical & Exchequer Accountant: Miss Nicola Roth. Tel: 232377.
Internal Business Support Accountant: Mr Robert Thorley. Tel: 235021.
Capital & Corporate Support Accountant: Mrs Jasmine Ross CPFA. Tel: 232448.
Estates & Facilities Manager: Ms Cheryl Mayer. Tel: 238656.
Transport Manager: Mr David Newbold. Tel: 232632.
PEOPLE SERVICES
Head of People Services: Vacant.
HR Senior Manager People Management: Vacant.
Performance Assessment: Supt Tim Martin.
People Performance Assessment Manager: Vacant.
Policy & Consultation Manager: Mrs Caroline Coombe MCIPD. Tel: 232562.
HR Support Manager: Miss Claire Arnold BA MCIPD. Tel: 232524.
HR System Development Manager: Ms Tracey Tyler. Tel: 232426.
HR Managers Business Support: Mrs Katherine Blundell. Tel: 232103. Mrs Janet Prescott. Tel: 235211.
Occupational Health, Safety & Welfare Manager: Ms Margaret Grahamslaw. Tel: 232037.
Learning & Development Managers: **Training Delivery:** Mr Philip Davies. Tel: 232268. **Strategic Development:** Mrs Linda Guthrie. Tel: 232431.

DEPUTY CHIEF CONSTABLE'S DIRECTORATE
Force Crime Manager: Mrs Tracy Shuker. Tel: 232597.
LEGAL SERVICES
Solicitor: Mr Herjinder Aoulick LLB(Hons). Tel: 232572.
CORPORATE COMMUNICATIONS
Head of Corporate Communications: Mr Ian Fegan. Tel: 232239.
Communications Managers: **Neighbourhood & Campaigns:** Mr David Bailey. Tel: 232425. **Public Relations:** Mrs Liz McGinn. Tel: 232230.
BENEFITS REALISATION
Head of Benefits Realisation: Mr Ralph Butler. Tel: 232537.
Benefits Realisation Consultants: Mr Paul Ross. Tel: 232521. Mr Neil Bullock. Tel: 232522. Mrs Catherine Acton. Tel: 232526.
Property Manager: Mrs Debbie Tallent.
Project Manager: Mrs Theresa Miles. Tel: 232462.

TECHNOLOGY SERVICES
Joint Head of ICT (Staffordshire & West Midlands forces): Mr Ron Bentley BSc(Hons) MBCS CEng CITP. Tel: 232197.
IS Development Manager: M Buckley. Tel: 232559.
IT Support Manager: Mr Paul Evans. Tel: 232277.
Communications Manager: Mr Christopher Bowen. Tel: 232424.
Service Delivery Manager: Mrs Sharon Athwal. Tel: 235028.
OPERATIONAL SERVICES
Head of Operational Services: Chief Supt Dave Forrest. Tel: 235177.
OPERATIONAL COMMUNICATIONS DEPARTMENT
Head of Operational Communications Department: Supt Peter Owen. Tel: 232792.
Deputy Head of Operational Communications Department: Chief Insp Paul Johnson. Tel: 235105.
CENTRAL JUSTICE SERVICES (STAFFORDSHIRE & WEST MIDLANDS POLICE)
Head of Central Justice Services: Chief Supt Stephen Anderson. Tel: 0845 113 5000 ext 078002614.
Deputy Head of Central Justice Services: Supt Peter Hall. Tel: 235239.
Continuous Improvement, ID & Traffic Process: Chief Insp Paul Trevor. Tel: 235284.
Custody: Chief Insp Karl Fellows. Tel: 0845 113 5000 ext 78002733.
Case Management, Witness Care & Court Liaison Manager: Mr Paul Gilbert. Tel: 234350.
Command Team Manager: Mrs Hilary Moss. Tel: 234350.
TACTICAL SUPPORT
Tactical Support Chief Inspector: Michael Boyle. Tel: 238881.
Tactical Support Inspector: Christopher Dawson. Tel: 238883.
CMPG Inspector: Derek Roberts.
Air Support Unit Sergeant: David Howell.
Firearms Licensing Manager: Mr Jonathan Cumberbatch. Tel: 232750.
CADRE
Cadre Superintendent: Vacant.
Business Continuity Chief Inspector: Amanda Davies. Tel: 232674.
Resourcing Chief Inspector: David Bird. Tel: 232726.
Tactical Planning Unit Chief Inspector: Michael Eyre. Tel: 233418.
Custody Chief Inspectors: Phil Fortun.
Roads Policing Chief Inspector: Stephen Smytheman. Tel: 232730.
INVESTIGATIVE SERVICES
Head of Investigative Services: Det Chief Supt Nick Baker. Tel: 232753.
Crime Review Team Manager: Mr Bernard Pearce. Tel: 238646.
INVESTIGATION NORTH
Det Supt David Mellor. Tel: 233011. Det Chief Insp Ricky Fields. Tel: 233328.
INVESTIGATION SOUTH
Det Supt Juliet Prince. Tel: 234750. Det Chief Insp David Garrett. Tel: 234751.
INTELLIGENCE
Head of Intelligence: Det Supt Stephan Popadynec. Tel: 238624.
Chief Insp Susan Hewett. Tel: 235119.
PROTECTING VULNERABLE PEOPLE
Head of Protecting Vulnerable People: Det Supt Ian Grant. Tel: 235290.
Deputy Heads of Protecting Vulnerable People: Det Chief Insp Helen Jones. Tel: 235156. Det Chief Insp Tim Martin. Tel: 2328639
STRATEGIC INVESTIGATION
Det Supt Wayne Jones. Tel: 232328.
Major Investigation Department: Det Chief Insp Darren Harding. Tel: 233676.
Serious & Organised Crime Unit/Economic Crime Unit: Det Chief Insp Paul Clews. Tel: 235101.
FORENSICS
Head of Forensics: Mr John Beckwith. Tel: 235252.
Digital Services Manager: Mr Howard Young.
Fingerprint Manager: Mr Tim Lee. Tel: 235285.
Forensic Services Manager: Mrs Claire Millar. Tel: 235113.
LOCAL POLICING
NORTH
Head of Local Policing, North: Chief Supt Bernie O'Reilly. Tel: 233050.
Superintendent Local Policing, Stoke-on-Trent: Laurie Whitby-Smith. Tel: 233051.

Local Policing Team Commanders
Stoke-on-Trent North: Chief Insp Adrian Roberts Tel: 235629.
Stoke-on-Trent South: Chief Insp Mark Dean. Tel: 233200.
Stoke-on-Trent Central: Chief Insp Jeffrey Moore. Tel: 233053.
Staffordshire Moorlands: Insp Clare Riley. Tel: 233812.
Newcastle Borough: Chief Insp Neil Hulme. Tel: 233451.
Integrated Offender Management Detective Chief Inspector: Simon Tweats. Tel: 233370.
Events & Football Liaison Manager: Mr Peter Aston. Tel: 234883.
Partnerships: Sgt Andrea Bayes.

SOUTH
Head of Local Policing, County: Chief Supt Jonathan Drake. Tel: 234050.
Superintendent, Local Policing: David Holdway. Tel: 234595.
Deputy Chief Officer, Special Constabulary: Simon Anderson. Tel: 233502.
Force Partnerships Co-ordinator: Mrs Helen Jarvie. Tel: 238333.

Local Policing Team Commanders
Stafford Borough: Chief Insp Scott Jones. Tel: 234040.
East Staffordshire: Chief Insp Steve Maskrey. Tel: 238251.
Tamworth Borough: Chief Insp Ian Coxhead. Tel: 234695.
Cannock Chase District: Chief Insp Carl Ratcliffe. Tel: 234200.
South Staffordshire: Insp Donna Gibbs. Tel: 238280.
Lichfield District: Insp Darren Oakey. Tel: 234560.

HM CORONERS

Staffordshire South: Mr Andrew A Haigh. Coroner's Office, 1 Staffordshire Place, Stafford ST16 2LP. Tel: 01785 276127. Fax: 01785 276128.

Stoke-on-Trent & North Staffordshire: Mr Ian S Smith. Coroner's Court Chambers, 547 Hartshill Road, Hartshill, Stoke-on-Trent ST4 6HF. Tel: 01782 234777. Fax: 01782 232074. Email: coroners@stoke.gov.uk

SUFFOLK CONSTABULARY
Martlesham Heath, Ipswich IP5 3QS.
Tel: 01473 613500. Fax: 01473 613585 (Control Room 24 hrs).
Email: headquarters@suffolk.pnn.police.uk
Website: www.suffolk.police.uk

Lord Lieutenant: Lord Tollemache.
Leader Suffolk County Council: Mr Mark Bee.
Police & Crime Commissioner: Tim Passmore.

Chief Constable: Mr Simon Ash.
T/Deputy Chief Constable: Mr Paul Marshall.
Assistant Chief Constable (*Norfolk & Suffolk Joint Protective Services*): Mr Charlie Hall.
T/Assistant Chief Constable (*Territorial Policing*): Mr Tim Newcomb.
T/Assistant Chief Constable (*Strategic Change & Collaboration*): Ms Sarah Hamlin.
Assistant Chief Officer (Resources): Mr Phillip Clayton ASCA.
Chief Officer, Special Constabulary: Mr Paul Goldsmith.
Staff Officer to the Chief Constable: Mr Andrew Doole.
Staff Officer to Assistant Chief Constables: Sgt Ben Hudson.

PROTECTIVE SERVICES COMMAND NORFOLK & SUFFOLK
Head of Protective Services Command (Crime) Norfolk & Suffolk: Det Chief Supt David Skevington. Tel: 01953 424853.
Head of Joint Protective Services Command (Operations) Norfolk & Suffolk: Chief Supt Bob Scully. Tel: 01953 424746.
Management Accountant Protective Services (Crime) Norfolk & Suffolk: Mr Mark Spratt. Tel: 01953 425699 ext 2858.
Management Accountant Protective Services (Operations) Norfolk & Suffolk: Ms Julie Hockley. Tel: 01473 613836.

CRIME
Head of Forensic Services Norfolk & Suffolk: Mr Alan Gilbert. Tel: 01953 424245.
Forensic Operations Manager Norfolk & Suffolk (Wymondham): Mr Mick House. Tel: 01953 424244.
Forensic Operations Manager Norfolk & Suffolk (Halesworth): Mr Paul Stafford. Tel: 01986 835051.
Forensic Support Manager Norfolk & Suffolk: Mr Julian Revitt-Smith. Tel: 01953 424246.
Head of Intelligence Level 1 Norfolk & Suffolk (Local & Central Intelligence): T/Det Supt Peter Hornby. Tel: 01953 424013.
Detective Chief Inspector Level 1 Intelligence Norfolk & Suffolk: Andy Quantrell. Tel: 01473 782631.
Head of Intelligence Level 2 Norfolk & Suffolk (Special Branch, CONFI Unit, CHIS): A/Det Supt David Cutler. Tel: 01473 613802.
Detective Chief Inspector Level 2 Intelligence Norfolk & Suffolk: Mark Afford. Tel: 01953 424306.
Head of Major Investigation Team Norfolk & Suffolk: Det Supt John Brocklebank. Tel: 01473 613707.
Detective Chief Inspector Major Investigation Team Norfolk & Suffolk: Neil Luckett. Tel: 01473 782025.
T/Detective Chief Inspectors Major Investigation Team Norfolk & Suffolk: Andy Guy. Tel: 01953 424544. Andy Smith. Tel: 01473 782044.
Head of Serious & Organised Crime Norfolk & Suffolk: Det Supt Alan McCullough. Tel: 01953 423682.
Operations Manager Serious & Organised Crime Norfolk & Suffolk: Det Chief Insp Stephen Mattin. Tel: 01473 613833.
High Tech Crime Unit Norfolk & Economic Crime Unit Suffolk: Det Insp Sean Coyne. Tel: 01953 423892.
Serious & Organised Crime Unit Norfolk & Suffolk: Det Insp Kathryn Thacker. Tel: 01953 424120.
Technical Support Unit Norfolk & Suffolk: Mr Adam Osborne. Tel: 01473 613856.
Head of Vulnerable People Directorate Norfolk: Det Supt Kate Elliott. Tel: 01603 276306.
Detective Chief Inspector Vulnerable People Directorate Norfolk: Julie Wvendth. Tel: 01603 276001.
Head of Public Protection Directorate Suffolk: Det Supt Alan Caton OBE. Tel: 01473 613701.
Detective Chief Inspector Public Protection Directorate Suffolk: Stuart McCallum. Tel: 01473 613899.

SPECIALIST OPERATIONS
Roads Policing & Firearms Operations: Chief Insp Chris Spinks. Tel: 01953 424872.
Operations Support: Chief Insp Adrian Dawson. Tel: 01473 613702.
Operations Planning: Mr Chris Eldridge. Tel: 01953 424894.
Firearms Licensing Services: Mr Richard Kennett. Tel: 01473 613608.

JUSTICE COMMAND NORFOLK & SUFFOLK
Command team for Norfolk & Suffolk

Norfolk & Suffolk Justice Commander: Chief Supt Les Parrett.
Norfolk & Suffolk Head of Criminal Justice Services: Mr Kevin Wilkins.
Norfolk & Suffolk Head of Custody Services: Chief Insp Roger Wiltshire.
Norfolk & Suffolk Head of Custody Investigations Unit: Det Chief Insp Kerry Cutler.
Norfolk Operational Business Manager: Mr Russell Wilkins.
Suffolk Operational Business Manager: Ms Jacqui Evans.

Norwich: CJS, Carmelite House, St James Court, Whitefriars, Norwich NR3 1SS. Tel: 01603 276952. Fax: 01603 276957.

King's Lynn: CJS, St James' Road, King's Lynn, Norfolk PE30 5DE. Tel: 01553 665052. Fax: 01553 665148.

NSPSIS Team: *Business Systems Administrator:* Carmelite House, as above. Tel: 01603 276281/276279. Fax: 01603 276957.

Streamline Processing Unit (based in Norwich): *Team Leader:* Mrs Amanda Ellis.

Central Ticket Office & Safety Camera Team (based in Norwich): c/o PO Box 3283, Norwich NR7 7ET. *CTO & Safety Camera Team Manager:* Mr Peter Anderson. Tel: 01603 276929. *Team Leader:* Mrs Amanda Wells. Tel: 02603 276402. Fax: 01603 276841.

Case Assessment Support: *Team Leader:* M Palmer. Tel: 01603 276875/276893. Fax: 01603 276906.

Case Assessment Team: *Team Leader:* Mr Barry Mason. Tel: 01603 276275/276893. Fax: 01603 276859.

Victim & Witness Services (based in Norwich): *Team Leader:* Mrs Simone Beaumont. Tel: 01603 276889. Fax: 01603 276261

Traffic Justice Unit (based in Lowestoft): *Team Leader:* Mrs Margaret Eaton. Tel: 01986 835162.

STRATEGIC CHANGE AND COLLABORATION
Strategic Change & Collaboration (Norfolk & Suffolk): T/Assistant Chief Constable Sarah Hamlin.

CORPORATE COMMUNICATIONS NORFOLK & SUFFOLK
Interim Head of Corporate Communications Norfolk & Suffolk Constabularies: Supt Malcolm Cooke.

HUMAN RESOURCES
Management team for HR – Norfolk & Suffolk

Director of HR: Mrs Rachel Wilkinson MCIPD.
Head of HR Operations (Norfolk & Suffolk): T/Chief Insp Lisa Hooper.
Head of HR Service Delivery (Norfolk & Suffolk): Mrs Marian Graveling LLM FCIPD.

PROFESSIONAL STANDARDS NORFOLK & SUFFOLK
Norfolk & Suffolk Head of Professional Standards: Supt Louisa Pepper.

PERFORMANCE AND ANALYSIS
Head of Performance & Analysis (Norfolk & Suffolk): Mrs Gemma Stannard.

ESTATES AND FACILITIES NORFOLK & SUFFOLK
Head of Estates & Facilities Manager (Norfolk & Suffolk): Mr Tony Byam MMIM MBIFM.
Estates Manager (Norfolk & Suffolk): Mr Duncan Potter BSc(Hons) MBA MRICS.
Facilities Manager (Norfolk & Suffolk): Mr Neil Critchley MBIFM.
PFI Contracts Manager (Norfolk & Suffolk): Mr Jonathan Henry MBIFM.

TRANSPORT SERVICES NORFOLK & SUFFOLK
Head of Transport Services (Norfolk & Suffolk): Mr Mark Davey MIMI.

FINANCIAL SERVICES
Joint Head of Finance (Norfolk & Suffolk): Mr Peter Jasper ACMA.
Payroll Services Manager: Mr Trevor Barnes.
Chief Accountant: Mrs Gillian Wreford.
Senior Financial Accountant: Mr Ivan Fearn.

PROCUREMENT AND SUPPLIES NORFOLK & SUFFOLK
Head of Procurement & Supplies (Norfolk & Suffolk): Mr Len Matthews.

INFORMATION SYSTEMS AND COMMUNICATIONS
Director of ICT (Norfolk & Suffolk): Mr James Close.
IT Service Improvement Manager: Mrs Lorraine Darling.
Project Managers: Mr Ronan Doorly; Mr Nigel Read; Mr Tom Howard; Mr Steve Johnson.
Airwave Services Manager: Mr David Woods.

INFORMATION MANAGEMENT
Information Compliance Manager: Mrs Hayley Youngs.
Information Security Manager: Mr Lee Scott.

COUNTY POLICING COMMAND
Tel: 01473 613500.
County Policing Commander: Chief Supt Jon Brighton.
CRIME INVESTIGATION
Detective Superintendent CPC Investigations: Stuart Sedgwick.
STRATEGIC COMMANDS
East
Lowestoft Police Station, Old Nelson Street, Lowestoft NR32 1PE.
Superintendent: Phil Aves.
Chief Inspector: Paul Sharp.
West
Bury St Edmunds Police Station, Raingate Street, Bury St Edmunds IP33 2AP.
Superintendent: Terry Byford.
Chief Inspectors: Kim Warner; Paul Bradford.
Ipswich
Landmark House, 4 Egerton Road, Ipswich IP1 5PF.
Superintendent: Martin Ransome. Tel: 01473 613888.
A/Chief Inspector: Andrew Mason. Tel: 01473 613888.
OPERATIONS
Tel: 01473 613500.
Chief Inspector (Operations Communications): Mike Bacon.
Chief Inspector (Community Safety): Jenny Powell.
Diversity Unit Manager: Mrs Liz Pettman.
Royalty & VIP Protection Norfolk & Suffolk: T/Supt Kevin Clarke. Tel: 01553 655210.
POLICE STATIONS AND OPENING TIMES
Tel: 01473 613500 (all stations)
Beccles: London Road, Beccles NR34 9TZ. (Daily 0900–1700, closed bank holidays.)
Brandon: 6 High Street, Brandon IP27 0AQ. (Mon, Thurs, Fri 1200–1400, closed bank holidays.)
Bungay & Southwold: Upper Olland Street, Bungay NR35 1BE. Station Road, Southwold IP18 6BB. (Open to public if officers are on duty/available.)
Bury St Edmunds: Raingate Street, Bury St Edmunds IP33 2AP. (Daily 0800–2000, bank holidays 0900–1700.)
Capel St Mary: Capel St Mary Police Station, Bentley Road, Capel St Mary IP9 2JN. (Mon, Wed, Fri 1000–1200, closed bank holidays.)
Felixstowe: 32 High Road West, Felixstowe IP11 9JE. (Daily 0900–1700, closed bank holidays.)
Framlingham: Fire Station, Saxmundham Road, Framlingham IP13 9DB. (Staffed by volunteers Mon, Tues, Thurs, Fri 0900–1300.)
Hadleigh: Magdalen Road, Hadleigh IP7 5AD. (Mon, Wed, Fri 1300–1500.)
Halesworth: Norwich Road, Halesworth IP19 8HJ. (Daily 0900–1700, closed bank holidays.)
Haverhill: Swan Lane, Haverhill CB9 9EQ. (Daily 0900–1700, closed bank holidays.)
Ipswich: Ipswich Police Station, Civic Drive, Ipswich IP1 2AW. (Daily 0800–2000, bank holidays 0900–1700.)
Ixworth: High Street, Ixworth IP31 2HN. (Mon, Wed, Fri 0900–1100.)
Leiston: 34 King's Road, Leiston IP16 4DA. (Daily, 0900–1700, closed bank holidays.)
Lowestoft: Old Nelson Street, Lowestoft NR32 1PE. (Daily 0800–2000, bank holidays 0900–1700.)
Mildenhall: Kingsway, Mildenhall IP28 7HS. (Daily 0900–1700, closed bank holidays.)
Newmarket: Vicarage Road, Newmarket CB8 8HR. (Daily 0900–1700, closed bank holidays.)
Stowmarket: Violet Hill Road, Stowmarket IP14 1NJ. (Daily 0900–1700, closed bank holidays.)
Sudbury: Acton Lane, Sudbury CO10 1QN. (Daily 0900–1700, closed bank holidays.)
Woodbridge: Grundisburgh Road, Woodbridge IP12 4HG. (Daily 0900–1700, closed bank holidays.)

Station or SNT base	Strategic Command	Station or SNT base	Strategic Command
Aldeburgh	East	Framlingham	East
Beccles	East	Hadleigh	West
Brandon	West	Halesworth	East
Bungay	East	Haverhill	West
Bury St Edmunds	West	Horringer	West
Capel Station	West	Ipswich	Ipswich
Clare	West	Ixworth	West
Debenham	West	Leiston	East
Elmswell	West	Lowestoft	East
Eye	West	Mildenhall	West
Felixstowe	East	Newmarket	West

Station or SNT base	*Strategic Command*	*Station or SNT base*	*Strategic Command*
Saxmundham	East	Sudbury	West
Southwold	East	Woodbridge	East
Stowmarket	West		

Locations in Suffolk designated under s35, P.A.C.E Act 1984 are: Police Investigation Centre (PIC), Police Headquarters, Martlesham Health, Ipswich; Police Investigation Centre (PIC), Bury St Edmunds.

HM CORONERS AND OTHER OFFICIALS

Suffolk: Dr Peter Dean. Bury St Edmunds Police Station, Raingate Street, Bury St Edmunds IP33 2AP. Tel: 01284 774167. Fax: 01284 774204.

Trading Standards
County Trading Standards Officer: Mr S Greenfield. Tel: 01473 264866.

SURREY POLICE

PO Box 101, Guildford, Surrey GU1 9PE.
Tel (non-emergency number and general contact): 101. Fax: 01483 634501(24 hrs).
Unless otherwise shown, telephone extensions in HQ can be obtained by dialling 01483 6 plus extension number.
X400: c = GB; a = CWMAIL; p = PNN45; o = SURREY POLICE; s = POSTMASTER.
Email: customerservice@surrey.pnn.police.uk
Email: unless otherwise stated, email addresses are all @surrey.pnn.police.uk
Website: www.surrey.police.uk

The following Surrey postal addresses are covered by 1) the Metropolitan Police: Addington, Addiscombe, Beddington, Belmont, Berrylands, Carshalton, Cheam, Chessington, Coulsdon, Croydon, Cuddington, Ditton Marsh, Hackbridge, Ham, Hook, Kenley, Kew, Kingston-upon-Thames, Malden & Coombe, Mitcham, Morden, Mortlake, Motspur Park, New Malden, Norbiton, Norbury, Petersham, Purley, Richmond, Sanderstead, Selsdon, Sheen East, Shirley, Stoneleigh, Surbiton, Sutton, Thornton Heath, Tolworth, Waddon, Wallington, Wimbledon, Worcester Park: 2) Hampshire Constabulary: Bentley, Blackwater, Bramshott Chase, Crondall, Darby Green, Ewshott, Frogmore, Grayshott, Hawley, Yateley: 3) Thames Valley Police: College Town, Little Sandhurst, Owlsmoor, Sandhurst (including the Royal Military Academy): 4) Sussex Police: Camelsdale, Fernhurst, Gatwick, Kingsley Green, Lynchmere & Marley.

Lord Lieutenant: Sarah Goad JP. Lord Lieutenant's Office, c/o County Hall, Penrhyn Road, Kingston-upon-Thames KT1 2DN.
Police & Crime Commissioner: Kevin Hurley.

Chief Constable: Lynne Owens. Ext: 39864. Email: owens3294
Staff Officer to Chief Constable: Insp Sarah Greenhalgh. Ext: 31141. Email: greenhalgh2219
PA to Chief Constable: Michaela Clements. Ext: 39864. Email: clements15060
Deputy Chief Constable: Craig Denholm. Ext: 31100. Email: denholm2997
Staff Officer to Deputy Chief Constable: Sgt Andy Crane. Ext: 37657. Email: crane1966
PA to Deputy Chief Constable: Mary Kennedy. Ext: 31406. Email: kennedy9951
Assistant Chief Constable: Jerry Kirkby. Ext: 31200. Email: kirkby958
Staff Officer to Assistant Chief Constable: Det Sgt Adam Tatton. Ext: 32114. Email: tatton2927
PAs to Assistant Chief Constable: Suzanne Hackett; Nicola Pope. Ext: 38037. Email: hackett7845; pope12266
Assistant Chief Constable (*Joint Command – Surrey/Sussex*): Olivia Pinkney. Email: pinkney242
Staff Officer to Assistant Chief Constable: Det Sgt Emma Heater. Tel: 01273 404005. Email: emma.heater@sussex.pnn.police.uk
PA to Assistant Chief Constable: Sgt Rachel Carr. Tel: 01273 404005. Email: rachel.carr@sussex.pnn.police.uk
Assistant Chief Officer: Clare Davies. Ext: 31400. Email: davies7455
Staff Officer to Assistant Chief Officer: Tamara Cooper. Ext: 37704. Email: cooper10732
Head of Audit Review Team (Force Crime & Incident Registrar): Frank Hemment. Ext: 30382. Email: hemment8924
Performance Manager: Jenny Stone. Ext: 38247. Email: stone13086

NEIGHBOURHOODS

Head of Neighbourhoods: Det Chief Supt Helen Collins. Ext: 38129. Email: collins1436
PAs to Head of Neighbourhoods: Louise Loader; Amanda Cusack. Ext: 32060. Email: loader14609; cusack11177
Northern Operating Base: Supt Jerry Westerman. Ext: 37172. Email: westerman1938
Western Operating Base: Chief Insp Mark Goodridge. Ext: 30768. Email: goodridge1599
Eastern Operating Base: Supt Matt Bristow. Ext: 38051. Email: bristow202
Central Neighbourhood Team: Insp Bob Jenkin. Ext: 32506. Email: jenkin2905

INVESTIGATIONS

Head of Investigation: Chief Supt Matthew Twist. Ext: tbc. Email: twist4687
PA to Head of Investigation: Sandie Devereux. Ext: 39490. Email: devereux13052
Reactive Investigation: T/Det Supt Darren McInnes. Ext: 39390. Email: mcinnes2536
Proactive Investigation: Det Supt Alan Sharp. Ext: 31344. Email: sharp327
Public Protection: Det Supt Jon Savell. Ext: 39421. Email: savell2616
Investigation Support & Criminal Justice: Det Supt R Blythe. Ext: 37169. Email: blythe186
Investigation Support: Chief Insp Santi Gil. Ext: 31086. Email: gil599
Criminal Justice Administration: Miss Samantha Goolding. Ext: 31289. Email: goolding8683

TASKING & CO-ORDINATION
Head of Tasking & Co-ordination: Chief Supt Charlie Doyle. Ext: 39385. Email: doyle210
PA to Head of Tasking & Co-ordination: Sandie Devereux. Ext: 39490. Email: devereux13052
Intelligence Support: T/Det Supt Maria Woodall. Ext: 30711. Email: woodall1249
Special Branch: T/Det Supt Stuart Sang. Ext: 31268. Email: sang1437
Operations: Supt Rachel Tills. Ext: 38747. Email: tills3776
Operations Planning: Chief Insp Paul Smith. Ext: 31130. Email: smith301
Covert Operations: Det Insp Ben Lee. Ext: 31744. Email: lee2353
Intelligence Management: Louise Sutton. Ext: 38244. Email: sutton9590
Intel Operations: Chief Insp David Mason. Ext: 31892. Email: mason2125

RESPONSE
Head of Response: Chief Supt David Miller. Ext: 33511. Email: miller4688
PA to Head of Response: Margie Jackson. Ext: 38055. Email: jackson10947
Contact Management: Supt Susan Lampard. Ext: 39051. Email: lampard242
Contact Centre Manager: Chief Insp Alison Barlow. Ext: 32526. Email: barlow1885
Targeted Response: Supt Johnny Johncox. Ext: 31814. Email: johncox1491
Targeted Patrol: T/Chief Insp Lynette Shanks. Ext: 31858. Email: shanks855
Force Control Rooms: Chief Insp Paul Farrow. Ext: 38728. Email: farrow76
Specialist Operations: Supt Johnny Johncox. Ext: 31814. Email: johncox1491
Superintendents' Secretariat. Ext: 39736. Email: secretarialpool

JOINT COMMAND – SURREY/SUSSEX
Head of Joint Command: Chief Supt Steve Barry. Tel: 07765 898067. Email: stephen.barry@sussex.pnn.police.uk
Forensic Investigations: Louise Whiteoak. Tel: 07920 501258. Email: louise.whiteoak@sussex.pnn.police.uk
Major Crime Team (MCT): Det Supt John Boshier. Ext: 37430. Email: boshier1820
Firearms: Supt Sharon Bush. Ext: 37428. Email: bush1492

CORPORATE COMMUNICATION
Head of Corporate Communications: Ruth Shulver. Ext: tbc. Email: tbc.
Media Relations Manager: Melenie Francis. Ext: 30881. Email: francis9427
Projects & Campaigns Manager: Helen Wilson. Ext: 30882. Email: wilson9503
Online & Production Manager: Catherine Holland. Ext: 30837. Email: holland12753
Officer Manager: Miss Natalie Gay. Ext: 38061. Email: gay12768

HUMAN RESOURCES
Head of Human Resources: Paul McElroy. Ext: 30416. Email: mcelroy12828
PA to Head of HR: Catherine De La Rue. Ext: 38928. Email: delarue8164
HR Operations Manager: Bill Davis. Ext: 38576. Email: davis14322
HR Policy & Development Manager (& Policy Lead): Dawn Runc. Ext: 31996. Email: runc10757
HR Consultancy Manager: Chris Milne. Ext: 34276. Email: milne14931
Occupational Health Manager: Liz Eades. Ext: 32003. Email: eades12901
Head of Learning & Development: Paul Cliff. Ext: 38272. Email: cliff9284

DIVERSITY
Head of Diversity: Mick Day. Ext: 30419. Email: day11585

LEGAL
Force Solicitor: Dawn Lelliott. Ext: 38024. Email: lelliott9282

PROFESSIONAL STANDARDS DEPARTMENT
Head of Professional Standards: Det Supt Ray Marley. Ext: 31736. Email: marley663
Office Manager: Stephen Howe. Ext: 39422. Email: howe12582

FINANCE AND SERVICES DEPARTMENT
Head of Finance: Paul Bundy. Ext: 39302. Email: bundy7922
PA to Head of Finance: Helen Tye. Ext: 31800. Fax: 01483 634857. Email: tye8718
Management Accounting Manager: Brian Sheriff. Ext: 36886. Email: sheriff13786
Finance Consultancy & Projects Manager: Bev Foad. Ext: 31943. Email: foad10815
Commercial Asset Manager: Liz Cannon. Ext: 39811. Email: cannon12675
Estates Project Manager: Judy Gavan. Ext: 32660. Email: gavan9563
Facilities Manager: Chris Jackson. Ext: 39844. Email: jackson8260
Procurement Manager: Dean Coulls. Ext: 39842. Email: coulls9476

INFORMATION AND COMMUNICATIONS TECHNOLOGY DEPARTMENT
Head of ICT: Ian Chandler. Ext: 38204. Email: chandler14709
Programme & Consultancy Manager: Rebecca Bee. Ext: 32059. Email: bee9071
Technical Design Manager: Paul Brimacombe. Ext: 32073. Email: 9685brimacombe
Operations Manager: Matthew Lockie. Ext: 32276. Email: lockie14628

POLICE FEDERATION
JBB Secretary: Simon Moxon. Ext: 31007. *Chairman:* Insp Mike Dodds. Ext: 37183. Fax: 01483 572828.
OSPRE Contact: Paul Richmond. Resource Officer, Training Centre, Surrey Police HQ, Mount Browne, Sandy Lane, Guildford GU3 1HG. Ext: 30440. Fax: 01483 634542.

Town	Division	Code	Town	Division	Code
Abinger Common	East	E	Eashing	West	W
			East Clandon	West	W
			East Horsley	West	W
Abinger Hammer	East	E	East Molesey	North	N
			Effingham	West	W
Addlestone	North	N	Egham	North	N
Albury	West	W	Ellen's Green	West	W
Alfold	West	W	Elstead	West	W
Alfold Crossways	West	W	Englefield Green	North	N
Ash	West	W	Epsom	East	E
Ashford	North	N	Esher	North	N
Ashtead	East	E	Ewell	East	E
Badshot Lea	West	W	Ewhurst	West	W
Bagshot	West	W	Ewhurst Green	West	W
Banstead	East	E	Fairlands	West	W
Beare Green	East	E	Farleigh	East	E
Betchworth	East	E	Farley Green	West	W
Bisley	West	W	Farncombe	West	W
Bletchingley	East	E	Farnham	West	W
Blindley Heath	East	E	Felbridge	East	E
Bowlhead Green	West	W	Felcourt	East	E
			Fetcham	East	E
Bramley	West	W	Flexford	West	W
Brockham	East	E	Forest Green	East	E
Brook	West	W	Fox Corner	West	W
Brookwood	West	W	Frensham	West	W
Buckland	East	E	Frimley	West	W
Burgh Heath	East	E	Godalming	West	W
Burntcommon	West	W	Godstone	East	E
Burpham	West	W	Gomshall	West	W
Burrowhill	West	W	Grayswood	West	W
Burstow	East	E	Great Bookham	East	E
Busbridge	West	W	Greyfriars	West	W
Byfleet	West	W	Guildford	West	W
Camberley	West	W	Hale	West	W
Capel	East	E	Hambledon	West	W
Caterham	East	E	Hascombe	West	W
Chaldon	East	E	Haslemere	West	W
Charlwood	East	E	Headley	East	E
Chertsey	North	N	Heath End	West	W
Chiddingfold	West	W	Henley Park	West	W
Chilworth	West	W	Hersham	North	N
Chipstead	East	E	Hindhead	West	W
Chobham	West	W	Holmbury St Mary	East	E
Churt	West	W			
Claygate	North	N	Hookwood	East	E
Cobham	North	N	Hooley	East	E
Coldharbour	East	E	Horley	East	E
Compton	West	W	Horne	East	E
Cranleigh	West	W	Horsell	West	W
Crowhurst	East	E	Hurst Green	East	E
Deepcut	West	W	Hydestile	West	W
Dippenhall	West	W	Jacob's Well	West	W
Donkey Town	West	W	Jayes Park	East	E
Dorking	East	E	Kenley	East	E
Dormans Park	East	E	Kingswood	East	E
Dormansland	East	E	Knaphill	West	W
Dunsfold	West	W	Laleham	North	N

Leatherhead	East	E
Leigh	East	E
Lightwater	West	W
Limpsfield	East	E
Lingfield	East	E
Littleton	North	N
Long Ditton	North	N
Longcross	North	N
Loxhill	West	W
Lyne	North	N
Mayford	West	W
Merstham	East	E
Mickleham	East	E
Milford	West	W
Millbridge	West	W
Mytchett	West	W
Newchapel	East	E
Newdigate	East	E
Normandy	West	W
North Holmwood	East	E
Norwood Hill	East	E
Nutfield	East	E
Ockham	West	W
Ockley	East	E
Okewood Hill	East	E
Onslow Village	West	W
Ottershaw	North	N
Outwood	East	E
Oxshott	North	N
Oxted	East	E
Parkgate	East	E
Peaslake	West	W
Peper Harow	West	W
Pirbright	West	W
Pitch Place	West	W
Puttenham	West	W
Pyrford Village	West	W
Pyrford	West	W
Ramsnest Common	West	W
Redhill	East	E
Reigate	East	E
Ripley	West	W
Rowledge	West	W
Rowly	West	W
Runfold	West	W
Rushmoor	West	W
Salfords	East	E
Seale	West	W
Send	West	W
Shackleford	West	W
Shalford	West	W
Shamley Green	West	W
Shepperton	North	N
Shere	West	W
Shipley Bridge	East	E
Shottermill	West	W
Sidlow	East	E
Smallfield	East	E
South Godstone	East	E
South Holmwood	East	E
South Nutfield	East	E
Spreakley	West	W
Staines	North	N
Stanwell	North	N
Stoke D'Abernon	North	N
Stoughton	West	W
Sunbury	North	N
Sutton Abinger	West	W
Sutton Green	West	W
Tadworth	East	E
Tandridge	East	E
Tatsfield	East	E
Thames Ditton	North	N
The Hermitage	East	E
Thorncombe Street	West	W
Thorpe	North	N
Thursley	West	W
Tilford	West	W
Tongham	West	W
Virginia Water	North	N
Walliswood	East	E
Walton-on-Thames	North	N
Walton-on-the-Hill	East	E
Warlingham	East	E
Wentworth	North	N
West Byfleet	West	W
West Clandon	West	W
West End	West	W
West Horsley	West	W
Westcott	East	E
Westfield	West	W
Westhumble	East	E
Weybridge	North	N
Wheelerstreet	West	W
Whiteley Village	North	N
Whyteleafe	East	E
Windlesham	West	W
Wisley	West	W
Witley	West	W
Woking	West	W
Woldingham	East	E
Woldingham Garden Villa	East	E
Wonersh	West	W
Wood Street Village	West	W
Woodham	North	N
Woodmansterne	East	E
Wormley	West	W
Worplesdon	West	W
Wotton	East	E
Wrecclesham	West	W

HM CORONER

County of Surrey: R Travers. Coroner's Court, Station Approach, Woking GU22 7AP. Tel: 01483 776138. Fax: 01483 765460.

SUSSEX POLICE

Sussex Police Headquarters, Church Lane, Lewes, Sussex BN7 2DZ.
Tel (non-emergency and general contact): 101. If calling from outside Sussex tel:
01273 470101. Minicom: 01273 483435. Fax: 01273 404274.
Email: chief.constable@sussex.pnn.police.uk
Website: www.sussex.police.uk

Lord Lieutenant, West Sussex: Mrs Susan Pyper.
Lord Lieutenant, East Sussex: Mr Peter Field.
Police & Crime Commissioner: Katy Bourne.

Chief Constable: Martin Richards. Ext: 544000.
Staff Officer: Det Chief Insp Michael Ashcroft.
EA: Jean Freeman.
Deputy Chief Constable: Giles York. Ext: 544010.
EA: Victoria Parsons.
Assistant Chief Constable: Robin Merrett. Ext: 544011.
Staff Officer: Vacant.
EA: Emma Chapman.
Assistant Chief Constable (Joint Command – Surrey/Sussex): Olivia Pinkney. Ext: 544473.
Staff Officer: Det Sgt Emma Heater.
EA: Sgt Rachel Carr. Ext: 5404005.
Director of Finance: Mark Baker. Ext: 544051.
Staff Officer: Kathy Wrathall.
EA: Michelle Redshaw.
Director of Human Resources: Marion Fanthorpe. Ext: 540585.
Executive Officer to DHR: Luella Bubloz.
EA: Julie Bishop.

DEPARTMENTS

OPERATIONS DEPARTMENT
Chief Supt Paul Morrison. Sussex Police Headquarters, as above. Ext: 544200.
HQ CRIMINAL INVESTIGATION DEPARTMENT
Det Chief Supt Steve Fowler. Sussex House, Brighton, East Sussex BN1 8AF. Ext: 559208.
INFORMATION TECHNOLOGY DEPARTMENT
Paul Hollister. HQ, as above. Ext: 540700.
CORPORATE DEVELOPMENT DEPARTMENT
David Paul. HQ, as above. Ext: 544475.
COMMUNICATIONS DEPARTMENT
Chief Supt Wayne Jones. HQ, as above. Ext: 544480.
COMMUNITY AND JUSTICE DEPARTMENT
Det Chief Supt Steve Fowler. Sussex House, Brighton BN1 8AF. Ext: 59208.
FINANCE DEPARTMENT
Mark Rowe. HQ, as above. Ext: 545450.
PROFESSIONAL STANDARDS DEPARTMENT
Supt Kenneth Taylor. HQ, as above. Ext: 540825.
ESTATES AND FACILITIES DEPARTMENT
Vaughan Williams. HQ, as above. Ext: 544059.
CORPORATE COMMUNICATIONS & PUBLIC ENGAGEMENT DEPARTMENT
Sue George. HQ, as above. Ext: 544230.

STAFF ASSOCIATIONS

Superintendents' Association: Chief Supt Graham Bartlett.
Police Federation Joint Branch Board: Insp Bob Brown.
UNISON: Andrew Stenning.

DIVISIONS
BRIGHTON & HOVE
John Street, Brighton, East Sussex BN2 0LA.
Hove Town Hall, Norton Road, Hove BN3 4AH.
Divisional Commander: A/Chief Supt Steve Whitton. Ext: 550300.
Neighbourhood Policing, Brighton & Hove: Chief Insp Helen West. Ext: 50567.

EAST SUSSEX
Grove Road, Eastbourne, East Sussex BN21 4UF.
Divisional Commander: Chief Supt Robin Smith. Ext: 567223.
Eastbourne District: Chief Insp Steve Biglands. Ext: 577425.
Lewes District: Chief Insp Jason Tingley. Ext: 540523.
Wealden District: Chief Insp Dick Coates. Ext: 568224.
Hastings District: Chief Insp Heather Keating. Ext: 560221.
Rother District: Chief Insp Katy Woolford. Ext: 564224.

GATWICK AIRPORT
Perimeter Road North, Gatwick, West Sussex RH6 0JE.
Head of Operations Department: Chief Supt Paul Morrison. Ext: 544200.
Crime & Operations Superintendent: Brian Bracher. Ext: 537200.

WEST SUSSEX
HQ: Crawley Police Station, Northgate Avenue, Crawley, West Sussex RH10 8BF.
Divisional Commander: Chief Supt Martin Walker. Ext: 531350.
Adur & Worthing District: T/Chief Insp Jo Banks. Ext: 581238.
Arun District: Chief Insp Jane Derrick. Ext: 585218.
Chichester District: T/Det Chief Insp Tanya Jones. Ext: 585235.
Crawley District: Chief Insp Justina Beeken. Ext: 531249.
Mid Sussex District: Chief Insp Jon Hull. Ext. 535225.
Horsham District: A/Chief Insp Howard Hodges. Ext: 530224.

Place	District	Place	District
Albourne	Mid Sussex	Colgate	Horsham
Aldingbourne	Arun	Copthorne	Mid Sussex
Alfriston	Wealden	Cowfold	Horsham
Amberley	Horsham	*Crawley	Crawley
Angmering	Arun	Crawley Down	Mid Sussex
Ardingly	Mid Sussex	Cross in Hand	Wealden
Arundel	Arun	Crowborough	Wealden
Ashington	Horsham	Cuckfield	Mid Sussex
Ashurst	Horsham	Dane Hill	Wealden
Ashurst Wood	Mid Sussex	Ditchling	Lewes
Balcombe	Mid Sussex	Duncton	Chichester
Barcombe	Lewes	*Eastbourne	Eastbourne
Barnham	Arun	East Dean	Eastbourne
Battle	Rother	*East Grinstead	Mid Sussex
Beckley	Rother	East Hoathly	Wealden
Bewbush	Crawley	East Preston	Arun
*Bexhill	Rother	Eridge	Wealden
Bignor	Chichester	Fairlight	Rother
Billingshurst	Horsham	Faygate	Horsham
Birdham	Chichester	Felpham	Arun
*Bognor Regis	Arun	Fernhurst	Chichester
Bolney	Mid Sussex	Ferring	Arun
Bosham	Chichester	Findon	Arun
Boxgrove	Chichester	Fishbourne	Chichester
Bramber	Horsham	Fittleworth	Chichester
Brede	Rother	Five Ashes	Wealden
*Brighton	Brighton & Hove	Fletching	Wealden
Broadbridge Heath	Horsham	Ford	Arun
Broadfield	Crawley	Forest Row	Wealden
Burgess Hill	Mid Sussex	Framfield	Wealden
Burpham	Arun	Frant	Wealden
Burwash	Rother	Fulking	Mid Sussex
Buxted	Wealden	Furnace Green	Crawley
Camber	Rother	*Gatwick	Gatwick
Chailey	Lewes	Gossops Green	Crawley
*Chichester	Chichester	Groombridge	Lewes
Chiddingly	Wealden	Guestling	Rother
Clapham	Arun	*Hailsham	Wealden
Clymping	Arun	Handcross	Mid Sussex
Cocking	Chichester	Hartfield	Wealden
Coldwaltham	Horsham	Harting	Chichester

Thank you for purchasing the Police and Constabulary Almanac.

 Don't miss important updates

So that you have all the latest information, the Police and Constabulary Almanac is published annually. Sign up today for a Standing Order to ensure you receive the updating copies as soon as they publish. Setting up a Standing Order with Sweet & Maxwell is hassle-free, simply tick, complete and return this FREEPOST card and we'll do the rest.

You may cancel your Standing Order at any time by writing to us at Sweet & Maxwell, PO Box 1000, Andover, SP10 9AH stating the Standing Order you wish to cancel.

Alternatively, if you have purchased your copy of the Police and Constabulary Almanac from a bookshop or other trade supplier, please ask your supplier to ensure that you are registered to receive the new editions.

All goods are subject to our 30 day Satisfaction Guarantee (applicable to EU customers only)

Yes, please send me new editions of the Police and Constabulary Almanac to be invoiced on publication, until I cancel the standing order in writing.

☐ All new editions

Title   Name

Organisation

Job title

Address

Postcode

Telephone

Email

S&M account number (if known)

PO number

All orders are accepted subject to the terms of this order form and our Terms of Trading (see www.sweetandmaxwell.co.uk). By submitting this order form I confirm that I accept these terms and I am authorised to sign on behalf of the customer.

Signed   Job Title

Print Name   Date

UK VAT Number: GB 900 5487 43. Irish VAT Number: IE 9513874E. For customers in an EU member state (except UK & Ireland) please supply your VAT Number. VAT No ☐

(BC003) V9 (03.2013) LC / KG

Delivery charges are not made for titles supplied to mainland UK. Non-mainland UK please add £4/€5 per delivery. Europe - please add £10/€13 for first item, £2.50/€3 for each additional item. Rest of World - please add £30/€38 for first item, £15/€19 for each additional item. For deliveries outside Europe please add £30/€42 for first item, £15/€21 for each additional item.

Goods will normally be dispatched within 3-5 working days of availability. The price charged to customers, irrespective of any prices quoted, will be the price specified in our price list current at the time of dispatch of the goods, as published on our website, unless the order is subject to a specific offer or discount in which case special terms may apply.

UK VAT is charged on all applicable sales at the prevailing rate except in the case of sales to Ireland where Irish VAT will be charged at the prevailing rate. Customers outside the EU will not be charged UK VAT.

Thomson Reuters (Professional) UK Limited – Legal Business (Company No. 1679046). 100 Avenue Road, Swiss Cottage, London NW3 3PF. Registered in England and Wales. Registered office: Aldgate House, 33 Aldgate High Street, London EC3N 1DL. Trades using various trading names, a list of which is posted on its website at sweetandmaxwell.co.uk

"Thomson Reuters" and the Thomson Reuters logo are trademarks of Thomson Reuters and its affiliated companies.

SWEET & MAXWELL

 **THOMSON REUTERS**

SWEET & MAXWELL

FREEPOST

PO BOX 1000

ANDOVER

SP10 9AH

UNITED KINGDOM

Place	District	Place	District
Hassocks	Mid Sussex	Rake	Chichester
*Hastings	Hastings	Ringmer	Lewes
*Haywards Heath	Mid Sussex	Robertsbridge	Rother
Heathfield	Wealden	Rodmell	Lewes
Henfield	Horsham	Rotherfield	Wealden
*Horsham	Horsham	Rudgwick	Horsham
Horsted Keynes	Mid Sussex	Rusper	Horsham
Houghton	Arun	Rustington	Arun
*Hove	Brighton & Hove	Rye	Rother
Hurst Green	Rother	Sayers Common	Mid Sussex
Hurstpierpoint	Mid Sussex	Seaford	Lewes
Icklesham	Rother	Sedlescombe	Rother
Ifield	Crawley	Selmeston	Wealden
Isfield	Wealden	Selsey	Chichester
Itchingfield	Horsham	Shermanbury	Horsham
Lancing	Adur	Shipley	Horsham
Langley Green	Crawley	*Shoreham	Adur
Lavant	Chichester	Sidlesham	Chichester
*Lewes	Lewes	Singleton	Chichester
Linchmere	Chichester	Slindon	Arun
Lindfield	Mid Sussex	Slinfold	Horsham
*Littlehampton	Arun	Sompting	Adur
Lodsworth	Chichester	South Stoke	Arun
Lower Beeding	Horsham	Southbourne	Chichester
Loxwood	Chichester	Southgate	Crawley
Lyminster	Arun	Southgate West	Crawley
Maidenbower	Crawley	Southwater	Horsham
Mannings Heath	Horsham	Southwick	Adur
Maresfield	Wealden	Staple Cross	Rother
Mark Cross	Wealden	Steyning	Horsham
Mayfield	Wealden	Storrington	Horsham
Maynards Green	Wealden	Sullington	Horsham
Merston	Chichester	Thakeham	Horsham
Middleton	Arun	Three Bridges	Crawley
Midhurst	Chichester	Ticehurst	Rother
Netherfield	Rother	Tilgate	Crawley
*Newhaven	Lewes	Tortington	Arun
Newick	Lewes	Trotton	Chichester
Newtimber	Mid Sussex	Turners Hill	Mid Sussex
Ninfield	Rother	Twineham	Mid Sussex
Northchapel	Chichester	Uckfield	Wealden
Northgate	Crawley	Upper Beeding	Horsham
Northiam	Rother	Wadhurst	Wealden
Nuthurst	Horsham	Warnham	Horsham
Nutley	Wealden	Warningcamp	Arun
Pagham	Arun	Washington	Horsham
Parham	Horsham	West Chiltington	Horsham
Partridge Green	Horsham	West Green	Crawley
Patching	Arun	West Grinstead	Horsham
Peacehaven	Lewes	West Hoathly	Mid Sussex
Pease Pottage	Mid Sussex	Westbourne	Chichester
Peasmarsh	Rother	Westfield	Rother
Petworth	Chichester	Westham	Wealden
Pevensey Bay	Wealden	Winchelsea	Rother
Plumpton	Lewes	Windmill Hill	Wealden
Polegate	Wealden	Wisborough Green	Chichester
Polling	Arun	Wiston	Horsham
Pound Hill	Crawley	Witterings	Chichester
Poynings	Mid Sussex	Wivelsfield	Lewes
Pulborough	Horsham	Woodmancote	Horsham
Pyecombe	Mid Sussex	Worth	Mid Sussex
Rackham	Horsham	*Worthing	Worthing

Place	District
Place	*District*
Yapton	Arun

* Denotes station designated under s35, P.A.C.E. Act 1984.

HM CORONERS AND OTHER OFFICIALS

City of Brighton & Hove: Veronica Hamilton-Deeley LLB. The Coroner's Office, Woodvale, Lewes Road, Brighton BN2 3QB. Tel: 01273 292046. Fax: 01273 292047.

East Sussex: Mr A R Craze LLB. 28–29 Grand Parade, St Leonard's-on-Sea TN37 6DR. Tel: 01424 200144. Fax: 01424 200145.

West Sussex: Penelope A Schofield. County Record Office, Orchard Street, Chichester, West Sussex PO19 1DD. Tel: 01243 753642. Fax: 01243 753644.

RSPCA

National HQ, Wilberforce Way, Southwater, Horsham, West Sussex RH13 9RS. Tel: 0870 010 1181. *Inspectors:* RSPCA, PO Box 313, Maidstone, Kent ME14 5YG. Tel: 0870 5555 999.

NSPCC

Children's Services Team, Broadfield House, Brighton Road, Crawley, West Sussex RH11 9RZ. Tel: 01293 449200.

THAMES VALLEY POLICE
Oxford Road, Kidlington, Oxfordshire OX5 2NX.
Tel: 101. Dialling code for all numbers is 01865, unless otherwise indicated.
Fax: 01865 846160 (operational).
Email: firstname.lastname@thamesvalley.pnn.police.uk
Website: www.thamesvalley.police.uk

The Thames Valley Police area consists of the historical counties of Berkshire, Buckinghamshire and Oxfordshire and is divided into 15 local policing areas (LPAs).

Police & Crime Commissioner: Anthony Stansfeld.

Chief Constable: Sara Thornton QPM CBE. Tel: 846002.
Deputy Chief Constable: Francis Habgood QPM. Tel: 846601.
Assistant Chief Constable (Crime & Counter Terrorism): Alan Baldwin. Tel: 846300.
Assistant Chief Constable (Operations): John Campbell. Tel: 846501.
Assistant Chief Constable (Neighbourhood Policing & Partnerships): Richard Bennett. Tel: 846200.
Director of Information, Science & Technology: Amanda Cooper. Tel: 846702.
Director of Human Resources: Dr Steven Chase MA DBACF CFCIPD. Tel: 855635. Fax: 855599.
Director of Corporate Finance: Linda Waters. Tel: 855400.

PORTFOLIOS
DEPUTY CHIEF CONSTABLE
Deputy Chief Constable: Francis Habgood QPM. Tel: 846601.
Head of Legal Services: Guy Lemon. Tel: 846305. Fax: 846305.
Head of Professional Standards: Det Chief Supt Nicola Ross.
Head of Performance: Peter Warner. Tel: 846113.
Head of Change: Daniel Hale.
Head of Corporate Support: Nick Harverson. Tel: 846264.
Collaboration & Protective Services: Supt Amanda Pearson.
Force Risk Manager & Business Continuity Manager: Jackie Orchard. Tel: 846278.
Head of Property Services: David Griffin FRICS. Tel: 283790.
Head of Transport Consortium: Sam Sloan. Tel: 01869 364815.
ASSISTANT CHIEF CONSTABLE CRIME & COUNTER-TERRORISM
Tel: 101, unless otherwise stated.
Assistant Chief Constable (Crime & Counter Terrorism): Alan Baldwin. Tel: 846300.
Force Crime & Investigations: Det Chief Supt Andrew Murray.
Intelligence & Specialist Operations: Chief Supt Brendan O'Dowda.
LPAS
Cherwell & West Oxfordshire: Supt Colin Paine.
Oxford City: Supt Christian Bunt.
South Oxfordshire & Vale of White Horse: Supt Andy Boyd.
ASSISTANT CHIEF CONSTABLE OPERATIONS
Tel: 101, unless otherwise stated.
Assistant Chief Constable (Operations): John Campbell. Tel: 846501.
Tasking & Resilience: A/Chief Supt Andrew Standen.
Control Room & Enquiries Department: Supt Howard Stone.
LPAS
Bracknell: Chief Insp Dave Gilbert.
Reading: Supt Stuart Greenfield.
Slough: Supt Richard Humphrey.
West Berkshire: Supt Robin Rickard.
Windsor & Maidenhead: Supt Simon Bowden.
Wokingham: Chief Insp Rob France.
JOINT OPERATIONS UNIT (HAMPSHIRE & THAMES VALLEY POLICE)
Email: operational.support@hampshire.pnn.police.uk
Chief Supt C Shead. Tel: 01962 871093.
Supt R Burrows. Tel: 023 8074 5358.
Operational Support (Operational Policy): Chief Insp J Malley. Tel: 01962 871501.
Emergency Planning: Mr G Snelgrove. Tel: 01962 871088.
Dog Section: Insp J Ramsbottom. Tel: 01993 814082.
Tactical Firearms Support Unit: Supt T Ismay; Chief Insp T Ashman. Tel: 023 8060 4741.

ASSISTANT CHIEF CONSTABLE NEIGHBOURHOOD POLICING & PARTNERSHIPS
Tel: 101, unless otherwise stated.
Assistant Chief Constable (Neighbourhood Policing & Partnerships): Richard Bennett. Tel: 846200.
Head of Neighbourhood Policing & Partnerships: Chief Supt Tim De Meyer.
Head of Criminal Justice: Supt Gez Chiariello.

LPAS
Aylesbury: Supt George Wrigley.
Milton Keynes: Supt Barry Halliday.
Chiltern & South Bucks: Supt Steve Hockin.
Wycombe: Supt Gilbert Houalla.

INFORMATION, SCIENCE & TECHNOLOGY
Director of Information, Science & Technology: Amanda Cooper. Tel: 846701.
Head of Corporate Communications: Michelle Nichols. Tel: 866482.
Head of Procurement: Sheena Evans. Tel: 293750.

INFORMATION COMMUNICATION TECHNOLOGY DEPARTMENT (HAMPSHIRE & THAMES VALLEY POLICE)
Email: it.services@hampshire.pnn.police.uk
Head of IT & Communications Services (Hampshire & Thames Valley Police): Steve Vercella. Tel: 01865 846603; 01962 875048.
Service Delivery Manager: Adrian Hudson. Tel: 01962 871228.
ICT Programme Manager: Brian Gibbins. Tel: 01962 871228.
Business Engagement Manager: Steve Bottom. Tel: 01865 846970.

JOINT INFORMATION MANAGEMENT DEPARTMENT (HAMPSHIRE & THAMES VALLEY POLICE)
Head of Information Management (Hampshire & Thames Valley Police): Marion Peulevé. Tel: 01865 846140.
Public Access Manager (Hampshire & Thames Valley Police): Jason Russell. Tel: 01962 871014.
Information Governance Manager (Hampshire & Thames Valley Police): Paul Church. Tel: 01865 846008.
Records Management (Hants & TVP): Mark Gould. Tel: 846179.

RESOURCES
Director of Human Resources: Dr Steven Chase MA DBACF CFCIPD. Tel: 855635. Fax: 855599.
Head of HR Business Services: Supt Jill Simpson. Tel: 855701. Fax: 855599.
Head of HR Business Partnering: John Summers. Tel: 855618.
Head of Learning & Development: David Backhouse. Tel: 0118 932 5600.
Director of Corporate Finance: Linda Waters. Tel: 855400.

HM CORONERS
Berkshire: Peter J Bedford. Yeomanry House, 131 Castle Hill, Reading RG1 7TA. Tel: 0118 93 3529. Fax: 0118 937 5448. Email: coroner@reading.gov.uk
Buckinghamshire: Richard A Hulett. The Gables, Market Square, Princes Risborough HP27 0AN. Tel: 01844 273121. Fax: 01844 275755. Email: c-rhulett@buckscc.gov.uk
Milton Keynes: Thomas Osborne. Milton Keynes Council, Civic Offices, 1 Saxon Gate, Milton Keynes MK9 3EJ. Tel: 01908 254326. Fax: 01908 253636. Email: coroners.office@milton-keynes.gov.uk
Oxfordshire: Darren Salter. Oxfordshire Coroner's Office, Oxford Register Office, 1 Tidmarsh Lane, Oxford OX1 1NS. Tel: 01865 815020. Fax: 01865 783391. Email: coroners.oxfordshire@oxfordshire.gov.uk

WARWICKSHIRE POLICE
PO Box 4, Leek Wootton, Warwick CV35 7QB.
Tel: 01926 415000. Fax: 01926 850362 (24 hrs). Fax: 01926 415188 (office hours).
The dialling code for all numbers is 01926, unless otherwise indicated.
Email: firstname.lastname@warwickshire.pnn.police.uk
Website: www.warwickshire.police.uk

Lord Lieutenant: Mr Martin Dunne JP.
Police & Crime Commissioner: Mr Ron Ball. Tel: 412322.

Chief Constable: Mr Andy Parker QPM.
Staff Officer: Sgt Mandy Crust. Tel: 415007.
PA: Ms Dawn Cross. Tel: 415002.
T/Deputy Chief Constable: Mr Neil Brunton. Tel: 415008.
PA: Ms Dawn Cross. Tel: 415002.
Assistant Chief Constable, Director Local Policing (*Warwickshire & West Mercia*): Mr Gareth Morgan.
PA: Ms Catherine Allsopp. Tel: 01905 332266.
Assistant Chief Constable, Director Protective Services (*Warwickshire & West Mercia*): Ms Karen Manners.
PA: Mrs Jan Horton. Tel: 415089.
Director of Enabling Services (*Warwickshire & West Mercia*): Mr Richard Elkin. Tel: 415016.
PA: Mrs Clare Dance. Tel: 415016.
Director of Finance (*Warwickshire & West Mercia*): Ms Heather Costello.
PA: Ms Pauline Hardwick. Tel: 01905 332287.
Specials Chief Officer: Mr Glyn Gardner. Ext: 8669.

Warwickshire Police has entered into a joint force collaboration with West Mercia Police. Each force retains a separate Chief Constable and Deputy Chief Constable, responsible for their respective geographical policing areas, who will commission policing services from the wider joint chief officer team which will serve both forces. Gold Command cover for major operational incidents in Warwickshire and West Mercia will also be provided by the joint chief officer team. See also www.westmercia.police.uk

LOCAL POLICING DIRECTORATE
Head of Territorial Policing: Det Chief Supt Martin McNevin. Ext: 3751.
North Warwickshire Territorial Policing Unit: Supt Martin Samuel. Ext: 3021.
South Warwickshire Territorial Policing Unit: Supt Debra Tedds. Ext: 4328.
Head of Operational Support (*Warwickshire & West Mercia*): Supt Charlie Hill. Tel: 03003 333000 ext 67894.

PROTECTIVE SERVICES DIRECTORATE
Head of Crime (*Warwickshire & West Mercia*): Det Chief Supt Andy Rowsell. Tel: 03003 333000 ext 2270.
Head of Force Intelligence (*Warwickshire & West Mercia*): Det Supt Mark Travis. Tel: 03003 333000 ext 2985.
Head of Major Investigation Unit (*MIU*) (*Warwickshire & West Mercia*): Det Supt Adrian McGee. Ext: 8088
Head of Protecting Vulnerable People (*PVP*) (*Warwickshire & West Mercia*): Det Supt Amanda Blakeman. Tel: 03003 333000 ext 5914.
Head of Force Operations (*Warwickshire & West Mercia*): Supt Lee Davenport. Tel: 03003 333000 ext 2795.
Head of Specialist Operations (*Warwickshire & West Mercia*): Det Supt Daryn Elton. Tel: 03003 333000 ext 60780.
Head of Forensic Services: Ms Amanda Harrison. Tel: 684947.
Crime Manager (*Warwickshire & West Mercia*): Det Supt Graeme Pallister. Tel: 415031.

ENABLING SERVICES DIRECTORATE
Head of Business Assurance & Improvement (*Warwickshire & West Mercia*): Ms Michelle Buttery BA(Hons). Tel: 01905 332332.
Head of Estates Services (*Warwickshire & West Mercia*): Mr Jim Stobie. Tel: 01905 331559.
Head of Contract & Procurement Services (*Warwickshire & West Mercia*): Ms Ann Church. Tel: 01905 331621.
Head of People Services (*Warwickshire & West Mercia*): Ms Tania Coppola. Tel: 415731.
Head of Workforce Development (*Warwickshire & West Mercia*): Supt Steve Eccleston. Tel: 03003 333000 ext 2470.

Head of Corporate Communications: Mr Carl Baldacchino. Tel: 415063.
Head of Information, Communication & Technology Services (Warwickshire & West Mercia): Mr Wayne Parkes. Tel: 415801.
Head of Transport Services: Mr Paul Raisen. Tel: 415034.

FINANCE DIRECTORATE

Head of Corporate Finance: Mr Jeff Carruthers. Tel: 415880.
Head of Resource Management (Warwickshire & West Mercia): Ms Rachel Hartland-Lane. Tel: 01905 332225.

STAFF ASSOCIATIONS

Superintendents' Association: *Chair:* Supt Steve Burrows. Warwickshire Police, PO Box 4, Warwick CV35 7QB. Tel: 415731.
Police Federation: *Chair:* PC Simon Payne. Police Federation Office, Warwickshire Police Federation, 8 Barford Exchange, Barford, Warwick CV35 8AQ.
UNISON: *Branch Secretary:* Mr Lee Bowers. Unison, 8 Barford Exchange, Barford, Warwick CV35 8AQ. Tel: 684387

POLICE LOCATIONS WITH DIRECT PUBLIC CONTACT POINTS

Warwickshire Justice Centre Nuneaton. Vicarage Street, Nuneaton CV11 4DW. Open: 24 hours. Tel: 02476 641111.
Warwickshire Justice Centre Leamington Spa. Newbold Terrace, Leamington Spa CV32 4EL. Open: daily 0800–2400. Tel: 01926 451111.
Rugby Police Station. Newbold Road, Rugby CV21 2DH. Open: daily 0800–2000. Tel: 01788 541111.
Stratford Police Station. Rother Street, Stratford-upon-Avon CV37 6RD. Open: daily 0800–2000. Tel: 01789 414111.

PARTNERSHIP LOCATIONS WITH DIRECT POLICE CONTACT POINTS

Alcester. Warwickshire Direct, Globe House, Priory Road, Alcester B49 5DZ. Open: Mon–Fri 0900–1700. Tel: 01789 762207.
Atherstone. Warwickshire Direct North Warwickshire, Council House, South Street, Atherstone CV9 1BD. Open: Mon–Fri 0830–1715. Tel: 01827 718092.
Bedworth. Warwickshire Direct Bedworth, Nuneaton & Bedworth Area Office, High Street, Bedworth CV12 8NF. Open: Mon–Fri 0900–1700. Tel: 02476 641111.
Coleshill. Warwickshire Direct Coleshill, 19a Parkfield Road, Coleshill B46 3LD. Open: Tues 0900–1900, Thurs 0900–1800; Fri 0900–1800, Sat 0930–1400. Tel: 01675 464444.
Kenilworth. Warwickshire Direct Kenilworth, Smalley Place, Kenilworth CV8 1QG. Open: Mon & Thurs 0900–1900, Tues & Fri 0900–1730, Wed 1030–1730, Sat 0900–1600. Tel: 01926 851111.
Shipston. Warwickshire Direct Shipston, 12 Church Street, Shipston-on-Stour CV36 4AP. Open: Mon 09300–1700, Tues & Thurs 0930–1900, Fri 0930–1300, Sat 0930–1230. Tel: 01608 661415.
Southam. Warwickshire Direct Southam, High Street, Southam CV47 0HB. Open: Mon, Wed, Fri 0900–1700, Tues & Thurs 0900–1900, Sat 0930–1330. Tel: 01926 812366.
Warwick. Warwickshire Direct, Shire Hall, Market Square, Warwick CV34 4SA. Open: Mon–Thurs 0800–1730, Fri 0800–1700, Sat 0900–1600. Tel: 01926 410111.
Full contact details to be used by members of the public can be found here: www.warwickshire.police.uk/contactingthepolice/Policepubliccontactpoints

PARISHES

Alcester	Bedworth	Burton Hastings	Dorsington
Alderminster	Bidford-on-Avon	Butlers Marston	Dunchurch
Alveston	Bilton	Caldecote	Earlswood
Ansley	Binton	Cawston	Eathorpe
Arley	Birdingbury	Charlecote	Ettington
Ash Green	Bishops Itchington	Cherrington	Exhall
Ashow	Bishops Tachbrook	Chesterton	Fenny Compton
Aston Cantlow	Blackdown	Church Lawford	Fillongley
Atherstone	Bourton-on-	Churchover	Frankton
Austrey	Dunsmore	Claverdon	Furnace End
Avon Dassett	Brailes	Clifford Chambers	Gaydon
Baddesley Clinton	Brandon	Clifton-on-Dunsmore	Grandborough
Baddesley Ensor	Brinklow	Coleshill	Great Alne
Baginton	Brownsover	Combrook	Great Wolford
Barford	Bubbenhall	Corley	Grendon
Barton-on-the-Heath	Budbrooke	Coughton	Halford
Baxterley	Bulkington	Cubbington	Hampton
Bearley	Burmington	Curdworth	Hampton Lucy
Beausale	Burton Dassett	Dordon	Harborough Magna

Harbury	Lower Shuckburgh	Ratley & Upton	Thurlaston
Hartshill	Loxley	Rowington	Tredington
Haseley	Mancetter	†Rugby	Tysoe
Haselor	Marton	Ryton-on-Dunsmore	Ufton
Hatton	Maxstoke	Salford Priors	Ullenhall
Henley-in-Arden	Monks Kirby	Sambourne	Upper Shuckburgh
Honiley	Moreton Morrell	Sherbourne	Wappenbury
Honington	Napton-on-the-Hill	Shilton	Warmington
Hunningham	Nether Whitacre	Shipston-on-Stour	Warwick
Ilmington	Newbold-on-Stour	Shotteswell	Wasperton
Kenilworth	Norton Lindsey	Shrewley	Water Orton
Keresley Part	†*Nuneaton	Shustoke	Welford-on-Avon
Kineton	Offchurch	Shuttington	Wellesbourne
Kingsbury	Old Milverton	Snitterfield	Weston-under-
Ladbroke	Over Whitacre	Southam	Wetherley
Langley	Oxhill	Southern Hastings	Whichford
Lapworth	Packington	Stockingford	Whitnash
Lea Marston	Pailton	Stockton	Willey
†Leamington Spa	Pillerton Priors	Stoneleigh	Willoughby
Leek Wootton	Polesworth	Stratford-upon-Avon	Wishaw
Lighthorne	Preston-on-Stour	Stretton-on-	Withybrook
Little Compton	Princethorpe	Dunsmore	Wolston
Long Compton	Priors Hardwick	Stretton-on-Fosse	Wolvey
Long Itchington	Priors Marston	Stretton-under-Fosse	Wormleighton
Long Lawford	Radford Semele	Studley	Wootton Wawen
Long Marston	Radway	Tanworth-in-Arden	Wroxall

* Denotes stations staffed 24 hours per day.
† Denotes stations designated under s35, P.A.C.E. Act 1984.

HM CORONER AND OTHER OFFICIALS

Warwickshire: Mr Sean McGovern. HM Coroner Office, Warwickshire Justice Centre, Newbold Terrace, Leamington Spa CV32 4EL. Tel: 01926 684228/9. Email: coronerofficer@warwickshire.pnn.police.uk

Trading Standards
Trading Standards Department, Old Budbrooke Road, Warwick. Tel: 01926 414040. Website: www.warwickshire.gov.uk/tradingstandards

NSPCC
Boole House, 76 Whitefriars Street, Coventry CV1 2DS. Tel: 024 7622 2456.

RSPCA
48 Regent Street, Leamington Spa CV32 5EG. Tel: 01926 425994. Website: www.rspca-warkssoutheast. org.uk

WEST MERCIA POLICE

Hindlip Hall, Hindlip, PO Box 55, Worcester WR3 8SP.
Tel: 0300 333 3000. Fax: 01905 454226. DX: 711780. The dialling code for all numbers is 01905, unless otherwise indicated.

Email: firstname.lastname@westmercia.pnn.police.uk

Website: www.westmercia.police.uk

(Comprising Herefordshire, Shropshire, Telford & Wrekin and Worcestershire)

Lords Lieutenant: The Countess of Darnley (Herefordshire); Mr Algernon Heber-Percy (Shropshire); Vacant (Worcestershire).
Police & Crime Commissioner: Mr Bill Longmore. Tel: 01743 860389.

Chief Constable: David Shaw.
Staff Officer: Alison Simpson. Tel: 332239.
Deputy Chief Constable: Simon Chesterman QPM.
Special Constabulary Chief Officer: Guy Fewtrel. Tel: 01547 540545.

JOINT CHIEF OFFICER TEAM
Assistant Chief Constable Local Policing: Gareth Morgan (West Mercia & Warwickshire).
Assistant Chief Constable Protective Services: Karen Manners (West Mercia & Warwickshire).
Director of Finance: Heather Costello (West Mercia & Warwickshire).
Director of Enabling Services: Richard Elkin (West Mercia & Warwickshire).
Staff Officers: T/Chief Insp Andy Milne; Mrs Julie Goodwin.

West Mercia Police has entered into a joint force collaboration with Warwickshire Police. Each force retains a separate Chief Constable and Deputy Chief Constable, responsible for their respective geographical policing areas, who will commission policing services from the wider joint chief officer team which will serve both forces. Gold Command cover for major operational incidents in Warwickshire and West Mercia will also be provided by the joint chief officer team. See also www.warwickshire.police.uk

FORCE HEADQUARTERS
Command fax: 01905 331806.
ACPO Armed Policing Subcommittee: Mr John MacDonald. Tel: 331708.

LOCAL POLICING COMMAND
Head of Territorial Policing: Chief Supt Nick Mason. Ext: 2932.
South Worcestershire Policing Area: Vacant.
North Worcestershire Policing Area: Supt Kevin Purcell. Ext: 3008.
Hereford Policing Area: Supt Ivan Powell. Ext: 4714.
Shrewsbury Policing Area: Supt Jim Tozer. Ext: 5838.
Telford & Wrekin Policing Area: Supt Nav Malik. Ext: 5914.

OPERATIONAL SUPPORT COMMAND
Head of Operational Support: Chief Supt Trevor Albutt. Ext: 67891.
Head of Criminal Justice: Mrs Coralie Jones. Ext: 67896.
Head of Safeguarding Services: Ms Kate Binnersley. Ext: 2666.
Head of Command, Control & Communications: Mrs Jolanta Czeren-Shorland. Ext: 67893.
Operational Support (Warwickshire & West Mercia): Supt Charlie Hill. Ext: 67894.

PROTECTIVE SERVICES COMMAND
Head of Crime (Warwickshire & West Mercia): Det Chief Supt Andy Rowsell. Ext: 2270.
Head of Force Intelligence (Warwickshire & West Mercia): Det Supt Mark Travis. Ext: 2985.
Head of Major Investigation Unit (MIU) (Warwickshire & West Mercia): Det Supt Adrian McGee. Tel: 01926 415000. Ext: 8088.
Head of Protecting Vulnerable People (PVP) (Warwickshire & West Mercia): Det Supt Amanda Blakeman. Ext: 5914.
Head of Force Operations (Warwickshire & West Mercia): Supt Lee Davenport. Ext: 2795.
Head of Specialist Operations (Warwickshire & West Mercia): Supt Daryn Elton. Ext: 60780.
Head of Forensic Services: Mr Tristram Elmhirst BSc MPhil DMS. Ext: 2616.
Crime Manager (Warwickshire & West Mercia): Det Supt Graeme Pallister. Tel: 01926 415031.

ENABLING SERVICES COMMAND
Head of Business Assurance & Improvement (Warwickshire & West Mercia): Ms Michelle Buttery. Ext: 2332.
Head of Estate Services (Warwickshire & West Mercia): Mr Jim Stobie. Ext: 2559.
Head of Contract & Procurement Services (Warwickshire & West Mercia): Ms Ann Church. Ext: 2621.

Head of People Services (Warwickshire & West Mercia): Ms Tania Coppola. Tel: 01926 415731.
Head of Workforce Development (Warwickshire & West Mercia): Supt Steve Eccleston. Ext: 2470.
Head of Corporate Communications: Vacant.
Head of Information, Communication & Technology Services (Warwickshire & West Mercia): Mr Wayne Parkes. Tel: 01926 415801.
Head of Transport Services: Vacant.

FINANCE
Head of Corporate Finance (Warwickshire & West Mercia): Mr Jeff Carruthers. Tel: 01926 415880.
Head of Resource Management (Warwickshire & West Mercia): Ms Rachel Hartland-Lane. Ext: 2225.
Central Counties Air Operations Unit. Wolverhampton Business Airport, Bobbington, Stourbridge, West Midlands DY7 5DY. Tel: 01384 221377. Fax: 01384 221340.

STAFF ASSOCIATIONS
Superintendents' Association: *Chairman:* Chief Supt Mark Turner (Head of Change & Strategic Partnerships). *Vice Chairman:* Supt Ivan Powell (Force Crime Manager). *Secretary/Treasurer:* Supt Adrian Pass (North Worcestershire TPU).
Police Federation. *JBB Chairman:* Insp Ken Mackaill. *Secretary/Treasurer:* PC Jamie Harrison. Tel: 332870.
UNISON: *Branch Secretary:* Mrs Val Mathison. Ext: 67505.

HM CORONERS AND OTHER OFFICIALS
Herefordshire: Mr H G M Bricknell. 36/37 Bridge Street, Hereford HR4 9DJ. Tel: 01432 355301. Fax: 01432 356619. Email: mb@lambecorner.co.uk
Mid & North-West Shropshire: Mr J P Ellery. c/o West Mercia Police, Clive Road, Monkmoor, Shrewsbury SY2 5RW. Tel: 01743 237445. Fax: 01743 264879.
South Shropshire: Mr J P Ellery. The Woodland, Pontesford Hill, Shropshire SY5 0UH. Tel: 01743 791937. Fax: 01743 792248.
Telford & Wrekin: Mr J P Ellery. c/o West Mercia Police, Wellington Police Station, Victoria Road, Wellington, Telford TF1 1LQ. Tel: 01743 791937. Fax: 01743 792248.
Worcestershire: Mr G U Williams. The Court House, Bewdley Road, Stourport-on-Severn DY13 8XE. Tel: 01299 824029. Fax: 01299 879238. Email: coroner@worcestershire.gov.uk

WEST MIDLANDS POLICE

PO Box 52, Lloyd House, Colmore Circus Queensway, Birmingham B4 6NQ.
Tel: 0345 113 5000. Fax: 0121 626 5642.
Email: initial.lastname@west-midlands.pnn.police.uk, unless otherwise indicated.
All email addresses @west-midlands.pnn.police.uk.
Website: www.west-midlands.police.uk

Comprising the district councils of Birmingham, Coventry, Dudley, Sandwell, Solihull, Walsall and Wolverhampton.

Police & Crime Commissioner: Bob Jones.

Chief Constable: C Sims QPM. Ext: 7800 2001.
Chief Constable's Staff Officer: Chief Insp S Russell. Ext: 7800 2012.
Deputy Chief Constable: D Thompson. Ext: 7800 2015.
Assistant Chief Constable (Crime): G Cann. Ext: 7800 2006.
Assistant Chief Constable (Security): M Beale. Ext: 7800 2015.
Assistant Chief Constable (Local Policing): S Rowe. Ext: 7800 6601.
Assistant Chief Constable (Operations): Mr G Forsyth. Ext: 7800 2017.
Director of Resources: David Wilkin. Ext: 7800 2126.
Force Solicitor: J Kilbey LLB(Hons). Ext: 7630 3385.
Chief Information Officer: Christopher Price.
Email for all the above: acpo@west-midlands.pnn.police.uk

DCC TASK FORCE
Chief Supt Richard Moore. Ext: 7861 6500.
Continuous Improvement Programme: A/Supt Alison Telford. Ext: 7800 2078.
    Email: a.l.telford

CORPORATE FUNCTIONS
LOCAL POLICING
Commander: Chief Supt L Bottomley.
Superintendent: A Shipman. Ext: 7822 6004 Email: a.p.shipman
CENTRAL JUSTICE SERVICES (STAFFORDSHIRE & WEST MIDLANDS POLICE)
Head of Central Justice Services: Chief Supt Stephen Anderson. Ext: 7800 2614.
Deputy Head of Central Justice Services: Supt Peter Hall. Tel: 01785 235239.
Superintendent: P Westlake. Ext: 7800 2367.
Continuous Improvement, ID & Traffic Process: Chief Insp Paul Trevor. Tel: 01785 235284.
Custody: Chief Insp Karl Fellows. Tel: 0845 113 5000 ext 7800 2733.
Case Management, Witness Care & Court Liaison Manager: Mr Paul Gilbert. Tel: 01785 234350.
Command Team Manager: Mrs Hilary Moss. Tel: 01785 234350.
Crown Court Police Liaison: S Knipe. Ext: 7800 2220.
INFORMATION SERVICES
Communications Manager: K Jeffries. Ext: 7630 3502. Email: kate.jeffries
Freedom of Information Unit: C Bird. Ext: 7630 6260.
Data Protection Unit: Kate Firkins. Ext: 7630 6136.
MOPI Force Records Manager: C Brazier. Ext: 7630 3335.
PROFESSIONAL STANDARDS
Commander: Chief Supt R Jones. Ext: 8800 31200.
Anti-corruption Chief Inspectors: D Doyle; J Harper. Ext: 8800 3129/7.
ORGANISATION & SERVICE DEVELOPMENT
Commander: Chief Supt S Manku QPM. Ext: 7244 6000.
Deputy Department Head: Chief Insp R Howat. Ext: 7800 2559.
Strategic Planning Manager: Mr D Leyland. Ext: 7800 2141.
Performance Support Manager: Mrs C Ewers. Ext: 7800 2558.
Research Manager: Insp G Rumble. Ext: 7800 2062.
LEARNING & DEVELOPMENT
Commander: Chief Supt J Byrne. Ext: 7800 2202.
Superintendent: S Parker. Ext: 7802 3112.
Business Manager: N Self. Ext: 7800 2737.
Training Centre: Tally Ho!, Pershore Road, Edgbaston, Birmingham B5 7RN.

COUNTER TERRORISM UNIT
Commander: Chief Supt K Bell.
Superintendents: G Tracey. Email: g.h.tracey. P Blackburn; N Beechey; J Denley; S Southern.
OPERATIONS
Commander: Chief Supt C McKeogh. Ext: 7800 2253.
Superintendent: R Burgess. Ext: 7800 2603. Email: rick.burgess
Airport Policing Unit: Insp R Williams. Ext: 7929 6242.
Dog Unit: Insp R Evans. Ext: 7601 6722. Email: russell.evans
Firearms Operations Unit: Chief Insp P Minor. Ext: 7982 6382.
INTELLIGENCE
Commander: Chief Supt S Graham. Ext: 7800 2240.
Superintendents: M Ward. Ext: 8800 3266. A/Supt M Howe. Ext: 7630 6442.
FORCE CID
Commanders: Det Chief Supt S Jupp. Ext: 7800 2160. Chief Supt C Foukes. Ext: 8800 3211.
Deputy Department Head: Supt T Bacon. Ext: 7800 2164.
Head of Major Investigation Unit: Det Supt R Baker. Ext: 7630 6300.
Forensic Services Unit: R Small. Ext: 7630 6787.
Gangs & Organised Crime Unit: Supt J Chilton Ext: 7630 6391.
PUBLIC PROTECTION
Commander: Chief Supt S Hyde. Ext: 7800 2639.
Public Protection Unit: Supt C Cowley. Ext: 7800 2660. Supt G Campbell. Ext: 7800 2541.
FINANCE
Head of Finance: D Wilkin. Ext: 7800 2126.
Head of Contracts & Procurement: G Jones. Ext: 7800 2057. Email: g.r.jones
Head of Exchequer Services: Ms C Parker. Ext: 7800 2041. Email: c.t.parker
CORPORATE SERVICES
Head of Corporate Services: S Middleditch. Ext: 7800 2456.
Design & Print Unit, Business Support Manager: I Kent. Ext: 7800 2110.
Facilities Manager: C Willetts. Ext: 7800 2409.
Firearms Licensing Manager: P Dale. Ext: 7800 2370.
Force Policy Co-ordinator: Insp G Rumble. Ext: 7800 2062.
Supplies Manager: T Venus. Ext: 7601 6051.
HUMAN RESOURCES
Head of Human Resources: C Rowson. Ext: 7800 2729. Email: c.j.rowson
Occupational Health Employee Support Manager: D Iles. Ext: 7800 6450.
HR Shared Services for West Midlands Police. Tel: 0345 1135 000 ext 8800 5100. Email: hr_ssc_general_enq@west-midlands.pnn.police.uk
PRESS AND PUBLIC RELATIONS
Head of Press & Public Relations: D Barton. Ext: 8800 3204.
LEGAL SERVICES
Deputy Force Solicitor: Ms L M Smith. Ext: 7630 3385. Email: l.m.smith
Chief Litigation Manager: J Goodwin. Ext: 7630 3218.
PROPERTY SERVICES
Head of Property Services: D Wilkin. Ext: 7630 3401.
FLEET SERVICES
Fleet Manager: A Kelly. Ext: 7982 6690. Email: andrew.kelly
CMPG
Commander: Chief Supt M Evans. Ext: 8843 6038.
Chief Inspector: C Flynn. Ext: 8843 6037.
Air Operations Unit: Sgt D Mitchell. Ext: 7630 6950.

LOCAL POLICING UNITS
HR Services have been centralised: see HR department above.
BIRMINGHAM WEST & CENTRAL
LPU Headquarters: Steelhouse Lane, Birmingham B4 6NW.
LPU Commander: Chief Supt C Burgess. Ext: 7861 6003.
Superintendent: D Long. Ext: 7861 6900.
Business Support. Ext: 7861 6350.
BIRMINGHAM EAST
LPU Headquarters: 338 Station Road, Stechford B33 8RR.
LPU Commander: Chief Supt A Murray. Ext: 7844 6200.
Superintendent: A Whitaker. Ext: 7844 6003.
Business Support. Ext: 7844 6100.

BIRMINGHAM NORTH
LPU Headquarters: Lichfield Road, Sutton Coldfield B74 2NR.
LPU Commander: Chief Supt L Bottomley.
Superintendent: R Youds. Ext: 7842 6550.
Business Support. Ext: 7601 6354.

BIRMINGHAM SOUTH
LPU Headquarters: 341 Bournville Lane, Birmingham B30 1QX.
LPU Commander: Chief Supt E Barnett. Ext: 7822 6003.
Superintendents: J Smallwood. Ext: 7822 6200. A Shipman. Ext: 7822 6004.
Business Support. Ext: 7822 6479.

COVENTRY
LPU Headquarters: Little Park Street, Coventry CV1 2JX.
LPU Commander: Chief Supt A Nicholson. Ext: 7931 6000.
Superintendents: R Winch. Ext: 7931 6500. C Bell. Ext: 7931 6222.
Business Support. Ext: 7931 6100.

DUDLEY
LPU Headquarters: Bank Street, Brierley Hill DY5 3DH.
LPU Commander: Chief Supt S Johnson. Ext: 7902 6000.
Superintendent: D Jobbins. Ext: 7902 6001.
Business Support. Ext: 7902 6100.

SANDWELL
LPU Headquarters: Moor Street, West Bromwich B70 7AQ.
LPU Commander: Chief Supt M Robinson. Ext: 8811 3000.
Superintendents: S Goose. Ext: 8811 3001. B Javid. Ext: 8811 3002.
Business Support. Ext: 8811 3060.

SOLIHULL
LPU Headquarters: Homer Road, Solihull B91 3QL.
LPU Commander: Chief Supt S Bourner. Ext: 7921 6001.
Superintendent: D Walker. Ext: 7921 6001.
Business Support. Ext: 7921 6100.

WALSALL
LPU Headquarters: Green Lane, Walsall WS2 8HL.
LPU Commander: Chief Supt D Sturman. Ext: 7881 6000.
Superintendents: K Fraser. Ext: 7881 6003. J Clews. Ext: 7881 6500.
Business Support. Ext: 7881 6111.

WOLVERHAMPTON
LPU Headquarters: Bilston Street, Wolverhampton WV1 3AA.
LPU Commander: Chief Supt N Evans. Ext: 7871 6000.
Superintendents: M Payne. Ext: 7871 6010. J Thomas-West. Ext: 7871 6002.
Business Support. Ext: 7871 6115.

HM CORONERS
Birmingham/Solihull: Mr Aidan K Cotter. Coroner's Court, 50 Newton Street, Birmingham B4 6NE. Tel: 0121 303 43228 Fax: 0121 233 4841. Email: coronercotter@birmingham.gov.uk
Coventry: Mr Sean P McGovern. Police HQ, Little Park Street, Coventry CV1 2JZ. Tel: 01926 684065. Fax: 02476 539804. Email: coroner@coventry.gov.uk
Black Country: Mr Robin J Balmain. HM Coroner's Office, Crocketts Lane, Smethwick B66 3BS. Tel: 0845 352 7483. Fax: 0845 352 7487. Email: barbara_powles@sandwell.gov.uk

WEST YORKSHIRE POLICE

PO Box 9, Wakefield, West Yorkshire WF1 3QP.
Tel: 101. Telex: 517704 WYPOL, WAKEFIELD.
Fax: 01924 293943 (24 hrs).
Email: firstname.lastname@westyorkshire.pnn.police.uk
Website: www.westyorkshire.police.uk

Lord Lieutenant: Dr Ingrid Roscoe.
Police & Crime Commissioner: Mark Burns-Williamson.

Chief Constable: Mr Mark Gilmore MA QPM.
T/Deputy Chief Constable: Mr Jawaid Akhtar.
Assistant Chief Constable Local Policing: Mr Geoff Dodd.
Assistant Chief Constable Specialist Operations: Mr Craig Guildford.
Assistant Chief Constable National Police Air Service: Mr Mark Milsom.
T/Assistant Chief Constable Specialist Crime: Mrs Ingrid Lee QPM.
Assistant Chief Constable Workforce Development and Standards: Mr John Robins.
Assistant Chief Officer Finance & Business Services: Mr Nigel G Brook BSc CPFA.
Chief Constable's Staff Officer: Chief Insp Samantha Millar.
Legal Services Manager: Mr Mike S Percival.
Force Headquarters. Laburnum Road, Wakefield WF1 3QP.

OPERATIONS SUPPORT UNIT
Divisional Commander: Chief Supt Barry South BA(Hons) MBA.
Superintendent Operations: Simon Whitehead.
Superintendent Support: Owen West.
Operations: Chief Insp Roger Essell.
Support: Chief Insp Derek Hughes.
Roads Policing: Chief Insp Neil Hunter.
Force Communications: Chief Insp Mick Hanks.
Training School: Chief Insp Kate Riley.
Cadre Chief Inspectors: Mick Quirk; Ian Gayles; Chris Corkindale; Paul Hepworth; Paula Booth.

COMMUNICATIONS
Head of Communications: Supt Owen West.
Operational Lead: Chief Insp Hanks.
Business Support Officer: Beverley Bedford.
Customer Contact Centre. Tel: 101. Fax: 01924 293943 (24 hrs).
Customer Contact Centre Supervisor: Tel: 01924 296635 (24 hrs).
PNC. Tel: 01924 296877 (24 hrs).

SCIENTIFIC SUPPORT
Tel: 01924 336201.
Director of Scientific Support YatH: Mr Kevin Morton.
Head of Operations YatH: Mr John Gilbody.
Head of Identifications YatH: Mr Neil Denison.
Head of Imaging: Mr Peter Burton.

TRAINING & DEVELOPMENT
Head of Training: Supt Owen West.
Crime Training: Det Insp Trevor Gasson.
Driver Training: Insp Joanne Field.
Public Order Training: Chief Insp Chris Corkindale.
Firearms Training: Chief Insp Andrew Dawson.
IT Training: *Team Leader:* Mrs Karen Strapps.
Leadership, Foundation & Management Training: Mrs Lisa Milner-Brown.
Business Engagement Officer: Mrs Carol Devereux BA(Hons).
Head of Quality Assurance/Learning Resource Centre: Mrs Rebecca Goring.

HOMICIDE AND MAJOR ENQUIRY TEAM
Head of Department: Det Chief Supt Andy Brennan QPM.
Head of MIRT: Det Supt Colin Prime.
Senior Investigating Officers: Det Supt Paul Taylor; Det Supt David Pervin; Det Supt Mark Ridley.
Crime Manager: Det Chief Insp Simon Bottomley.
Finance & Business Support Manager: Anne Benson.

CRIME

Divisional Commander: T/Det Supt David Knopwood. Tel: 01924 821400. Fax: 01924 821591.
Finance & Business Support Manager: Anne Benson. Tel: 01924 821300. Fax: 01924 821591.
Force Authorising Officer: Det Supt Steve Bennett. Tel: 01924 821448. Fax: 01924 821591.
Head of Organised Crime: Det Supt Knopwood. Tel: 01924 821413. Fax: 01924 821591.
Director of Intelligence: Det Supt Dean Henson. Tel: 01924 821409. Fax: 01924 821591.
Intelligence Bureau Manager: Dave Pegg. Tel: 01274 376530. Fax: 01924 821514.
Deputy Director of Intelligence: Det Chief Insp Andy Williams. Tel: 01274 376635. Fax: 01274 376727.
Operation (Quartz): Det Supt Dean Henson. Tel: 01924 821409. Fax: 01924 821591.
Head of Economic Crime: Det Chief Insp Mick Lawrenson. Tel: 01274 373725.
Head of Safeguarding Central Governance Unit: Det Chief Insp Susan Jenkinson. Tel: 01924 292314. Fax: 01924 292496.

CENTRAL PROCESS UNIT

PO Box 1105, Bradford BD1 4WA. Tel: 01274 376928/376888. Fax: 01274 376895 (Mon–Thur 0900–1700; Fri 0900–1630).

Includes fixed and mobile camera section; collision management; central ticket office; DVLA and summons preparation input. All correspondence should be addressed to the appropriate section within the unit.

Head of Unit: Lillian MacFarlane.
Operation Support Services: Chief Supt Barry South.
DVLA Police Liaison Section. Tel: 01274 376858.
Evidence Investigations. Tel: 01274 376829.

HUMAN RESOURCES

Director of Human Resources: Mrs Hilary Sykes FCIPD.
Head of Corporate HR: Mr John Hughes MSc(HR) FCIPD.
Employee Relations Manager: Mr Steven Davies FCIPD.
Resourcing Manager: Mr Danny Wilks MA MCIPD.
HR Information Manager: Mr Paul Fowler.
Head of Operational HR: Mrs Helen Parkinson FCIPD.
Head of Health & Wellbeing: Mrs Karen McGinnity FCIPD.
Force Medical Officer: Dr Christopher P Shinn MB ChB BSc.
Force Occupational Health Physician: Dr Juliet A Pearlman MB ChB MRCGP AFOM.
Health & Safety Manager: Mr Steven Thorley-Lawson MIOSH MCMI BEng(Hons).

INFORMATION TECHNOLOGY

Fax: 01924 293493 (weekdays 0830–1700).

Director of Information Services: Paul Whiteley.
Head of IT Support: Priscilla Dalton.
Head of IT Systems: Mark Homer.
Head of IT Technical: Andrew Fidler.
Secretaries to the Director of Information Services: Helen Burton-Laws; Jayne Booth.

CORPORATE SUPPORT

Head of Department: Chief Supt Alan Ford. Tel: 01924 292345.
Head of Organisational Development: Mr Ian Newsome.
Head of Strategy, Policy & Organisational Learning: Ms Rebecca Tennyson-Mason.
Business Change Managers: Mr Martin Rahman; Ms Donna Tranter.
Chief Inspector Organisational Development: Carl Burkey.
Engagement & Accountability: Supt Martin Deacon.
Performance Review Manager: Ms Jayne Sykes.
Strategic Partnerships: Chief Insp Hector Mackay.
Legal Services Manager: Mr Mike Percival.
Corporate Communications Manager: Mr Nigel Swift.

PROFESSIONAL STANDARDS

Quality and standards, information management, integrity management, anti-corruption and vetting.

Head of Department: Chief Supt Marc Callaghan.

LOCAL POLICING SUPPORT

Tel: 01924 292162/292505.

Head of Department: Chief Supt S Willsher MBA BSocSc(Hons).
Head of Operations: Supt M Hussain. Chief Insp M McManus; Chief Insp J Turton; Mr C Joyce.
Head of Criminal Justice: Supt R Whitehead. Chief Insp P Wiggins; Mrs J Zunda.
PROSECUTION TEAMS WEST YORKSHIRE
Criminal Justice Unit Manager: Julie Zunda (central contact for all prosecution teams). Tel: 01924 292886.

ESTATES, TRANSPORT & LOGISTICS

Director of Estates, Transport & Logistics: Mr John Prentice.
Head of Transport: Mr Steven Thompson.
Head of Logistics: Mr Neil Wilson.
Head of Property & Projects: Mr Matthew Saunders.
Head of Police National Legal Database: Mr Nigel Hughes. (See p xx.)
Viper Bureau Manager: Mr Wayne Collins. (See p xx.)

FINANCE & BUSINESS SUPPORT

Director of Finance & Business Support: Mr Martin A Stubbs BA(Hons) ACMA.
Head of Accountancy, Payments & Revenues: Mrs Wendy Scatchard ACCA.
Head of Payroll & Pensions: Mrs Jan L Swales BSc(Hons) MIPPM(Dip).
Head of Risk Management & Insurance: Mrs Beverley Nichol-Culff RRP.

REGIONAL PROCUREMENT TEAM
Policing Yorkshire and the Humber

Director of Regional Procurement: Ms Chris Mottershaw MCIPS.
Head of Procurement & Category Management: Mrs Joanne Osborne MCIPS.
Head of Contract Management & Performance: Mrs Sandy Campbell MCIPS.

STAFF ASSOCIATIONS

Police Federation: *Chairman:* Mr Jon Christopher. *JBB Secretary:* Mr Simon Gelder. *Deputy Secretary/Equality Leader:* Gary Maloney. Police Federation Office, Trenarren, 3 Eastmoor Road, Wakefield WF1 3RY. Tel: 01924 295494/5 ext 35194/5. Fax: 01924 295497 (weekdays 0900–1700).
UNISON: Branch Office: 6 Laburnum Road, Wakefield WF1 3QP. Tel: 01924 292842/3 (direct). Fax: 01924 292844 (weekdays 0900–1700). *Joint Branch Secretaries:* Mr Garry Bull; Mrs Jane Wilkinson.

DIVISIONS

Although the following areas have a West Yorkshire postal address, they are located within the North Yorkshire Police area and all correspondence should be addressed to the Skipton subdivision of that force: Bradley, Cononley, Cowling, Cross Hills, Farnhill, Glusburn, Kildwick, Lothersdale, Sutton-in-Craven.

NORTH WEST LEEDS

300 Otley Road, Leeds LS16 6RG.
Divisional Commander: Chief Supt David Oldroyd.
Superintendent Operations: Michael Hunter.
Chief Inspector Neighbourhood Operations: James McNeil.
Chief Inspector Operations Support: Damon Solley.
Detective Chief Inspector: Frances Naughton.
Otley Police Station. Bridge Street, Otley LS21 3BA.
Pudsey Police Station. Dawson's Corner, Pudsey, Leeds LS28 5TA.

NORTH EAST LEEDS

10 Stainbeck Lane, Leeds LS7 3QU.
Divisional Commander: Chief Supt Richard Jackson.
Superintendent Operations: Martin Snowden.
Chief Inspector Operations: Nik Adams.
Chief Inspector NPT: Matt Davison.
Crime Manager: Det Chief Insp Elizabeth Belton.
Killingbeck Police Station. Foundry Lane, Seacroft, Leeds LS14 6NN.
Wetherby Police Station. Boston Road, Wetherby LS22 5HA.
Garforth Police Station. Lidgett Lane, Garforth, Leeds LS25 1LJ.

CITY AND HOLBECK

10 Burton Road, Leeds LS11 5EF.
Divisional Commander: Chief Supt Paul Money.
Superintendent Operations: Patrick Twiggs.
Chief Inspector Operations: Mark Jessop.
Crime Manager: Det Chief Insp Michael Oddy.
City Centre Commander: Chief Insp Stephen Palmer.
Millgarth Police Station. Millgarth Street, Leeds LS2 7HX.
Morley Police Station. Corporation Street, Morley LS27 9NB.
Rothwell Police Station, 92 Haigh Road, Rothwell LS26 0LP.

WAKEFIELD DIVISION

Wood Street, Wakefield WF1 2HD.
Divisional Commander: Chief Supt Andy Battle.
Superintendent Operations: Patrick Casserley.
Superintendent Community Safety: Tyron Joyce.
Crime Manager: Det Chief Insp Karen Gayles.
Operations & Support (including Standards): Chief Insp Vicki White.

Chief Inspector Neighbourhood Policing: Phill Wright.
Chief Inspector Partnerships: Mel Williams.
Normanton Police Station. High Street, Normanton WF6 2AL.
Ossett Police Station. Bank Street, Ossett WF5 8NW.
PONTEFRACT
Normanton Police Station. High Street, Normanton, Wakefield WF6 2AL.
Ossett Police Station. Bank Street, Ossett WF5 8NW.
Castleford Police Station. Jessop Street, Castleford WF10 1DQ.
Pontefract & Knottingley NPT. Pontefract Fire Station, Stump Cross Lane, Pontefract WF8 2WJ.
South Kirkby Police Station. White Apron Street, Stockingate, South Kirkby WF9 3XA.
KIRKLEES
Castlegate, Huddersfield HD1 2NJ.
Divisional Commander: Chief Supt Tim Kingsman.
Superintendent Partnerships: Ged McManus.
Superintendent Operations: David Lunn.
Chief Inspector Operations: Marianne Huison.
Chief Inspector NPT: Justine Plumb.
Crime Manager: Det Chief Insp Paul Jeffrey.
Holmfirth Police Station. Huddersfield Road, Holmfirth, Huddersfield HD7 2TT.
Slaithwaite Police Station. Manchester Road, Slaithwaite, Huddersfield HD7 5HH.
Kirkburton Police Station. 2 Shelley Lane, Kirkburton, Huddersfield HD8 0SJ.
Dewsbury Police Station. Aldams Road, Dewsbury WF12 8AP.
Batley Police Station. Market Place, Batley WF17 5DJ.
Heckmondwike Police Station. Claremont, Heckmondwike WF16 9LJ.
Mirfield Police Station. Knowle Road, Mirfield WF14 8DQ.
CALDERDALE
HQ Halifax Police Station, Richmond Close, Halifax HX1 5TW.
Divisional Commander: Chief Supt Chris Hardern.
Superintendent Operations: Martin Lister.
Crime Manager: Det Chief Insp Terence Long.
Chief Inspector Operations: Viv Cutbill.
Chief Inspector Local Policing: Kate Jowett.
Sowerby Bridge Police Station. Station Road, Sowerby Bridge HX6 3AB.
Brighouse Police Station. Bradford Road, Brighouse HD6 4AA.
Hebden Bridge Police Station. Hope Street, Hebden Bridge HX7 8AG.
Todmorden Police Station. Burnley Road, Todmorden OL14 5EY.
Elland Police Station. Burley Street, Elland HX5 0AQ.
AIREDALE AND NORTH BRADFORD
Divisional Headquarters: Keighley Police Station, Airedale House, Royd Ings Avenue, Keighley BD21
    4BZ. Tel: 01535 617059. Fax: 01535 617099. Open 24/7.
Divisional Commander: Chief Supt Angela Williams.
Superintendent: Paul Dixon.
Crime Manager: Det Chief Insp Steve Thomas.
Chief Inspector Operations: Suzanne Akeroyd.
Chief Inspector NPT: Darren Williams.
Eccleshill Police Station. Javelin House, Javelin Close, Eccleshill, Bradford BD10 8SD. Open Mon–Sat
    1000–1800.
Ilkley Police Station. Riddings Road, Ilkley LS29 9LU. Open Tues–Sat 1000–1800.
Bingley Police Station. Bradford Road, Bingley. Not open to the public.
Shipley Police Station. Manor Lane, Shipley BD18 3RR. Open Tues–Sat 1000–1800.
BRADFORD SOUTH
Trafalgar House Police Station, Nelson Street, Bradford BD5 0DX.
Divisional Commander: Chief Supt Simon Atkin.
Superintendent: Scott Bisset.
Chief Inspector Neighbourhood Management: Damien Miller.
Chief Inspector Neighbourhood Operations: Jaene Booth.
Crime & Community Justice: Chief Insp Peter Craig.
The following are to be regarded as Designated Police Stations under s.35, P.A.C.E. Act 1984:

Airedale & North Bradford	Leeds Central Charge Office	Stainbeck
Dewsbury	Pontefract	Trafalgar House (Bradford)
Halifax	Pudsey	Wakefield
Huddersfield		

HM CORONERS AND OTHER OFFICIALS

Eastern District: Mr D Hinchcliff. Coroner's Office, 71 Northgate, Wakefield WF1 3BS. Tel: 01924 302180. Fax: 01924 302184. Email: leedscoroner@wakefield.gov.uk; hmcoroner@wakefield.gov.uk

Western District: Mr P H Straker. Coroner's Office, The City Courts, The Tyrls, Bradford BD1 1LA. Tel: 01274 391362. Fax: 01274 721794. Email: hmc@bradford.gov.uk

State Veterinary Service

Animal Health Defra: AHVLA Leeds Field Services, Olympia House, Gelderd Lane, Gelderd Road, Leeds LS12 6DD. Tel: 0113 279 6121. Fax: 0113 261 0212. Nightline: 0113 279 6121. Email: AHROYorksandHumber@ahvla.gsi.gov.uk (Leeds & Bradford Airport is nominated for the import and export of animals).

WILTSHIRE POLICE
London Road, Devizes, Wiltshire SN10 2DN.
Tel: 101. If calling from outside England and Wales, tel: 01380 735735.
Textphone: 18001 101. DX: 132830. Fax: 01380 734135 (24 hrs); 01380 734176
(0830–1700).
The dialling code for all numbers is 01380, unless otherwise indicated.
s = POSTMASTER, o = WILTSHIRE POLICE; p = PNN54; a = CWMAIL; c
= GB
Email: firstname.lastname@wiltshire.pnn.police.uk
Website: www.wiltshire.police.uk

Lord Lieutenant: Mrs Sarah Rose Troughton.
Police & Crime Commissioner: Mr Angus MacPherson.
Chief Executive for the Police & Crime Commissioner: Mr Kieran Kilgallen.
Chief Finance Officer for the Police & Crime Commissioner: Mr Mike Prince.
Office of the Police & Crime Commissioner for Wiltshire: London Road, Devizes SN10 2DN. Tel:
734022.

Chief Constable: Mr Patrick Geenty BEd MA.
Deputy Chief Constable: Mr Michael Veale.
Assistant Chief Constable: Mr Stephen Hedley.
Chief Constable's Staff Officer: Det Insp Nicki Davey. Ext: 720 2218.
PA to Chief Constable: Barbara Masters. Tel: 734221.
PA to Deputy Chief Constable: Kath Binks. Tel: 734031.
PA to Assistant Chief Constable: Julie Lawless. Tel: 734185.
BUSINESS IMPROVEMENT AND TRANSFORMATION
Head of Business Improvement & Transformation: Chief Supt Andrew Tatam.
Head of Performance, Planning & Assurance: Helen Westmacott.
Senior Project Manager: David Mayes.
Senior Technical Project Manager (ICT): Andrew Smith.
Assurance & Service Delivery Manager (ICT): Robert Tofield.
PA to Head of Business Improvement & Transformation: Sharon Innes. Tel: 734052.
CORPORATE COMMUNICATIONS
Head of Communications: Clare Mills. Ext: 720 4687.
Head of Media Services: Helen Kennedy. Ext: 720 2231.
PA to Head of Communications: Sharon Innes. Tel: 734052.
FINANCE AND LOGISTICS
Head of Finance & Logistics: Mr Clive A Barker CPFA. Tel: 734030.
Accountancy Manager: Mrs Dawn Young.
Exchequer Manager: Ms Sarah Holbrook.
Estates Manager: Mrs Kim Glenister. Tel: 734172.
Fleet & Services Manager: Mr Stephen C Botham MIMI AMIRTE. Tel: 734117.
PA to Head of Finance & Logistics: Wendy Colyer. Ext: 720 4629.
PEOPLE SERVICES
Head of People Services: Mrs Zoe Durrant FCIPD. Tel: 734053.
Senior People Services Partners: Mrs Sharon Williams BA(Hons) MCIPD. Tel: 734067. Mrs Julie
Curtis FCIPD. Tel: 734068. Mrs Sonia Grewal MCIPD.
Health & Safety Manager: Mrs Sarah Somers. Tel: 734125.
Occupational Health Nurse Manager: Mrs Penny Fuller RGN BSc(Hons) OH. Tel: 734073.
Head of People Development: Chief Insp Fraser Howorth. Tel: 734198.
Training Development Manager: Insp Graham Fisher.
Specialist Operations Training Manager: Insp Glynn Ashforth.
Force Resourcing Manager: Mark Levitt. Tel: 07980 236307.
PA to Head of People Services: Lorraine Briggs. Tel: 734053.
PEOPLE STANDARDS & SUPPORT
Head of People Standards & Support: Supt Charlie Armstrong.
Protective Security Manager: Mr Keith Lewis.
Office Manager: Ms Jean Coombes.
PA to Head of People Standards & Support: Lorraine Briggs. Tel: 734053.

STAFF ASSOCIATIONS

Superintendents' Association: *Secretary:* Supt Nick Ashley. Ext: 720 2035.
Police Federation: *JBB Secretary:* Sgt Mel Rolph. Tel: 720 2336. Fax: 729446 (0900–1700).
UNISON: *Secretary:* Mr Nick Maslen. Ext: 720 4640. *Chairman:* Mr Colin Parkinson-Hill. Tel: 734062.

OPERATIONAL SUPPORT SERVICES

Head of Operational Support Services: Mrs Sue Leffers.
Head of Custody: Chief Insp Marion Deegan. Tel: 734077.
PA to Head of Operational Support Services: Julia Green. Tel: 720 2198

PROTECTIVE SERVICES

Head of Protective Services: Det Chief Supt Kier Pritchard.
Head of Intelligence: Det Supt Willie Glasgow.
Deputy Head of Intelligence: Det Chief Insp Craig Holden
Head of Crime Investigations: A/Det Supt Nick John.
Head of Public Protection Unit: Det Supt Jerry Dawson.
Deputy Head of Public Protection Unit: Det Chief Insp Andrew Carr.
Head of Forensic Services: Ms Barbara Lockwood.
Forensic Operations Manager: Mr Cliff Bassett.
Forensic Support Manager: Mr Nicholas Hunt. Tel: 734173.
Special Branch: Det Insp Angela Rees.
Major Crime Investigation Team: Det Chief Insp Ian G Saunders.
Major Crime Review & Crime Strategy: Mr Guy Turner.
PA to Head of Protective Services: Ceri Sonnet. Ext: 720 3644.
PA to Head of Intelligence & Head of Crime Investigation: Rosemary Waterkeyn. Ext: 720 4654.
PA to Head of Public Protection: Wendy Colyer. Ext: 720 4629.

LOCAL POLICING

Head of Local Policing: Chief Supt Paul Mills. Ext: 720 3415.
Headquarters Response: Supt Nick Ashley. Ext: 720 2035. Chief Insp Sean Memory. Ext: 720 3416.
Force Specialist Operations: Insp Chris Chammings. Ext: 720 3340.
Armed Response Group: Insp Dave Eddy Ext: 720 3427.
Head of Roads Policing: Insp Steven Cox. Ext: 720 4002.
Wildlife Liaison: PC Tony Miles. Tel: 07817 689640.
Major Incident Planning: Mr Robert Young. Tel: 01380 734101.
Air Support Unit: Mr Graham Saunders. Ext: 720 3405.
Head of Contact Management – Emergency Contact Centre, Force Contact Centre: Chief Insp Madge Lynch. Tel: 720 3454.
Deputy Head of Contact Management: John Flynn. Tel: 720 5540.
PA to Head of Local Policing Commander: Karen Dyke. Tel: 731479.
PA to Superintendent, Headquarters Response: Elisabeth Clarkson. Ext: 720 3617.

LOCAL POLICING NORTH

Superintendent, Local Policing North: Gavin Williams. Ext: 760 512.
North Response: T/Chief Insp Roger Bull. Ext: 760 311.
North Neighbourhoods: Chief Insp Keith Ewart. Ext: 760 311.
T/PA to Superintendent, Local Policing North: Sarah Porter. Tel: 01793 507918.
NEIGHBOURHOOD POLICING SECTORS: NORTH
Swindon North (Moredon, Haydon Wick, Northern Expansion, Highworth, Swindon Rural North, Upper Stratton, Stratton St Margaret & Covingham Communities): Insp Antony C Ducker. Swindon Police Station, Gablecross, Shrivenham Road, South Marston, Swindon SN3 4RB. Ext: 760 514.
Swindon Central (Town Centre, Broadgreen, Eastcott & Kingshill Communities): Insp Adrian Burt. Swindon Police Station, as above. Ext: 760 843.
Swindon East (Parks & Walcot, Lawn, Walcot West & Old Town, Swindon Rural South & Eldene Communities): A/Insp Aileen Conway. Swindon Police Station, as above. Ext: 760 354.
Swindon West (Penhill, Pinehurst, Rodbourne & Cheney Manor, Gorsehill & West Swindon North & South Communities): Insp Paul Hacker. Swindon Police Station, as above. Ext: 760 842.
Royal Wootton Bassett, Cricklade & Malmesbury Communities: Insp Mark Thompson. Royal Wootton Bassett Police Station, Lime Kiln, Royal Wootton Bassett SN4 7AA. Ext: 730 813.
Chippenham, Calne & Corsham Communities: Insp Phil Staynings Police Station, Wood Lane, Chippenham SN15 3DH. Ext: 722 813.

LOCAL POLICING SOUTH

Superintendent, Local Policing South: Matt Pullen. Ext: 723 811.
South Response: Chief Insp Charlie Dibble. Ext: 725 513.
South Neighbourhoods: Chief Insp Mark Sellers. Ext: 728 213.

PA to Superintendent, Local Policing South & Customer Services Officer: **Salisbury:** Sarah Perkins. Tel: 01722 435348.

NEIGHBOURHOOD POLICING SECTORS: SOUTH

Bradford-on-Avon, Melksham & Trowbridge Communities: Insp Lisette Harvey. Trowbridge Police Station, Polebarn Road, Trowbridge BA14 7EP. Ext: 725 813.

Amesbury & Tidworth Communities: Insp Christian Lange. Amesbury Police Station, Salisbury Road, Amesbury SP4 7HQ. Ext: 724 813.

Salisbury, Alderbury & Wilton Communities: Insp Andrew Noble. Salisbury Police Station, Wilton Road, Salisbury SP2 7HR. Ext: 723 813.

Warminster, Westbury, Tisbury & Mere Communities: Insp Lindsey Winter. Warminster Police Station, Station Road, Warminster BA12 9BR. Ext: 726 813.

Devizes, Marlborough & Pewsey Communities: Insp Matt Armstrong. Devizes Borough Police Station, New Park Street, Devizes SN10 1DZ. Ext: 737 813.

DESIGNATED POLICE STATIONS
Police stations designated under s35, P.A.C.E. Act 1984

North: Chippenham, Royal Wootton Bassett, Swindon Gablecross.

South: Salisbury, Amesbury, Devizes, Marlborough, Melksham, Trowbridge, Warminster.

The Royal Military College of Science, Shrivenham, is in the area of Thames Valley Police.

HM CORONER AND OTHER OFFICIALS
Wiltshire & Swindon: Mr David W G Ridley. Lloyds Bank Chambers, 6 Castle Street, Salisbury SP1 1BB. Tel: 01722 326870. Fax: 01722 332223. Email: david.ridley@wiltshire.gov.uk

Prevention of Cruelty to Children

Swindon Service Centre, 35 Victoria Road, Swindon SN1 3AS. Tel: 01793 431501.

Tidworth Family Centre, Drummer Lane, Tidworth SP9 7NR. Tel: 01980 846164.

SCOTLAND

THE SCOTTISH GOVERNMENT
The Scottish Parliament, Edinburgh EH99 1SP.
Website: www.scotland.gov.uk
Cabinet Secretary for Justice: Kenny MacAskill MSP.
Minister for Community Safety & Legal Affairs: Roseanna Cunningham MSP.

DIRECTOR GENERAL JUSTICE AND COMMUNITIES
St Andrew's House, Regent Road, Edinburgh EH1 3DG.
Tel: 0131 556 8400; 08457 721741.
Email: dglj@scotland.gsi.gov.uk
Director General Learning & Justice: Leslie Evans.
Director of Safer Communities: Paul Johnston.
Director of Justice: Bridget Campbell.

HM INSPECTORATE OF CONSTABULARY FOR SCOTLAND
1st Floor West, St Andrew's House, Regent Road, Edinburgh EH1 3DG.
Tel: 0131 244 5614. Fax: 0131 244 5616.
Email: hmics@scotland.gsi.gov.uk
Her Majesty's Inspector of Constabulary: Mr Andrew Laing.
PA to Her Majesty's Inspector of Constabulary: Mrs Susan Archibald. Tel: 0131 244 5617.
Principal Inspection Managers: Mr David McCracken; Mr Brian Plastow.
Inspection Managers: Supt Gavin Buist; Supt Paul Bullen; Supt Frank Gallop.
Head of Performance Analysis Unit: Mr Stephen Woodhouse. Tel: 0131 244 5625.

CROWN OFFICE & PROCURATOR FISCAL SERVICE (COPFS)

The Crown Office and Procurator Fiscal Service (COPFS) is responsible for the prosecution of crime in Scotland, the investigation of sudden or suspicious deaths, and the investigation of complaints against the police. COPFS is brigaded into four federations: National, East, North and West. The National Federation comprises Corporate Services and Serious Casework, headed by the Deputy Chief Executive and Director of Serious Casework.

CROWN OFFICE

25 Chambers Street, Edinburgh EH1 1LA. Tel: 0844 561 2000. Fax: 0844 561 4089. Website: www.copfs.gov.uk

Crown Agent/Chief Executive: Catherine Dyer.
Deputy Chief Executive: Peter Collings.
Director of Serious Casework: David Harvie.
COPFS National Enquiry Point. Tel: 0845 561 3000.

PROCURATOR FISCAL SERVICE FEDERATIONS

Tel: 0844 561 3000 (from landlines); 01389 739557 (from mobiles).
Website: www.copfs.gov.uk/About-Us/Service-Overview/Our-Federations

EAST OF SCOTLAND

Procurator Fiscal for the East of Scotland: John Logue.
Head of Business Management for the East of Scotland: Paul Lowe.
Procurator Fiscal, High Court for the East of Scotland: Michelle Macleod.
Procurator Fiscal, Sheriff & Jury for the East of Scotland: Fiona Cameron.
Procurator Fiscal, Initial Case Processing for the East of Scotland: Anne Donaldson.
Procurator Fiscal, Summary for the East of Scotland: Adrian Cottam.

OFFICES IN THE EAST OF SCOTLAND

Edinburgh: Procurator Fiscal's Office, 29 Chambers Street, Edinburgh EH1 1LB. *Procurator Fiscal:* Michelle Macleod.
Alloa: Procurator Fiscal's Office, Sheriff Court, Alloa FK10 1HR. *Procurator Fiscal:* Mr L Brown.
Cupar: Procurator Fiscal's Office, Sheriff Court, Cupar KY15 4LS. *Procurator Fiscal:* Fiona Cameron.
Dunfermline: Procurator Fiscal's Office, Carnegie Drive, Dunfermline KY12 7HW. *Procurator Fiscal:* Fiona Cameron.
Falkirk: Procurator Fiscal's Office, Mansionhouse Road, Camelon, Falkirk FK1 4LW.
Haddington: Procurator Fiscal's Office, 10–12 Court Street, Haddington EH41 3JA. *Procurator Fiscal:* Michelle Macleod (based in Edinburgh).
Jedburgh: Procurator Fiscal's Office, Sheriff Court, Jedburgh TD8 6AR. *Procurator Fiscal:* Mr G Fraser.
Kirkcaldy: Procurator Fiscal's Office, Carlyle House, Carlyle Road, Kirkcaldy KY1 1DB. *Procurator Fiscal:* Fiona Cameron.
Livingston: Procurator Fiscal's Office, West Lothian Civic Centre, Howden South Road, Livingston EH54 6FF. *Procurator Fiscal:* Adrian Cottam.
Selkirk: Procurator Fiscal's Office, Sheriff Court, Selkirk TD7 4LE. *Procurator Fiscal:* Mr G Fraser.
Stirling: Procurator Fiscal's Office, Carseview House, Castle Business Park, Stirling FK9 4SW. *Procurator Fiscal:* Mr L Brown.

NORTH OF SCOTLAND

Procurator Fiscal for the North of Scotland: David Harvie.
Head of Business Management for the North of Scotland: Bill Comrie.
Deputy Head of North Federation & Procurator Fiscal, High Court for the North of Scotland: Ruth McQuaid.
Procurator Fiscal, Sheriff & Jury for the North of Scotland: Andrew McIntyre.
Procurator Fiscal, Initial Case Processing for the North of Scotland: Andrew Richardson.
Procurator Fiscal, Summary for the North of Scotland: Andrew Laing.

OFFICES IN THE NORTH OF SCOTLAND

Aberdeen: Procurator Fiscal's Office, Atholl House, 84–88 Guild Street, Aberdeen AB11 6QA. *Procurator Fiscal:* Andrew Richardson.
Arbroath: Procurator Fiscal's Office, Aitken House, 15 Hill Street, Arbroath DD11 1AQ. *Procurator Fiscal:* Ms E Miller.
Banff: Procurator Fiscal's Office, Sheriff Court, Banff AB45 1AU. *Procurator Fiscal:* Mr D Thorburn.
Dingwall: Procurator Fiscal's Office, Sheriff Court, Ferry Road, Dingwall IV15 9QX. *Procurator Fiscal:* Mr A MacDonald.
Dundee: Procurator Fiscal's Office, PO Box 39, Caledonian House, Greenmarket, Dundee DD1 4QA. *Procurator Fiscal:* Ms H Nisbet.

Elgin: Procurator Fiscal's Office, 48 South Street, Elgin, Moray. *Procurator Fiscal:* Mr A Shanks.
Forfar: Procurator Fiscal's Office, Sheriff Court, Forfar DD8 3LA. *Procurator Fiscal:* Ms E Miller.
Fort William: Procurator Fiscal's Office, 2nd Floor, Tweeddale, High Street, Fort William PH33 6EU. *Procurator Fiscal:* Ms A Wyllie.
Inverness: Procurator Fiscal's Office, Inverness IV1 1QL. *Procurator Fiscal:* Ms E Knox.
Kirkwall: Procurator Fiscal's Office, Sheriff Court, Kirkwall KW15 1PD. *Procurator Fiscal:* Ms S Foard.
Lerwick: Procurator Fiscal's Office, Sheriff Court, Lerwick ZE1 0HD. *Procurator Fiscal:* Ms S Foard.
Lochmaddy: Procurator Fiscal's Office, Sheriff Court, Lochmaddy HS6 5AE. *Procurator Fiscal:* Mr D Teale.
Perth: Procurator Fiscal's Office, 82 Tay Street, Perth PH2 8NN. *Procurator Fiscal:* Ms H Nisbet.
Peterhead: Procurator Fiscal's Office, 70 St Peter Street, Peterhead AB42 1QB. *Procurator Fiscal:* Mr D Thorburn.
Portree: contact Procurator Fiscal's Office, Sheriff Court, Ferry Road, Dingwall IV15 9QX. *Procurator Fiscal:* Mr A MacDonald.
Stonehaven: contact Procurator Fiscal's Office, Atholl House, 84–88 Guild Street, Aberdeen AB11 6QA. *Procurator Fiscal:* Andrew Richardson.
Stornoway: Procurator Fiscal's Office, Sheriff Court, Lewis Street, Stornoway HS1 2JF. *Procurator Fiscal:* Mr D Teale.
Tain: Procurator Fiscal's Office, 11 Stafford Street, Tain IV19 1BP. *Procurator Fiscal:* Mr A N MacDonald.
Wick: Procurator Fiscal, Sheriff Court, Wick KW1 4AJ. *Procurator Fiscal:* Mr A N MacDonald.

WEST OF SCOTLAND

Procurator Fiscal for the West of Scotland: John Dunn.
Head of Business Management for the West of Scotland: John Tannahill.
Procurator Fiscal, High Court for the West of Scotland: Vacant.
Procurator Fiscal, Sheriff & Jury for the West of Scotland: Anne Currie.
Procurator Fiscal, Initial Case Processing & Summary for the West of Scotland: Geri Watt.

OFFICES IN THE WEST OF SCOTLAND
Glasgow: Procurator Fiscal's Office, 10 Ballater Street, Glasgow G5 9PS. *Procurator Fiscal:* John Dunn.
Airdrie: Procurator Fiscal's Office, 87A Graham Street, Airdrie ML6 6DE. *Procurator Fiscal:* Ms L McPherson.
Ayr: Procurator Fiscal's Office, 37 Carrick Street, Ayr KA7 1NS. *Procurator Fiscal:* Ms M Watson.
Campbeltown: Procurator Fiscal's Office, Sheriff Court, Campbeltown PA28 6AN. *Procurator Fiscal:* Mr D Glancy.
Dumbarton: Procurator Fiscal's Office, St Mary's Way, Dumbarton G82 1NL. *Procurator Fiscal:* Mr J Service.
Dumfries: 44 Buccleuch Street, Dumfries DG1 2AP. *Interim Procurator Fiscal Dumfries & Kirkcudbright:* Mr S Cassidy.
Dunoon: Procurator Fiscal's Office, Sheriff Court, Dunoon PA23 8BQ. *Procurator Fiscal:* Mr D L Webster.
Greenock: Procurator Fiscal's Office, Victory Court, Cartsburn Maritime, Arthur Street, Greenock PA15 4RT. *Procurator Fiscal Greenock/Rothesay:* Mr J Farrell.
Hamilton: Procurator Fiscal's Office, Cameronian House, 3/5 Almada Street, Hamilton ML3 0HG. *Procurator Fiscal:* Mr L Murphy.
Kilmarnock: Procurator Fiscal's Office, St Marnock Street, Kilmarnock KA1 1DZ. *Procurator Fiscal:* Ms M Watson.
Lanark: Procurator Fiscal's Office, Sheriff Court, Lanark ML11 7NE. *Procurator Fiscal:* Ms L McPherson.
Oban: Procurator Fiscal's Office, Boswell House, Argyle Square, Oban PA34 4BD. *Procurator Fiscal:* Mr D Glancy.
Paisley: Procurator Fiscal's Office, 1 Love Street, Paisley PA3 2DA. *Procurator Fiscal:* Mr K Donnelly.
Stranraer: Procurator Fiscal's Office, Sheriff Court, Stranraer DG9 7AA. *Interim Procurator Fiscal:* Lyndsay Hunter.

POLICE SCOTLAND

Police Scotland Headquarters, PO Box 21184, Alloa FK10 9DE.
Tel: 01786 289070.
Email: contactus@scotland.pnn.police.uk
Website: www.scotland.police.uk

Police Scotland, the national police service of Scotland, came into effect on 1 April 2013, replacing the eight regional Scottish police forces and the Scottish Crime and Drug Enforcement Agency. Police Scotland consists of over 25,000 police officers and police staff, serving a population of almost 5.3 million people. The key focus for Police Scotland is 'Keeping People Safe'. It will deliver local policing services which are professional, effective, visible, accessible and responsive to the concerns and needs of the communities it serves.

Police Scotland is led by a command team of one chief constable, four deputy chief constables, six assistant chief constables and three directors. There are 14 local policing divisions across the country, each led by a divisional commander with responsibility for local policing in his/her area.

This edition of the *Almanac* includes details of the chief officers of Police Scotland, 14 Local Policing Divisions, Specialist Crime Division and Operational Support Division. For any other information or enquiries please visit www.scotland.police.uk. Further details of Police Scotland will be published in future editions of the Almanac.

The services previously provided by the Scottish Police Services Authority are now provided by the Scottish Police Authority.

Scottish Police Authority: c/o Elphinstone House, 65 West Regent Street, Glasgow G2 2AF.

Chief Constable: Stephen House QPM.
Deputy Chief Constable (Designate): Neil Richardson QPM.
Deputy Chief Constable (Local Policing): Rose Fitzpatrick QPM.
Deputy Chief Constable (Crime & Operational Support): Iain Livingstone QPM.
Deputy Chief Constable (Commonwealth Games & Major Events): Steve Allen QPM.
Assistant Chief Constable (Local Policing East): Mike McCormick.
Assistant Chief Constable (Local Policing North): Derek Penman.
Assistant Chief Constable (Local Policing West): Wayne Mawson.
Assistant Chief Constable (Major Crime & Public Protection): Malcolm Graham.
Assistant Chief Constable (Organised Crime & Counter Terrorism): Ruaraidh Nicolson QPM.
Assistant Chief Constable (Operational Support): Bernard J Higgins BA.
Staff Officer to Chief Constable. Tel: 01259 732208.
Staff Officer to Deputy Chief Constable (Designate). Tel: 01259 732378.
Staff Officer to Deputy Chief Constable (Local Policing). Tel: 01259 732379.
Staff Officer to Deputy Chief Constable (Crime & Operational Support). Tel: 01259 732378.
Staff Officers to Assistant Chief Constables. Tel: 01259 732399/732398/732397.
PA to Chief Constable. Tel: 01259 732209.
PA to Deputy Chief Constable (Designate). Tel: 01259 732237.
PA to Deputy Chief Constable (Local Policing). Tel: 01259 732237.
PA to Deputy Chief Constable (Crime & Operational Support). Tel: 01259 732249.
PA to Deputy Chief Constable (Commonwealth Games & Major Events). Tel: 01259 732236.
PAs to Assistant Chief Constables. Tel: 01259 732383/732300/732301.

DIVISIONS
ABERDEEN CITY DIVISION
Divisional Headquarters: Queen Street, Aberdeen AB10 1ZA. Tel: 0845 600 5700.
Divisional Commander: Chief Supt A Watson.

ABERDEENSHIRE & MORAY DIVISION
Divisional Headquarters: Blackhall Road, Inverurie AB51 3QD. Tel: 0845 600 5700.
Divisional Commander: Chief Supt M McLaren.

TAYSIDE DIVISION
Divisional Headquarters: West Bell Street, Dundee DD1 9JU. Tel: 0800 358 8460.
Divisional Commander: Chief Supt H MacPherson.

HIGHLAND & ISLANDS DIVISION
Divisional Headquarters: Old Perth Road, Inverness IV2 3SY. Tel: 0845 603 3388.
Divisional Commander: Chief Supt J Innes.

FORTH VALLEY DIVISION
Divisional Headquarters: West Bridge Street, Falkirk FK1 5AP. Tel: 01786 456000.
Divisional Commander: Chief Supt D Flynn.

EDINBURGH DIVISION
Divisional Headquarters: Fettes Avenue, Edinburgh EH4 1RB. Tel: 0131 311 3131.
Divisional Commander: Chief Supt M Williams.

THE LOTHIANS & SCOTTISH BORDERS DIVISION
Divisional Headquarters: Newbattle Road, Dalkeith, Midlothian EH22 3AX. Tel: 0131 311 3131.
Divisional Commander: Chief Supt J McDiarmid.

FIFE DIVISION
Divisional Headquarters: Detroit Road, Glenrothes, Fife KY6 2RJ. Tel: 0845 600 5702.
Divisional Commander: Chief Supt G McEwan.

GREATER GLASGOW DIVISION
Divisional Headquarters: 923 Helen Street, Glasgow G52 1EE. Tel: 0141 532 5400.
Divisional Commander: Chief Supt A Bates.

AYRSHIRE DIVISION
Divisional Headquarters: 10 St Marnock Street, Kilmarnock KA1 1TJ. Tel: 01563 505000.
Divisional Commander: Chief Supt J Thomson.

LANARKSHIRE DIVISION
Divisional Headquarters: 217 Windmillhill Street, Motherwell, North Lanarkshire ML1 1 RZ. Tel: 01698 483000.
Divisional Commander: Chief Supt N Telfer.

ARGYLL & WEST DUNBARTONSHIRE DIVISION
Divisional Headquarters: Stirling Road, Dumbarton G82 3PT. Tel: 01389 822000.
Divisional Commander: Chief Supt R Dunn.

RENFREWSHIRE & INVERCLYDE DIVISION 13
Divisional Headquarters: Mill Street, Paisley PA1 1JU. Tel: 0141 532 5900.
Divisional Commander: Chief Supt A Speirs.

DUMFRIES & GALLOWAY DIVISION
Divisional Headquarters: Cornwall Mount, Dumfries DG1 1PZ. Tel: 0845 600 5701.
Divisional Commander: Chief Supt K Thomson.

SPECIALIST CRIME DIVISION
Organised Crime & Counter Terrorism: Det Chief Supt John Cuddihy. Tel: 0141 532 2423.
Major Crime: Det Chief Supt Campbell Thomson. Tel: 01224 306070.
Divisional Crime & Public Protection: Det Chief Supt Gillian Imery. Tel: 0131 311 3007.
Intelligence: Det Chief Supt Colin Field. Tel: 0141 532 2375.
Safer Communities: Chief Supt Grant Manders. Tel: 0141 532 2241.

OPERATIONAL SUPPORT DIVISION
Specialist operations: Chief Supt Derek Robertson. Tel: 0131 311 3322.
Plannning: Chief Supt Billy Gordon. Tel: 01259 732301.

NORTHERN IRELAND

NORTHERN IRELAND OFFICE
Castle Buildings, Stormont, Belfast BT4 3SG. Website: www.nio.gov.uk

Secretary of State: Rt Hon Theresa Villiers.
Minister of State (Policing & Security): Rt Hon Hugo Swire MP.
Director General: Hilary Jackson.
Her Majesty's Lord Lieutenants for the Counties & County Boroughs
Belfast: Dame Mary Peters DBE.
City of Londonderry: Dr Donal A J Keegan OBE.
Antrim: Mrs Joan Christie OBE.
Armagh: The Rt Hon The Earl of Caledon.
Down: Mr David Lindsay.
Fermanagh: The Rt Hon The Earl of Erne JP.
Londonderry (County): Mr Denis F Desmond CBE.
Tyrone: Mr Robert Scott OBE.

NORTHERN IRELAND POLICING BOARD
Waterside Tower, 31 Clarendon Road, Clarendon Dock, Belfast BT1 3BG. Tel: 028 9040 8500. Fax: 028 9040 8540. Email: information@nipolicingboard.org.uk Website: www.nipolicingboard.org.uk

Chairman: Mr Brian Rea MBE JP.

FORENSIC SCIENCE NORTHERN IRELAND
151 Belfast Road, Carrickfergus, Co Antrim BT38 8PL. Tel: 028 9036 1888. Fax: 028 9036 1900. Website: www. www.dojni.gov.uk/fsni

Chief Executive: Mr Stan Brown. Tel: 028 9036 1800.

POLICE SERVICE OF NORTHERN IRELAND
Brooklyn, 65 Knock Road, Belfast BT5 6LE.
Tel: 0845 600 8000. Criminal Records Office tel: 028 9070 0061 (weekdays 0900–1700).

Email: comsec1@psni.pnn.police.uk

Website: www.psni.police.uk

Chief Constable: Mr Matt Baggott CBE QPM BA(Hons).
Deputy Chief Constable: Judith Gillespie OBE BA(Hons) MSt.
Chief Constable's Staff Officer: Sgt Tommy Johnston. Tel: 028 9070 0003.
    Email: tommy.johnston@psni.pnn.police.uk
Chief Constable's Senior Personal Secretary: Suzanne Robson. Tel: 028 9056 1613. Fax: 028 9056 1645.
    Email: suzanne.robson@psni.pnn.police.uk
Deputy Chief Constable's Staff Officer: Insp Robin Dempsey. Tel: 028 9056 1615.
Deputy Chief Constable's Personal Secretary: Sandra Chalmers. Tel: 028 9056 1614.
Assistant Chief Constable (Crime Operations): J A Harris OBE.
Assistant Chief Constable (Service Improvement): George Hamilton.
Assistant Chief Constable (Operational Support): A G Finlay OBE.
Assistant Chief Constable (Urban Region): W Kerr.
Assistant Chief Constable (Rural Region): D G Jones.
Head of Command Secretariat: Supt R Henderson.

FINANCE & SUPPORT SERVICES
Brooklyn, as above.

Director: Mr David W Best BSc(Econ) FCA MBA.
Head of Finance Management Services: Mr Mark McNaughten.
Head of Finance Reporting & Accounting Services: Mr M Burton.

Procurement & Logistic Services: Mr C M Browne.
Estate Services: Mr I Moore.
Transport: *Head:* David Graham.
Information & Communications Services: Mr Ian Radcliffe.

HUMAN RESOURCES DEPARTMENT
Lisnasharragh, 42 Montgomery Road, Belfast BT6 9LD. Fax: 028 9092 2943.
Director: Mr Joe Stewart OBE LLB FCIPD.
Deputy Director (incorporates Personnel Department): Mr Michael Cox.
A/Head of Equality & Diversity: Louise Crothers.
Head of Training & Development: Chief Supt Kevin Dunwoody.
Chief Medical Advisor (OHW): Dr Geoff Crowther.
Head of Health & Safety: Mr David Orr.
Head of Business Services: Mr Iain Murphy.
PERSONNEL DEPARTMENT
HR Planning & Appointments: Mr Lawrence Clarke.
Head of People Development: Mrs Carmel McCormack.
OHW
Seapark, 151 Belfast Road, Carrickfergus BT38 8PL.
PE Unit Director: Mr W J Henderson.
Chief Nursing Advisor: Joanna Elliott.
Health & Safety. Fax: 028 9070 0713.
TRAINING, EDUCATION & DEVELOPMENT
Garnerville Road, Belfast.
Head of Training & Development: Chief Supt Kevin Dunwoody.
Business Services: Ian Murphy.
Foundation Programmes: Vacant.
Operational Development: Supt A McInnes.
Leadership Development Programmes: Chief Insp M Dornan.
Learning Support: Philip Smith.

LEGAL SERVICES BRANCH
Brooklyn, as above.
Head of Legal Services: Donna Scott.
Assistant Legal Advisors: Mr G Steenson; Mr V Lynagh; Mr C Hanna.
Human Rights & Employment Lawyer: Mr R Roche.
Personal Secretary: Valerie Neill.

CRIME OPERATIONS
Brooklyn, as above.
Assistant Chief Constable: J A Harris OBE.
Organised Crime: Det Chief Supt Roy McComb.
Serious Crime: Det Chief Supt Tim Hanley QPM.
Intelligence: Det Chief Supt Pete Todd.
Special Operations: Det Chief Supt Hugh Hume.
Scientific Support: Mr Jim McQuillan.
Staff Officers: Ms Jeanette McMurray; Sgt Robert Orr.
Personal Secretary: Valerie Graham.

SERVICE IMPROVEMENT DEPARTMENT
Knocknagoney, 29 Knocknagoney Road, Belfast BT4 2PP.
Assistant Chief Constable: George Hamilton.
Personal Secretary: Ms Julie Maitland.
Deputy Head of Department: Chief Supt Peter Farrar.
Community Safety – CJ1: Supt Alan Skelton.
Justice – CJ2: Supt Andrea Wallace.
Public Protection – CJ3: Supt Alister Wallace.
Anti Corruption S4: Det Supt C Taylor.
Investigations: Supt Noel Mullan.
Head of Human Resources: Mrs Heather Palmer.

OPERATIONAL SUPPORT DEPARTMENT
Brooklyn, as above. Tel: 028 9056 1664 (weekdays 0900–1700).
Assistant Chief Constable: Alistair Finlay.
Staff Officer: Insp Rosie Thompson.
Personal Secretary: Mrs Alison Mayes.
Central Statistics Unit: Mr Tony Mathewson.

Corporate Governance: Mr Sam Hagen.
Road & Armed Support: Supt Mark Purdon.

CORPORATE COMMUNICATIONS
Brooklyn, as above.
Director of Media & Public Relations: Liz Young.
Head of Public Relations: Mrs Una Williamson.
Staff Officer: Trevor Scroggie.

DISTRICT POLICING COMMAND
URBAN REGION
Assistant Chief Constable: Will Kerr.
Staff Officer: Kellie McMillan.
Personal Secretary: Corrine Brown.

RURAL REGION
Assistant Chief Constable: Dave Jones.
Territorial Support: Chief Supt Alan Todd.
Deputy/Staff Officer: Sgt Gary McMullan.
Personal Secretary: Shirley Kennedy.

POLICE FEDERATION FOR NORTHERN IRELAND
Garnerville Complex, Garnerville Road, Belfast BT4 2NL.
Chairman: Sgt T Spence.
Secretary: Mr S McCann.

Station	District				
Antrim	D	Enniskillen	F	Newcastle	C
Antrim Road	A	Fintona	F	Newtownabbey	D
Ardmore	E	Garnerville	B	Newtownards	C
Armagh	E	Training		Newtownbutler	F
Armagh (Gough	E	College		Newtownhamilton	E
Barracks)		Garvagh	H	North Queen	A
Ballycastle	H	Glenarm	H	Street	
Ballyclare	D	Glengormley	D	Oldpark	A
Ballymena	H	Grosvenor Road	A	Omagh	F
Ballymoney	H	Hillsborough	D	Pomeroy	F
Ballynafeigh	B	Holywood	C	Portadown	E
Ballynahinch	C	Irvinestown	F	Portaferry	C
Banbridge	E	Keady	E	Portglenone	H
Bangor	C	Kells	H	Portrush	H
Beragh	F	Kesh	F	Rathfriland	E
Bessbrook	E	Kilkeel	E	Saintfield	C
Broughshane	H	Killyleagh	C	Seapark	D
Carrickfergus	D	Knock	B	Sprucefield	D
Castlederg	G	Knocknagoney	B	Steeple Barracks	D
Castlereagh	C	Larne	H	Stewartstown	F
Coleraine	H	Limavady	G	Strabane	G
Comber	C	Lisburn	D	Strand Road	G
Cookstown	F	Lisburn Road	B	Strandtown	A
Craigavon	E	Lislea Drive	B	Tandragee	E
Crossgar	C	Lisnasharragh	C	Tempo	F
Cushendall	H	Lisnaskea	F	Tennent Street	A
Donegall Pass	B	Lurgan	E	Warrenpoint	E
Downpatrick	C	Maghera	G	Waterside	G
Dromore (Down)	E	Magherafelt	G	Woodbourne	A
Dundonald	C	Mahon Road	E	*York Road	A
Dungannon	F	Markethill	E	Industrial &	D
Dungiven	G	Maydown	G	Forensic	
Dunmurry	D	Moira	D	Science Lab	
Eglinton	G	Musgrave Street	B		
		New Barnsley	A		

VETERINARY SERVICE
Ms S Dunbar MRVCS. Portal Inspectorate, Magnet House, Frederick Street, Belfast. Tel: 028 9054 7104.

ISLE OF MAN CONSTABULARY

Police Headquarters, Dukes Avenue, Douglas, Isle of Man IM2 4RG.
Tel: 01624 631212. Fax: 01624 628113 (24 hrs). The dialling code for all numbers is 01624.

Email: firstname.lastname@gov.im, unless otherwise indicated.

General email: police@gov.im

Website: www.gov.im/dha/police

Lieutenant-Governor: His Excellency the Lieutenant Governor Mr Adam Wood.
Chief Minister: Hon J Watterson MHK.
Chief Secretary: Mr W Greenhow.
HM Attorney-General: Mr S M Harding.
Chief Constable: Gary Roberts. Tel: 631222.
Deputy Chief Constable: Vacant. Tel: 631222.
PA: Miss Linda Magee. Tel: 631222.
National Operational Commander: Supt Paul Cubbon. Tel: 631223.
Crime & Intelligence: Det Chief Insp Kevin Willson. Tel: 631224.
Operations: Chief Insp Sid Caine. Tel: 631215.
Organisational Development: Chief Insp Simon Lowe. Tel: 631217.
Complaints & Discipline: Insp Terry Stephen. Tel: 631410.
Financial Crime Unit: Det Insp John Scarffe. Tel: 686001.
Public Protection Unit: Det Insp Jed Bibby. Tel: 631490.
Multi-agency Public Protection Unit: Insp Phil Drowley. Tel: 687573.
Proactive & Intelligence Unit: A/Det Insp Stephen Maddocks. Tel: 631348.
Custody & Call Handling: Insp Derek Flint Tel: 631371.

NEIGHBOURHOOD POLICING TEAMS

Central NPT: Insp Phil Shimmin. Tel: 631420.
Northern NPT: Insp Juan Kinley. Tel: 812234.
Southern NPT: Insp Mark Newey. Tel: 832222.
Western NPT: Insp Will Campbell. Tel: 842208.

CORPORATE SERVICES

Organisational Development: Ms Clare Porter. Tel: 631545.
Staff Development: A/Sgt Adrian Shimmin. Tel: 631540.
Information Technology: Mr Clive Wild BSc BA. Tel: 631255.
Communications: Mr Dave Caley. Tel: 631240.
Finance: Mr Iain Richardson. Tel: 631237.
Facilities: Mr Andrew Quayle. Tel: 631270.

STATES OF JERSEY POLICE
PO Box 789, St Helier, Jersey, Channel Islands JE4 8ZD.
Tel: 01534 612612. Telex: 4192222.
Fax (control room): 01534 612613 (24 hrs). Fax (Criminal Justice Department):
01534 612319 (Mon–Fri 0700–1700).
The dialling code for all numbers is 01534.
Email: sojp@jersey.pnn.police.uk
Website: www.jersey.police.uk

Lieutenant-Governor: General Sir John McColl KCB CBE DSO
Chief Minister: Senator Ian Gorst.
Minister for Home Affairs: Senator Ian Le Marquand.
Home Affairs Department. Tel: 447923.
Chairman of the Jersey Police Complaints Authority: Mrs Debbie Prosser. Tel: 877555.

THE ROYAL COURT
Royal Court House, Royal Square, St Helier JE1 1BA. Tel: 441102.
Bailiff of Jersey: Sir Michael C St J Birt.
HM Attorney-General: Mr Timothy Le Cocq QC.

STATES OF JERSEY POLICE
All enquiries and correspondence to be addressed to The Chief Officer.
Chief Officer: Mr Mike Bowron QPM BA(Hons). Tel: 612500.
Staff Officer: Sgt Matt Le Monnier. Tel: 612627.
PA to the Chief Officer: Mrs Pauline Oliver. Tel: 612502. Fax: 612503.
Deputy Chief Officer: Mr Barry Taylor BA DipAppCrim. Tel: 612520.
PA to the Deputy Chief Officer: Ms Rosie Evans. Tel: 612512. Fax: 612503.

OPERATIONS
Head of Crime Services: Det Supt Stewart Gull QPM. Tel: 612522.
Head of Operations: Supt Rob Bastable. Tel: 612522.
Crime Services: Det Chief Insp Alison Fossey. Tel: 612081.
Uniform Operations: Chief Insp John Sculthorp. Tel: 612400.
Intelligence: Det Chief Insp Chris Beechey. Tel: 612522.
Operations Support: T/Chief Insp Alan Williamson. Tel: 612401.
Operational Support Unit: Vacant. Tel: 612751.
Joint Financial Crimes Unit: Det Insp Dave Burmingham. Tel: 612259. Fax: 870537.
Force Intelligence Bureau: Det Insp Mark Hafey. Tel: 612270.
Priority Crime Team: Det Insp Lee Turner. Tel: 612289.
Public Protection: Det Insp Paul Kennea. Tel: 612240.
Criminal Investigation: Det Insp Steve Langford. Tel: 612200.
Special Branch: Det Sgt Simon Thomas. Tel: 612700.

SUPPORT SERVICES
Senior Human Resources Manager: Mrs Elizabeth Webster. Tel: 447938.
Finance Director: Ms Elizabeth Middleton. Tel: 447929.
Head of Corporate Development: Mr Andrew Sugden. Tel: 612531.
Corporate Communications Manager: Mrs Carol Saunders-Long. Tel: 612107.
Press Officer: Ms Hannah Collier. Tel: 612109.
Head of Information Services: Mr Andrew Gillyett. Tel: 612181.
Scientific Services Manager: Mrs Vicky Coupland. Tel: 612439.
Training: Insp Sara Garwood. Tel: 612134.
Firearms Training: Sgt Dean Machin. Tel 612381.
Professional Standards Department: Det Insp Mark Smith. Tel: 612512. Fax: 612626.
Projects & Facilities Manager: Mr Rob Moy. Tel: 612549.
Head of Criminal Justice Department: Dr Helen Miles. Tel: 612580.
Welfare: Mr Mark Lamerton. Tel: 612600.

OTHER DEPARTMENTS
Law Officers' Department: *Force Legal Advisor:* Mr Laurence O'Donnell. Tel: 441201. Fax: 441220.
Emergency Planning: *States of Jersey Emergency Planning Officer:* Mr Michael Long. Tel: 440621.
Mob: 07797 716451.
Official Analyst's Department: *Senior Analyst:* Mr Nicholas Hubbard BSc MChemA CChem MRCS.
Tel: 736455.

Driver & Vehicle Standards Department: *Head of DVS:* Mr Alan Muir. Tel: 448600.
Customs & Immigration Service: *Chief Executive:* Mr Mike Robinson. Tel: 448000.

GUERNSEY POLICE

Police Headquarters, Hospital Lane, St Peter Port, Guernsey, Channel Islands GY1 2QN.
Tel: 01481 725111. Fax: 01481 256432 (24 hrs). The dialling code for all departments is 01481, unless otherwise indicated.
Email: hq@guernsey.pnn.police.uk; controlroom@guernsey.pnn.police.uk (24 hrs)
Website: www.guernsey.police.uk

Alderney, Channel Islands, is within the jurisdiction of Guernsey and communications in respect of this island should be addressed to the Chief Officer of Police, Guernsey.

Lieutenant-Governor & Commander-in-Chief: Air Marshal Peter Walker CB CBE.
Secretary to the Lieutenant-Governor: Major Marco Ciotti. Tel: 726666.
Minister for the Home Department: Deputy J Le Tocq. Tel: 717000.
THE ROYAL COURT
Bailiff of Guernsey: Mr R Collas. Tel: 726161.
Deputy Bailiff: Mr R McMahon. Tel: 726161.
HM Procureur (Attorney-General): Mr H Roberts QC. Tel: 723355.

GUERNSEY POLICE
Chief Officer of Police: Mr Patrick Rice LLB(Hons).
Deputy Chief Officer of Police: Mr Ian Morellec.
PA to the Chief Officer: Mrs C O'Meara. Tel: 734530.
Head of Operations: Supt P Dowding. Tel: 719485

UNIFORM OPERATIONS
Head of Uniform Operations: Chief Insp N Taylor. Tel: 719406.
Neighbourhood Policing: Insp T Coule; Sgt A Randall. Tel: 734521.
Operational Support (Firearms/Dogs/Traffic): Insp J-P Le Breton. Tel: 719476.
Traffic: Sgt J Tostevin. Tel: 734525.
Operational Planning: Sgt M Harris. Tel: 719411.

CRIME SERVICES
Head of Crime Services: Det Chief Insp R Hardy. Tel: 719450
Criminal Investigation: Det Insp R Medhurst. Tel: 719402.
Public Protection Unit: Det Insp C Cuthbert. Tel: 719458.
Scientific Support: Sgt D Senior. Tel: 719438.
Joint Police & Guernsey Border Agency Intelligence Unit: Mr C McVean. Tel: 755814.

SPECIALIST SERVICES
Head of Specialist Services: Det Chief Insp P Breban. Tel: 719426.
Special Branch: Det Sgt P Mellon. Tel: 719490.
Commercial Fraud: Det Sgt S-J Snowdon. Tel: 719449. Email: gpolfraud@guernsey.net
Professional Standards Department: Det Insp A Whitton. Tel: 719495.
Data Protection & Information Security: Mrs R Masterton. Tel: 719451.

CORPORATE SERVICES
Corporate Services: Chief Insp A Read. Tel: 719412.
Criminal Justice & Licensing Department: Mr P Falla. Tel: 719403.
Process Unit: Insp I Scholes. Tel: 719428.
Royal Court Liaison: Mr N Burnard. Tel: 719478.
Liquor Licensing: Mrs A Cann. Tel: 719461.
Corporate Development: Insp T Coleman. Tel: 719466.
Administration: Mrs C Eley. Tel: 719460.
Human Resources: Miss R Bean. Tel: 717000. (Home Department, Central Services.)
IT Department: Mr G Le Cheminant. Tel: 717000. (Home Department, Central Services.)
Training Department: Mr J Bell. Tel: 719488.
Vehicle Examiners & Fleet Maintenance: Mr G Le Page. Ext: 2474.
Disclosure Unit: Miss G Cale. Tel: 734528. Fax: 734538.

OTHER DEPARTMENTS
Force Medical Examiner: Dr M P R Downing MB BS MSc DCH DRCOG. Tel: 723322.
Emergency Planning Officer: Mrs C Veron. Tel: 717000 ext 2337.

GUERNSEY BORDER AGENCY
Chief Officer of the Guernsey Border Agency: Mr Patrick Rice LLB(Hons).
Immigration & Nationality Division: Mr P Taylor. Tel: 741421.
Customs & Excise Division: Mr T Robin. Tel: 741412.
Operations Branch: Mr P Ferbrache. Tel: 230307.
Detection, Professional Standards & Training: Mr P Knee. Tel: 741432.
Financial Investigation Unit: Mr P Hunkin. Tel: 755817.
Corporate Services: Mrs M Halliday. Tel: 230303.

GARDA SÍOCHÁNA
Garda Headquarters, Phoenix Park, Dublin 8.
Tel: Dublin (00 353) 1 666 0000. The dialling code for all numbers is (00 353) 1
666, unless otherwise indicated.
Email: firstname.lastname@garda.ie, unless otherwise indicated.
Website: www.garda.ie

Commissioner: Martin Callinan. Garda Headquarters. Tel: 01 666 2020. Fax: 01 666 2013. Email: commissioner@garda.ie
Chief Administrative Officer (Strategic & Resource Management): Vacant. Tel: 2078. Fax: 2084. Email: srmstaff@garda.ie
Deputy Commissioner (Operations): Noreen P O'Sullivan. Tel: 2057. Fax: 2060. Email: commissioner_ops@garda.ie
Deputy Commissioner (Strategy & Change Management): Ignatious Rice. Tel: 1253. Fax: 1692. Email: commissioner_scm@garda.ie
Assistant Commissioner, Organisational Development & Strategic Planning: Jack Nolan. Tel: 1901. Email: commissioner_st@garda.ie
Assistant Commissioner, Traffic: Gerry Philips. Tel: 2729. Fax: 1958. Email: commissioner_traffic@garda.ie
Assistant Commissioner, Human Resource Management & Professional Standards: Fintan Fanning. Tel: 2347. Fax: 2338. Email: commissioner_hrm@garda.ie
Assistant Commissioner, Crime & Security: John O'Mahony. Tel: 2801. Fax: 2882. Email: commissioner_cs@garda.ie
Assistant Commissioner, National Support Services: Derek Byrne. Tel: 3429. Fax: 3428. Email: commissioner_nss@garda.ie
Assistant Commissioner, Dublin Metropolitan Region: John Twomey. Tel: 3000. Fax: 3077. Email: commissioner_dmr@garda.ie
Assistant Commissioner, Regional Office (Eastern), Mullingar: Gerry Phillips. Tel: 044 938 4007. Fax: 044 938 4080. Email: commissioner_east@garda.ie
Assistant Commissioner, Regional Office (Northern), Sligo: Kieran Kenny. Tel: 071 915 7007. Fax: 071 915 7080. Email: commissioner_north@garda.ie
Assistant Commissioner, Regional Office (South Eastern), Kilkenny: Jack Nolan. Tel: 056 7775006. Fax: 056 777 5080. Email: commissioner_southeast@garda.ie
Assistant Commissioner, Regional Office (Southern), Anglesea Street, Cork: Thomas Quilter. Tel: 021 452 2007. Fax: 021 452 2083. Email: commissioner_south@garda.ie
Assistant Commissioner, Regional Office (Western), Galway: Donal O'Cualain. Tel: 091 538007. Fax: 091 538080. Email: commissioner_western@garda.ie
Executive Director of Finance & Services: Mr M Culhane. Tel: 1759. Fax: 1966. Email: finance@garda.ie
Chief Medical Officer: Dr Donal Collins. Tel: 2326. Fax: 2365. Email: hrm.occupationalhealthservice@garda.ie
Executive Director, Information & Communication Technology (ICT): Mr Liam Kidd. Tel: 1451. Fax: 1659. Email: ict_executive_director@garda.ie
PA to Commissioner: Chief Supt Orla McPartlin. Tel: 2026. Fax: 2013. Email: commissioner@garda.ie
Private Secretary to the Commissioner: Supt Frank Walsh. Tel: 2022. Fax: 2013. Email: commissioner@garda.ie
Director of Communications: Vacant. Tel: 2031. Fax: 2033. Email: communications@garda.ie

CHIEF SUPERINTENDENTS, ORGANISATIONAL DEVELOPMENT AND STRATEGIC PLANNING
Change Management: Supt Margaret Nugent. Tel: 2583. Fax: 2578.
Community Relations & Community Policing: Anne McMahon. Tel: 3882. Fax: 3801.
CHIEF SUPERINTENDENTS, HUMAN RESOURCE MANAGEMENT AND PROFESSIONAL STANDARDS
HR Director: Mr Alan Mulligan. Tel: 046 903 6800 Fax: 046 903 6899.
Human Resource Management: John Grogan. Tel: 2349. Fax: 2305.
Professional Standards: Pat Clavin. Tel: 2583. Fax: 2578.
Internal Affairs: Pat Clavin. Tel: 2358. Fax: 2351.
Director of Training & Development: Anne McMahon. Tel: 0504 35406. Fax: 0504 35451. Email: college_dv@garda.ie

CHIEF SUPERINTENDENTS, CRIME AND SECURITY
Crime Policy & Administration: Vacant. Tel: 2611. Fax: 2698.
Security & Intelligence: Peter Kirwan. Tel: 2801. Fax: 1704.
Liaison & Protection: John Gilligan. Tel: 2842. Fax: 1733.
Special Detective Unit: Kevin Donohoe. Tel: 3500. Fax: 01 478 0060.
Garda National Traffic Bureau: Aidan Reid. Tel: 1950. Fax: 1958.
CHIEF SUPERINTENDENTS, NATIONAL SUPPORT SERVICES
National Bureau of Criminal Investigation: Padraig M Kennedy. Tel: 3300. Fax: 3347.
Garda Bureau of Fraud Investigation: David Dowling. Tel: 2842. Fax: 3798.
Criminal Assets Bureau: Eugene Corcoran. Tel: 3200. Fax: 3224.
Garda National Drugs Unit: John McMahon. Tel: 9990. Fax: 9985.
Garda National Immigration Bureau: John J O'Driscoll. Tel: 9155. Fax: 9154.
Technical Bureau: Supt John Nolan. Tel: 2624. Fax: 2531. Email: technical_bureau_hq@garda.ie.
CHIEF SUPERINTENDENTS, TRAFFIC
DMR Traffic Division: Aidan Reid. Tel: 9890. Fax: 9899.
CHIEF SUPERINTENDENTS, INFORMATION & COMMUNICATION TECHNOLOGY (ICT)
IT: Supt Denis Ferry. Tel: 2424. Fax: 2419.
Telecommunications: Supt Michael Flynn Tel: 1940. Fax: 1929.

DIVISIONS

DMR East
Chief Supt Jeremiah O'Sullivan. Tel: 5092. Fax: 5099.
DMR North
Chief Supt Francis Clerkin. Tel: 4493. Fax: 4099.
DMR North Central
Chief Supt Patrick Leahy. Tel: 8092. Fax: 8099.
DMR South
Chief Supt Brendan Mangan. Tel: 6292. Fax: 6299.
DMR South Central
Chief Supt Michael V O'Sullivan. Tel: 9092. Fax: 9099.
DMR West
Chief Supt Declan Coburn. Tel: 7000. Fax: 7099.
Garda Reserve Management Unit
Chief Supt John Grogan. Tel: 01 6662568. Email: gardareserve@garda.ie
Anglesea Street
Chief Supt Michael Finn. Tel: 021 452 2011. Fax: 021 452 2081.
Bandon
Chief Supt Thomas Hayes. Tel: 023 885 2211. Fax: 023 885 2281.
Bray
Chief Supt T Conway. Tel: 01 6665392. Email: thomas.g.conway@garda.ie
Castlebar
Chief Supt T Curley. Tel: 094 903 8211. Fax: 094 903 8281. Email: thomas.a.curley@garda.ie
Drogheda
Chief Supt Patrick McGee. Tel: 041 987 4211. Fax: 041 987 4281.
Ennis
Chief Supt John Kerin. Tel: 065 684 8116. Fax: 065 684 8181.
Fermoy
Chief Supt William Dillane. Tel: 025 82111. Fax: 025 33473.
Mill Street
Chief Supt Michael O'Sullivan Tel: 091 538011. Fax: 091 538081. Email: michael.d.osullivan@garda.ie
Henry Street
Chief Supt David Sheahan. Tel: 061 212411. Fax: 061 212481.
Kilkenny/Carlow
Chief Supt Michael McGarry. Tel: 056 777 5006. Fax: 056 777 5080. Email: michael.a.mcgarry@garda.ie
Letterkenny
Chief Supt Terry McGinn. Tel: 074 67100. Fax: 074 28452.
Monaghan
Chief Supt James Sheridan. Tel: 047 77211. Fax. 047 77281.
Mullingar
Chief Supt Mark Curran. Tel: 044 938 4011. Fax: 044 938 4081.
Naas
Chief Supt Michael Byrnes. Tel: 045 884311. Fax: 045 884382. Email: michael.a.byrnes@garda.ie
Navan

Chief Supt Aidan Glackan. Tel: 046 903 6300. Fax: 046 903 6315.
Portlaoise
Chief Supt John Scanlan. Tel: 057 867 4112. Email: john.b.scanlan@garda.ie
Roscommon
Chief Supt P Rattigan. Tel: 090 663 8311. Fax: 090 663 8381.
Sligo
Chief Supt Michael Clancy. Tel: 071 915 7011. Fax: 071 915 7081. Email: michael.p.clancy@garda.ie
Thurles
Chief Supt Catherine Kehoe. Tel: 0504 25111. Fax: 0504 25181.
Tralee
Chief Supt Patrick Sullivan. Tel: 066 710 2311. Fax: 066 710 2381.
Waterford
Chief Supt P V Murphy. Tel: 051 305309. Fax: 051 305381.
Wexford
Chief Supt J Roche. Tel: 0539 165211. Fax: 0539 165281. Email: john.j.roche@garda.ie

BRITISH TRANSPORT POLICE

Force Headquarters: 25 Camden Road, London NW1 9LN.
Tel: 0121 254 8906 (general enquiries). Freephone: 0800 405 040.
Email: firstname.lastname@btp.pnn.police.uk
Website: www.btp.police.uk

British Transport Police is the national police for the railways providing a policing service to rail operators, their staff and passengers.

Chief Constable: Andrew Trotter OBE QPM BSc(Hons).
Deputy Chief Constable: Paul Crowther.
Assistant Chief Constable (Territorial Policing & Crime): Alan Pacey.
Assistant Chief Constable (Central Operations): Stephen Thomas QPM.
Assistant Chief Constable(Scotland): David McCall.
T/Assistant Chief Constable (Director of Corporate Resources): Mark Newton.
Media & Marketing Department. Tel: 020 7830 8854. Fax: 020 7830 8944.
Freedom of Information. Tel: 029 2052 5326.
Professional Standards. Tel: 020 7830 8828.
Counter Terrorism Risk Advisor: Adrian Dwyer OBE MSc MInstRE MIExpE. Tel: 020 7830 8817.
CID: Chief Supt Miles Flood. Tel: 020 7830 8844.
Director of Intelligence: Det Supt Paul Shrubsole. Tel: 020 7830 6428.
Command Support: Elaine Derrick. Tel: 020 7521 6437.
Head of Justice & Forensic Science: Hacer Evans. Tel: 020 7752 4368.
Head of Learning & Development: Peter Ward. Tel: 020 7830 8852.
Force Control Room London: Chief Insp Paul Garrett. Tel: 020 7380 1400. Fax: 020 7383 5989.
Administration of Justice: Supt Peter Rowe. Tel: 020 7830 8931.
Head of Central Ticket Office: David Hards. Tel: 020 7023 6732.
T/Head of HR: Kerry McCafferty. Tel: 020 7830 8920.
Force Safety Advisor: Bob Kenwrick. Tel: 020 7830 6301.
Chief Information Officer: Cliff Cunningham. Tel: 020 7830 8858.
Freedom of Information Manager: Brian Coleman. Ext: 8893.
Head of Finance: Simon Hart. Ext: 8852.
Financial Controller: Andrew Clark. Ext: 8921.
Procurement Manager: Tony Foster. Tel: 020 7830 8930.
Estates & Facilities Manager: Scott Ambrose. Tel: 020 7521 6268.
Vehicle Fleet Manager: Graham Tillett. Tel: 020 7521 6285.

SCOTLAND
Area Headquarters: 90 Cowcaddens Road, Glasgow G4 0LU.
Area Commander: Chief Supt Ellie Bird.
NEIGHBOURHOOD POLICING TEAMS
Aberdeen
Aberdeen Railway Station, Guild Street, Aberdeen AB9 2DQ.
Inverness Police Station. Inverness Railway Station, Academy Street, Inverness IV1 1LE.
Ayrshire Inverclyde
Kilwinning Railway Station, Townhead, Kilwinning KA13 6NT.
Bathgate
British Transport Police, Lothian & Borders Police Office, 18 South Bridge Street, Bathgate EH48 1TW.
Dalmuir
Duntocher Road, Clydebank G81 3QT.
Dundee
Dundee Railway Station, South Union Street, Dundee DD1 4BY.
Edinburgh
Platform 19, Waverley Railway Station, Edinburgh EH1 1BB.
Edinburgh to Glasgow
Platform 19, Waverley Railway Station, Edinburgh EH1 1BB.
Glasgow City Centre
Glasgow Central Station, Glasgow G1 3SL.
Inverness
Inverness Railway Station, Academy Street, Inverness IV1 1LE.
Kirkcaldy
Station Road, Kirkcaldy KY1 1YL.
Motherwell

Muir Street, Motherwell ML1 1BH.
Paisley
Gilmour Street, County Square, Paisley PA1 1RS.
Perth
Perth Railway Station, Leonard Street, Perth PH2 8HF.
Stirling
Goosecroft Road, Stirling FK8 1PF.
RESPONSE TEAMS
Glasgow
90 Cowcaddens Road, Glasgow G4 0LU.
Edinburgh
Platform 19, Waverley Railway Station, Edinburgh EH1 1BB.

NORTH EASTERN
Area Headquarters: 1st Floor, West Gate House, Grace Street, Leeds LS1 2RP.
Area Commander: Chief Supt Terry Nicholson.
DARLINGTON POLICE STATION
Bank Top Railway Station, Darlington DL1 4AA.
Officer in Charge: Sgt Tim Woolven.
Middlesbrough Police Station. Railway Station, Zetland Road, Middlesbrough, Cleveland TS1 1EG.
DERBY POLICE STATION
Railway Terrace, Derby DE1 2RU.
Officer in Charge: Sgt Rob Bowley.
DONCASTER POLICE STATION
7 Trafford Court, Trafford Way, Doncaster DN1 1PD.
Officers in Charge: Insp Andy Selby; Sgt Mark Burgess.
HULL POLICE STATION
Hull Railway Station, Hull HU1 3QX.
Officer in Charge: Sgt Simon Litchfield.
Grimsby Police Station. Grimsby Railway Station, Grimsby, Humberside DN31 1LY.
LEEDS POLICE STATION
Leeds City Bradford Police Station, Leeds City Railway Station, Leeds LS1 4PR.
Officer in Charge: Insp Richard Price.
Bradford Police Station. Bradford Interchange Railway Station, Bradford.
Shipley Police Station. Bradford Interchange, as above.
LEICESTER POLICE STATION
1st Floor, 27 East Street, Leicester LE1 6NB.
Officer in Charge: Sgt Rob Bowley.
LINCOLN POLICE STATION
Central Railway Station, St Mary's Street, Lincoln LN5 7EW.
Officer in Charge: Sgt Steve Broughton.
NEWCASTLE POLICE STATION
Newcastle Sunderland Police Station, 1 Neville Street, Newcastle-upon-Tyne NE1 5DP.
Officer in Charge: Insp Brian Buddo.
Sunderland Police Station. Railway Station, Athenaeum Street, Sunderland SR1 3HD.
NOTTINGHAM POLICE STATION
1 Queens Road, Nottingham NG2 3AS.
Officer in Charge: Insp Granville Sellers.
SHEFFIELD POLICE STATION
Platform 1, Railway Station, Sheaf Street, Sheffield S1 2BP.
Officer in Charge: Sgt Shaun Kenyon.
YORK POLICE STATION
York Railway Station, Station Road, York YO24 1AY.
Officer in Charge: Sgt Joanne Christon.

NORTH WESTERN
Area Headquarters: 2nd Floor, No 1 Portland Street, Manchester M1 3BE.
Area Commander: Chief Supt Peter Holden.
CARLISLE POLICE STATION
Citadel Station, Carlisle, Cumbria CA1 1QZ.
Officer in Charge: Insp Derek McCutcheon.
Lancaster Police Station. Railway Station, Station Road, Lancaster LA1 5NW.

CREWE POLICE STATION
Pedley Street, Crewe, Cheshire CW2 7AA.
Officer in Charge: Insp Sonja Simister.
Chester Police Station. General Railway Station, Station Road, Chester CH1 3NS.
Stoke Police Station. Railway Station, Station Road, Stoke-on-Trent, Staffordshire ST4 2AA.
LIVERPOOL POLICE STATION
2nd Floor, Rail House, Lord Nelson Street, Liverpool L1 1JF.
Officer in Charge: Chief Insp Neil Moffatt.
MANCHESTER POLICE STATION
Manchester Piccadilly Manchester Airport Police Station. Tower Block, Piccadilly Railway Station, Manchester M60 9AJ.
Officer in Charge: Chief Insp Graham Bamford.
PRESTON POLICE STATION
Railway Station, Fishergate Hill, Preston PR1 8AP.
Officer in Charge: Insp Adrian Yorston.
Blackpool Police Station. Blackpool North Railway Station, Talbot Road, Blackpool FY1 2AB.
WIGAN POLICE STATION
North Western Railway Station, Wallgate, Wigan WN1 1BJ.
Officer in Charge: Sgt Andrew Tomkins.

WALES AND WESTERN
Area Headquarters: 1st Floor, The Axis, 10 Holliday Street, Birmingham B1 1UP.
Area Commander: Chief Supt Peter Davies.
BANGOR POLICE STATION
Bangor Railway Station, Holyhead Road, Bangor, Gwynedd LL57 2EG.
Officer in Charge: Sgt Karl Anderson.
BIRMINGHAM POLICE STATION
PO Box 5585, New Street Railway Station, Birmingham B2 4QB.
Officer in Charge: Insp Stuart Middlemiss.
BRISTOL POLICE STATION
Temple Meads Railway Station, Bristol BS1 6QF.
Officer in Charge: Insp Shawn Taylor.
CARDIFF POLICE STATION
1st Floor, 3 Callaghan Square, Cardiff CF10 5BT.
Officer in Charge: Insp Michael Jones.
COVENTRY POLICE STATION
Coventry Railway Station, Station Square, Coventry CV1 2GT.
Officer in Charge: Sgt Martin Smith.
EXETER POLICE STATION
St David's Railway Station, Exeter EX4 4NT.
Officer in Charge: Sgt David Mannion.
GLOUCESTER POLICE STATION
Gloucester Railway Station, Bruton Way, Gloucester GL1 1DE.
Officer in Charge: Sgt Geoff Walker.
NEWPORT POLICE STATION
High Street Railway Station, Newport NP9 4RA.
Officer in Charge: PC Debbie Rouse.
PLYMOUTH POLICE STATION
Plymouth Railway Station, North Road, Plymouth PL4 6AB.
Officer in Charge: Sgt Paul Curtis.
SHREWSBURY POLICE STATION
Railway Station, Castle Foregate, Shrewsbury SY1 2DQ.
Officer in Charge: Sgt Karl Anderson.
SWANSEA POLICE STATION
High Street Railway Station, Swansea SA1 1NU.
Officer in Charge: Sgt Steve Dawkins.
TRURO POLICE STATION
Truro Railway Station, Truro TR1 6HH.
Officers in Charge: Sgt Paul Curtis.
WOLVERHAMPTON POLICE STATION
Wolverhampton Railway Station, Railway Drive, Wolverhampton WV1 1LE.
Officer in Charge: Sgt Julie Everett.

LONDON NORTH
Area Headquarters: 423–425 Caledonian Road, London N7 9BQ.
Area Commander: Det Chief Supt Martin Fry. Tel: 020 7391 8291.
CAMBRIDGE POLICE STATION
Cambridge Station, Station Road, Cambridge CB1 2JW.
Officer in Charge: Sgt Linda Welch.
CAMDEN ROAD POLICE STATION
Camden Road Railway Station, Camden Road, London NW1 9LS.
Officer in Charge: Sgt Charles McGrotty.
COLCHESTER POLICE STATION
Colchester North Rail Station, North Station Road, Colchester CO1 1XD.
Officer in Charge: Insp Paul Mauger.
EBBSFLEET POLICE STATION
Ebbsfleet International Station, International Way, Dartford DA10 1EB.
Officer in Charge: Sgt Martin Keep.
EUSTON POLICE STATION
Euston Station, Melton Street, London NW1 2DU.
Officer in Charge: Insp Tony Lodge.
KINGS CROSS POLICE STATION
Platform 8, Kings Cross Station, London N1 9AP.
Officer in Charge: Sgt John Redman.
LIVERPOOL STREET POLICE STATION
c/o City of London Police, Bishopsgate Police Station, 182 Bishopsgate, London EC2M 4NP.
Officers in Charge: Insp Bob Munn; Insp Paul Mauger.
MILTON KEYNES POLICE STATION
66 Sherwood Drive, Bletchley, Buckinghamshire MK3 6DT.
Officer in Charge: Insp Mike Steer.
NORWICH POLICE STATION
Norwich Station, Thorpe Road, Norwich NR1 1EF.
Officer in Charge: Sgt Andy Cook.
PADDINGTON POLICE STATION
4th Floor, E Block, Macmillan House, Paddington Station, London W21 HA.
Officer in Charge: Sgt Mike Conroy.
PETERBOROUGH POLICE STATION
4 Lincoln Court, Lincoln Road, Peterborough PE1 2RP.
Officer in Charge: Insp Andrew Pickles.
OXFORD POLICE STATION
Oxford Station, Park End Street, Oxford OX1 1HN.
Officer in Charge: Insp Justin Archer.
READING POLICE STATION
Brunel Arcade, Reading Railway Station, Reading RG1 1LT.
Officer in Charge: Insp Justin Archer.
ST PANCRAS POLICE STATION
St Pancras International Railway Station, St Pancras Road, London NW1 2QP.
Officer in Charge: Insp John Clark.
SOUTHEND POLICE STATION
Southend Victoria Station, Southend-on-Sea SS2 6AE.
Officer in Charge: T/Insp Alan Judd.

LONDON SOUTH
Area Headquarters: Ivason House, 8A London Bridge Street, London SE1 9SG.
Area Commander: Chief Supt Steve Morgan.
ASHFORD POLICE STATION
Floor 5, International House, Dover Place, Ashford, Kent TN23 1HU.
Officer in Charge: A/Insp Tim Bradley.
BRIGHTON POLICE STATION
Brighton Railway Station, Queens Road, Brighton BN1 3XP.
Officer in Charge: Insp Gary Ancell.
CROYDON POLICE STATION
Knolly's House, 17 Addiscombe Road, Croydon, Surrey CR0 6SR.
Officer in Charge: Insp Jack Ioannou QPM.

DARTFORD POLICE STATION
Dartford Railway Station, Hythe Street, Dartford DA1 1BP.
Officer in Charge: Sgt Rick Usher.
EBURY BRIDGE POLICE STATION
3 Ebury Bridge, London SW1W 8RR.
Officer in Charge: Insp Dave Brady.
HOLMES HOUSE
Holmes Terrace, Waterloo, London SE1 8BL.
Officer in Charge: Chief Insp Alison Evans.
SOUTH WEST QUADRANT
Central Railway Station, Overline House, Blechynden Terrace, Southampton SO15 1AL.
Officer in Charge: Insp M Morriss.
Bournemouth Police Station. Central Railway Station, Holdenhurst Road, Bournemouth BH8 8HX.
Officer in Charge: Sgt Noel Lilly.
Guildford Police Station. Station View, Walnut Tree Close, Guildford GU1 4UT. *Officer in Charge:* Sgt
Justin Waite.
Portsmouth Police Station. Portsmouth Southsea Station, Commercial Road, Portsmouth PO1 1EQ.
Officer in Charge: Sgt Derek Bish.
Southampton Police Station. Central Railway Station, Overline House, as above. *Officer in Charge:* Sgt
Noel Lilly.

LONDON UNDERGROUND & DLR
Area Headquarters: 55 Broadway, London SW1H 0BD.

Area Commander: Chief Supt Paul Brogden. Tel: 020 7027 6386.
Bakerloo Line: T/Insp Matt Carroll.
Central Line: Insp Mick McGinty.
Circle, Hammersmith & City Line: Insp Alison Martin.
District Line: Insp Kevin Jacobs.
Jubilee Line: T/Insp Andrew Hickling.
Metropolitan Line: T/Insp Dawn Skinner.
Northern Line: T/Insp John Sanderson.
Piccadilly Line: Insp Becky Warren.
Victoria Line: T/Insp Andrew Jackson.
Docklands Light Railway: Insp Kate Shaw.

BRITISH TRANSPORT POLICE FEDERATION
134 Thurlow Park Road, West Dulwich, London SE21 8HN.

Tel: 020 8761 8071. Fax: 01689 893438. Email: infobtpf@btconnect.com. Website: btpolfed.org.uk
Chairman: Mr George Lewis.
General Secretary: Mr Roger Randall.

AREA, POPULATION, STRENGTH, AGE REQUIREMENTS

PLEASE NOTE THAT INFORMATION FOR POLICE SCOTLAND, THE NEW NATIONAL POLICE SERVICE OF SCOTLAND LAUNCHED ON 1 APRIL 2013, WAS NOT AVAILABLE AT TIME OF GOING TO PRESS. THIS INFORMATION WILL BE INCLUDED IN THE 2014 EDITION.

Police force or constabulary Area / population	Strength Police strength (Part-time)	PCSOs (Part-time)	Police staff Full-time or equivalent (Part-time)	Age require- ments
AVON AND SOMERSET 1,186,972 acres/1,511,600	2940 (FTE)	358 (FTE)	2034 (FTE)	18½
BEDFORDSHIRE 123,465 hectares/602,500 305,082 acres	1147	108	878	18½
CAMBRIDGESHIRE 842,390 acres/605,400	1306	185	798	18½
CHESHIRE 576,450 acres/1,006,100	1908 (109)	188 (16)	1147 (255)	18½
CLEVELAND 59,653 hectares/563,000 147,402 acres	1459	166	258	18½
CUMBRIA 1,681,926 acres/496,000	1127	95	655	18
DERBYSHIRE 650,00 acres/1,007,000	1982 (1942 FTE)	170 (167 FTE)	1411 (1207 FTE)	18½ (18 to apply)
DEVON AND CORNWALL 1,024,086 hectares/1,680,370 2.5 million acres	3212 (3132 FTE)	385 (370 FTE)	1818 (1661 FTE)	18
DORSET 655,659 acres/744,000	1316 (FTE)	142	907 (FTE)	18½
DURHAM 243,500 hectares/591,300	1372	169	738	18½
DYFED-POWYS 2,704,305 acres/476,000	1141 (FTE 1120)	127	660 (FTE 608)	18½
ESSEX 1420 square miles/1,729,000	3408 (FTE)	380 (FTE)	1681	18
GLOUCESTERSHIRE 269,878 hectares/575,225	1199	131	634	18
GREATER MANCHESTER 500 square miles/2,500,000	7282 (FTE)	784 (FTE)	3238 (FTE)	18
GUERNSEY 19,411 acres/65,000	153	0	56	18½
GWENT 155,600 hectares/561,751 384,488 acres	1412	241	719	18½
HAMPSHIRE 418,000 hectares/1,884,160	3361	337	1977	18
HERTFORDSHIRE 164,306 hectares/1,100,000	1948	262	1467	18½
HUMBERSIDE	1865	299	1678	18

Police force or constabulary Area / population	Strength Police strength (Part-time)	PCSOs (Part-time)	Police staff Full-time or equivalent (Part-time)	Age require-ments
1356 square miles/914,846	(156)	(19)	(465)	
ISLE OF MAN 226 square miles/80,058	236		50	18½
JERSEY 28,800 acres/100,000	237		90	18½
KENT 390,811 hectares/1,705,300	3374	326	2108	18½ (18 to apply)
LANCASHIRE 2903 square km/1,451,426	3178	409 (28)	1757 (329)	18–60
LEICESTERSHIRE 2538km²/992,700	2008	207	1017	18
LINCOLNSHIRE 2,284 square miles/701,972	1138 (51)	152 (18)	862 (194)	18½
LONDON, CITY OF 779 acres/300,000 day; 8000 night	791	16	310	18½
LONDON, METROPOLITAN 620 square miles/7,200,000	31,124 (1418)	2594 (165)	11,824 (1938) (2362)	18
MERSEYSIDE 64,750 hectares/1,353,596 253 square miles	4033	410	2174	18
NORFOLK 537,085 hectares/850,800 2,074 sq. miles	1516	246	87	18
NORTH WALES 1,554,858 hectares/629,000	1464 (FTE)	251	811 (FTE)	18½
NORTH YORKSHIRE 2,053,984 acres/750,000	1444	104	1096	18½
NORTHAMPTONSHIRE 584,979 acres/657,000	1276 (1244 FTE)	131 (129 FTE)	962 (844 FTE)	18
NORTHERN IRELAND 3,495,255 acres/1,547,400	7033 (550 POPT)		2381 (354)	18
NORTHUMBRIA 1,375,000 acres/1,396,374	3810	407	1435	18½
NOTTINGHAMSHIRE 2,161 sq km/1,086,590	2119 (FTE)	257 (FTE)	1248 (FTE)	18
SOUTH WALES 812 square miles/1,225,900	2876 (FTE)	374 (FTE)	1589 (FTE)	18
SOUTH YORKSHIRE 385,605 acres/1,291,200	2803 (173)	299 (28)	2230 (703)	18
STAFFORDSHIRE 671,175 acres/1,058,269	1795 (149)	189 (26)	998 (286)	18
SUFFOLK	1166	167	907	18½

Police force or constabulary Area / population	Strength Police strength (Part-time)	PCSOs (Part-time)	Police staff Full-time or equivalent (Part-time)	Age require- ments
939,510 acres/728,200				
SURREY 645 square miles/1,098,200	1941 (FTE)	207 (FTE)	2041 (FTE)	18½
SUSSEX 932,100 hectares/1,259,130	2731' (268)	317 (340)	1650 (441)	18
THAMES VALLEY 2,200 square miles/2,253,400	4197 (FTE)	490 (FTE)	2447 (FTE)	18½
WARWICKSHIRE 764 square miles/535,100	779 (56)	99 (6)	558 (134)	18
WEST MERCIA 2868 square miles/1,181,900	2146	261	1608	18½
WEST MIDLANDS 1,299,830 hectares/5,601,847	7872 (7639 FTE)	787 (692 FTE)	3235 (3133 FTE)	18½
WEST YORKSHIRE 780 square miles/2,200,000	5435	765	3795	18
WILTSHIRE 1346 acres/661,590	1057 (FTE)	147 (FTE)	841 (FTE)	18
BRITISH TRANSPORT	2815	378	1396	18½
GARDA SÍOCHÁNA 2,843,912 acres/4,222,100	13,505		2476 (2039 FTE)	18–35

CHIEF POLICE OFFICERS
METROPOLITAN POLICE DISTRICT
Commissioner: Sir Bernard Hogan-Howe QPM MBA MA(Oxon)
Deputy Commissioner: Craig Mackey QPM
Assistant Commissioners

Allison, C	Byrne, S, MA	Dick, C, QPM	Rowley, M

Deputy Assistant Commissioners

Ball, H	Gallan, P	Osborne, S	Simmons, M, QPM
de Brunner, M	Hewitt, M		

Commanders

Basu, N	Gibson, A	Morris, R	Spindler, P
Bennett, J	Jones, C	Newcomb, A	Taylor, F
Chishty, M	Loughborough, P, QPM	Quinton, I	Walton, R
Eastaugh, T	Martin, D	Rodhouse, S	Watson, S
Ephgrave, N	Martin, R		

CITY OF LONDON
Commissioner: Adrian Leppard QPM MBA
Assistant Commissioner: Ian Dyson
T/Commanders: Wayne Chance; Steve Head.

CHIEF CONSTABLES IN ENGLAND AND WALES (INCLUDING ACTING AND TEMPORARY)

Ash, S (Suffolk) 2007
Barton, M, LLB (Durham) 2012
Bliss, A, QPM (Hertfordshire) 2011
Cheer, J, QPM BA MBA Dip (Cleveland) 2013
Cole, S, BA MA DipCrim (Leicestershire) 2010
Creedon, M F, BA MA (Derbyshire) 2007
Crompton, D, QPM (South Yorkshire) 2012
Cunningham, M, QPM (Staffordshire) 2009
Curran, J (Humberside) 2013
Davenport, S (Gloucestershire) 2013
Eyre, C, QPM (Nottinghamshire) 2012
Fahy, Sir P, QPM MA (Greater Manchester) 2008
Finnigan, S, CBE QPM MA BA MA Diploma AC & PS (Lancashire) 2005
Gargan, N (Avon and Somerset) 2013
Geenty, P, BEd MBA (Wiltshire) 2012
Gilmore, M, MA QPM (West Yorkshire) 2013
Gormley, P, QPM BA DipAppCrim (Norfolk) 2010
Hitchcock, A, QPM BSc MA MBA (Bedfordshire) 2010
Kavanagh, S (Essex) 2013
Lawson, B, QPM, MSt (Cumbria) 2012 (Temporary)
Learmonth, I (Kent) (2010)
Lee, A (Northamptonshire) 2009

Madgwick, T (North Yorkshire) 2012 (Temporary)
Marsh, A (Hampshire) 2013
Murphy, J, QPM LLB (Merseyside) 2010
Napier, C, QPM (Gwent) 2011
Owens, L (Surrey) 2012
Parker, A, QPM (Warwickshire) 2011
Parr, S (Cambridgeshire) 2010
Polin, M, MBA QPM (North Wales) 2009
Rhodes, N, LLB (Lincolnshire) 2012
Richards, M (Sussex) 2007
Roberts, J, QPM (Dyfed-Powys) 2012
Sawyer, S (Devon & Cornwall) 2012
Shaw, D (West Mercia) 2011
Sim, S, QPM BA MBA FCMI DipAppCrim (Northumbria) 2010
Simpson, D (Dorset) 2012
Sims, C, QPM (West Midlands) 2009
Thornton, S, QPM CBE (Thames Valley) 2005
Trotter, A, OBE QPM BSc (British Transport) 2009
Vaughan, P, QPM CCMI BSc DipAppCrim (South Wales) 2009
Whatton, D, QPM (Cheshire) 2008

DEPUTY CHIEF CONSTABLES IN ENGLAND AND WALES (INCLUDING ACTING AND TEMPORARY)

Adams, A (Hertfordshire)
Akhtar, J (West Yorkshire) (Temporary)
Bailey, S (Norfolk)
Banks, M, BA (Durham) (Temporary)
Beckley, R, QPM (Avon and Somerset)
Benson, D (Essex)
Vacant (Cleveland)
Brunton, N (Warwickshire) (Temporary)
Chesterman, S, QPM (West Mercia)
Cross, S (North Yorkshire) (Temporary)
Crowther, P (British Transport)
Donholm, C (Surrey)
Edens, S (Leicestershire)
Farrar, J, BSc MPA (Gwent)
Feavyour, J (Cambridgeshire)
Fletcher, J, BA (Bedfordshire)
Goodman, P (East Midlands)
Goodwin, A J, QPM BA (Derbyshire)
Griffin, D, QPM MA (Humberside)

Habgood, F, QPM (Thames Valley)
Hopkins, I, MBA FCMI (Greater Manchester)
Ingram, N (Dyfed-Powys)
King, H, QPM MA (Cheshire)
Lambert, K (Gloucestershire)
Lawson, B, BSc, MSt (Merseyside) (seconded to Cumbria)
Marshall, P (Suffolk)
Parkinson, J (West Yorkshire)
Paul, C, BA (South Wales)
Paxton, D, BA (Staffordshire)
Pughsley, A (Kent)
Sahota, M (South Yorkshire)
Scarrott, P (Nottinghamshire)
Shannon, I, BA MA (North Wales)
Skeer, M, BA (Cumbria) (Temporary)
Thompson, D (West Midlands)
Veale, M (Wiltshire)
Ward, A (Merseyside) (Temporary)

Weigh, C (Lancashire)
Whiting, A J, QPM (Dorset)
Wood, A (Lincolnshire)

York, G (Sussex)
Zinzan, D (Devon & Cornwall)

ASSISTANT CHIEF CONSTABLES IN ENGLAND AND WALES (INCLUDING ACTING AND TEMPORARY)

Armitt, C (Merseyside) (Temporary)
Ashman, S (Northumbria)
Baldwin, A (Thames Valley)
Bangham, A (Avon and Somerset)
Bannister, R (Lincolnshire)
Bates, M (Lancashire)
Beale, M (West Midlands)
Beautridge, G (Kent and Essex)
Bennett, R (Thames Valley)
Berry, R (Gloucestershire)
Blazeby, J (Staffordshire)
Boarland, C (Devon & Cornwall)
Boutcher, J (Hertfordshire)
Brandon, P (Kent)
Campbell, J (Northumbria)
Campbell, J (Thames Valley)
Cann, G (West Midlands)
Collins, D, BA (Derbyshire)
Cooke, A, BA (Merseyside)
Copley, D (Greater Manchester)
Cotterill, S (Derbyshire)
Crook, S (Gloucestershire)
Dodd, G (West Yorkshire)
Donald, S, QPM MA (Humberside)
Fish, S, OBE (Nottinghamshire)
Forsyth, Mr G (West Midlands)
Frost, A (Northamptonshire)
Graham, J, BA MA (Cumbria)
Guildford, C (West Yorkshire)
Hall, C (Norfolk and Suffolk)
Hamlin, S (Norfolk and Suffolk) (Temporary)
Hansen, R (Avon and Somerset)
Harrison, S (Essex)
Hedley, S (Wiltshire)
Heywood, S (Greater Manchester)
Holt, A (South Yorkshire)
Hopkins, M (Cambridgeshire)
Jelley, M (Northamptonshire)
Jukes, M, MA MSc (South Wales)
Kirby, J, BSc (South Wales)
Kirkby, J (Surrey)
Langley, C (Dyfed-Powys)
Leaver, A (Humberside)
Lee, I, QPM (West Yorkshire) (Temporary)
Lewis, R (South Wales) (Acting)
Long, J (Avon and Somerset)
McCall, D (British Transport)

McCormick, J (Cheshire)
Manners, K (West Mercia & Warwickshire)
Mason, M (Essex)
Merrett, R (Sussex)
Milsom, M (West Yorkshire)
Morgan, G (West Mercia & Warwickshire)
Morgan, S, BA MSc (Leicestershire)
Netherton, P (Devon and Cornwall)
Newcomb, T (Suffolk) (Temporary)
Newton, M (British Transport) (Temporary)
Nicholson, L (Hampshire)
Nix, M (Kent) (Temporary)
Orford, D (Durham) (Temporary)
Pacey, A (British Transport)
Pickard, D, BA (Cleveland)
Pilling, I (Merseyside) (Temporary)
Pinkney, O (Surrey and Sussex)
Prince, S (Gwent)
Pritchard, H G, MA (North Wales)
Pryde, D (Hampshire)
Pughsley, A (Kent)
Purdie, R (Cheshire)
Rhodes, A, BA (Lancashire)
Richer, A, BA MA (Bedfordshire)
Roberts, A, BSc Dip(Cantab) (Cleveland)
Robins, J (West Yorkshire)
Roome-Gifford, A, LLB (Hertfordshire)
Rowe, S (West Midlands)
Sawyers, J (Staffordshire)
Scarrott, P (Nottinghamshire)
Shewan, G (Greater Manchester)
Smy, K, BSc MBA PgDip PM FInstLM (Lincolnshire)
Spittal, I (North Yorkshire)
Taylor, S (Devon and Cornwall)
Thomas, C (Leicestershire) (Temporary)
Thomas, S, QPM (British Transport)
Torr, S (South Yorkshire) (Temporary)
Vant, G (Northumbria)
Vaughan, J (Dorset)
Ward, A (Merseyside)
Waterfield, I (Nottinghamshire) (Temporary)
White, P (Lancashire)
White, S, BA MBA (Cleveland)
Wiggett, I (Greater Manchester)
Wilson, G (Norfolk)
Wortley, J (Essex) (Temporary)

CHIEF CONSTABLE, POLICE SCOTLAND

House, S, QPM (2013)

DEPUTY AND ASSISTANT CHIEF CONSTABLES, POLICE SCOTLAND

Allen, S, QPM (Deputy)
Fitzpatrick, R, QPM (Deputy)
Livingstone, I (Deputy)
Richardson, N, QPM (Deputy) (Designate)
Graham, M (Assistant)

Higgins, B J, BA (Assistant)
McCormick, M (Assistant)
Mawson, W (Assistant)
Nicolson, R, QPM (Assistant)
Penman, D (Assistant)

CHIEF CONSTABLE IN NORTHERN IRELAND

Baggott, M, CBE QPM BA

DEPUTY AND ASSISTANT CHIEF CONSTABLES IN NORTHERN IRELAND

Gillespie, J, OBE BA MSt (Deputy)
Finlay, A G OBE (Assistant)
Hamilton, G (Assistant)

Harris, J A, OBE (Assistant)
Jones, D G (Assistant)
Kerr, W (Assistant)

POLICE ASSOCIATIONS

ASSOCIATION OF CHIEF POLICE OFFICERS OF ENGLAND, WALES AND NORTHERN IRELAND

10 Victoria Street, London SW1H 0NN.
Tel: 020 7084 8950. Website: www.acpo.police.uk

OFFICERS OF THE ASSOCIATION
President: Sir Hugh Orde OBE QPM.
Vice Presidents: Miss Sara Thornton CBE QPM (Chief Constable, Thames Valley Police); Sir Peter Fahy QPM (Chief Constable, Greater Manchester Police); Vacant.
Chief Executive: Mr Thomas Flaherty.
Chief of Staff: Mr David Lewis.
Director of Communications: Mr Oliver Cattermole.

BUSINESS AREAS

Children & Young People
Head: Ms Jacqui Cheer (Chief Constable, Cleveland).
Crime
Head: Mr Jon Murphy QPM (Chief Constable, Merseyside).
Criminal Justice
Head: Mr Chris Eyre QPM (Chief Constable, Nottinghamshire).
Equality, Diversity & Human Rights
Head: Mr Alfred Hitchcock (Chief Constable, Bedfordshire).
Finance & Resources
Head: Nigel Brook (Assistant Chief Officer, West Yorkshire).
Futures
Head: Mr Alex Marshall (Chief Executive, College of Policing).

Information Management
Head: Ms Ailsa Beaton OBE (Metropolitan).
Local Policing & Partnership
Head: Mr Simon Cole (Chief Constable, Leicestershire).
Performance Management
Head: Mr Stephen Finnigan QPM (Chief Constable, Lancashire).
Terrorism and Allied Matters
Head: Ms Cressida Dick (Assistant Commissioner, Metropolitan).
Uniformed Operations
Head: Mr Philip Gormley (Chief Constable, Norfolk).
Workforce Development
Head: Sir Peter Fahy QPM (Chief Constable, Greater Manchester).

CHIEF POLICE OFFICERS' STAFF ASSOCIATION (CPOSA)

Chairman: Mr Craig Mackey (Deputy Commissioner, Metropolitan).
Vice-Chairman: Mr David Griffin (Deputy Chief Constable, Humberside).
Negotiating Secretary: Mr D Jones (Assistant Chief Constable, Police Service Northern Ireland).
Secretary: Mr Thomas Flaherty.

THE POLICE SUPERINTENDENTS' ASSOCIATION OF ENGLAND AND WALES

67A Reading Road, Pangbourne, Berkshire RG8 7JD.
Tel: 01189 844005. Fax: 01189 845642. Email: enquiries@policesupers.com.
Website: www.policesupers.com

The Police Superintendents' Association is the sole representative body for all police officers in the ranks of Superintendent and Chief Superintendent in all Home Office police forces in England and Wales, Isle of Man Constabulary, Civil Nuclear Constabulary and British Transport Police.

NATIONAL OFFICERS
President: Chief Supt Irene Curtis (Lancashire).
Vice President: Chief Supt Gavin Thomas (Gloucestershire).
National Secretary: Chief Supt Graham Cassidy (South Yorkshire).
National Deputy Secretary: Chief Supt Tim Jackson (Cheshire).

NATIONAL EXECUTIVE COMMITTEE
A District
Chair: Chief Supt Richard Kerman (Humberside).
Secretary: Supt Alan Lees (West Yorkshire).
B District
Chair: Supt Alan Greene (Greater Manchester).
Secretary: Chief Supt Mark Turner (West Mercia).

C District
Chair: Chief Supt Gavin Thomas (Gloucestershire).
Secretary: Chief Supt Paul Symes (Gwent).
D District
Chair: Chief Supt Alan Horton (Kent).
Secretary: Chief Supt Bob Scully (Norfolk).
E District
Chair: Chief Supt Steve Lovelock (Metropolitan).
Secretary: Chief Supt Joanna Young (Metropolitan).
Reserved Places
Women: Supt Emma Webber (Devon and Cornwall).
BME: Chief Supt John Molloy (Kent).
LGBT: Vacant.

POLICE FEDERATION OF ENGLAND AND WALES
Police Federation of England and Wales, Federation House, Highbury Drive, Leatherhead, Surrey KT22 7UY.
Tel: 01372 352000. Website: www.polfed.org

The Police Federation is the representative body for the police service for all ranks up to and including chief inspectors. It was established in accordance with the Police Act 1964.

JOINT CENTRAL COMMITTEE
Chairman: Mr S Williams (North Wales).
Vice Chairman: Mr S White (Avon and Somerset).
General Secretary: Mr I Rennie (Greater Manchester).
Deputy General Secretary: Mr S Smith (Durham).
Treasurer: Mr M Mordecai (Metropolitan).
Deputy Treasurer: George Gallimore (Greater Manchester).
CONSTABLES' CENTRAL COMMITTEE
Chairman: Mr W Riches (Metropolitan).
General Secretary/Treasurer: Mr P Barker (Greater Manchester).
SERGEANTS' CENTRAL COMMITTEE
Chairman: Mr J F M Giblin MA BSc(Hons) (Gwent).
General Secretary/Treasurer: Mrs A M Kirkwood (West Midlands).
INSPECTORS' CENTRAL COMMITTEE
Chairman: Mr S White (Avon and Somerset).
General Secretary/Treasurer: Mr I Trueman (Hampshire).
REGIONAL MEMBERS OF THE NATIONAL COMMITTEE
All regional members of the National Committee can be contacted at Police Federation HQ, Leatherhead, as above.

No 1 Region
Mr P Barker
Mr G Gallimore BSc(Hons)
Mr I Rennie
No 2 Region
Mr A Jones
Mr S A Smith
Mr M G Taylor
No 3 Region
Mrs A Kirkwood
Ms J Willetts
Mr P Ford
No 4 Region
Mr P R Davis
Mr S Evans BA(Hons)
Mr A Ogg
No 5 Region
Mr K Huish
Ms Karen Stephens

Mr I R Trueman
No 6 Region
Mr J Coppen
Mr A Dumbiotis FInstLEx
Mr S White
No 7 Region
Mr J F M Giblin MA BSc(Hons)
Mr Z Mader
Mr S Williams
No 8 Region
Mr R Nelson
Mr P Huitson
Mr A Fittes
Mr M J Mordecai BA(Hons)
Mr W Riches
Mr G Stuttaford
Policewomen
Ms C Davies
Mrs J Lawrence BA(Hons)

THE ASSOCIATION OF SPECIAL CONSTABULARY CHIEF OFFICERS

Website: www.ascco.org.uk

Hon President: Sir Peter Fahy (Chief Constable, Greater Manchester).
Chair: Debi Potter.
ASCCO Council PA: Denise Maynard. c/o Essex Police Headquarters, F Block, PO Box 2, Springfield, Chelmsford CM2 6DA. Email: denise.maynard@essex.pnn.police.uk

THE ASSOCIATION OF SCOTTISH POLICE SUPERINTENDENTS (ASPS)

Secretariat: 99 Main Street, Glasgow G62 6JH.
Tel: 0141 532 4022. Fax: 0141 532 4019. Email: secretariat@scottishpolicesupers.org.uk. Website: www.scottishpolicesupers.org.uk

President: Chief Supt David O'Connor.
General Secretary: Ms Carol Forfar.
Office Manager: Ms Ruth Todd.

SCOTTISH POLICE FEDERATION

5 Woodside Place, Glasgow G3 7QF.
Tel: 0141 332 5234. Fax: 0141 331 2436. Twitter: @scotspolfed Website: www.spf.org.uk

General Secretary: Calum Steele.
Chairman: Brian Docherty.
Deputy General Secretary: Robert Milligan.
Vice Chairman: David Ross.
Treasurer: Graham Neilson.
The Federation is the representative body for the Scottish police service for all ranks up to and including chief inspectors. It was established in accordance with the Police Acts 1919 and 1964.

THE SUPERINTENDENTS' ASSOCIATION OF NORTHERN IRELAND

Secretariat: PSNI College, Garnerville, Belfast BT4 2NX.
Tel: 028 9092 2201/2160. Fax: 028 9092 2169. Email: mail@policesuperintendentsni.org Website: www.policesuperintendentsni.org

President: Chief Supt N Grimshaw.
Honorary Secretary: Supt A Kearney.
Office Manager: Ms Alison Smyth.

POLICE FEDERATION FOR NORTHERN IRELAND

77–79 Garnerville Road, Belfast BT4 2NX.
Tel: 028 9076 4200. Fax: 028 9076 1367. Website: www.policefed-ni.org.uk Email: pfni@btconnect.com

Chairman: Mr Terry Spence.
Secretary: Mr Stevie McCann.
Assistant Secretary: Marty Whittle.
Treasurer: Ronald Kenning.
Vice Chairman: Mark Lindsay.

MINISTRY OF DEFENCE POLICE

Headquarters, Ministry of Defence Police, Wethersfield, Braintree, Essex CM7 4AZ.

Tel: 01371 854000. Fax: 01371 854030.

For HQ extensions tel: 01371 85 followed by the extension number.

The Ministry of Defence Police is a statutory civil police force with particular responsibility for the provision of armed security and specialist policing services to the MOD. It contributes significantly to the physical protection of property and personnel within its jurisdiction and delivers a specific policing service in accordance with the MOD Mandate and Statement of Requirement for MDP services.

CENTRE OFFICE
Chief Constable/Chief Executive: Stephen B Love QPM MA. Ext: 4109.
PA: Jeanette Beswick. Ext: 4316.
Staff Officer: Chief Insp Colin Fiske. Ext: 4317.
Deputy Chief Constable: Gerard P McAuley MSc MCIM. Ext: 4057.
PA: Jenny Norton. Ext: 4108.
Staff Officer: Insp Steve Rochester. Ext: 4067.
Driver: Robbie Boyle. Ext: 4319.

AGENCY BUSINESS SERVICES
Head of ABS: Chief Supt Dave Long MA. Ext: 4401.

STANDARDS
Fax: 01371 854040.
Head of PSD: Supt Mark Foulger. Ext: 4854. Fax: 01371 854307.
Complaints: Chief Insp Richard Willcocks. Ext: 4305. Mob: 07920 750566.
Investigations: Det Chief Insp Graham Byrne BSc(Hons). Ext: 4722. Mob: 07780 957299.
Misconduct: Chief Insp Graham Seale LLB(Hons). Ext: 4187. Mob: 07802 332028.
Intelligence Manager (PSIU): Det Insp Roger Griffiths. Ext: 4654.
PSD Support Manager: Chief Insp Martin Johnston MA. Ext: 4775.
Case Support Unit: Amanda Johnston. Ext: 4324.

INFORMATION MANAGEMENT
Head of Police Information Management: Insp Adam Morris. Ext: 4370.
Retention & Disposal Unit (RRDU). Ext: 4106.
ISO (Business); iHub: Martin Brett. Ext: 4104.

OPERATIONAL STANDARDS
Head of Operational Standards: Chief Insp C Groves. Ext: 4318.
Force Crime & Incident Registrar: Insp Ken Thomson. Ext: 4636.
IT Security Officer: Keith Hardy. Ext: 4218.
Force Protective Security Officer: Ext: 4218.

AGENCY COMPLEMENTING TEAM
Head of ACT: Insp Paul Sadler. Ext: 4410. Sgt Gill Norwood. Ext: 4770.

DIVISIONAL OPERATIONS
Fax: 01371 854241.
Assistant Chief Constable: David J Allard. Ext: 4251.
Staff Officer & Head of Community Safety: Insp D Barber. Ext: 4786.
Superintendent Divisional Operations: Dave Hewitt. Ext: 4374.
Personal Secretary: Rosemary Marshall. Ext: 4291.
Business Manager: Lesley McCarthy. Ext: 4287.
Budget Officer: Sarah Hill BA(Hons). Ext: 4255.
Assistant Business Coordinator: Nikki Coe BA(Hons). Ext: 4274.
Administrative Officer: Vacant. Ext: 4377.
Critical National Infrastructure Team: *Head of CNI Team:* Supt Derry Montgomery. Ext: 4283. Insp Jo Thompson. Ext: 4032. Sgt Yasmine Singh. Ext: 4021. Fax: 01371 854001.
Central Control Room. *Shift Inspector.* Ext: 4398. **General Enquiries.** Ext: 4444. Fax: 01371 854030. Secure fax only (MOD CUSEFAX): 01371 854423.

HUMAN RESOURCES
As a business unit of the MOD, the MDP is served by the Department's corporate HR teams at Defence Business Services, supported locally by HR business partners.
MDP-HQ HRD-Senior HRBP: Glen McDermott. Ext: 4141.
MDP-HQ HRD-HRBP 1: Rachael Simpson. Ext: 4309.
MDP-HQ HRD-HRBP 2: Vacant.

COMMUNICATIONS & INFORMATION SYSTEMS
Fax: 01371 854673.
Head of Communications & Information Systems: Chris Lansbury. Ext: 4668.
Service Desk Manager: Tony Petterson. Ext: 4113.
Authorised Telecommunications Officer: Michelle Cole. Ext: 4356.
Head of CIS Systems Design: Andrew Wallbank. Ext: 4202.
Service Level & Problem Manager: Andrew Chaplin. Ext: 4012.
Server Support Manager: Stuart Doughty. Ext: 4939.
System Design Manager: Ray Maycock. Ext: 4112.
Technical Security Officer: Jon Nelson. Ext: 4215.
Configuration Manager: Denise Mulley. Ext: 4225.
Security Compliance Manager: Paul Wisher. Ext: 4204.
AICC Manager (Airwave, ICCS, Command & Control): Sgt Steve Woodgate. Ext: 4502.

CENTRAL OPERATIONS
Fax: 01371 854050.
Assistant Chief Constable: Robert Chidley MA. Ext: 4301.
Staff Officer: Insp D Finn. Ext: 4299.
Personal Secretary. Ext: 4519.
Business Coordinator: Mr L James. Ext: 4424.
Head of Department: Chief Supt R Hoblin. Ext: 4428. Supt C Yates. Ext: 4418.
Exercise Planning Team: Sgt P Goward. Ext: 4585.
Operational Support Unit (South) MDP Wethersfield: Chief Insp K McDonaugh. Tel: 01371 854566.
Operational Support Unit (North) (Linton-on-Ouse Yorkshire): Chief Insp G Bruce. Tel: 01347 847650.

OPERATIONAL CAPABILITY CENTRE
Head of OCC: Supt Kevin McAndrew. Ext: 4506.
Head of Operational Delivery: Chief Insp Tom Falconer.
Head of Operational Capability Services: Chief Insp Matt Spiers. Ext: 4501.
Head of Capability Management: Chief Insp Tom Falconer. Ext: 4090.
Head of Central Administration: Debbie Law. Ext: 4153.
Dog Section: Sgt Matt Busby. Ext: 94451 8692.

INTERNATIONAL POLICING
Fax: 01371 854353.
Head of Afghan Police Unit: Chief Insp Melvin Goudie. Ext: 4327.
PJHQ Liaison Officer: Insp Alistair Elvers. Ext: 4902.
Operations Manager: Sgt David McIllwraith. Ext: 4798.
Administration: PC Sharon Beaney. Ext: 4925. Beverly Freeman. Ext: 4265. Sue Hanslip. Ext: 4705.

CRIMINAL INVESTIGATION DEPARTMENT
Head of CID: T/Det Chief Supt S Mace. Ext: 4381. Fax: 01371 854417.
Head of Force Intelligence Bureau/Special Branch: Det Chief Insp S Russell. Ext: 4184. Fax: 4284.
Head of Fraud Squad/CID Management: Det Chief Insp P Mayne MA Cert Ed. Ext: 4383/4612. Fax: 4552.
Criminal Justice Unit: Det Insp M Goodwin. Ext: 4382. Fax: 4649.
Senior Crime Managers: **Northern Area (including Scotland & Northern Ireland):** Det Chief Insp J Grieg. Tel: 01748 874070. **Southern Area:** Chief Insp G O'Shea. Ext: 4499.
Force Counter Terrorism Security Advisor: PC S C Read. CTSA, MOD Police, Room 048A, Old War Office, Whitehall, London SW1A 2EU. Tel: 020 7218 0854. Mobile: 07799 343411

AUDIO VISUAL
Head of Audio Visual: Neil Parry. Ext: 4076.
Deputy Head: Paul Kemp. Ext: 4176.

CORPORATE SERVICES
Fax: 01371 854025 (to DRP only).
Agency Secretary (Senior Civil Service): Mr David King. Ext: 4289.
Personal Secretary: Mrs Irene MacIntyre. Ext: 4293.
Clothing & Equipment: Mr M Lowden. Ext: 4250. Ms J Nixon. Ext: 4248.
Vehicle Fleet Manager: Vacant. Ext: 4668.
Head of SHEF: Mr A Clapp. Ext: 4128.
Occupational Health Advisor: Ms Maria Hale. Ext: 4889.
Head of Diversity & Equality: Vacant.

BUSINESS MANAGEMENT AND FINANCE
Fax: 01371 854080.
Head of Department: Mr J J Oliver. Ext: 4240.
Parliamentary Business: Mrs D J Browne. Ext: 4206.

Freedom of Information & Data Protection Officer: Mr R Harney. Ext: 4399.
In Year Manager: Mr H Moore. Ext: 4714.

CORPORATE COMMUNICATIONS
Fax: 01371 854010.
Head of Corporate Communications: Patrick Nealon. Ext: 4616.
Communications Hub: Mr Norman Hicks. Ext: 4216.
Press Officer: Vacant. Ext: 4416.
Publicity Officer: Mrs Judith Slater. Ext: 4275.

WETHERSFIELD STATION ADMINISTRATION
Fax: 01371 854195.
Head of Department: Chris Lansbury. Ext: 4668.

NUCLEAR DIVISION
Ministry of Defence Police, Central Gatehouse, MoD Abbey Wood, Bristol BS34 8JH..
Nuclear Divisional Command Designate: Chief Supt P McLaughlin. Tel: 030 6798 4822.
Superintendent Operations: J O'Donnell. Tel: 030 6798 4821.

TERRITORIAL DIVISION
Territorial Division HQ, Building 116, Wetherby Block, Imphal Barracks, Fulford Road, York YO10 4HD. Tel: 01904 66 plus extension.
Divisional Commander: Chief Supt D S Walker. Ext: 5688.
Divisional Operations: Supt M O'Byrne. Ext: 5022.

VEHICLE REGISTRATION INDEX
Enquiries with regard to HM Forces Vehicles and Ministry of Defence Vehicles should be directed to: Service Police Crime Bureau, Southwick Park, Fareham, Hampshire PO17 6EJ. Tel: 023 9228 5170. Fax: 023 9228 5179.

FORENSIC EXPLOSIVES LABORATORY
Forensic Explosives Laboratory, DSTL, Building S12, Fort Halstead, Sevenoaks, Kent TN14 7BP.
Tel: 01959 892735/892507. Out of hours contact MOD Police. Tel: 01959 892709.

Head of FEL: David Groves.
National Liaison Officer: Geoff Lewry. Tel: 01959 892735.

ARMED FORCES POLICE

ROYAL NAVY POLICE (RNP)

The RNP includes the policing arm of the Royal Marines, known as the Royal Marines Police Troop. Collectively, the RNP provides the policing capabilities for all HM ships, naval and RM establishments in the United Kingdom. The RM Police Troop also provides support to the Royal Marines on operations in both peace and war. The head of the RNP is Provost Marshal (Navy).

PROVOST MARSHAL (NAVY) HQ
Building 25, HMS Excellent, Whale Island, Portsmouth PO2 8ER.
Provost Marshal (Navy): Cdr C A Moran RN. Tel: 023 9254 7293.
Deputy Provost Marshal (Navy): Lt Cdr A Day RN. Tel: 023 9254 7821.
SO3 Police Operations: Lt S Hunnybun RN. Tel: 023 9254 7294.
SO3 Police Policy: Lt A Williams RN. Tel: 023 9254 7195.
Training & Recruitment: WO1(MAA) K C Williams MBE. Tel: 023 9254 7060.
Professional Standards Unit: Lt C McNaught RN. Tel: 023 9254 7051. WO1(MAA) P Brook. Tel: 023 9254 7058.

RN SPECIAL INVESTIGATIONS BRANCH (EASTERN)
Barham Block, HMS Nelson, Queen Street, Portsmouth PO1 3HH.
Officer i/c: Lt Cdr A Bright RN. Tel: 023 9272 3131.
Deputy Officer i/c (Eastern): Lt M Thompson RN. Tel: 023 9272 2607.
Duty Investigator. Tel: 023 9272 3898.

RN SPECIAL INVESTIGATIONS BRANCH (WESTERN)
Frobisher Block, HMS Drake, Plymouth PL2 2BG.
Deputy Officer i/c (Western): Lt S Stewart RN. Tel: 01752 557557.

ROYAL NAVY POLICE HEADQUARTERS (EASTERN)
RNPHQ(E), HMS Nelson, Queen Street, Portsmouth PO1 3HH.
Naval Provost Marshal: Lt Cdr N Jayes RN. Tel: 023 9272 4117.
Deputy Naval Provost Marshal: Lt E Grant RN. Tel: 023 9272 5836.
Duty Provost Operations. Tel: 023 9272 3966.
A central register of RN and RM missing persons is held by the Naval Provost Marshal (Eastern).

ROYAL NAVY POLICE HEADQUARTERS (WESTERN)
RNPHQ(W), HMS Drake, Plymouth PL2 2BG.
Naval Provost Marshall: Lt Cdr R Colley RN. Tel: 01752 555323.
Assistant Naval Provost Marshal: WO1(MAA) A T Sharpe. Tel: 01752 555135.
Duty Provost Operations. Tel: 01752 555315.

ROYAL NAVY POLICE HEADQUARTERS (NORTHERN)
RNPHQ(N) 9–12 Churchill Square, Helensburgh, Argyll & Bute G84 9HL.
Naval Provost Marshal: Lt M Youngman RN. Tel: 01436 674321 ext 3293.
Assistant Naval Provost Marshal: WO1(MAA) J S Newbury. Tel: 01436 673452.
Duty Provost Operations. Tel: 01436 673452.

ROYAL MARINES POLICE TROOP
RM Barracks, Stonehouse, Plymouth PL1 3QS.
Officer Commanding: Capt Tom Blackmore (RMP). Tel: 01752 836362.
Troop Sergeant Major. Tel: 01752 836321.
Police Office Manager. Tel: 01752 836428.
Investigation Section Sergeant. Tel: 01752 836372. Fax: 01752 836320.
Investigation Office. Tel: 01752 836338.
Duty Officer. Mob: 07799 657867.
Duty Investigator. Mob: 07799 657869.

ROYAL MARINES POLICE DETACHMENT, COMMANDO TRAINING CENTRE ROYAL MARINES
CTCRM, Lympstone, Nr Exmouth, Devon EX8 5AR.
Police Office. Tel: 01392 414139.

ROYAL MARINES POLICE DETACHMENT, ROYAL MARINES CONDOR
RM Condor, Arbroath, Angus DD11 3SP.
Police Office. Tel: 01241 822135.

ROYAL MARINES POLICE DETACHMENT, ROYAL MARINES BARRACKS CHIVENOR
RMB Chivenor, Barnstaple, Devon EX31 4AZ.
Police Office. 01271 857248.

ROYAL MARINES DISCIPLINE

STAFF OFFICER RM DISCIPLINE
Navy Command Headquarters, Leach Building, Whale Island, Portsmouth PO2 8BY.
Staff Officer: Maj C J March MBE RM. Tel: 023 926 25816.
Email: cameron.march953@mod.uk
Staff Assistant: Ms Kirstin Knowlson-Clark. Tel: 023 926 25962. Email: kirstin.knowlson-clark826@mod.uk

COMMANDO TRAINING CENTRE ROYAL MARINES
Lympstone, Exmouth EX8 5AR.
Discipline Advisor: WO1 C M Thomas RM. Tel: 01392 414166.
Police Office. Tel: 01392 414117.

3 COMMANDO BRIGADE ROYAL MARINES
Royal Marine Barracks, Stonehouse, Plymouth PL1 3QS.
Discipline Advisor: WO2 A MacFarlane RM. Tel: 01752 836522.
Mrs S Walters. Tel: 01752 836519.
Staff Officer: Maj S Richardson RM. Tel: 01752 836517. Email: simon.richardson851@mod.uk

COMMANDO LOGISTICS REGIMENT ROYAL MARINES
Royal Marine Barracks, Chivenor, Barnstaple EX31 1AZ.
Discipline Advisor: WO2 S Betts RM. Tel: 01271 857284.

1 ASSAULT GROUP ROYAL MARINES
Hamworthy, Poole BH15 4HQ.
Discipline Advisor: WO2 J Worthy RM. Tel: 01202 202334.

40 COMMANDO ROYAL MARINES
Norton Manor Camp, Taunton TA2 6PF.
Discipline Advisor: WO2 W Staff RM. Tel: 01823 362256.

42 COMMANDO ROYAL MARINES
Bickleigh Barracks, Plymouth PL6 7AJ.
Discipline Advisor: WO2 R Taylor RM. Tel: 01752 727034.

45 COMMANDO ROYAL MARINES
RM Condor, Arbroath DD11 3SJ.
Discipline Advisor: WO2 M Elfverson RM. Tel: 01241 872201 ext 2009.
Police Detachment. Tel: 01241 822135.

43 COMMANDO FLEET PROTECTION GROUP ROYAL MARINES
Gibraltar Building, HMNB Clyde, Helensburgh G84 8HL.
Discipline Advisor: WO2 G Guy RM. Tel: 01436 674321 ext 5483.

30 COMMANDO IX GP ROYAL MARINES
Royal Marine Barracks, Stonehouse, Plymouth PL1 3QS.
Discipline Advisor: WO2 P Mitchell RM. Tel: 01752 836368

ROYAL MILITARY POLICE

For all police enquiries contact: Service Police Crime Bureau, Southwick Park, Fareham, Hampshire PO17 6EJ.
Tel: 023 9228 5170/5180/5218. Fax: 023 9228 5179.

The Royal Military Police is the Army's police force. Its role of policing the Army at home and overseas in peace and war may be summarised as follows: the provision of garrison police facilities; law enforcement and crime prevention, and liaison with Home Office and other police forces worldwide when army interests are involved or suspected; tactical military police support to the Army in all phases of military operations; the provision of close protection worldwide to those deemed by the MOD to warrant it.

HEADQUARTERS PROVOST MARSHAL (ARMY)
2nd Floor, Zone 5, Ramillies Building (1DL 431), Marlborough Lines, Monxton Road, Andover, Hampshire SP11 8HJ. Tel: 01264 381823. Fax: 01264 381935.
Provost Marshal (Army): Brig R W Warren MBE. Tel: 01264 383515.
Personal Secretary: Ms L Salter. Tel: 01264 381799.
Deputy Provost Marshal (Operations) (Chief of Staff): Col D S Neal. Tel: 01264 383321.
Deputy Provost Marshal (Investigations): Col P S M A Cairns. Tel: 01264 381779.
Deputy Provost Marshal (Historic Inquiries): Col L S Wassell. Tel: 01980 615968.

INVESTIGATIONS & POLICING BRANCH & TRAINING
SO1 Investigations & Policing: Lt Col P Hagues AGC(RMP). Tel: 01264 381821.
SO2 Investigations & Policing (A): Maj L Bowen AGC(RMP). Tel: 01264 381807.
SO2 Investigations & Policing (B): Maj J Harvey AGC(RMP). Tel: 01264 381877.

SA Investigations & Policing: WO1 J Turner AGC(RMP). Tel: 01264 381808.
INVESTIGATIONS & POLICING STANDARDS
SO2 Investigations & Standards: Lt Cdr (Retd) A Mickleburgh. Tel: 01264 381877.
WO Investigations & Standards: WO2 J Saunders. Tel: 01264 381777.
HEADQUARTERS SUPPORT COMMAND
Provost Marshal Special Command. Provost Branch, Steeles Road, Aldershot, Hampshire GU11 2DP.
Tel: 01252 347009.
MILITARY POLICE STATIONS IN THE UNITED KINGDOM
150 Provost Company RMP: Catterick, North Yorkshire. Tel: 01748 872875/6. Police Post Edinburgh.
Tel: 0131 441 6488/9811. Police Post Inverness. Tel: 01463 234241.
156 Provost Company RMP: Colchester, Essex CO2 7NZ. Tel: 01206 816830. Police Post Bassinbourn.
Tel: 01223 204306. Police Post Chilwell. Tel: 01159 572413. Police Post Wattisham. Tel: 01449
728299.
158 Provost Company RMP: Bulford, Wiltshire SP4 9J2. Tel: 01980 672251/672334. Police Post
Blandford. Tel: 01258 482510. Police Post Warminster. Tel: 01985 21400.
160 Provost Company RMP: Aldershot, Hampshire GU11 2DN. Tel: 01252 347323. Detachment
London. Tel: 020 7414 5130. Detachment Shorncliffe. Tel: 01303 495451 ext 2197. Detachment
Bicester. Tel: 01869 253311. Detachment Bordon. Tel: 01420 465421.
174 Provost Company RMP: Donnington, Telford, Shropshire TF2 8LS. Tel: 01952 672000.
Detachment Brecon. Tel: 01874 613922.
SPECIAL INVESTIGATION BRANCH RMP UK
Campion Lines, High Street, Bulford, Wiltshire SP4 9DT.
Commanding Officer. Tel: 01980 673600.
Adjutant. Tel: 01980 673602.
HQ Southern Region SIB (UK) RMP. Aldershot. Tel: 01252 340433/383. Bulford. Tel: 01980 673672.
Plymouth. Tel: 01752 836374. Colchester. Tel: 01206 816835.
Northern Region SIB (UK) RMP. York. Tel: 01904 662283. Edinburgh. Tel: 0131 310 5104. Catterick.
Tel: 01748 872872. Donnington. Tel: 01952 672859.

ROYAL AIR FORCE POLICE

General enquiries: Service Police Crime Bureau, Southwick Park, Fareham, Hampshire PO17 6EJ. Tel: 023 9228 5170/5180. Fax: 023 9228 5179.

Intelligence related enquiries: RAF Police Force Intelligence Bureau, HQ RAF Police, RAF Henlow, Bedfordshire SG16 6DN. Tel: 01462 851515 ext 8236. Fax: 01462 857669. (Outside working hours contact Service Police Crime Bureau, as above.)

RAF Police Confidential Crime Line: 0800 432 0771. Individuals tel: 01462 851515 plus extension number.

The Royal Air Force Police is the RAF's police force. Its role is to provide a policing and security service to the RAF at home and overseas. The RAF Police is responsible for providing station policing, criminal investigations, law enforcement, crime prevention and liaison with Home Office and other police forces. In addition, the RAF Police provides specialist advice on all aspects of physical and personnel security in relation to air operations undertaken by the RAF both in the United Kingdom and overseas. Capabilities include higher level investigations, SB, close protection, forensics (computer and CSI), specialist search dogs, air transport security, general policing, crime prevention, law enforcement and counter intelligence support to cyber defence and protective security.

HEADQUARTERS ROYAL AIR FORCE POLICE
HQ Royal Air Force Police, Bldg 143, RAF Henlow, Bedfordshire SG16 6DN. Tel: 01462 851515 plus extension number.
Provost Marshal (RAF): Group Captain M S Sexton MA BA RAF. Ext: 8200.
Deputy Provost Marshal (RAF): Wg Cdr S McCleery BSc RAF. Ext: 8202.
Squadron Leader Administration: K Upham MSc RAF. Ext: 7219.
Squadron Leader Plans, Equipment & MWD: D M Dixon BA RAF. Ext: 6097.
Squadron Leader Policy: Vacant. Ext: 7573.
Squadron Leader Operations & Media: J F Duffy MSc LLB RAF. Ext: 8227.
Squadron Leader Professional Standards: A C Walker LLB RAF. Ext: 7476.
Force Legal Advisor: Sqn Ldr M J Greenway LLB RAF. Ext: 7542.
Budget Officer: Ms L C Barlow BEd MAAT. Ext: 8240.
NO 1 RAF POLICE WING (& RAF SQUADRONS IN THE UK)
OC No 1 RAF Police Wing/Assistant Provost Marshal (Nth): Wg Cdr G J Darby MSc RAF. Ext: 8203.
Squadron Leader 2IC No 1 RAF Police Wing: J Disley RAF. Ext: 7255.
RAF Police Special Investigations & Intelligence Branch (Nth): Sqn Ldr B Youd BA RAF. Ext: 6100.
OC No 4 RAF Police Squadron (Scotland & Northern Ireland): Sqn Ldr Vacant. Lossiemouth, Morayshire IV31 6SD. Tel: 01343 816164.
OC No 5 RAF Police Squadron (North England & North Wales): Sqn Ldr A C Mildon BA RAF. RAF Waddington, Lincoln LN5 9NB. Tel: 01522 727670.
NO 2 RAF POLICE WING (& RAF SQUADRONS IN THE UK)
OC No 2 RAF Police Wing/Assistant Provost Marshal (Sth): Wg Cdr M C Dixon MSc RAF. Ext: 8221.
Squadron Leader 2IC No 2 RAF Police Wing: D Davies BA RAF. Ext: 6174.
Warrant Officer No 2 RAF Police Wing: B McGuire. Ext: 6176.
RAF Police Special Investigations & Intelligence Branch (Sth): Sqn Ldr N J Card RAF. Ext: 8237.
OC No 6 RAF Police Squadron (Central, West & East England & Central Wales): Sqn Ldr J C Mills MA RAF. Marham, King's Lynn PE33 9NP. Tel: 01760 337987.
OC No 7 RAF Police Squadron (South & West England & South Wales): Sqn Ldr S Carroll. RAF Brize Norton, Carterton, Oxfordshire OX18 3LX. Tel: 01993 896603.
NO 3 RAF POLICE WING
OC No 3 RAF Police Wing/Assistant Provost Marshal (Ops): Wg Cdr A J Gillespie RAF. Ext: 6372.
OC No 1 RAF (Tactical) Police Squadron: Sqn Ldr A Y Drake BA Dip BA RAF. Ext: 6384.
OC Specialist Capabilities Squadron: Sqn Ldr J A Park MA MLitt RAF. Ext: 6067.
OC No 3 RAuxAF (Tactical) Police Squadron: Sqn Ldr S J Kirkbride RAF. Ext: 6374.

CIVIL NUCLEAR CONSTABULARY

Building F6, Culham Science Centre, Abingdon, Oxfordshire OX14 3DB.
Tel: 01235 466466 (24 hrs). Fax: 01235 466566 (24 hrs).
Tel: 01235 46 plus extension, unless otherwise indicated.
Email: enquiries and messages to staff whose email address is not known:
ccc@cnc.pnn.police.uk. Individuals: firstname.lastname@cnc.pnn.police.uk.
Recruitment enquiries: jobs@cnc.pnn.police.uk
Website: www.cnc.police.uk

The Civil Nuclear Constabulary is charged with safeguarding civil nuclear material in the UK and internationally. We defend our sites, deny unauthorised access to nuclear material, and, if necessary, recover control of any lost material, using a proportionate armed response to any potential threat.

CHIEF CONSTABLE'S OFFICE
Fax: 6764.

Chief Constable: Mr M Griffiths. Ext: 6760.
Staff Officer to CC: Supt C Robinson. Ext: 6918.
Senior Executive Assistant to CC: Ms L Ramsden. Ext: 6756.
Deputy Chief Constable: Mr J Sampson. Ext: 6761.
Staff Officer to DCC: Supt C Robinson. Ext: 6918.
Executive Secretary to DCC: Mrs A McInnerny. Ext: 6763.
Assistant Chief Constable: Mr A Cooper. Ext: 6917.
Staff Officer to ACC: Sgt M Taylor. Ext: 6416.
T/Executive Secretary to ACC: Miss A Citovska. Ext: 6976.
Director of Corporate Services: Mr J Rees. Ext: 6453.
Executive Secretary to DCS: Mrs A McInnerny. Ext: 6763.

EXECUTIVE OFFICE
Chairman: Sir P Trousdell. Ext: 6797.
Interim Head of Executive Office: Mr R Cawdron. Ext: 6536.
Senior Executive Assistant to Chairman: Ms L Ramsden. Ext: 6756.
Senior Board & Committee Administrator: Mrs R Powdrill. Ext: 6214.
Board & Committee Administrator: Ms T Shaw. Ext: 6356.
Administrative Assistant: Vacant. Ext: 6861.
Legal Advisor: Mr R Cawdron. Ext: 6536.
Secretary to Legal Advisor: Mrs C Wilmshurst. Ext: 6764.
T/Legal Assistant: Miss A Rathbone. Ext: 6552

STRATEGIC PORTFOLIO OFFICE
Portfolio Director: Chief Supt J L Robertson. Ext: 6304.
Portfolio Delivery: Supt M O'Kane. Ext: 6864. Tel: 01847 802126.
Governance & Assurance: Mr M Mooney. Ext: 6515.
Portfolio Definition: Mr P Mould. Ext: 6815.
Programme Manager: Chief Insp G Shaw. Tel: 01946 786008.
Programme Manager: Insp S Burnett. Ext: 6790.
PA/Secretary to Programme Director: Miss E Masters. Ext: 6478.

CORPORATE DEVELOPMENT
Fax: 6279.

Interim Head of Department: Chief Supt J Robertson. Ext: 6304.
Principal Analyst: Mrs H White. Ext: 6929.
Performance Management Officer: Mrs M Atkinson. Tel: 01946 781908.
Business Planning Co-ordinator: Mrs C Roscoe. Ext: 6903.
Risk Manager: Ms L Shaw. Ext: 6804.
Head of Inspections & Professional Standards: Chief Insp S Exelby. Ext: 6389.
Inspections Manager: Mrs L Townsend. Ext: 6361.
Inspections & Professional Standards Manager: Det Insp G Allan. Ext: 6720.
Security Manager: Mr G Balmer. Ext: 6612.
Professional Standards & Security Officer: Ms S Woodward. Ext: 6614.

CORPORATE SERVICES
Fax: 6279.

Financial Controller: Mr K Kilpatrick. Ext: 6563. Fax: 6334.
Chief Information Officer: Mr M Verrier. Ext: 6920.
Deputy Chief Information Officer: Mr P Stone. Ext: 6591.
Information Assurance Manager: Mr M Root. Ext: 6544

Operational Communications Manager: Ms S Maclean. Ext: 6701.
IT Services Manager: Mrs L Ford. Ext: 6523.
Head of Procurement & Estates: Mr M Jenner. Ext: 6562.
Senior Contracts Officer: Miss P Crook. Ext: 6332.
Estates & Facilities Manager: Mrs A Dunnill. Ext: 6593.

HUMAN RESOURCES
Fax: 6391.

Head of Profession: Mr P Leigh. Ext: 6312.
A/Head of HROD: Mrs A Stubbington. Ext: 6733.
Corporate HROD Manager: Ms G Prince. Ext: 6571.
HR Services Manager: Mrs L Sexton. Ext: 6216.
Recruitment. Ext: 6666. Fax: 6483.

CENTRE FOR LEARNING AND DEVELOPMENT
Building F7, Culham Science Centre, Abingdon OX14 3DB.
Head of Learning & Development: Insp J Vance. Ext: 6840.

FIREARMS TRAINING DEPARTMENT
B496 Firearms Training Unit, Sellafield, Seascale, Cumbria CA20 1PG. Tel: 01946 785126. Fax: 01946 785903.
Head of Firearms Training (based in Culham): Supt K Carter. Ext: 6847.
Chief Firearms Instructor: Chief Insp I Kendall. Tel: 01946 785293.
Firearms Training Administrator. Tel: 01946 785126.

DOG TRAINING FACILITY
B937 Dog Training Facility, Yottenfews, Sellafield, Seascale, Cumbria CA20 1PG. Tel: 01946 773645. Fax: 01946 776553.
Force Dogs Officer: Insp T McCully. Tel: 01946 787765.
Dog Training Administrator. Tel: 01946 773645.

CIVIL NUCLEAR POLICE FEDERATION
Gosforth Suite, Innovation Centre, Westlakes Science Park, Moor Row, Whitehaven, Cumbria CA24 3TP.
Chief Executive Officer: Mr N Dennis. Tel: 01946 694252. Mob: 07595 006192. Email: admin@cnpolfed.co.uk

NORTH & SCOTLAND DIVISION
Divisional Commander: Chief Supt P Bishop. Tel: 01946 781974.
Divisional Superintendents: B Stephenson. Tel: 01847 802250. Fax: 01847 802240. D Worsell. Tel: 01946 773630.
North Subdivision Chief Inspector: J Weeden. Tel: 0151 473 4978.
Scotland Subdivision Chief Inspector: A Brotherston. Tel: 01847 802123.
Divisional Administrator: Miss E Driver. Tel: 01946 781907.
HR Officer: Mrs C Ashfield. Tel: 01946 777320.
Duty Planning Managers: Ms G O'Connell. Tel: 01946 771131. Mrs T Chisholm. Tel: 01847 802127.
DOUNREAY
Civil Nuclear Constabulary, Dounreay, Thurso, Caithness KW14 7TZ.
Operational Unit Commander: Chief Insp A Brotherston. Tel: 01847 802123. Fax: 01847 802136.
Support Services Inspector: S Jack. Tel: 01847 802217. Fax: 01847 802136.
Police Control Room (24 hrs). Tel: 01847 802130/802131. Fax: 01847 802137.
CHAPELCROSS
Civil Nuclear Constabulary, Chapelcross Power Station, Annan, Dumfriesshire DG12 6RF. Fax: 01461 203455.
Operational Unit Commander: Insp J Ferguson. Tel: 01461 208261. Fax: 01461 203455.
Police Control Room (24 hrs). Tel: 01461 208468.
HUNTERSTON
Civil Nuclear Constabulary, Hunterston Power Station, West Kilbride, Ayrshire KA23 9QJ. Fax: 01294 826264.
Operational Unit Commander: Insp A MacRae. Tel: 01294 821872.
TORNESS
Civil Nuclear Constabulary, Torness Power Station, Dunbar, East Lothian EH42 1QS. Fax: 01368 873984.
Operational Unit Commander: Insp J Hannah. Tel: 01368 873981.
SELLAFIELD
Civil Nuclear Constabulary, Sellafield, Seascale, Cumbria CA20 1PG.
Operational Unit Commander: Supt D Worsell. Tel: 01946 773630. Fax: 01946 785960.
PA/Secretary: Mrs C Henderson. Tel: 01946 773558. Fax: 01946 785960.

Police Control Centre (24 hrs). Tel: 01946 776011.
CAPENHURST
Civil Nuclear Constabulary, URENCO UK Ltd, Capenhurst Works, Capenhurst, Chester CH1 6ER.
Fax: 0151 473 4905.
Operational Unit Commander: Insp L Cotterell. Tel: 0151 473 4969. Fax: 0151 473 4343.
Police Control Room (24 hrs). Tel: 0151 473 4985. Fax 0151 473 4905.
HARTLEPOOL
Civil Nuclear Constabulary, Hartlepool Power Station, Tees Road, Hartlepool, Cleveland TS25 2BZ.
Fax: 01429 853543.
Operational Unit Commander: Insp G Elms. Tel: 01429 853312.
HEYSHAM
Civil Nuclear Constabulary, Heysham Power Station, Morecambe LA3 2XQ.
Operational Unit Commander: Insp S Wade. Tel: 01524 863349. Fax: 01524 854218.
SPRINGFIELDS
Civil Nuclear Constabulary, Springfields, Salwick, Preston PR4 OXJ. Fax: 01772 763002.
Operational Unit Commander: T/Insp S Benson. Tel: 01772 763061.
Police Control Room (24 hrs). Tel: 01772 764345. Fax: 01772 762705.
Duty Sergeant. Tel: 01772 763519.
WYLFA
Civil Nuclear Constabulary, Wylfa Power Station, Anglesey, Gwynedd LL67 0DH. Fax: 01407 711623.
Operational Unit Commander: Insp H Townsend. Tel: 01407 711623.

SOUTH, OPERATIONS SUPPORT, SPECIAL BRANCH DIVISION
Civil Nuclear Constabulary, Culham Science Centre, Abingdon OX14 3DB.
Divisional Commander South, Operations Support, Special Branch: T/Chief Supt W Walker. Ext: 6752.
Divisional Administrator: Ms S Bolton. Ext: 6986.
Deputy Divisional Commander: T/Supt A Peden. Ext: 6705.
Divisional Chief Inspector South OPU (excluding Harwell): M Vance. Ext: 6852.
DUNGENESS
Civil Nuclear Constabulary, Dungeness B Power Station, Romney Marsh, Kent TN29 9PX. Fax: 01797
343092.
Operational Unit Commander: T/Insp A Potter. Tel: 01797 343091.
HARWELL
Civil Nuclear Constabulary, B591, Rutherford Avenue, Harwell, Didcot OX11 0DF.
Operational Unit Commander: Chief Insp D Jackson. Tel: 01235 434048. Fax: 01235 432022.
Operations Inspector: R Kemsley. Tel: 01235 434656. Fax: 01235 434058.
Police Control Room (24 hrs). Tel: 01235 433030/432501. Fax: 01235 435531.
HINKLEY POINT
Civil Nuclear Constabulary, Hinkley Point B Power Station, nr Bridgwater, Somerset TA5 1UD. Fax:
01278 658065.
Operational Unit Commander: Insp P Fox. Tel: 01278 658042.
OLDBURY
Civil Nuclear Constabulary, Oldbury Power Station, Oldbury Naite, Thornbury, Gloucestershire BS35
1RQ. Fax: 01454 893737.
Operational Unit Commander: Insp M Lester. Tel: 01454 893541.
SIZEWELL
Civil Nuclear Constabulary, Sizewell B Power Station, nr Leiston, Suffolk IP16 4UR.
Operational Unit Commander: Insp A Hill. Tel: 01728 653789.

OPERATIONS SUPPORT & ESCORT OPERATIONS
Fax: 6833.
ESCORT OPERATIONS
CNC, Building F7, Culham Science Centre, Abingdon OX14 3DB.
Escort Operations: Chief Insp R Murray. Ext: 6650. Mob: 07702 098767.
Escort Operations Inspector: S Edwards. Tel: 01925 833832. Mob: 07834 495978.
Firearms Training: Sgt K Atkinson. Tel: 01946 776491. Mob: 07889 703835.
Planning: Sgt S Hutchinson. Ext: 6296. Mob: 07768 710482.
Administrator: Ms C Lamorinière. Ext: 6654.
OPERATIONS SUPPORT
Operations Support: T/Chief Insp C Adamczyk. Ext: 6386.
Operations Support Inspector: T/Insp S Owen. Ext: 6696.
Operational Policies & Procedures: Insp G Bell. Ext: 6560.
Stakeholder Liaison Officer: Insp T Howes. Ext: 6418.
Exercise Resilience Lead Manager: Mr S Ginn. Ext: 6793.

Health, Safety & Environmental Manager: Mr B Rowles. Ext: 6210.
Health & Safety Advisor: Mr M Carrick. Ext: 6290.
Emergency/Resilience Manager: Mr E Johnson. Ext: 6482.
Command & Control Centre: *Duty Officer.* Ext: 6466 (24 hrs). Fax: 6566.

SPECIAL BRANCH
Constabulary Headquarters, Culham Science Centre, Abingdon, Oxfordshire, OX14 3DB. Email:
cnc.sb.hq@cnc.pnn.police.uk
General Enquiries. Ext: 6751.

AIRPORTS POLICE

Aberdeen Airport: Police Scotland (Police Scotland Border Command), Aberdeen Airport Police Office (24 hrs), Viscount House, Brent Road, Dyce AB21 ONU. Tel: 0845 600 5700. Fax: 01224 723915. *Airport Police Commander:* Insp Alan Keith.

*(**George Best**) **Belfast City Airport:** The Police Service of Northern Ireland (Strandtown Sub-Division), 1–5 Dundela Avenue, Belfast BT4 3BQ. Tel: 028 9090 1758. *Airport Police Commander:* Insp David Gibson. Email: david.gibson@psni.pnn.police.uk Sgt Jonathan Ireland. Email: jonathan.ireland@psni.pnn.police.uk

Belfast International Airport Constabulary: Belfast International Airport, Belfast BT29 4AB. Tel: 028 9448 4400 (Airport Control Centre: ask for duty sergeant). Fax: 028 9442 3985.
Sworn as constables under Art 19(3) of the Airport (Northern Ireland) Order 1994, employed by Belfast International Airport Ltd which is authorised by the Secretary of State for Northern Ireland to nominate constables.

Birmingham Airport: West Midlands Police, Operations Aviation Unit, Diamond House, Birmingham International Airport, Birmingham B26 3QJ.
Airport Policing Unit: Insp R Williams. Tel: 0345 113 5000 ext 7929 6242. Email: r.williams@west-midlands.pnn.police.uk

Bournemouth Airport: Dorset Police (County Division, Christchurch Section), Barrack Road, Christchurch, Dorset BH23 1PN. Tel: 01202 222908. Fax: 01202 222917. *Airport Police Commander:* Insp Lance Cliff. Email: lance.cliff@dorset.pnn.police.uk

Bristol Airport: Avon & Somerset Constabulary (HQ CID District), Police Office Administration Building, Bristol International Airport, Lulsgate, Bristol BS48 3DY. Tel: 01275 473764/473875. Mob: 07825 756409. Fax: 01275 473876. *Airport Police Commander:* Insp Barney Gardom. Email: barney.gardom@avonandsomerset.police.uk

Cardiff Airport: South Wales Police Operational Support Division, Police Headquarters, Cowbridge Road, Bridgend CF31 3SU.
Airport Policing Group: Insp Steve Morris. Tel: 01656 306111.

***Carlisle Airport:** Cumbria Constabulary (Headquarters). Tel: 01768 517844. Fax: 01768 868867. Unit responsible: Counter Terrorism Branch Ports Unit.

***Durham Tees Valley Airport:** Durham Constabulary (Darlington Division), 6 St Cuthbert's Way, Darlington, Co Durham DL1 5LB. Tel: 0345 606 0365.

***East Midlands Airport:** Leicestershire Constabulary, Building 13, Castle Donnington DE74 2SA. Tel: 0116 222 2222.

Edinburgh Airport: Police Scotland (Police Scotland Border Command), Airport Police Station, Almond House, Almond Road, Edinburgh EH12 9DN. Tel: 0131 335 5000. Fax: 0131 335 5018. *Airport Police Commander:* Insp Paul McDonald. Tel: 0131 335 5002.

***Farnborough Airport:** Hampshire Constabulary, Southampton Central Police Station, Southern Road, Southampton SO15 1AN. Tel: 023 8053 3283. Email: strategic.operations@hampshire.pnn.police.uk

Glasgow International Airport: Police Scotland (Police Scotland Border Command), Airport Police Station, St Andrew's Drive, Glasgow Airport, Abbotsinch PA3 2ST. Tel: 0141 532 6099. Fax: 0141 889 7717. *Airport Police Commander:* Insp Nicola Burns.

Isle of Man Aviation Security: Isle of Man Airport, Ballasalla, Isle of Man IM9 2AS. Tel: 01624 821612/3. Fax: 01624 821619. *Airport Standards Manager:* D E Georgeson. *Duty Sgts:* S F C Moffitt; G A Lee; D A Berry; P R Smith. Email: dutyofficers.airport@gov.im Tel: 01624 821712. Fax: 01624 821713.
The force is responsible to the Department of Infrastructure, a department of the Isle of Man government, and officers are sworn as Constables under the Police Act 1993.

***Leeds/Bradford Airport:** West Yorkshire Police (NW Leeds Division), 300 Otley Road, Leeds LS16 6RG. Tel: 101. *Airport Police Commander:* Insp Richard Coldwell. Tel: 0113 241 3450. *Chief Inspector:* Jim McNeil. Tel: 0113 241 3412.

***Liverpool John Lennon Airport:** Merseyside Police (South Liverpool Area), Ganworth Road, Speke, Liverpool L24 2XQ. Tel: 0151 222 6671. Mob: 07764 656490 (24 hrs). Fax: 0151 777 5299. *Airport Inspector:* Bob Daly. *Designated Airport Officers:* Sgt Mark Hankin; A/Sgt Mal Webster.

***London City Airport:** Heathrow & London City Airport Police, Heathrow Police Station, Unit 3, Polar Park, Bath Road, Sipson, West Drayton UB7 0DG. Tel: 020 3276 1460 (24 hours). *OCU Commander:* Chief Supt Bert Moore. Tel: 020 3276 1248. *Superintendent Deputy to OCU Commander:* Martin Hendy.

London Gatwick Airport: Sussex Police (Gatwick Division), Police Station, Perimeter Road North, Gatwick Airport, West Sussex RH6 0JE. Tel: 0845 607 0999 (Call Resourcing Centre). Fax: 01293 506830 (Gatwick Control Room). *Head of Operations:* Chief Supt Paul Morrison. Ext: 44200. *Crime & Operations Superintendent:* Brian Bracher. Ext: 37200. Fax: 01293 592801. Email: brian.bracher@sussex.pnn.police.uk

London Heathrow Airport: Heathrow & London City Airport Police, Heathrow Police Station, Unit 3, Polar Park, Bath Road, Sipson, West Drayton UB7 0DG. Tel: 020 3276 1460 (24 hours).
OCU Commander: Chief Supt Bert Moore. Tel: 020 3276 1248. *Superintendent Deputy to OCU Commander:* Martin Hendy.
London Stansted Airport: Essex Police (KD Division), Enterprise House, Bassingbourn Road, Stansted Airport, Essex CM24 1PS. Tel: 01279 680298 or 101. Fax: 01279 680018.
Airport Commander: Chief Insp Graham Stubbs.
*Luton Airport: Bedfordshire Police, Woburn Road, Kempston, Bedford MK43 9AX. Tel: 01582 473483. Fax: 01582 473489.
Airport Police Commander: David Ford. Tel: 01582 473485.
Manchester Airport: Greater Manchester Police, Manchester Airport Section, Wythenshawe, Manchester M90 1NN. Tel: 0161 856 0250 (Communications Room). Fax: 0161 856 0206.
Airport Police Commander: Supt Bob Lomas. Tel: 0161 856 0201. Fax: 0161 856 0206. Chief Insp Mike Miskell. Tel: 0161 856 0202. **General enquiries:** 0161 856 0250.
*Newcastle Airport: Northumbria Police Operational Support (Airport Police Team), Main Terminal Building, Newcastle Airport, Woolsington, Newcastle-upon-Tyne NE13 8BZ. Tel: 0191 214 3603; 01661 872555 ext 69543 (sergeant's office). Mob: 07920 500230. Fax: 0191 214 3435.
Newcastle Airport Beat Officer: Sgt Andy Reay.
Prestwick Airport: Police Scotland (Police Scotland Border Command), Airport Police Office, Tactical Command Building, RVP South, McIntyre Road, Prestwick KA9 0BU. Tel: 01292 511234/511322/664000. Fax: 01292 511344.
Airport Police Commander: Insp Paul Seditas. Email: paul.seditas@strathclyde.pnn.police.uk
*Southampton Airport: Hampshire Constabulary, Southampton Central Police Station, Southern Road, Southampton SO15 1AN. Tel: 023 8053 3283. Email: strategic.operations@hampshire.pnn.police.uk

*These airports do not have a dedicated 24-hour police response on site, but the relevant police station covering the airport is given here.

This entry was first compiled for the *Police and Constabulary Almanac* by Supt T P Burgess of Greater Manchester Police.

PARKS POLICE

EPPING FOREST: FOREST KEEPERS
The Warren, Loughton, Essex IG10 4RW. Tel: 020 8532 1010. Fax: 020 8508 2176. Email: epping.forest@cityoflondon.gov.uk
Head Forest Keeper: Mr K French.
Forest Keepers are sworn in as Constables under Section 43 of the Epping Forest Act 1878.

KENSINGTON AND CHELSEA, ROYAL BOROUGH OF, PARKS POLICE
Stable Yard, Holland Park, London W8 6LU. Tel: 020 7938 8190; 07973 124066. Email: parkspolice@rbkc.gov.uk
Chief Officer: Insp Mike Rumble MCMI. *Deputies:* C Ellinson; M Thompson.
Strength of force: 13. Members of the service are sworn in as constables under Section 18, Ministry of Housing and Local Government Provisional Order Confirmation (Greater London Parks and Open Spaces) Act 1967.

ROYAL BOTANIC GARDENS KEW CONSTABULARY
Headquarters: The Royal Botanic Gardens, Kew, Richmond, Surrey TW9 3AB. Tel: 020 8332 5121.
Manager of Constabulary: J Deer. Tel: 020 8332 5130. Fax: 020 8332 5176. Email: j.deer@kew.org

ROYAL PARKS OCU, METROPOLITAN POLICE SERVICE, ENGLAND
See Metropolitan Police, Westminster Borough.

WANDSWORTH EVENTS POLICE SERVICE
Events Police Headquarters, Battersea Park, London SW11 4NJ. Tel: 020 8871 7532. Fax: 020 7223 2750. Email: sbiggs@wandsworth.gov.uk
Chief Officer: Insp Stephen Biggs. *Deputy Sergeant:* Laurie Black.
Members of the service are sworn in as constables under Article 18, Ministry of Housing and Local Government Provision Order Confirmation (Greater London Parks and Open Spaces) Act 1967. The service specialises in the policing of public events in parks and open spaces and can provide assistance and training by accredited instructors in conflict management and the use of general purpose police dogs and dog handlers.

WILDLIFE POLICE

UK NATIONAL WILDLIFE CRIME UNIT

Old Livingston Police Station, Almondvale South, Livingston, West Lothian EH54 6PX.
Tel: 01506 833722. Fax: 01506 443447.
Email: ukwildlifecrime@nwcu.pnn.police.uk.
Individual email: firstname.lastname@nwcu.pnn.police.uk.

Head of Unit: Det Insp Nevin Hunter. Tel: 07919 690392.
Senior Analyst: Sue Eddy. Tel: 01506 833724.
Senior Intelligence Officer: Colin Pirie. Tel: 01506 833727.
Intelligence Officer: Helen Bulmer. Tel: 01506 833729.
Analyst: Miranda Gray. Tel: 01506 833723.
Indexer & Administration Officer: Alison Midgley. Tel: 01506 833726.
Investigative Support Officers: Andy McWilliam. Tel: 07884 116585. Alan Roberts. Tel: 07884 116749. Charles Everitt. Tel: 07917 599690.

PORT, WATERWAYS & TUNNEL POLICE

BELFAST, BELFAST HARBOUR POLICE
Port Operations Centre, Milewater Basin, Belfast Harbour Estate, Belfast BT3 9AF. Tel: 028 9055 3000. Fax: 028 9055 3001. Email: port.police@belfast-harbour.co.uk
Chief Officer: S Reid. Email: stephen.reid@belfast-harbour.co.uk

BRISTOL, PORT OF BRISTOL POLICE
Royal Portbury Dock, Bristol BS20 7XQ. Tel: 01275 375787; 0117 982 0000 ext 4510. Fax: 0117 938 0205. Email: port.police@bristolport.co.uk
Chief Police Officer: Keith Wood. Email: police.chief@bristolport.co.uk. *Deputy:* Carl Bromfield.
The force polices the Avonmouth and Royal Edward Docks situated in the Bristol district, and the Royal Portbury Dock situated in the district of North Somerset.

BROADS AUTHORITY
Yare House, 62–64 Thorpe Road, Norwich NR1 1RY. Tel: 01603 610734. Fax: 01603 765710.
River Control. Tel: 01603 756056. Email: broads.control@broads-authority.gov.uk
Chief Executive: Dr John Packman. *Director of Waterways:* Trudi Wakelin. *Head of Ranger Services:* Adrian Vernon.
The Authority is the statutory navigation authority for the Norfolk and Suffolk Broads rivers system. Uniformed patrolling of the system by launch and road is maintained for the purposes of assisting and informing the public, protection of the environment and ensuring that navigational and licensing regulations are observed. Close liaison is maintained with Norfolk Constabulary.

CANAL & RIVER TRUST ENFORCEMENT OFFICERS
Head office: First Floor North, Station House, 500 Elder Gate, Milton Keynes MK9 1BB. National Customer Service Centre tel: 0303 040 4040. Emergency out of hours contact tel: 0800 479 9947. Email: customer.services@canalrivertrust.org.uk
To contact the relevant Canal & River Trust patrol officer responsible for any given location, call the Trust's customer service team on the number above.
The Enforcement Unit is a uniformed body and its duties include enforcing the bye-laws and pleasure boat licensing legislation covering Canal & River Trust canals and river navigations across England and Wales. Staff are available to liaise with the police and can assist in tracing and identifying boat owners.

DOVER, PORT OF DOVER POLICE
Police Station, Eastern Docks, Dover CT16 1JA. Tel: 01304 216084. Fax: 01304 241956 (operational); 211059 (CID & administration).
Email: portofdoverpolice@kent.pnn.police.uk or police@doverport.co.uk
Chief Officer: Chief Supt S J Masters.
Strength of force: 48. Support staff: 10.

FALMOUTH
The Falmouth Docks & Engineering Co Ltd, The Docks, Falmouth, Cornwall TR11 4NR. Tel: 01326 212100. Fax: 01326 319433.
Head of Security: G Renfree. *Deputy:* Sgt J Mulgrew. *Marine Operations Manager:* T Lowe.

FELIXSTOWE
Port of Felixstowe Security & Port Police Unit, The Dock, Felixstowe, Suffolk IP11 3SY. Tel: 01394 604747. Fax: 01394 604929.
Chief Officer: Chief Insp John I Whitby. *Deputy:* Insp Malcolm Hayward. *Station Sergeant:* Andreas Miaoulis.

ISLE OF MAN
Isle of Man Port Security, Sea Terminal Building, Douglas, Isle of Man IM1 2RF. Tel: 01624 686630. Fax: 01624 686918.
Chief Officer: Mr F W Keown.
The force is responsible to the Department of Transport, a department of the Isle of Man Government, and officers are sworn under the Police Act 1993.

KENT PORTS (INCLUDING EUROTUNNEL TERMINAL IN COQUELLES, FRANCE)
Ports Co-Ordination Centre, Longport Police Station, Ashford Road, Newington, Folkestone, Kent CT18 8AP. Tel: 01303 297320 (24 hours). Fax: 01303 289269.

LARNE
Larne Harbour Police, Larne Harbour Ltd, 9 Olderfleet Road, Larne, Co Antrim BT40 1AS. Port Police tel: 028 2887 2137 (24 hrs). Port Control tel: 028 2887 2179 (24 hrs). Fax: 028 2887 2182.
Security Manager: A J Synnott.
The Harbour Police derives authority from the Harbour, Docks & Piers Clauses Act 1847 and is responsible to Larne Harbour Ltd. Jurisdiction extends one mile beyond the harbour complex.

LIVERPOOL, PORT OF LIVERPOOL POLICE
Headquarters: Liverpool Freeport, Liverpool L21 1JD. Tel: 0151 949 1212. Fax: 0151 949 6399.
Chair of the Police Committee: Gary Hodgson. *Clerk to the Police Committee:* Caroline Marrison. Tel: 0151 949 6349. *Chief Officer:* Peter Clarke. Ext: 322.

LONDON, PORT OF TILBURY
Police Headquarters, Tilbury Freeport, Tilbury, Essex RM18 7DU. **Communications Room.** Tel: 01375 846781. Fax: 01375 852404. **Administration.** Tel: 01375 857633. Email: colette.clark@potll.com
Chief Officer: Insp Andy Masson. Tel: 01375 846781.
Strength of force: 20. Qualifications of candidates for the force: age 18½–45.

MERSEY TUNNELS POLICE
Merseyside Integrated Transport Authority, Merseytravel, PO Box 1976, Liverpool L69 3XN. Tel: 0151 330 1999 (Police Control Room). Fax: 0151 346 9699. Email: police@merseytravel.gov.uk
Interim Chief Executive & Director General – Merseytravel: Mr J Barclay. *Director of Customer Services – Merseytravel:* Mr F Rogers. *Chief Police Officer/Head of Service – Tunnel Operations:* Supt K Haggar. Tel: 0151 330 4450. Email: superintendent@merseytravel.gov.uk or chief.officer@mt.cjsm.net *Deputy Chief Officer/Operations Manager:* Chief Insp A P Tierney. Tel: 0151 330 4451. Email: chief.inspector@merseytravel.gov.uk or chief.inspector@mt.cjsm.net
The Mersey Tunnels Police is a specialist force created by an Act of Parliament. Its aims and objectives are to ensure the safe and efficient passage of vehicles through the Mersey Tunnels under the Mersey estuary. The force consists of officers from constable to superintendent. All are trained in first aid, fire fighting, breathing apparatus and general police duties, with particular emphasis on road policing, which is their primary role.

PORTLAND PORT POLICE
Portland Port, Castletown, Portland, Dorset DT5 1PP. Tel: 01305 824044. Fax: 01305 824055.
Senior Constable: James Grant. Tel: 01305 825353. Mob: 07990 898919. Email: j.grant@portland-port.co.uk
Portland Port has five sworn constables under Section 79 of the Harbours, Docks and Piers Clauses Act 1847. These five constables currently form the basis of Portland Port Police under the direction of the Senior Constable.

TEES & HARTLEPOOL HARBOUR POLICE, TEESPORT
Harbour Police, Harbour Master's Office, Tees Dock, Grangetown, Middlesbrough, Cleveland TS6 6UD. Tel: 01642 277216. Fax: 01642 277227.
Chief Officer: Denis M Murphy MSc. Tel: 01642 277561. *Sergeants.* Tel: 01642 277215.

OVERSEAS POLICE

OVERSEAS POLICE FORCES

BERMUDA POLICE SERVICE
10 Headquarters Hill, Devonshire DV 02. PO Box HM 530, Hamilton, HM CX, Bermuda. Tel: (00 1) 441 295
0011. Fax: (00 1) 441 299 4459. Website: www.bermudapolice.bm
Commissioner: Michael A DeSilva FCMI.

SOVEREIGN BASE AREAS CYPRUS
Sovereign Base Areas Police Headquarters, British Forces Episkopi, BFPO 53. Tel: 00 357 2596 3175. Email:
sbapolice-gmb@mod.uk. Website: www.sba.mod.uk
Chief Constable: David J Kelly QPM MBA MCIPD.
The two British Sovereign Base Areas occupy 98 square miles of territory situated 60 miles apart within the Republic
of Cyprus. The SBA Police provide a civil policing service in all the SBAs including the military garrisons and the
RAF station. Although funded wholly by the Ministry of Defence, the SBA Police is an independent UK service and
has no connection with the MoD Police.
Western Sovereign Base Areas. Tel: 00 357 2596 7227/7262/7263/7264.
Eastern Sovereign Base Areas. Dhekelia Police Station tel: 00 357 2474 4333. Ay Nicolaos Police station tel: 00
357 2395 7695.

ROYAL ANGUILLA POLICE SERVICE
PO Box 60, Parliamentary Drive, The Valley, Anguilla. Tel: (00 1) 264 497 2333. Fax: (00 1) 264 496 5112.
Website: www.gov.ai/department.php?id=4&dept=34
Commissioner of Police: Rudolph Proctor.

ROYAL CAYMAN ISLANDS POLICE SERVICE
69A Elgin Avenue, George Town, Grand Cayman, Cayman Islands. Tel: (00 1) 345949 4222. Email:
rcipsinfo@gov.ky. Website: www.rcips.ky
Commissioner: David Baines. *Deputy Commissioner:* Anthony Ennis.

ROYAL FALKLAND ISLANDS POLICE
Ross Road, Stanley, Falkland Islands FIQQ 1ZZ. Tel: (00 500) 28100. Fax: (00 500) 28110. Email:
reception@police.gov.fk. Website: www.falklands.gov.fk/police.html
Director of Community Safety & Chief Police Officer: Chief Supt Gary Finchett.
Email: chiefpoliceofficer@police.gov.fk
The Royal Falkland Islands Police has jurisdiction over the whole of the two main and 200 smaller islands that make
up the United Kingdom Overseas Territory of the Falkland Islands, an area of some 4700 square miles. The Royal
Falkland Islands Police also assists the South Georgia government, when requested, with police matters on the Island
of South Georgia, South Sandwich Islands and British Antarctica.

ROYAL GIBRALTAR POLICE
Police Headquarters: Royal Gibraltar Police HQ, Rosia Road, Gibraltar. Tel: (00 350) 200 72500. Email:
info@royalgib.police.gi. Website: www.police.gi
Commissioner: Edward Yome CPM.
The Royal Gibraltar Police is the oldest police force in the Commonwealth, founded in 1930 only nine months after
Sir Robert Peel founded the Metropolitan Police. The RGP polices a community of approximately 30,000 residents
and some 9 million annual visitors to Gibraltar's 6 km². The surrounding territorial waters, international airport,
cruise liner port and a land frontier with Spain also fall within its jurisdiction.

ROYAL MONTSERRAT POLICE SERVICE
Police Headquarters, Brades, Montserrat, West Indies. Tel: (00 1) 664 491 2555. Email: monpol@candw.ms
Website: www.gov.ms
Deputy Commissioner: Bradley Siddell.

ROYAL VIRGIN ISLANDS POLICE FORCE
Police Headquarters, Waterfront Drive, Tortola, British Virgin Islands. Tel: (00 1) 284 494 2945. Website:
www.rvipf.freshmango.com
A/Commissioner: David Morris.

ROYAL TURKS AND CAICOS ISLANDS POLICE FORCE
Church Folly, Grand Turk, Turks & Caicos Islands. Tel: (00 1) 649 946 2371. Fax: (00 1) 649 946 2099. Email:
policehq@tcipolice.tc. Website: www.tcipolice.tc
Commissioner: Colin Farquhar. *Deputy Commissioner:* Brad Sullivan.

OVERSEAS TERRITORIES LAW ENFORCEMENT ADVISOR

Foreign & Commonwealth Office, Overseas Territories Directorate, King Charles Street, London
SW1A 2AH.

*Foreign & Commonwealth Office Overseas Territories Directorate Law Enforcement Advisor for the Caribbean
Overseas Territories & Bermuda:* Mr Larry Covington OBE MA. British Consulate-General Miami, 1001
Brickell Bay Drive (Suite 2800), Miami, Florida 33131–4940, USA. Tel: 400 6968. Fax: (001) 305 400 6868.
Mob: (001) 305 815 4909. Email: larry.covington@fco.gov.uk; larry.covington@fconet.fco.gov.uk;
larry.covington@bellsouth.net

The Caribbean & Bermuda overseas territories are: Anguilla, Bermuda, British Virgin Islands, Cayman Islands, Montserrat and Turks and Caicos Islands.

OVERSEAS POLICE REPRESENTATIVES

Australian Federal Police: Australian High Commission, Australia House, Strand, London WC2B 4LA. Tel: 020 7887 5164 (direct line). Fax: 020 7465 8213.

Royal Canadian Mounted Police: Liaison Office: Canadian High Commission, Macdonald House, 1 Grosvenor Square, London W1K 4AB. Tel: 020 7258 6340/6497/6685 (direct lines). Out of hours tel: 020 7258 6600 (main switchboard). Fax: 020 7258 6305.

INTERPOL MEMBER COUNTRIES

Afghanistan	Czech Republic	Lebanon	Samoa
Albania	Denmark	Lesotho	San Marino
Algeria	Djibouti	Liberia	Sao Tome & Principe
Andorra	Dominica	Libya	Saudi Arabia
Angola	Dominican Republic	Liechtenstein	Senegal
Antigua & Barbuda	Ecuador	Lithuania	Serbia
Argentina	Egypt	Luxembourg	Seychelles
Armenia	El Salvador	Madagascar	Sierra Leone
Aruba	Equatorial Guinea	Malawi	Singapore
Australia	Eritrea	Malaysia	Sint Maarten
Austria	Estonia	Maldives	Slovakia
Azerbaijan	Ethiopia	Mali	Slovenia
Bahamas	Fiji	Malta	Somalia
Bahrain	Finland	Marshall Islands	South Africa
Bangladesh	Former Yugoslav	Mauritania	South Sudan
Barbados	Republic of	Mauritius	(Republic of)
Belarus	Macedonia	Mexico	Spain
Belgium	France	Moldova	Sri Lanka
Belize	Gabon	Monaco	Sudan
Benin	Gambia	Mongolia	Suriname
Bhutan	Georgia	Montenegro	Swaziland
Bolivia	Germany	Morocco	Sweden
Bosnia &	Ghana	Mozambique	Switzerland
Herzegovina	Greece	Myanmar	Syria
Botswana	Grenada	Namibia	Tajikistan
Brazil	Guatemala	Nauru	Tanzania
Brunei	Guinea	Nepal	Thailand
Bulgaria	Guinea-Bissau	Netherlands	Timor-Leste
Burkina-Faso	Guyana	New Zealand	Togo
Burundi	Haiti	Nicaragua	Tonga
Cambodia	Honduras	Niger	Trinidad & Tobago
Cameroon	Hungary	Nigeria	Tunisia
Canada	Iceland	Norway	Turkey
Cape Verde	India	Oman	Turkmenistan
Central African	Indonesia	Pakistan	Uganda
Republic	Iran	Panama	Ukraine
Chad	Iraq	Papua New Guinea	United Arab Emirates
Chile	Ireland	Paraguay	United Kingdom
China	Israel	Peru	United States of
Colombia	Italy	Philippines	America
Comoros	Jamaica	Poland	Uruguay
Congo	Japan	Portugal	Uzbekistan
Congo (Democratic	Jordan	Qatar	Vatican City State
Republic)	Kazakhstan	Romania	Venezuela
Costa Rica	Kenya	Russia	Vietnam
Côte d'Ivoire	Korea (Republic of)	Rwanda	Yemen
Croatia	Kuwait	St Kitts & Nevis	Zambia
Cuba	Kyrgyzstan	St Lucia	Zimbabwe
Curaçao	Laos	St Vincent &	
Cyprus	Latvia	Grenadines	

GOVERNMENT MINISTRIES AND BODIES

DEPARTMENT FOR BUSINESS INNOVATION & SKILLS: LEGAL SERVICES (CRIMINAL ENFORCEMENT)
1 Victoria Street, London SW1H 0ET.
Investigation Officers Branch (IOB): PO Box 280, Exchange House, Exchange Road, Watford WD18 0GA.
Chief Investigation Officer: Mr C Duggan. Tel: 01923 655601. Fax: 01923 655615.
Email: chris.duggan@bis.gsi.gov.uk
Intelligence & Financial Investigations: Floor 2, No 3 Piccadilly Place, Manchester M1 3BN. Fax: 0161 234 8687.
Deputy Chief Investigation Officer: Mr P Thomas. Tel: 0161 234 8677. Email: peter.thomas@bis.gsi.gov.uk
Senior Investigation Officer: Mr M Clarke. Tel: 0161 234 8678. Email: michael.clarke@bis.gsi.gov.uk
North Team: Floor 2, No 3 Piccadilly Place, Manchester M1 3BN.
Deputy Chief Investigation Officer: Mr M R Williams. Tel: 0161 234 8670. Email: michael.williams1@bis.gsi.gov.uk
East Team: Apex Court, City Link, Nottingham NG2 4LA.
Deputy Chief Investigation Officer: Mr G Wicks. Tel: 0115 872 4701. Fax: 0115 872 4798. Email: glenn.wicks@bis.gsi.gov.uk
South Team A: PO Box 280, Exchange House, Exchange Road, Watford WD18 0GA. Fax: 01923 655615.
Deputy Chief Investigation Officer: Mr L Mannall. Tel: 01923 655640. Email: liam.mannall@bis.gsi.gov.uk
South Team B: PO Box 280, Exchange House, Exchange Road, Watford WD18 0GA.
Deputy Chief Investigation Officer: Mr I West. Tel: 01923 655176. Email: ian.west@bis.gsi.gov.uk
West Team: Room 3:153, Companies House, Crown Way, Cardiff CF14 3UZ.
Deputy Chief Investigation Officer: Mr L Mannall Tel: 02920 381204. Fax: 02920 381249. Email: liam.mannall@bis.gsi.gov.uk
Insolvency Service: Investigations & Enforcement Services (IES). 21 Bloomsbury Street, London WC1B 3SS. Tel: 020 7596 6123. Fax: 020 7596 6106.
Head of Investigations & Enforcement Services & Inspector of Companies: Vacant.
Director of Company Investigations South & Deputy Inspectors of Companies: Ms Angela Crossley. Tel: 020 7637 6660. Email: angela.crossley@cib.gsi.gov.uk
Director of Company Investigations North & Deputy Inspector of Companies: Ms C Entwistle. Floor 2, No 3 Piccadilly Place, Manchester M1 3BN. Tel: 0161 234 8653. Fax: 0161 234 8660. Email: claire.entwistle@cib.gsi.gov.uk
The main aim of the Legal Services Directorate (Criminal Enforcement), Investigation Officers Branch (IOB) is to increase the confidence of consumers, the business community, and investors by contributing to the reduction of commercial malpractice. Its objectives are: to carry out criminal investigations and prosecutions into offences of fraud, perjury, theft and breaches of the Insolvency Act, Companies Act, Company Directors Disqualification Act and Financial Services Act. The main powers of the Companies Investigation & Enforcement Services are to examine on a confidential basis the records of a company under s447 and the investigation of the affairs or ownership of a company under ss431, 432, or 442 of the Companies Act 1985. It seeks, in the public interest, the winding up of companies and the disqualification of offenders from action as company directors.

DEPARTMENT FOR ENVIRONMENT FOOD AND RURAL AFFAIRS (DEFRA) INVESTIGATION SERVICES
First Floor 13, Apex Court, Woodlands, Bradley Stoke, Gloucestershire BS32 4JT. Tel: 01454 870055.
Head of Service: Martin Leslie Bell.
Senior Investigation Officers: **North & Scotland:** Brian Lynch BA. **South & Northern Ireland:** Derrick Arthur Langley Price OBE MA PgDipCrim, PgDipCouns.
Intelligence Manager & Administrative Support: Phil Nicholls MBE.
The Investigation Service undertakes enquiries into frauds and irregularities affecting department interests. Officers are based throughout the United Kingdom and work in conjunction with other government agencies, police forces and local authorities.

DEPARTMENT OF HEALTH: NHS PROTECT
Department of Health, Weston House, 246 High Holborn, London WC1B 7EX. Tel: 020 7895 4500. Email: firstname.lastname@nhsprotect.gsi.gov.uk Website: www.nhsbsa.nhs.uk/protect
Managing Director: Dermid McCausland. Tel: 020 7895 4505.
Head of Deterrence & Engagement: Mark Richardson. Tel: 020 7895 4500.
Head of Deterrence & Engagement National Investigation Services: Susan Frith. Tel: 020 7895 4630.
Head of Information & Intelligence: Richard Rippin. Tel: 020 7895 4570.
Regional Offices: Coventry; Newcastle-upon-Tyne; St Helens.

DEPARTMENT FOR TRANSPORT (DFT): TRANSPORT SECURITY & CONTINGENCIES
Department for Transport, Great Minster House, 33 Horseferry Road, London SW1P 4DR. Tel: 0300 330 3000 (helpdesk); 020 7944 5999 (out of hours). Individuals tel: 020 7944 plus extension. Fax: 020 7944 9643. Email: transec@dft.gsi.gov.uk Individuals email: firstname.lastname@dft.gsi.gov.uk
Divisional Manager, Transport Security Strategy: Tim Symington.
Divisional Manager, Transport Security Compliance: Gillian Underwood.
Divisional Manager, Maritime & Land Transport Security: Caroline Billingham (Maritime); John Fuller (Land).
Divisional Manager, Aviation Security: Tim Figures.

Aviation: Training & Recruitment. Sean Birch. Ext: 5287. **Regulation.** Richard Davies. Ext: 3416. **Compliance.** Robert John. Ext: 2863.
Maritime: Regulation. Mark Traquair. Ext: 2845. **Compliance.** John Mills. Ext: 2865.
Land Transport: Regulation. David Pike. Ext: 5933. **Compliance.** David Goodchild. Ext: 2858.
Dangerous Goods by Road & Rail: Regulation. Leon Brain. Ext: 6982. **Compliance.** David Goodchild. Ext: 2858.
The Department for Transport regulates the transport industries for security purposes by developing and enforcing security measures with regard to their deliverability and proportionality, based on the nature and scale of the prevailing threat. The security regimes also take account of financial and operational costs to the industry and the consequences of a terrorist attack. Responsibility for delivering and paying for these measures rests with the regulated industries: aviation, maritime, railways (including the London Underground, Docklands Light Railway and Glasgow Subway), the Channel Tunnel and the movement of dangerous goods by road and rail. For further details see http://www.dft.gov.uk/topics/security/.

DFT: AIR ACCIDENTS INVESTIGATION BRANCH (AAIB)
Berkshire Copse Road, Aldershot, Hampshire GU11 2HH. Tel: 01252 510300. Accident/incident reporting tel: 01252 512299. Fax: 01252 376999. Email: enquiries@aaib.gov.uk; investigations@aaib.gov.uk Website: www.aaib.gov.uk
Chief Inspector of Air Accidents: Keith Conradi.
Deputy Chief Inspector of Air Accidents: David Miller.
The Air Accidents Investigation Branch is empowered by European Regulation EC/996/2010 and the Civil Aviation (Investigation of Accidents and Incidents) Regulations 1996 to investigate all accidents and serious incidents arising out of or in the course of air navigation which occur to civil aircraft in or over the United Kingdom and its overseas territories and crown dependencies. All such occurrences should be reported to the Chief Inspector of Accidents.

DEPARTMENT FOR WORK AND PENSIONS (JOB CENTRE PLUS) FRAUD INVESTIGATION SERVICE (FIS)
Daryl House, Bridge Road, Stockton-on-Tees, Cleveland TS18 3BW.
Head of Fraud Investigation Service: Dave White. Tel: 01642 413314.
Group Manager (South): Nick Owen. Tel: 020 8535 6139.
Group Manager (North): Phil Crozier. Tel: 01524 598145.
Area Fraud Investigators FIS (Organised): Chris Hare. Tel: 0115 944 8138.
Area Fraud Investigator FIS (Intelligence): Stewart Brooks. Tel: 07741 005799
FIS deals with all attacks on the DWP benefit system. The bulk of staff work within seven group fraud commands based in the regions of England, Scotland and Wales, mainly investigating fraud committed by individual benefit customers misrepresenting or not reporting changes in circumstances. FIS (Organised) investigates organised and systematic abuse of DWP claims and payments, and liaises with police and other investigation agencies. Activities investigated include the use of false identities to make fraudulent applications for benefit, as well as the use of stolen, manipulated and counterfeit instruments of payment material. FIS (Intelligence) provides support to all teams in the form of referral management, intelligence gathering and criminal analysis; it also handles information requests via a national disclosure unit based at Lewes.

AVIATION REGULATION ENFORCEMENT DEPARTMENT
Headquarters: Room K504, CAA House, 45–59 Kingsway, London WC2B 6TE. Tel: 020 7453 6186; 020 7453 6193 (outside office hours). Fax: 020 7453 6163.
The Investigation Branch undertakes enquiries into all breaches of aviation legislation relating to UK aircraft anywhere in the world and foreign aircraft operating within the United Kingdom.

CHARITY COMMISSION INVESTIGATIONS AND ENFORCEMENT DEPARTMENT
London Office: 1st Floor, 30 Millbank, London SW1P 4DU.
Liverpool Office: 12 Princes Dock, Princes Parade, Liverpool L3 1DE. Tel: 0845 300 0218.
Head of Investigations & Enforcement: Michelle Russell.
Heads of Investigation Teams: Iain Hewitt; Steve Law.
Head of Intelligence: Dave Hawkins.
The Charity Commission's functions include identifying and investigating abuse within or connected to charities and their trustees. Its Investigation and Enforcement Department's investigation, assessment and monitoring units carry out this work. The intelligence unit is the principal point of contact for liaison and the exchange of information with other bodies, including the police.

FINANCIAL SERVICES AUTHORITY (FSA)
25 The North Colonnade, Canary Wharf, London E14 5HS. Tel: 020 7066 1000. Fax: 020 7066 1009. Website: fsa.gov.uk
Central Intelligence Tasking Team. Tel: 020 7066 2474.
Manager of Intelligence Team: Neil Hughes. Tel: 020 7066 1572.
Team Leader, Intelligence Team: Michael Buggy. Tel: 020 7066 9808.
FSA is the central UK authority responsible for supervising banks and regulating investment business. It has statutory powers under the Financial Services and Markets Act 2000. These powers enable it to take action, in criminal and civil matters: where regulated firms and approved persons fall seriously short of its regulatory standards; where business is carried on without authorisation; where investment funds fail to meet their statutory requirements; for the purposes of fighting financial crime and market abuse. The intelligence team acts as principal point of contact for requests for assistance from police forces and other law enforcement bodies.

FOOD STANDARDS AGENCY
Investigation Branch: Area 2B, 125 Kingsway, London WC2B 6NH. Tel: 020 7276 8648. Website: www.food.gov.uk
Senior Investigation Officer: Dave Hickman. Mob: 07770 281947.

Investigation Manager: Gareth Williams.
The Branch investigates offences in England, Wales and Scotland on its own account and on behalf of Defra, the Welsh Assembly government and the Scottish government.
Wine Standards: Enforcement and Local Authority Delivery Division, 125 Kingsway, as above. Tel: 020 7276 8351. Fax: 020 7276 8289.
Email: john.boodle@foodstandards.gsi.gov.uk Website: www.food.gov.uk/wine
Wine Standards within the FSA is an enforcement authority responsible for the provisions of European Community wine regulations in the non-retail sector. These include checks on wine sector products in tax warehouses, wholesale premises and vineyards, which are carried out by a small team of regionally based inspectors, often drawing on expertise from previous careers in the police force. Investigations where criminal deception charges may arise (Theft Act) can involve co-ordination with the police service.

GANGMASTERS LICENSING AUTHORITY
PO Box 10272, Nottingham NG2 9PB. Tel: 0845 602 5020. Website: www.gla.defra.gov.uk
Chief Executive: Paul Broadbent. *PA:* Jane Riley. Tel: 0115 959 7077. Email: jane.riley@gla.gsi.gov.uk
Intelligence Manager: Ian Walker. Tel: 0115 959 7060. Email: intelligence@gla.gsi.gov.uk
General Operational Enquiries. Tel: 0115 959 7032 (switches to out-of -hours officer after 17:00).
The GLA is the central UK authority responsible for regulating gangmasters and investigating illegality and the unlicensed supply of workers in agriculture, shellfish gathering, and the processing and packaging of food and drink products. This is in accordance with the requirements set out in the Gangmasters (Licensing) Act 2004. Its mission is to safeguard the welfare and interests of workers while ensuring gangmasters operate within the law. The GLA works across the UK with a wide range of government departments, agencies and police forces, as well as foreign embassies and authorities, to tackle labour exploitation. A register of licensed gangmasters and details of those who have had their licences revoked can be seen at www.gla.defra.gov.uk.

HEALTH AND CARE PROFESSIONS COUNCIL (HCPC)
Park House, 184 Kennington Park Road, London SE11 4BU. Tel: 0845 300 6184. Fax: 020 7820 9684. Website: www.hpc-uk.org
Chief Executive: Marc Seale.
The HPC currently regulates the following professions: arts therapists; biomedical scientists; chiropodists/ podiatrists; clinical scientists; dietitians; hearing aid dispensers; occupational therapists; operating department practitioners; orthoptists; paramedics; physiotherapists; practitioner psychologists; prosthetists/orthotists; radiographers; social workers in England; speech and language therapists. All these professions have at least one professional title that is protected by law; anyone using such a title must be registered with the HPC.

HM REVENUE & CUSTOMS CENTRE FOR EXCHANGE OF INTELLIGENCE
Gateway Exchange Team London. Custom House Annexe, 20 Lower Thames Street, London EC3R 6EE. Tel: 0870 785 2296. Fax: 0870 785 2240. Email: get.london@hmrc.gsi.gov.uk
Contacts: Paul Wright. Tel: 087 0785 2220. Julie Larkins. Tel: 087 0785 2801. Susan Evans. Tel: 087 0785 2875.
Gateway Exchange Team Cardiff. Room G.72, CEI Cardiff, Ty-Glas Road, Llanishen, Cardiff CF14 5TS. Tel: 029 2032 6567. Email: cri.gatewaydisclosure@hmrc.gsi.gov.uk
Contacts: Judith Hall. Tel: 029 2032 6567. Jason James. Tel: 029 2032 6574. John Richards. Tel: 029 2032 5147.

INFORMATION COMMISSIONER'S OFFICE
Wycliffe House, Water Lane, Wilmslow, Cheshire SK9 5AF. Tel: 0303 123 1113. DX: 20819 Wilmslow. Fax: 01625 524510.
Information Commissioner: Christopher Graham.
Head of Enforcement: Stephen Eckersley.
Enforcement Group Managers: Sally-Anne Poole; Andy Curry.
Intelligence Hub: Adam Stephens. Tel: 01625 545785. Email: ih@ico.gsi.gov.uk
Enquiries: Deirdre Rogers. Tel: 01625 545725.
The Enforcement Department deals with criminal and non-criminal breaches of the Data Protection Act 1998, the Freedom of Information Act 2000 and the Privacy & Electronic Communications Regulations.

MEDICINES & HEALTHCARE PRODUCTS REGULATORY AGENCY (MHRA)
151 Buckingham Palace Road, London SW1W 9SZ. Out of hours tel: 020 3080 6000 (urgent enquiries).
Medicines Sector, Enforcement Group
A/Group Manager: Nimo Ahmed. Tel: 020 3080 6576.
A/Head of Intelligence: Gift Minta. Tel: 020 3080 6617.
Head of Operations: Danny Lee-Frost. Tel: 020 3080 6618.
Case Referral Centre. Tel: 020 3080 6330. Email: casereferrals@mhra.gsi.gov.uk
To report suspected counterfeit products tel: 020 3080 6701 or email: counterfeit@mhra.gsi.gov.uk
The Enforcement Group deals with policy on safety, quality and efficacy of medicinal products, including international aspects of medicines control. The main function of the group is to enforce the Human Medicines Regulations 2012 and associated legislation. Investigations range from unlawfully manufactured medicines, including counterfeited and diverted products, to the illegal sale, supply and importation of medicinal products. Investigators are trained to CID standards in interviewing and investigating techniques and maintain close liaison with SOCA, police forces, UKBA and Trading Standards.

Devices Sector, Compliance & Enforcement Unit
Compliance & Enforcement Unit Manager: Bruce Petrie. Tel: 020 3080 7335.
Compliance Policy Manager: David Batten. Tel: 020 3080 7254.
General enquiries. Tel: 020 3080 6000. Out of hours (urgent enquiries) tel: 020 7210 3000.
The Devices Sector deals with policy on the safety, quality and performance of medical devices, including international aspects of medical devices control. The Compliance & Enforcement Unit's main function is to enforce

the European Union Medical Devices Directives. Investigations include the unlawful manufacturing and illegal marketing of counterfeit, fraudulent, and non-compliant medical devices.

NATS (FORMERLY NATIONAL AIR TRAFFIC SERVICES): CORPORATE SECURITY SERVICES
PO Box 31, Sopwith Way, Swanwick, Southampton SO31 7AY. Tel: 01489 612125. Fax: 01489 612688.
Head of Department & Counter-terrorism & Crime Prevention: Peter Bath. Tel: 01489 612146. Mob: 07768 710520. Email: pete.bath@nats.co.uk
Security Advisers: Alan Bailey. Tel: 01489 612659. Email: alan.bailey@nats.co.uk. Keri-Anne Barnjum. Tel: 01489 612659. Email: keri-anne.barnjum@nats.co.uk
Vetting Manager: Melanie English. Tel: 01489 612125. Email: melanie.english@nats.co.uk
Security Administration: Janet Mori. Tel: 01489 612030.
Corporate Security Services are responsible for crime prevention, security advice, personnel vetting, protection of information and the investigation of criminal and security matters affecting the NATS infrastructure and estate.

OFCOM (OFFICE OF COMMUNICATIONS)
Riverside House, 2A Southwark Bridge Road, London SE1 9HA. Tel: 0300 123 3000; 020 7981 3000. Fax: 020 7981 3333. Website: www.ofcom.org.uk
Chief Executive: Ed Richards.
Ofcom is the communications regulator, operating under the Communications Act 2003.It enforces the Wireless Telegraphy Acts and associated legislation and acts against illegal users of radio. The service is able to assist the police in tracing illegal radio communications, through its regional offices. As well as providing technical expertise, the regional offices also have non-technical investigations officers (ex-police) who investigate matters such as the suppliers of illegal equipment and the backers of pirate broadcasters.

SECURITY INDUSTRY AUTHORITY (SIA)
90 High Holborn, London WC1V 6BH. Tel: 020 7025 4100.
Chief Executive: Bill Butler. Email: bill.butler@sia.gsi.gov.uk
Assistant Directors: Compliance & Investigation: John Montague. Email: john.montague@sia.gsi.gov.uk
Intelligence: David Porter. Email: intelligence@sia.gsi.gov.uk
The SIA is an executive non-departmental public body (NDPB) responsible for regulating the private security industry in England, Wales, Scotland and Northern Ireland, according to the requirements set out by the Private Security Industry Act 2001. In October 2010, the Government announced a 'phased transition to a new regulatory regime' for the private security industry. The SIA is working in consultation with the industry to draw up these plans, and while future regulation is subject to parliamentary approval, the key elements are likely to include: a new regulatory body outside Government; the licensing of businesses; and the registration of individuals. The final decisions on future regulation in Scotland and Northern Ireland are subject to decision by the devolved administrations, but it is expected that the new regime should be capable of working across the UK.

UK FOOTBALL POLICING UNIT (UKFPU)
PO Box 51997, London SW9 6TN. Email: footballdesk@fpu.pnn.police.uk. Email for individuals: firstname.lastname@fpu.pnn.police.uk
Director: Bryan Drew QPM. Tel: 020 7785 7161.
Assistant Director Operations: Roger Evans. Tel: 020 7785 7163.
Assistant Director Information Management: Tony Conniford. Tel: 020 7785 7162.
Business Manager: Liam Rackham. Tel: 020 7785 7166.
FBOA enquiries. Tel: 020 7785 7183. Fax: 020 7785 7160.
The UKFPU was established in November 2005 and is funded by the Home Office and ACPO. Its aim is to ensure that effective arrangements are in place to provide a coherent national police response to all aspects of football related crime. The unit is responsible for football policy issues, co-ordination of the football intelligence network in England and Wales, and management of the Football Banning Orders Authority (FBOA).

SAFETY AND SECURITY ORGANISATIONS

ART LOSS REGISTER, THE
1st Floor, 63–66 Hatton Garden, London EC1N 8LE. Tel: 020 7841 5780. Fax: 020 7841 5781. Email: info@artloss.com. Website: www.artloss.com
Directors: Julian Radcliffe OBE; Simon Wood; Tony Le Fevre; Eric Westropp.
The Art Loss Register (ALR) provides a free service to the police and law enforcement agencies worldwide to assist with the identification and recovery of stolen art, antiques and collectibles on behalf of owners. Clients include insurance companies, Lloyd's syndicates, and auction houses. The ALR is endorsed by the Home Office and ACPO.

THE ASSOCIATION FOR UK INTERACTIVE ENTERTAINMENT (UKIE)
167 Wardour Street, London W1F 8WP. Tel: 020 7534 0580. Fax: 020 7534 0581. Email: piracy@ukie.org.uk
    Website: www.ukie.org.uk
Chief Executive: Joe Twist.
The trade association for the games and interactive entertainment industry in the United Kingdom. Investigators are available to assist police and trading standards officers in the prosecution of cases under the Copyright, Designs and Patents Act 1988 and Trade Mark Act 1994.

BANK OF ENGLAND
Head of Security: Don Randall MBE. Tel: 020 7601 4560. Fax: 020 7601 5521.
    Email: don.randall@bankofengland.co.uk
Senior Security Manager Investigations: Terry Burke. Tel: 020 7601 4000. (Contact for all security risk-related matters, including physical, information, IT, fraud management, money laundering and criminal investigations.)
Senior Operations & Technology Manager: David Cox. Tel: 020 7601 5960.
Security Operations Centre (24 hrs). Tel: 020 7601 3333. (Out-of-hours operational contact point for all urgent enquiries or security support.)

BBC SECURITY AND INVESTIGATION SERVICES
Head of Corporate Security: Eddie Halling. Rm BC4 C1, Broadcast Centre, 201 Wood Lane, London W12 7TS. Tel: 020 8743 8000. Fax: 020 8008 3279. Email: eddie.halling@bbc.co.uk
Head of Investigation Service: Kit Kitson. Rm 1540, White City, 201 Wood Lane, London W12 7TS. Tel: 020 8752 5542. Fax: 020 8752 4213. Email: investigation.service@bbc.co.uk
One of the functions of the investigators is to liaise with the police in all matters relating to BBC radio and television. Their services are readily available to police officers requiring assistance or information.

BRITISH HORSERACING AUTHORITY LEGAL, INTEGRITY & RISK DEPARTMENT
75 High Holborn, London WC1V 6LS. Tel: 020 7152 0168. Fax: 020 7152 0171.
    Email: intel@britishhorseracing.com. Website: www.britishhorseracing.com
Director: Mr A Brickell. Tel: 020 7152 0134. Email: abrickell@britishhorseracing.com
PA: Ms F Carlin. Tel: 020 7152 0178. Email: fcarlin@britishhorseracing.com
Head of Integrity (Operations): Mr P Beeby. Tel: 020 7152 0180. Email: pbeeby@britishhorseracing.com
Licensing Team Leader: Ms Annette Baker. Tel: 020 7152 0143. Email: abaker@britishhorseracing.com
The department's primary aim is to protect the integrity of British horseracing using the regulatory powers of the British Horseracing Authority (BHA). It conducts investigations and gathers intelligence relating to malpractice, corruption or criminal activity in relation to breaches of the Rules of Racing. On completion of investigations, the compliance team submits findings to the BHA's disciplinary panel and, where appropriate, external law enforcement agencies. The department also licenses the sport's participants to ensure they are suitable persons, and employs staff to protect racehorses from interference while in the secure area of the racecourse stable yard and to maintain integrity in the weighing rooms.

BRITISH SKY BROADCASTING LTD
Headquarters: Grant Way, Isleworth, Middlesex TW7 5QD. Website: www.sky.com
Director of Group Security: Michael Barley.
Government & LEA Service Manager, Compliance: Sandra Miles.
Government & LEA Service Unit. Tel: 020 7032 7010. Fax: 020 7900 8558. Email: spoc@bskyb.scn.gov.uk
Single contact point for all law enforcement enquiries. Responsible for liaison with police, government agencies and public authorities in all matters relating to BSkyB customer and employee data and also for broadcast data, film footage and fleet enquiries. Full BSkyB written protocols and procedures for submission of requests for data are published on SpocBook or are available on request.

BRITISH VEHICLE RENTAL & LEASING ASSOCIATION
BVRLA, River Lodge, Badminton Court, Amersham HP7 0DD. Tel: 01494 434747. Email: info@bvrla.co.uk
    Website: www.bvrla.co.uk
The BVRLA is the representative trade body for companies providing short-term self-drive rental, contract hire and fleet management services to corporate users and consumers: its members operate a combined fleet of 2.5m vehicles throughout the United Kingdom. BVRLA's Risk Management and Security Committee works with the police and other law enforcement agencies to raise and promote awareness of industry risk-related issues and encourage the use of 'best practice' to minimise the financial and operational impact of vehicle crime and fraud.

BT SECURITY
BT Centre, 81 Newgate Street, London EC1A 7AJ.
Managing Director BT Security: Mark Hughes. Tel: 01277 328111. Email: mark.hughes@bt.com
BT Security Incident Management: St Giles ATE, Spring Garden, Northampton NN1 1LZ. General enquiries tel: 0800 321999 (24 hrs); 01908 238372.

General Manager BT Corporate Investigations: Tom Mullen. Tel: 07710 029792.
  Email: tom.mullen@bt.com
Managers Detective Operations BT Corporate Investigations: Steve Beach. Tel: 020 3279 0662.
  Email: steve.beach@bt.com. Lesley Green. Tel: 020 3279 0672. Email: lesley.a.green@bt.com
BT Corporate Investigations Intelligence Team Manager: John Millar. Tel: 020 3279 0685. Email:
  john.2.millar@bt.com
Payphone Crime Investigation Manager: Steve Hewitt. Tel: 01327 872003. Email: steve.g.hewitt@bt.com
BT Corporate Investigations Crime Advice Manager: Joe Fitzgerald. Tel: 020 3279 0671. Email:
  joe.fitzgerald@bt.com
BT Security is responsible for investigating crime committed against BT and assisting the police in respect of all
criminal matters affecting the company.

CABLE & WIRELESS WORLDWIDE – POLICE LIAISON UNIT
Atlas Business Park, Simonsway, Wythenshawe, Manchester M22 5RR. Tel: 0161 266 5153 (law enforcement
enquiries). Fax: 0161 957 6471. Email: policeliaisonunit@cw.com
Police Liaison Unit Manager: Ms S Kirkman. Tel: 07957 809916.
Manager Compliance & Disclosure: Mr P Mackay. Tel: 07957 802899.
The Police Liaison Unit is the primary contact point for FIBs in all police forces.

DEDICATED CHEQUE AND PLASTIC CRIME UNIT
PO Box 39913, London EC2A 1YE. Tel: 020 7709 6600. Fax: 020 7709 6630.
  Email: dcpcu@dcpcu.pnn.police.uk. Website: www.dcpcu.org.uk
Head of Unit: Det Chief Insp David Carter.
Managers: Det Insp Sarah Ward; Det Insp David Timmins.
The DCPCU is a Home Office approved, payments industry sponsored, multi-agency unit. Its principal role is to
combat payments fraud to NIM Level 3. It is staffed by police officers, bank investigators and staff from the UK
Payments Authority (formerly APACS). The DCPCU consists of the payments industry and Police Joint Intelligence
Unit (PIPJIU), which liaises and manages relationships with industry stakeholders and manages law enforcement and
banking industry intelligence, data-sharing initiatives and operational intelligence on behalf of the unit, and the
Operations and Investigations Unit (OIU), which investigates cheque, ATM and payment card fraud, linked identity
fraud and the counterfeiting of plastic cards, where serious organised crime is involved.

EE
Law Enforcement Liaison Department (Bristol): 800 Park Avenue, Aztec West, Almondsbury, Bristol BS32
4TR. Tel: 0870 376 4800. Fax: 0870 376 0802.
Manager: Mr J Butcher. Email: bristol.disclosures@ee.co.uk
Law Enforcement Liaison Department (Hatfield): Hatfield Business Park, Hatfield AL10 9BW. Tel: 01707
315599. Fax: 01707 319014.
Manager: Paul Fennelly. Email: hatfield.pl@ee.co.uk

FEDERATION AGAINST COPYRIGHT THEFT LTD (FACT)
Europa House, Church Street, Old Isleworth, Middlesex TW7 6DA. Tel: 020 8568 6646. Fax: 020 8560 6364.
  Email: contact@fact-uk.org.uk. Website: www.fact-uk.org.uk
FACT is the UK's leading non-profit trade organisation established to protect and represent the interests of the film
and broadcasting industry against copyright and trademark infringements. It works closely with statutory law
enforcement agencies to combat the growth in pirate DVDs, film and other forms of broadcast material, including the
increasing threat of internet-based piracy. FACT has trained investigators throughout the United Kingdom and offers
free assistance with investigations, intelligence gathering and forensics. FACT can be found on the PNLD: search
under piracy.

FEDERATION AGAINST SOFTWARE THEFT
York House, 18 York Road, Maidenhead SL6 1SF. Tel: 0845 521 8630. Fax: 0845 521 8625. Email:
info@fast.org Website: www.fastiis.org
The Federation is a not for-profit organisation and a key remit is enforcement. It uses the sanctions of copyright and
trade mark legislation to tackle software theft, from under-licensing in business to unlawful distribution over the
internet to the sale of counterfeit and copied software. It works with enforcement agencies and provides expert
assistance to the police and trading standards on these issues. It represents any software publisher member, regardless
of size, whose intellectual property is being violated. The Federation has 120 software industry members, including
resellers, distributors, audit software producers and consultants.

INSTITUTE OF TRAFFIC ACCIDENT INVESTIGATORS
The Institute of Traffic Accident Investigators, Column House, London Road, Shrewsbury SY2 6NN. Tel:
0845 621 2066. Fax: 0845 621 2077. Email: admin@itai.org. Website: www.itai.org
The Institute draws its membership from a wide variety of professions including police officers, forensic scientists and
private consultants. It aims to provide a means for communication, education, representation and regulation in the
field of traffic accident investigation. Affiliate membership is open to any person with an interest in this field.
Transfer to associate or full membership status is available according to qualifications and experience.

INTERNATIONAL FEDERATION OF SPIRITS PRODUCERS (IFSP) LTD
Website: www.ifspglobal.com
Chief Executive: Mr D Bolt. Tel: 07775 333918 Email: david.bolt@ifspglobal.com
Europe: *Director Europe:* Mr M Heasman. Tel: 07711 979952. Email: mheasman.ifspeurope@ifspglobal.com
  Deputy Director Europe: Ms S Lyons. Tel: 07791 831909. Email: slyons.ifspeurope@ifspglobal.com
UK & Ireland: Mr J Fitzpatrick. Tel: 07775 344805. Email: john.fitzpatrickifspuk@ifspglobal.com
Created in the early 1990s to combat worldwide counterfeiting of spirits, IFSP represents major producers of
internationally-sold brands and operates in over 30 countries, including the United Kingdom. It works with law

enforcement and regulatory agencies to protect consumers from counterfeit products and with traders to prevent loss of government tax revenues and preserve company profits, sharing intelligence about counterfeit production, distribution and sales. IFSP trains enforcement agencies in counterfeit recognition and provides support including forensic testing and analysis of seized goods, and taking action against offenders.

NATIONAL PLANT & EQUIPMENT REGISTER (TER), THE
Station House West, Ashley Avenue, Lower Weston, Bath BA1 3DS. Tel: 01225 464599. Fax: 01225 317698. Email: info@ter-europe.org. Website: www.ter-europe.org
Chairman: Mr J G Y Radcliffe OBE TD. *Manager:* Mr G Barwill.
The National Plant & Equipment Register (TER) provides a free, 24-hour, seven days a week service to the police and law enforcement agencies worldwide to assist with the identification and recovery of items of stolen construction, demolition and quarrying plant and equipment, tractors and agricultural machinery, trailers, and caravans. TER maintains a database of owned and stolen equipment and runs a team of investigators in the UK and Northern Ireland.

NATIONAL PUBWATCH
PO Box 3523, Barnet EN5 9LQ. Tel: 020 8755 3222. Email: admin@nationalpubwatch.org.uk Website: www.nationalpubwatch.org.uk
Chairman: Steve Baker.
National Pubwatch is a voluntary organisation which aims to encourage a safe and secure environment in and around licensed premises by supporting existing pubwatches and encouraging the creation of new watches. To help police officers and licensees, it provides a best practice guide, a quarterly newsletter, a database of watches, a national voice on watch issues and access to other agencies that can help or provide the services needed by watches.

NATIONAL SECURITY INSPECTORATE (NSI)
Sentinel House, 5 Reform Road, Maidenhead SL6 8BY. Tel: 01628 637512. Fax: 01628 773367. Email: nsi@nsi.org.uk. Website: www.nsi.org.uk
Chief Executive: Jeff Little OBE.
NSI is an independent, not-for-profit provider of inspection and certification services for electronic security system installers, fire detection and manned security providers. NSI approved companies must consistently meet appropriate British and European Standards as well as ACPO requirements where appropriate. Details of NSI approved companies can be accessed via the NSI website.

POST OFFICE LTD SECURITY
Support Team. Tel: 0161 869 7205. (Mon–Fri 0830–1700.)
24/7 Control Room (Grapevine). Tel: 0845 603 4004.
(Grapevine is owned by Post Office Ltd and is an intelligence focused single point of contact for the reporting of all suspicious activity.)
Head of Security: John M Scott MSc FSyI. Email: john.m.scott@postoffice.co.uk
Post Office Ltd is recognised by the Home Office as a non-police prosecuting authority. It has a dedicated security team whose primary aim is to minimise crime against Post Office Ltd in order to protect the business. Post Office Ltd has a prosecution policy, criminal law team and trained security managers who conduct criminal investigations on behalf of the business. It also has accredited financial investigators who utilise powers under Parts 2 & 8 of the Proceeds of Crime Act 2002 to pursue recovery of money stolen from the business.

ROAD HAULAGE ASSOCIATION SECURITY COMMITTEE
Road Haulage Association, The Old Forge, South Road, Weybridge, Surrey KT13 9DZ. Tel: 01932 838905. Fax: 01932 852516. Website: www.rha.uk.net
Chairman: John Traynor TNT. *Secretary:* Chrys Rampley.
The Committee consists of members of the Road Haulage Association, HM Revenue and Customs, Association of British Insurers, SOCA, Distribution Industry Project Scotland (DIPS), the RHA Insurance and Truckpol, People United Against Crime.

ROYAL MAIL GROUP LTD
Headquarters: 100 Victoria Embankment, London EC4Y 0HQ. **Security Headquarters:** 6a Eccleston Street, London SW1W 9LT. **Security Helpdesk.** Tel: 020 7239 6655 (24 hours). Email: securityhelpdesk@royalmail.com
Group Security Director: Tony Marsh MBA. Tel: 020 7881 4300. Email: tony.marsh@royalmail.com
Director of Criminal Investigation: Phil Gerrish. Tel: 020 7881 4311. Email: phil.gerrish@royalmail.com
Director of Security Risk Management: Martin Dunckley. Tel: 07850 733874. Email: martin.dunckley@royalmail.com
Head of Security Intelligence: Roger Duckworth. Tel: 07801 985960. Email: roger.duckworth@royalmail.com
DSO & Head of Aviation & Protective Security: David Davies. Tel: 07711 036065. Email: david.j.davies@royalmail.com
Royal Mail Security is responsible for the security of employees, customers, Royal Mail businesses and customers' assets. These businesses include Royal Mail, Parcelforce Worldwide and General Logistic Services. The team is also responsible for the investigation and prosecution of all non-violent offences against Royal Mail Group and its businesses and for supporting relevant authorities in the investigation of violent crime against the group. Royal Mail Group is a designated public authority under the Regulation of Investigatory Powers Act and law enforcement single points of contact (SPOCs) should contact the Royal Mail SPOC using established procedures or via the Security Helpdesk.

VISA
Visa International Service Association, PO Box 253, London W8 5TE. Tel: 020 7937 1179 (Visa Service Centre).

The Visa Service Centre's (VSC) telephone number was introduced in 1986 as a contact point for law enforcement assistance. All collect calls are accepted. While VSC operators are restricted in the type of information they are permitted to release on Visa cards and travellers' cheques, they can provide contact information on Visa member banks worldwide 24 hours a day, every day.

VODAFONE – FRAUD, RISK & SECURITY
The Connection, Baird House, First Floor, Newbury, Berkshire RG14 2FN. Tel: 07770 999999 (24/7). Fax: 01635 673122.

Head of Fraud, Risk & Security: Mark Hughes. Tel: 07825 044049.

Vodafone Fraud Risk and Security Department focuses on reducing all criminal activity affecting Vodafone UK. This includes criminal investigations, customer fraud management, risk management, information security and security awareness. The department liaises with the police and other law enforcement agencies to assist in the prevention and detection of crime.

EMERGENCY PLANNING

EMERGENCY PLANNING COLLEGE
The Hawkhills, Easingwold, York YO61 3EG.
Tel: 01347 821406 Fax: 01347 822575.
Website: www.epcollege.com

Director: Ronnie Coutts.
Head of Sales & Marketing: Simon Barter.
The Emergency Planning College (EPC) seeks to enhance UK resilience through the provision of world-class training, exercising and consultancy by the UK's leading experts in emergency planning and crisis management. Established in 1989, the EPC is now managed and operated by Serco in partnership with, and on behalf of, the Cabinet Office.

THE EMERGENCY PLANNING SOCIETY
The Media Centre, Culverhouse Cross, Cardiff CF5 6XJ.
Tel: 0845 600 9587. Fax: 029 2059 0397.
Email: generalmanager@the-eps.org Website: www.the-eps.org

Chair of Society: Helen Hinds.
Director of Finance: Julie Bell.
Directors: Sanda Petakovic; Chris Spry; Bill Whitlock, Sandra Walker.
The Emergency Planning Society is the professional body for all those involved with any form of emergency, disaster or crisis planning and management. It aims to: (a) promote the views of its members in all issues relating to emergency planning and management; (b) provide a forum for the study of the most effective means of planning and managing local emergency preparation and response, and dissemination of good practice; (c) influence policy relating to emergency planning; (d) encourage the professional development of its members. Members come mainly from local authorities, the emergency services and industry.

LONDON FIRE BRIGADE EMERGENCY PLANNING DEPARTMENT
First Floor, LFB Operations Centre, Jubilee Way, London SW19 3XD.
Tel: 020 8555 1200.

Head of Emergency Planning: Andrew Pritchard. Ext: 50700.
    Email: andrew.pritchard@london-fire.gov.uk
Deputy Head of Emergency Planning Local Resilience Forum Manager: John Hetherington. Ext: 50715.
Deputy Head of Emergency Planning Local Authority Liaison Manager: Mark Sawyer. Ext: 50703.
Deputy Head of Emergency Planning Contingency Planning Manager: Toby Gould. Ext: 50704.
The London Fire Brigade Emergency Planning Department is responsible for discharging the following duties on behalf of the London Fire & Emergency Planning Authority. 1. Under the Civil Contingencies Act 2004: provision of the secretariat to London's Sub Regional Resilience Fora; provision of the pan-London local authority arrangements pertaining to Local Authority Gold and the London Local Authority Co-ordination Centre; and the provision of training and exercises in support of pan-London local authority arrangements. 2. Contingency planning: leading on the production of multi-agency off-site emergency plans for industrial sites designated 'top tier' under the Control of Major Accident Hazards (COMAH) Regulations 1999, the Radiation (Emergency Preparedness & Public Information Regulations) (REPPIR) 2001, and the Pipelines Safety Regulations 1996.

POLICE/MILITARY LIAISON

ACPO (TAM) Police Military Liaison Officer: Chief Insp Mark Scoular. 5th Floor, 8–10 Victoria Street, London SW1H 0NN. Tel: 020 7084 8830. Mob: 07595 010447. Email: mark.scoular@acpo.pnn.police.uk
ACPO (TAM) Deputy Police Military Liaison Officer: Sgt Will Llewellyn Jones. 5th Floor, 8–10 Victoria Street, London SW1H 0NN. Tel: 020 7084 8832. Mob: 07825 257267. Email: will.jones@acpo.pnn.police.uk
The ACPO (TAM) Police Military Liaison Officer for England and Wales is Chief Insp Mark Scoular. The role seeks to provide a single point of contact for the MOD in respect of national policing issues and support linkages between the police and the military chain of command in matters relating to UK resilience, counter-terrorism, protective security and overseas operations involving UK military forces.

FIRE AND RESCUE SERVICES

ENGLAND

Department for Communities and Local Government, Eland House, Bressenden Place, London SW1E 5DU. Tel: 0303 444 0000.
Website: www.communities.gov.uk/fire

Chief Fire & Rescue Advisor: Sir Ken Knight. Eland House, as above. Tel: 0303 444 3153.

Avon: Fire & Rescue Service HQ, Temple Back, Bristol BS1 6EU. Tel: 0117 926 2061. Website: www.avonfire.gov.uk

Bedfordshire & Luton: Fire & Rescue Service HQ, Southfields Road, Kempston MK42 7NR. Tel: 01234 845000. Website: www.bedsfire.com

Berkshire: Fire & Rescue Service HQ, 103 Dee Road, Tilehurst, Reading RG30 4FS. Tel: 01189 452888. Website: www.rbfrs.co.uk

Buckinghamshire: Fire & Rescue Service HQ, Stocklake, Aylesbury HP20 1BD. Tel: 01296 744600. Website: www.bucksfire.gov.uk

Cambridgeshire: Fire & Rescue Service HQ, Hinchingbrooke Cottage, Brampton Road, Huntingdon PE29 2NA. Tel: 01480 444500. Website: www.cambsfire.gov.uk

Cheshire: Fire Brigade HQ, Sadler Road, Winsford CW7 2FQ. Tel: 01606 868700. Website: www.cheshirefire.gov.uk

Cleveland: Fire Brigade HQ, Endeavour House, Stockton Road, Hartlepool TS25 5TB. Tel: 01429 872311. Website: www.clevelandfire.gov.uk

Cornwall: Brigade Headquarters, Old County Hall, Station Road, Truro TR1 3HA. Tel: 01872 273117. Website: www.cornwall.gov.uk/fire

Cumbria: Carleton Avenue, Penrith CA10 2FA.Tel: 01768 812612. Website: www.cumbriafire.gov.uk

Derbyshire: Fire & Rescue Service HQ, The Old Hall, Burton Road, Littleover, Derby DE23 6EH. Tel: 01332 771221. Website: www.derbys-fire.gov.uk

Devon & Somerset: Fire & Rescue Service HQ, The Knowle, Clyst St George, Exeter EX3 0NW. Tel: 01392 872200. Website: www.dsfire.gov.uk

Dorset: Fire & Rescue Service HQ, Peverell Avenue West, Poundbury, Dorchester DT1 3SU. Tel: 01305 252600. Website: www.dorsetfire.gov.uk

County Durham & Darlington: Fire & Rescue Brigade HQ, Finchale Road, Framwellgate Moor, Durham DH1 5JR. Tel: 0191 384 3381. Website: www.ddfire.gov.uk

East Sussex: Fire & Rescue Service HQ, 20 Upperton Road, Eastbourne BN21 1EU. Tel: 0845 130 8855. Website: www.esfrd.org

Essex: Fire & Rescue Service HQ, Kelvedon Park, Rivenhall, Witham CM8 3HB. Tel: 01376 576000. Website: www.essex-fire.gov.uk

Gloucestershire: Fire & Rescue Service HQ, Waterwells Drive, Quedgeley, Gloucester GL2 2AX. Tel: 01452 753333. Website: www.glosfire.gov.uk

Greater Manchester: County Fire Service HQ, 146 Bolton Road, Swinton, Manchester M27 8US. Tel: 0161 736 5866. Website: www.manchesterfire.gov.uk

Hampshire: Fire & Rescue Service HQ, Leigh Road, Eastleigh SO50 9SJ. Tel: 02380 644000. Website: www.hantsfire.gov.uk

Hereford & Worcester: Fire & Rescue Service HQ, 2 Kings Court, Charles Hastings Way, Worcester WR5 1JR. Tel: 0845 122 4454. Website: www.hwfire.org.uk

Hertfordshire: Fire & Rescue Service HQ, Old London Road, Hertford SG13 7LD. Tel: 01992 507507. Website: www.hertsdirect.org/yrcouncil/hcofire

Humberside: Fire & Rescue Service HQ, Summergroves Way, Kingston-upon-Hull HU4 7BB. Tel: 01482 565333. Website: www.humbersidefire.gov.uk

Isle of Wight: Fire & Rescue Service HQ, St Nicholas, 58 St John's Road, Newport, Isle of Wight PO30 1LT. Tel: 01983 823194. Website: www.iwfire.org

Kent: Fire & Rescue Service HQ, The Godlands, Straw Mill Hill, Tovil, Maidstone ME15 6XB. Tel: 01622 692121. Website: www.kent.fire-uk.org

Lancashire: Service Headquarters, Garstang Road, Fulwood, Preston PR2 3LH. Tel: 01772 862545. Website: www.lancsfirerescue.org.uk

Leicestershire: Fire & Rescue Service HQ, Anstey Frith, Leicester Road, Glenfield, Leicester LE3 8HD. Tel: 0116 287 2241. Website: www.leicestershire-fire.gov.uk

Lincolnshire: Fire & Rescue Service HQ, South Park Avenue, Lincoln LN5 8EL. Tel: 01522 582222. Website: www.lincolnshirefire.org.uk

London: Fire & Emergency Planning Authority, 169 Union Street, London SE1 0LL. Tel: 020 8555 1200. Website: www.london-fire.gov.uk

Merseyside: Fire & Rescue Service, Bridle Road, Bootle, Liverpool L30 4YD. Tel: 0151 296 4000. Website: www.merseyfire.gov.uk

Norfolk: Fire & Rescue Service HQ, Whitegates, Hethersett, Norwich NR9 3DN. Tel: 01603 810351. Website: www.norfolkfireservice.gov.uk

Northamptonshire: Fire & Rescue Service HQ, Moulton Way, Moulton Park, Northampton NN3 6XJ. Tel: 01604 797000. Website: www.northamptonshire.gov.uk

Northumberland: Fire & Rescue Service HQ, Loansdean, Morpeth NE61 2ED. Tel: 01670 533000. Website: www.northumberland.gov.uk

North Yorkshire: Fire & Rescue Service HQ, Thurston Road, Northallerton DL6 2ND. Tel: 01609 780150. Website: www.northyorksfire.gov.uk

Nottinghamshire: Fire & Rescue Service HQ, Bestwood Lodge, Arnold, Nottingham NG5 8PD. Tel: 0115 967 0880. Website: www.notts-fire.gov.uk

Oxfordshire: Fire & Rescue Service HQ, Sterling Road, Kidlington OX5 2DU. Tel: 01865 842999. Website: www.oxfordshire.gov.uk/fireandrescueservice/

Scilly, Isles of: Fire Brigade Admin Centre, St Mary's Airport, St Mary's, Isles of Scilly TR21 0NG. Tel: 01720 424331. Website: www.scilly.gov.uk

Shropshire: Fire & Rescue Service HQ, St Michael's Street, Shrewsbury SY1 2HJ. Tel: 01743 260200. Website: www.shropshirefire.gov.uk

South Yorkshire: Headquarters, Eyre Street, Sheffield S1 3FG. Tel: 0114 272 7202. Website: www.syfire.gov.uk

Staffordshire: Fire & Rescue Service HQ, Pirehill, Aston, Stone ST15 0BS. Tel: 0845 122 1155. Website: www.staffordshirefire.gov.uk

Suffolk: County Fire Service HQ, Endeavour House, Russell Road, Ipswich IP4 2BX. Tel: 01473 588888. Website: www.suffolkcc.gov.uk/fire

Surrey: Fire & Rescue Service HQ, Croydon Road, Reigate RH2 0EJ. Tel: 01737 242444. Website: www.surrey-fire.gov.uk

Sussex: see East Sussex and West Sussex.

Tyne and Wear: Fire & Rescue Service HQ, PO Box 1196, Nissan Way, Barmston Mere, Sunderland SR5 3QY. Tel: 0191 444 1500. Website: www.twfire.gov.uk

Warwickshire: Fire & Rescue Service HQ, Warwick Street, Leamington Spa CV32 5LH. Tel: 01926 423231. Website: www.warwickshire.gov.uk/fireandrescue

West Midlands: Fire Service HQ, 99 Vauxhall Road, Birmingham B7 4HW. Tel: 0845 500 0900. Website: www.wmfs.net

West Sussex: Fire Brigade HQ, Northgate, Chichester PO19 1BD. Tel: 01243 786211. Website: www.westsussex.gov.uk

West Yorkshire: Fire Service HQ, Oakroyd Hall, Bradford Road, Birkenshaw, Bradford BD11 2DY. Tel: 01274 682311. Website: www.westyorksfire.gov.uk

Wiltshire: Fire Brigade HQ, Manor House, Potterne, Nr Devizes SN10 5PP. Tel: 01380 723 601. Website: www.wiltsfire.gov.uk

WALES

North Wales: Fire & Rescue Service HQ, Ffordd Salesbury, St Asaph Business Park, Denbighshire LL17 0JJ. Tel: 01745 535250. Website: www.nwales-fireservice.org.uk

Mid & West Wales: Fire & Rescue Service HQ, Lime Grove Avenue, Carmarthen SA31 1SP. Tel: 0370 606 0699. Email: mail@mawwfire.gov.uk Website: mawwfire.gov.uk

South Wales: Fire & Rescue Service, Forest View Business Park, Llantrisant CF72 8LX. Tel: 01443 232000. Email: swfs@southwales-fire.gov.uk Website: www.southwales-fire.gov.uk

SCOTLAND

Scottish Fire & Rescue Service (SFRS)
Chief Officer: Alasdair Hay.
Chair: Pat Watters.
HQ: 5 Whitefriars Crescent, Perth PH2 0PA. Tel: 01738 475260.
North Service Delivery Area: 19 North Anderson Drive, Aberdeen AB15 6TP. Tel 01224 696666. Fax: 01224 692224.
East Service Delivery Area: Fire Station, 21 Claylands Road, Newbridge, Midlothian EH28 8LF. Tel: 0131 335 9600.
West Service Delivery Area: Bothwell Road, Hamilton ML3 0EA. Tel: 01698 300999. Fax: 01698 338444.
HM Fire Service Inspectorate (HMFSI): Floor 1 West, St Andrew's House, Regent Road, Edinburgh EH1 3DG. Tel: 0131 556 8400. Fax: 0131 244 2564.

NORTHERN IRELAND

Northern Ireland Fire & Rescue Service Headquarters: 1 Seymour Street, Lisburn, Co Antrim BT27 4SX. Tel: 028 9266 4221. *Chief Executive:* Mr Jim Wallace. *Chief Fire Officer:* Mr Chris Kerr.
Eastern Area Headquarters: 6 Bankmore Street, Belfast BT7 1AQ. Tel: 028 9031 0360.
Northern Area Headquarters: 22–26 Waveney Road, Ballymena BT43 5BA. Tel: 028 2564 3370.
Southern Area Headquarters: Thomas Street, Portadown BT62 3AH. Tel: 028 3833 2222.
Western Area Headquarters: 10 Crescent Link, Londonderry BT47 1FR. Tel: 028 7131 1162.
Training Centre: 79 Boucher Crescent, Belfast BT12 6HU. Tel: 028 9038 9800.

ISLE OF MAN AND CHANNEL ISLANDS

Isle of Man Fire & Rescue Service: Isle of Man Fire & Rescue Service Headquarters, Homefield, 88 Woodbourne Road, Douglas, Isle of Man IM2 3AP. Tel: 01624 647300. Email: iomfire@gov.im Website: www.iomfire.com *Chief Fire Officer:* Mr Brian Draper.

States of Guernsey Fire & Rescue Service: Town Arsenal, St Peter Port, Guernsey GY1 1UW. Tel: 01481 724491. Fax: 01481 715988. Website: www.gov.gg/gfrs

States of Jersey Fire & Rescue Service: Fire & Rescue Service – Administration, Rouge Bouillon, St Helier, Jersey JE2 3ZA. Tel: 01534 445906. Fax: 01534 445999. Email: s.admin@gov.je Website: www.fire.gov.je *Fire Chief Officer:* Mr Mark James. Tel: 01534 445911.

AMBULANCE SERVICES

ENGLAND

Department of Health. Email: urgent&emergencycare@dh.gsi.gov.uk

East of England Ambulance Service NHS Trust: Trust Headquarters, Cambourne Building 1020, Cambourne Business Park, Cambourne, Cambridgeshire CB23 6EB. Tel: 0845 601 3733. Website: www.eastamb.nhs.uk *Chief Executive:* Hayden Newton.

East Midlands Ambulance Service NHS Trust: Trust Headquarters, 1 Horizon Place, Mellors Way, Nottingham Business Park, Nottingham NG8 6PY. Tel: 0115 884 5000. Website: www.emas.nhs.uk *Acting Chief Executive:* Phil Milligan.

Great Western Ambulance Service NHS Trust: Executive Office, Jenner House, Langley Park, Chippenham SN15 1GG. Tel: 01249 858500. Website: www.gwas.nhs.uk *Interim Chief Executive:* Ken Wenman.

Isle of Wight NHS Primary Care Trust: St Mary's Hospital, Parkhurst Road, Newport, Isle of Wight PO30 5TG. Tel: 01983 524081. Website: www.iow.nhs.uk *Chief Executive:* Kevin Flynn.

London Ambulance Service NHS Trust: 220 Waterloo Road, London SE1 8SD. Tel: 020 7921 5100 . Website: www.londonambulance.nhs.uk *A/Chief Executive:* Martin Flaherty OBE.

North East Ambulance Service NHS Foundation Trust: NEAS Headquarters, Bernicia House, Goldcrest Way, Newburn Riverside, Newcastle-upon-Tyne NE15 8NY. Tel: 0191 430 2000. Website: www.neambulance.nhs.uk *Chief Executive:* Simon Featherstone.

North West Ambulance Service NHS Trust: Ladybridge Hall, 399 Chorley New Road, Bolton BL1 5DD. Tel: 01204 498400. Website: www.nwas.nhs.uk *Chief Executive:* Darren Hurrell.

South Central Ambulance Service NHS Foundation Trust: Units7 and 8, Talisman Business Centre, Talisman Road, Bicester, Oxfordshire OX26 6HR. Tel: 01869 365000. Website: www.southcentralambulance.nhs.uk *Chief Executive:* Will Hancock.

South East Coast Ambulance Service NHS Foundation Trust: 40–42 Friars Walk, Lewes, East Sussex BN7 2XW. Tel: 01273 489444. Website: www.secamb.nhs.uk *Chief Executive:* Paul Sutton.

South Western Ambulance Service NHS Foundation Trust: Abbey Court, Eagle Way, Sowton Industrial Estate, Exeter EX2 7HY. Tel: 01392 261500. Website: www.swast.nhs.uk *Chief Executive:* Ken Wenman.

West Midlands Ambulance Service NHS Trust: Regional Ambulance Headquarters, Millennium Point, Waterfront Business Park, Waterfront Way, Brierley Hill DY5 1LX. Tel: 01384 215555. Website: www.wmas.nhs.uk *Chief Executive:* Anthony Marsh.

Yorkshire Ambulance Service NHS Trust: Springhill, Brindley Way, Wakefield 41 Business Park, Wakefield WF2 0XQ. Tel: 0845 124 1241. Website: www.yas.nhs.uk *Chief Executive:* David Whiting.

WALES

Website: www.ambulance.wales.nhs.uk

Welsh Ambulance Services NHS Trust: Trust Headquarters, HM Stanley Hospital, St Asaph, Denbighshire LL17 0RS. Tel: 01745 532900. Fax: 01745 532901.

North Region: PO Box 1064, HM Stanley Hospital, as above. Tel: 01745 532900. Fax: 01745 532904.

Central & West Region: Ty Maes Y Gruffudd, Cefn Coed Hospital, Cockett, Swansea SA2 0GP. Tel: 01792 562900. Fax: 01792 281184.

South East Region: Vantage Point House, Vantage Point Business Park, Ty Coch Way, Cwmbran NP44 7HF. Tel: 01633 626262.

SCOTLAND

Website: www.scottishambulance.com

Scottish Ambulance Service National Headquarters: Gyle Square, 1 South Gyle Crescent, Edinburgh EH12 9EB. Tel: 0131 314 0000.

Scottish Ambulance Service North Division – Aberdeen: Ashgrove Road West, Aberdeen AB16 5EG. Tel: 01224 812200. Fax: 01224 812201.

Scottish Ambulance Service North Division – Inverness: Thistle House, Beechwood Park North, Inverness IV2 3Ed. Tel: 01463 667700. Fax: 01463 712717.
East Central Division: 76 West School Road, Dundee DD3 8PQ. Tel: 01382 882400. Fax: 01382 882401.
West Central Division: Range Road, Motherwell ML1 2JE. Tel: 01698 264201. Fax: 01698 276746.
South East Division: 111 Oxgangs Road North, Edinburgh EH14 1ED. Tel: 0131 446 2600. Fax: 0131 446 2601.
South West Division: Maryfield House, Maryfield Road, Ayr KA8 9DF. Tel: 01292 284101. Fax: 01292 289962.

NORTHERN IRELAND

Northern Ireland Ambulance Service: Northern Ireland Ambulance Service HSC Trust, Site 30, Knockbracken Healthcare Park, Saintfield Road, Belfast BT8 8SG. Tel: 028 9040 0999. Fax: 028 9040 0900. Website: www.niamb.co.uk

ISLE OF MAN

Isle of Man Ambulance Service, Ambulance HQ, Cronk Coar, Noble's Hospital, Braddan, Isle of Man IM4 4BR. Tel: 01624 642157. Email: ambulancecare@dh.gov.im Website: http://www.gov.im/health/services/AandP/

CHANNEL ISLANDS

Guernsey Ambulance & Rescue Service: The Ambulance & Rescue Service, Ambulance Station, Rohais, St Peter Port, Guernsey GY1 1YN. Tel: 01481 725211. Fax: 01481 724095. Email: chiefofficer@ambulance.org.gg Website: www.ambulance.org.gg
States of Jersey Ambulance Service: Rouge Bouillon, St Helier, Jersey JE2 3ZA. Tel: 01534 444710. Fax: 01534 444730. Email: health@gov.je Website: www.gov.je/emergency

THE GAMBLING COMMISSION

4th Floor, Victoria Square House, Victoria Square, Birmingham B2 4BP.
Tel: 0121 230 6666. Fax: 0121 230 6720.
Email: info@gamblingcommission.gov.uk Email individuals:
initial.lastname@gamblingcommission.gov.uk
Website: www.gamblingcommission.gov.uk

Chief Executive: Mrs Jenny Williams. Tel: 0121 230 6503.
Director of Regulation: Mr Nick Tofiluk. Tel: 0121 230 6505.
Executive Assistant: Mrs Jayne Cunnington. Tel: 0121 230 6502.

COMPLIANCE OFFICE

4th Floor, Victoria Square House, Birmingham B2 4BP. This address should be used for all the regions below.
Quality Assurance & Improvement Administration Team. Tel: 0121 230 6600. Email: qualityassurance&improvementteam@gamblingcommission.gov.uk
Quality Assurance & Improvement Manager: Stephen Coley. Ext: 6595.
Quality Assurance & Improvement Administrators: Angie Fanshawe. Ext: 6563. Jacqueline Russell. Ext: 6557.

LONDON & SOUTH EAST REGION

Regional Compliance Manager: Clive Noblett. Tel: 0121 230 6931.
Hertfordshire, Bedfordshire, Northamptonshire, Oxfordshire, Aylesbury Vale & Buckinghamshire, Buckinghamshire South: East & North Hertfordshire, Central Bedfordshire, Luton Town, Milton Keynes, Bedford, Watford, South Northamptonshire, Northampton, Wellingborough, East Northamptonshire, Daventry, Kettering, Corby, Vale of White Horse, South Oxfordshire, Oxford, West Oxfordshire, Cherwell, Aylesbury Vale, Broxbourne, Stevenage, Three Rivers, Welling & Hatfield, St Albans, Hertsmere, & Dacorum. *Inspector:* James Reynolds. Tel: 0121 230 6608.
Berkshire & East & West Surrey: County of Surrey, districts of Spelthorne, Elmbridge, Epsom & Elwell, Mole Valley, Reigate & Banstead & Tandridge. London boroughs of Kingston-upon-Thames, Merton & Sutton, Slough, Windsor & Maidenhead. County of Berkshire/county of Surrey, districts of Surrey Heath, Runnymede, Woking, Guildford, Waverley, Bracknell Forest, Reading & West Berkshire. *Inspector:* Clive Noblett. Tel: 0121 230 6931.
East Essex: County of Essex (outside M25), including Tendring, Colchester, Braintree, Maldon, Chelmsford, Rochford, Brentwood, Basildon, Castle Point, Thurrock & Southend. *Inspector:* Heidi Hards. Tel: 0121 230 6908.
East & West Sussex: County of East Sussex, Wealden, Rother, Lewes, Eastbourne, Hastings, County of West Sussex including City of Brighton & Hove, Mid Sussex, Crawley, Horsham, Adur, Worthing, Arun, Chichester. *Inspector:* Andrew Isaacs. Tel: 0121 230 6920.
Kent: County of Kent (outside M25), including districts of Thanet, Dover, Canterbury, Ashford, Shepway, Maidstone, Swale, Tunbridge Wells, Tonbridge & Malling, Medway & Gravesham. *Inspector:* David Bragg. Tel: 0121 230 6904.
Norfolk, Suffolk & Cambridgeshire: Babergh Council, Ipswich Council, Suffolk Coastal, Mid Suffolk, Forest Heath, Waveney, St Edmundsbury, South Norfolk, Norwich, Breckland, Great Yarmouth, Broadland, North Norfolk, Kings Lynn & West Norfolk, South Cambridgeshire, East Cambridgeshire, Fenland, Huntingdonshire, Cambridgeshire County, Cambridge. *Inspector:* Tony Arnold. Tel: 0121 230 6932.
North & West London: London boroughs of Enfield, Barnet, Haringey, Waltham Forest, Camden, Islington & Hackney. West London boroughs of Harrow, Brent, Hillingdon, Hounslow, Ealing & Hammersmith & Fulham. *Inspector:* Chander Kala. Tel: 0121 230 6749.
South London & Kent: South London boroughs of Richmond-upon-Thames, Wandsworth, Lambeth, Kensington & Chelsea, City of Westminster, City of Southwark, Lewisham, Greenwich, Bexley, Bromley & Croydon. County of Kent, districts of Sevenoaks & Dartford. *Inspector:* Henry Kirkup. Tel: 0121 230 6909.
Essex: County of Essex (within M25), including districts of Uttlesford, Epping Forest & Harlow. London boroughs of Redbridge, Newham, Tower Hamlets, Barking & Dagenham. *Inspector:* Timothy Poon. Tel: 0121 230 6927.

NORTH EAST REGION

Regional Compliance Manager: Andrew Turrell. Tel: 0121 230 6917.
Derbyshire & Nottinghamshire: The counties of Derbyshire, Nottinghamshire, Rushcliffe, City of Nottingham, Gedling, Broxtowe, Ashfield, Newark & Sherwood, Mansfield, Bassetlaw, South Derbyshire, City of Derby, South Derbyshire Dales, Erewash, Amber Valley, North East Derbyshire, Chesterfield, Bolsover & High Peak. *Inspector:* Fay Callaghan. Tel: 0121 230 6907.

Leicestershire, Peterborough, Rutland & the North & South Kesteven areas of Lincolnshire: City of Peterborough, Rutland, North Kesteven, South Kesteven, Harborough, Hinckley & Bosworth, Blaby, City of Leicester, North West Leicestershire, Charnwood, Melton, Oadby & Wigston. *Inspector:* Graham Burgin. Tel: 0121 230 6925.

North & East Yorkshire: York, Selby, Scarborough, Ryedale, Hambleton, East Riding of Yorkshire, City of Kingston-upon-Hull, Redcar & Cleveland, Middlesbrough. *Inspector:* Tim Bright. Tel: 0121 230 6915.

North & West Yorkshire: Craven, Bradford, Calderdale, Kirklees, Wakefield, Harrogate, Leeds & Richmond. *Inspector:* Pippa Coombes. Tel: 0121 230 6913.

North Lincolnshire & Scunthorpe, North East Lincolnshire, Grimsby & Cleethorpes & all of Lincolnshire County including Boston & Lincoln: South Holland, Boston, East Lindsay, North East Lincolnshire, West Lindsay, Lincoln District & North Lincolnshire. *Inspector:* Neil Rayson. Tel: 0121 230 6926.

Northumberland & North Tyneside: Northumberland County (includes Berwick-upon-Tweed, Alnwick, Castle Morpeth, Tynedale, Wansbeck & Blyth Valley), Newcastle-upon-Tyne, North Tyneside. *AIInspector:* Mel Potter. Tel: 0121 230 6727.

South Tyneside, Durham, Teesside: South Tyneside, Gateshead, Sunderland, Chester-le-Street, Durham, Easington, Sedgefield, Wear Valley, Teesdale, Derwentside, Darlington, Stockton-on-Tees & Hartlepool. *Inspector:* Mel Potter. Tel: 0121 230 6923.

South Yorkshire: Barnsley, Doncaster, Sheffield & Rotherham. *Inspector:* Damian Chapman. Tel: 0121 230 6928.

NORTH WEST & NORTH WALES REGION

Regional Compliance Manager: Alan Green. Tel: 0121 230 6905.

Cheshire & Stoke: Cheshire West & Chester, Cheshire East, Newcastle-under-Lyme, Stoke-on-Trent, Halton & Warrington. *Inspector:* Joanne Craig. Tel: 0121 230 6937.

Cumbria & North Lancashire: Allerdale, Barrow-in-Furness, Carlisle, Eden, Copeland, South Lakeland, Lancaster, Wyre, Blackpool, Ribble Valley & Fylde. *Inspector:* Peter Kirkbride. Tel: 0121 230 6929.

Greater Manchester: Trafford, Salford, Wigan, Manchester, Tameside, Stockport & Oldham. *Inspector:* Mohammed Shafiq. Tel: 0121 230 6912.

Liverpool, South West Lancashire & Sefton: Liverpool City Centre, Sefton, West Lancashire, Knowsley & St Helens. *Inspector:* Claire Wilson. Tel: 0121 230 6930.

North Wales & The Wirral, North Shropshire: Flintshire, Wrexham, Denbighshire, Conwy, Gwynedd, Anglesey, North Powys, Shropshire (North), Wirral & Cheshire West (Ellesmere Port & Neston). *Inspector:* Derek Bebbington. Tel: 0121 230 6906.

South Lancashire & Greater Manchester: Preston, Chorley, Rochdale, Bury, Bolton, Blackburn & Darwen, South Ribble, Pendle, Rossendale, Burnley & Hyndburn. *Inspector:* Dale Allen. Tel: 0121 230 6919.

Staffordshire including Lichfield, Tamworth, Walsall, East Birmingham, Solihull, Sutton Coldfield & Coventry City: South Staffordshire, Stafford, East Staffordshire, Staffordshire Moorlands, Lichfield, Tamworth, Newcastle-under-Lyme, Cannock Chase, Walsall, Coventry, Nuneaton & Bedworth, Solihull, Birmingham East. *Inspector:* Darren Shenton. Tel: 0121 230 6903.

Wolverhampton, Dudley, Sandwell (including West Bromwich), Shropshire (including Oswestry), Wrekin, Telford, Shrewsbury & Bridgnorth, Birmingham West: Wolverhampton, Dudley, Bridgnorth, Sandwell, Shropshire, Shrewsbury & Atcham, Wrekin District, Oswestry. Birmingham West. *Inspector:* Anne Maginnis. Tel: 0121 230 6933.

SOUTH WEST REGION

Regional Compliance Manager: Barry Stone. Tel: 0121 230 6746.

Bristol, South Somerset & West Somerset, South Gloucestershire: City & County of Bristol, North Somerset, districts of Sedgemoor & Mendip, South Somerset, Taunton Dean & West Somerset & Unitary Authority of South Gloucestershire. *Inspector:* Peter Lintern. Tel: 0121 230 6731.

Devon, Cornwall, West Somerset & Taunton Deane: Devon, Cornwall, Plymouth & Torbay. *Inspector:* Barrie Davis. Tel: 0121 230 6936.

Dorset, Bournemouth & South Somerset: County of Dorset, Bournemouth, Poole & Christchurch. *Inspector:* Nicola Dowse. Tel: 0121 230 6934.

Gloucestershire, North East Somerset, Bath, The Forest of Dean, Worcestershire, South Warwickshire, Herefordshire, Torfaen, Monmouthshire, Caerphilly, Blaenau Gwent & Newport City: County of Gloucestershire, Bath & North East Somerset, Forest of Dean, district of Gloucestershire, Redditch, Bromsgrove, Wychavon, Wyre Forest, Worcester, Malvern Hills, Warwick, Stratford-upon-Avon & Rugby, Caerphilly, Newport, Blaenau Gwent, Torfaen, Monmouthshire, the County of Herefordshire. *Inspector:* Alastair Henry. Tel: 0121 230 6724.

South & Mid Wales: Cardiff, Rhondda Cynon Taff, Ceredigion, Pembrokeshire, Camarthenshire, the area of Powys separately administered from Llandrindodd Wells & Brecon, Swansea, Neath Port Talbot, Bridgend, the Vale of Glamorgan & Merthyr Tydfil. *Inspector:* Paul Edmunds. Tel: 0121 230 6548.

Wiltshire, Hampshire & Isle of Wight: Wiltshire, Swindon, Hampshire, Southampton, Isle of Wight & Portsmouth. *Inspector:* Rod Davis. Tel: 0121 230 6901.

SCOTLAND REGION

Regional Compliance Manager: Douglas Greenshields. Tel: 0121 230 6636.

North & Mid West Scotland: Clackmannan, Stirling, Inverclyde, Renfrewshire, Glasgow, West Dumbarton, East Dumbarton, Argyll & Bute, Western Isles. *Inspector:* David Nicholson. Tel: 0121 230 6728.

North Scotland: City of Dundee, Angus, Perth & Kinross, Falkirk, Moray, Highland, Shetlands, Orkney, Aberdeenshire & Fife. *Inspector:* Kevin Brown. Tel: 0121 230 6921.

South Scotland: Dumfries & Galloway, Borders, East Lothian, Mid Lothian, West Lothian & Edinburgh. *Inspector:* Steven McWhirter. Tel: 0121 230 6729.

South West Scotland: South Ayrshire, East Ayrshire, North Ayrshire, North Lanarkshire, South Lanarkshire & East Renfrewshire. *Inspector:* Scott Markwick. Tel: 0121 230 6939.

DEPARTMENT FOR TRANSPORT

Great Minster House, 76 Marsham Street, London SW1P 4DR.
Enquiries tel: 0300 330 3000. Website: www.gov.uk/dft

TRAFFIC COMMISSIONERS

Traffic Commissioners for Public Service Vehicles under the Public Passenger Vehicles Act 1981, as amended and Authorities for Goods Vehicles under the Goods Vehicles (Licensing of Operators) Act, 1995.

Traffic Area	Name	Address	Tel:
South Eastern & Metropolitan	Nick Denton	Ivy House, 3 Ivy Terrace, Eastbourne, Sussex BN21 4QT.	0300 123 9000
North East of England	Kevin Rooney	Hillcrest House, 386 Harehills Lane, Leeds LS9 6NF.	0300 123 9000
North West of England	Beverley Bell	Suite 4, Stone Cross Place, Stone Cross Lane, Golborne, Warrington WA3 2SH.	0300 123 9000
Wales & the West Midlands	Nick Jones	38 George Road, Edgbaston, Birmingham B15 1PL.	0300 123 9000
East of England	Richard Turfitt	City House, 126–130 Hills Road, Cambridge CN2 1NP.	0300 123 9000
West of England	Sarah Bell	Jubilee House, Croydon Street, Bristol BS5 0DA.	0300 123 9000
Scotland	Joan Aitken	Level 6, The Stamp Office, 10 Waterloo Place, Edinburgh EH1 3EG.	0300 123 9000

Traffic Area Network (Central Office) Zone 1/11, Great Minster House, 76 Marsham Street, London SW1P 4DR.

DVLA LOCAL OFFICES

ENGLAND AND WALES
Tel: 0300 790 6802 (all offices).

Bangor: Ground Floor, Ty Glyder, 339 High Street, Bangor LL57 1YA.

Beverley: Crosskill House, Mill Lane, Beverley HU17 9JB.

Birmingham: 30 Granby Avenue, Garretts Green, Birmingham B33 0SD.

Bournemouth: Ground Floor, Bourne Gate, 25 Bourne Valley Road, Poole BH12 1DR.

Brighton: 4th Floor, Mocatta House, Trafalgar Place, Brighton BN1 4UE.

Bristol: Northleigh House, Lime Kiln Close, Stoke Gifford, Bristol BS34 8SR.

Cardiff: Archway House, 77 Ty Glas Avenue, Cardiff CF14 5DX.

Carlisle: Ground Floor, 3 Merchants Drive, Parkhouse, Carlisle CA3 0JW.

Chelmsford: Swift House, 18 Hoffmanns Way, Chelmsford CM1 1GU.

Chester: Norroy House, Nuns Road, Chester CH1 2ND.

Exeter: Hanover House, Manaton Close, Matford Business Park, Marsh Barton, Exeter EX2 8EF.

Ipswich: Podium Level, St Clare House, Greyfriars, Ipswich IP1 1UT.

Leeds: Unit 9, Finch Drive, Temple Point, Colton, Leeds LS15 9JQ.

Lincoln: Firth Court, Firth Road, Lincoln LN5 7WD.

London – Borehamwood: Units 2 & 3, Elstree Gate, Elstree Way WD6 1JD.

London – Sidcup: 12/18 Station Road, Sidcup DA15 7EQ.

London –Wimbledon: Ground Floor, Connect House, 133–137 Alexandra Road, Wimbledon SW19 7JY.

Maidstone: Coronet House, 11 Queen Anne Road, Maidstone ME14 1XB.

Manchester: Trafford House, Chester Road, Stretford, Manchester M32 0SL.

Newcastle-upon-Tyne: Eagle Star House, Regent Farm Road, Newcastle-upon-Tyne NE3 3QF.

Northampton: Ground Floor, Riverside House, Riverside Way, Bedford Road, Northampton NN1 5PE.

Norwich: 11 Prince of Wales Road, Norwich NR1 1UP.

Nottingham: Nottingham Business Park, Unit D, Orchard Place, off Woodhouse Way, Nottingham NG8 6PX.

Oxford: Ground Floor, 3 Cambridge Terrace, Oxford OX1 1RW.

Peterborough: 88 Lincoln Road, Peterborough PE1 2ST.

Portsmouth: 5th Floor, The Connect Centre, Kingston Crescent, Portsmouth PO2 8AH.

Preston: Fulwood Park, Caxton Road, Fulwood, Preston PR2 9NZ.

Reading: 77–81 Basingstoke Road, Reading RG2 0ER.

Sheffield: Cedar House, Hallamshire Court, 63 Napier Street, Sheffield S11 8HA.

Shrewsbury: Stafford Drive, Battlefield Enterprise Park, Shrewsbury SY1 3BF.

Stockton: St Mark's House, St Mark's Court, Thornaby, Stockton-on-Tees TS17 6QR.

Swansea: 1 Sandringham Park, Ground Floor East, Swansea Vale, Llansamlet SA6 8AJ.

Theale: Buliding B, Theale House, Brunel Road, RG7 4AQ.

Truro: Pydar House, Pydar Street, Truro TR1 2TG.

Worcester: Clerkenleap Barn, Broomhall, Worcester WR5 3HR.

SCOTLAND
Tel: 0300 790 6802 (all offices).

Aberdeen: Greyfriars House, Gallowgate, Aberdeen AB10 1WG.
Dundee: Caledonian House, Greenmarket, Dundee DD1 4QP.
Edinburgh: Wallace House, Lochside Avenue, Edinburgh EH12 9DJ.

Glasgow: 46 West Campbell Street, Glasgow G2 6TT.
Inverness: Longman House, 28 Longman Road, Inverness IV1 1SF.

NORTHERN IRELAND
Driver and Vehicle Agency, County Hall, Castlerock Road, Coleraine BT51 3TA. Tel: 0845 601 4094.
Website: www.dvani.gov.uk

Armagh: Dobbin Centre, Dobbin Lane, Armagh BT61 7PQ.
Ballymena: County Hall, Galgorm Road, Ballymena BT42 1QE.
Belfast: 1 Cromac Avenue, Ormeau Road, Belfast BT7 2JA.
Coleraine: County Hall, Castlerock Road, Coleraine BT51 3TA.

Downpatrick: Rathkeltair House, Market Street, Downpatrick BT30 6AT.
Enniskillen: County Buildings, East Bridge Street, Enniskillen BT74 7BN.
Londonderry: Orchard House, 40 Foyle Street, Londonderry BT48 6AT.
Omagh: Boaz House, 15 Scarffes Entry, Omagh BT78 1JE.

REPUBLIC OF IRELAND MOTOR TAX OFFICES

All telephone numbers below should be prefixed with 00 353 when calling from the UK. Website: www.motortax.ie

COUNTY COUNCILS

Carlow: Athy Road, Carlow. Tel: 59 917 0342.
Cavan: Courthouse, Cavan. Tel: 49 437 8430.
Clare: New Road, Ennis, Co Clare. Tel: 65 684 4661.
Cork: Model Business Park, Model Farm Road, Cork. Tel: 21 454 4566.
Donegal: The Three Rivers Centre, Lifford. Tel: 74 917 2266.
Donegal: Neil T Blaney Road, Letterkenny. Tel: 74 919 4200.
Donegal: Malin Road, Cardonagh. Tel: 77 937 3700.
Donegal: Gweedore Road, Dungloe. Tel: 74 956 1300.
Donegal: Main Street, Milford. Tel: 74 915 3900.
Donegal: Stranorlar Public Service Centre. Tel: 74 917 2222.
Donegal: Drumlonagher, Donegal Town. Tel: 74 972 4400.
Galway: County Hall, Prospect Hill, Galway. Tel: 91 509 304.
Galway: Civic Offices, Bridge Street, Ballinasloe. Tel: 90 964 8007.
Galway: An Cheathrú Rua. Tel: 91 595 788.
Kerry: Ratass, Tralee, Co Kerry. Tel: 66 712 2300.
Kildare: Aras Chill Dara, Devoy Park, Newbridge Road, Naas. Tel: 45 980 591.
Kilkenny: County Hall, John's Street, Kilkenny. Tel: 56 779 4100.
Laois: County Hall, Portlaoise, Co Laois. Tel: 50 264 008.
Leitrim: Park Lane House, Carrick-on-Shannon. Tel: 71 965 0431.

Limerick: Lissanalta House, Dooradoyle. Tel: 61 316 444.
Limerick: Aras Wm Smith O'Brien, Newcastle West. Tel: 06 962 100.
Longford: Great Water Street, Longford. Tel: 43 434 00.
Louth: Millennium Centre, Dundalk. Tel: 42 933 5457.
Louth: Bolton St, Drogheda. Tel: 41 984 6469.
Mayo: Glenpark, The Mall, Castlebar. Tel: 94 902 4444.
Meath: Railway Street, Navan. Tel: 46 902 2416.
Monaghan: Market Street, Monaghan. Tel: 47 81175.
Offaly: Aras An Chontae, Charleville Road, Tullamore. Tel: 50 646 831.
Roscommon: Abbey St, Roscommon. Tel: 90 663 7250.
Sligo: Cleveragh Road, Sligo. Tel: 71 916 2221.
Sligo: Teach Laighne, Tubbercurry. Tel: 71 911 1719.
Tipperary (North): Civic Offices, Limerick Road, Nenagh, Co Tipperary. Tel: 67 447 01.
Tipperary (South): Emmet St, Clonmel. Tel: 52 613 4444
Tipperary (South): Friar Street, Cashel. Tel: 62 647 00.
Waterford: Shandon Road, Dungarvan. Tel: 58 220 87.
Westmeath: Civic Offices, Mullingar,Westmeath. Tel: 44 933 2232.
Wexford: County Hall, Wexford. Tel: 53 763 33.
Wicklow: Council Buildings, Wicklow. Tel: 40 420 118.
Wicklow: Civic Offices, Main Street, Bray. Tel: 12 014 186.
Wicklow: Civic Offices, Main Street, Blessington. Tel: 45 858 031.

CITY COUNCILS

Dublin: Nutgrove Shopping Centre, Rathfarnham, Dublin 14. Tel: 1 222 8000.
Dublin: Block B, Blackhall Walk, Queen Street, Dublin 7. Tel: 1 222 8000.
Dublin: 9th Lock Road, Clondakin, Dublin 22. Tel: 1 222 8300.

Dublin: Ballymum Civic Centre, Main Street, Ballymum, Dublin 9. Tel: 1 222 8250.
Limerick: City Hall, Merchant's Quay. Tel: 61 415 799.
Waterford: The Deanery, Cathedral Square. Tel: 51 849 951.

MOTOR INDEX

Three-letter marks are formed by prefixing the letters of the alphabet to the original index marks shown in the following list, thus: NA (Manchester), ANA, BNA, CNA, etc. (Manchester). To find the place of origin of a three-letter mark look up the last two letters of the index mark on these lists.

The following list of index marks and the offices of origin need revision from 1981 as a result of the closure of a number of Vehicle Registration Offices. Local series registration marks from the offices which have closed have been made available to the public through nominated offices upon written request. VROs that have closed, their prime marks and the nominated offices are given at the end of this table.

Note: The **SK, VS, YJ**, and **FF** marks to be added to the SU and SV for issue to vehicles which require a non-suffix mark = vehicles manufactured between 1 January 1931 and 31 December 1962 (3 Alpha & 3 Numeric).

The **SL, DS**, and **SV** marks for issue to vehicles manufactured from 1 January 1906 to 31 December 1930 (2 Alpha & 4 Numeric).

The **BS** mark for issue to vehicles manufactured before 31 December 1905 (2 Alpha & 4 Numeric).

For index marks, after 1 September 2001, see the end of this section.

ENGLAND, WALES AND SCOTLAND

Index Mark	Office				
AA	Bournemouth	CA	Chester	EA	Birmingham
AB	Worcester	CB	Manchester	EB	Peterborough
AC	Coventry	CC	Bangor	EC	Preston
AD	Gloucester	CD	Brighton	ED	Liverpool
AE	Bristol	CE	Peterborough	EE	Lincoln
AF	Truro	CF	Reading	EF	Middlesbrough
AG	Hull	CG	Bournemouth	EG	Peterborough
AH	Norwich	CH	Nottingham	EH	Stoke-on-Trent
AJ	Middlesbrough	CJ	Gloucester	EJ	Haverfordwest
AK	Sheffield	CK	Preston	EK	Liverpool
AL	Nottingham	CL	Norwich	EL	Bournemouth
AM	Swindon	CM	Liverpool	EM	Liverpool
AN	Reading	CN	Newcastle-upon-Tyne	EN	Manchester
AO	Carlisle	CO	Exeter	EO	Preston
AP	Brighton	CP	Leeds	EP	Swansea
AR	Chelmsford	CR	Portsmouth	ER	Peterborough
AS	Inverness	CS	Glasgow	ES	Dundee
AT	Hull	CT	Lincoln	ET	Sheffield
AU	Nottingham	CU	Newcastle-upon-Tyne	EU	Bristol
AV	Peterborough			EV	Chelmsford
AW	Shrewsbury	CV	Truro	EW	Peterborough
AX	Cardiff	CW	Preston	EX	Norwich
AY	Leicester	CX	Leeds	EY	Bangor
		CY	Swansea		
BA	Manchester			FA	Stoke-on-Trent
BB	Newcastle-upon-Tyne	DA	Birmingham	FB	Bristol
		DB	Manchester	FC	Oxford
BC	Leicester	DC	Middlesbrough	FD	Birmingham
BD	Northampton	DD	Gloucester	FE	Lincoln
BE	Lincoln	DE	Haverfordwest	FF	Bangor
BF	Stoke-on-Trent	DF	Gloucester	FG	Brighton
BG	Liverpool	DG	Gloucester	FH	Gloucester
BH	Luton	DH	Birmingham	FJ	Exeter
BJ	Ipswich	DJ	Liverpool	FK	Birmingham
BK	Portsmouth	DK	Manchester	FL	Peterborough
BL	Reading	DL	Portsmouth	FM	Chester
BM	Luton	DM	Chester	FN	Maidstone
BN	Manchester	DN	Leeds	FO	Gloucester
BO	Cardiff	DO	Lincoln	FP	Leicester
BP	Portsmouth	DP	Reading	FR	Preston
BR	Newcastle	DR	Exeter	FS	Edinburgh
BS	Aberdeen	DS	Glasgow	FT	Newcastle-upon-Tyne
BT	Leeds	DT	Sheffield		
BU	Manchester	DU	Coventry	FU	Lincoln
BV	Preston	DV	Exeter	FV	Preston
BW	Oxford	DW	Cardiff	FW	Lincoln
BX	Haverfordwest	DX	Ipswich	FX	Bournemouth
BY	Stanmore	DY	Brighton	FY	Liverpool
				GA	Glasgow

GB	Glasgow	JR	Newcastle-upon-	MH	London NE
GC	Wimbledon		Tyne	MJ	Luton
GD	Glasgow	JS	Inverness	MK	London NE
GE	Glasgow	JT	Bournemouth	ML	London NE
GF	Wimbledon	JU	Leicester	MM	London NE
GG	Glasgow	JV	Lincoln	MN	(not used)
GH	Wimbledon	JW	Birmingham	MO	Reading
GJ	Wimbledon	JX	Leeds	MP	London NE
GK	Wimbledon	JY	Plymouth	MR	Swindon
GL	Truro	KA	Liverpool	MS	Edinburgh
GM	Reading	KB	Liverpool	MT	London NE
GN	Wimbledon	KC	Liverpool	MU	London NE
GO	Wimbledon	KD	Liverpool	MV	Sidcup
GP	Wimbledon	KE	Maidstone	MW	Swindon
GR	Durham	KF	Liverpool	MX	Sidcup
GS	Luton	KG	Cardiff	MY	Sidcup
GT	Wimbledon	KH	Hull	NA	Manchester
GU	Sidcup	KJ	Maidstone	NB	Manchester
GV	Ipswich	KK	Maidstone	NC	Manchester
GW	Sidcup	KL	Maidstone	ND	Manchester
GX	Sidcup	KM	Maidstone	NE	Manchester
GY	Sidcup	KN	Maidstone	NF	Manchester
HA	Birmingham	KO	Maidstone	NG	Norwich
HB	Cardiff	KP	Maidstone	NH	Northampton
HC	Brighton	KR	Maidstone	NJ	Brighton
HD	Leeds	KS	Edinburgh	NK	Luton
HE	Sheffield	KT	Maidstone	NL	Newcastle-upon-
HF	Liverpool	KU	Sheffield		Tyne
HG	Preston	KV	Coventry	NM	Luton
HH	Carlisle	KW	Sheffield	NN	Nottingham
HJ	Chelmsford	KX	Luton	NO	Chelmsford
HK	Chelmsford	KY	Sheffield	NP	Worcester
HL	Sheffield	LA	Stanmore	NR	Leicester
HM	London C	LB	Stanmore	NS	Glasgow
HN	Middlesbrough	LC	Stanmore	NT	Shrewsbury
HO	Bournemouth	LD	Stanmore	NU	Nottingham
HP	Coventry	LE	Stanmore	NV	Northampton
HR	Swindon	LF	Stanmore	NW	Leeds
HS	Glasgow	LG	Chester	NX	Birmingham
HT	Bristol	LH	Stanmore	NY	Cardiff
HU	Bristol	LJ	Bournemouth	OA	Birmingham
HV	London C	LK	Stanmore	OB	Birmingham
HW	Bristol	LL	Stanmore	OC	Birmingham
HX	London C	LM	Stanmore	OD	Exeter
HY	Bristol	LN	Stanmore	OE	Birmingham
IA–IZ	See Northern	LO	Stanmore	OF	Birmingham
	Ireland page	LP	Stanmore	OG	Birmingham
JA	Manchester	LR	Stanmore	OH	Birmingham
JB	Reading	LS	Edinburgh	OJ	Birmingham
JC	Bangor	LT	Stanmore	OK	Birmingham
JD	London C	LU	Stanmore	OL	Birmingham
JE	Peterborough	LV	Liverpool	OM	Birmingham
JF	Leicester	LW	Stanmore	ON	Birmingham
JG	Maidstone	LX	Stanmore	OO	Chelmsford
JH	Reading	LY	Stanmore	OP	Birmingham
JJ	Maidstone	MA	Chester	OR	Portsmouth
JK	Brighton	MB	Chester	OS	Glasgow
JL	Lincoln	MC	London NE	OT	Portsmouth
JM	Reading	MD	London NE	OU	Bristol
JN	Chelmsford	ME	London NE	OV	Birmingham
JO	Oxford	MF	London NE	OW	Portsmouth
JP	Liverpool	MG	London NE	OX	Birmingham
				OY	Stanmore

PA	Guildford	SO	Aberdeen	VC	Coventry
PB	Guildford	SP	Dundee	VD	Luton (series
PC	Guildford	SR	Dundee		withdrawn)
PD	Guildford	SS	Aberdeen	VE	Peterborough
PE	Guildford	ST	Inverness	VF	Norwich
PF	Guildford	SU	Glasgow	VG	Norwich
PG	Guildford	SV	Spare	VH	Leeds
PH	Guildford	SW	Dumfries	VJ	Gloucester
PJ	Guildford	SX	Edinburgh	VK	Newcastle-upon-
PK	Guildford	SV,	See below		Tyne
PL	Guildford	SY		VL	Lincoln
PM	Guildford			VM	Manchester
PN	Brighton	TA	Exeter	VN	Middlesbrough
PO	Portsmouth	TB	Liverpool	VO	Nottingham
PP	Luton	TC	Bristol	VP	Birmingham
PR	Bournemouth	TD	Manchester	VR	Manchester
PS	Aberdeen	TE	Manchester	VS	Luton
PT	Durham	TF	Reading	VT	Stoke-on-Trent
PU	Chelmsford	TG	Cardiff	VU	Manchester
PV	Ipswich	TH	Swansea	VV	Northampton
PW	Norwich	TJ	Liverpool	VW	Chelmsford
PX	Portsmouth	TK	Exeter	VX	Chelmsford
PY	Middlesbrough	TL	Lincoln	VY	Leeds
		TM	Luton		
QA-	London C	TN	Newcastle-upon-	WA	Sheffield
QY			Tyne	WB	Sheffield
		TO	Nottingham	WC	Chelmsford
RA	Nottingham	TP	Portsmouth	WD	Birmingham
RB	Nottingham	TR	Portsmouth	WE	Sheffield
RC	Nottingham	TS	Dundee	WF	Sheffield
RD	Reading	TT	Exeter	WG	Sheffield
RE	Stoke-on-Trent	TU	Chester	WH	Manchester
RF	Stoke-on-Trent	TV	Nottingham	WJ	Sheffield
RG	Newcastle-upon-	TW	Chelmsford	WK	Coventry
	Tyne	TX	Cardiff	WL	Oxford
RH	Hull	TY	Newcastle-upon-	WM	Liverpool
RJ	Manchester		Tyne	WN	Swansea
RK	Stanmore			WO	Cardiff
RL	Truro	UA	Leeds	WP	Worcester
RM	Carlisle	UB	Leeds	WR	Leeds
RN	Preston	UC	London C	WS	Bristol
RO	Luton	UD	Oxford	WT	Leeds
RP	Northampton	UE	Birmingham	WU	Leeds
RR	Nottingham	UF	Brighton	WV	Brighton
RS	Aberdeen	UG	Leeds	WW	Leeds
RT	Ipswich	UH	Cardiff	WX	Leeds
RU	Bournemouth	UJ	Shrewsbury	WY	Leeds
RV	Portsmouth	UK	Birmingham	X	Northumberland
RW	Coventry	UL	London C		CC
RX	Reading	UM	Leeds		
RY	Leicester	UN	Exeter	XA	Greater London C
		UO	Exeter		and Kirkcaldy
SA	Aberdeen	UP	Newcastle-upon-		DC
SB	Glasgow		Tyne	XB	Greater London C
SC	Edinburgh	UR	Luton		and Monklands
SD	Glasgow	US	Glasgow		DC (Coatbridge)
SE	Aberdeen	UT	Leicester	XC	Greater London C
SF	Edinburgh	UU	London C		and MB Solihull
SG	Edinburgh	UV	London C	XD	Greater London C
SH	Edinburgh	UW	London C		and B of Luton
SJ	Glasgow	UX	Shrewsbury	XE	Greater London C
SK	Inverness	UY	Worcester		and B of Luton
SL	Dundee			XF	Greater London C
SM	Carlisle	VA	Peterborough		and B of Torbay
SN	Dundee	VB	Maidstone	XG	Middlesbrough BC

XH	Greater London C	XX	Greater London C	YK	London C
XI	Central Office,	XY	Greater London C	YL	London C
	Coleraine	XZ	Central Office.	YM	London C
XJ	Manchester City C		Coleraine	YN	London C
XK	Greater London C			YO	London C
XL	Greater London C		**Note:** The XA-XY series has	YP	London C
XM	Greater London CO		not been issued since	YR	London C
XN	Greater London CO		October 1974.	YS	Glasgow
XO	Greater London C	YA	Taunton	YT	London C
XP	Greater London C	YB	Taunton	YU	London C
XR	Greater London C	YC	Taunton	YV	London C
XS	Renfrew DC	YD	Taunton	YW	London C
	(Paisley)	YE	London C	YX	London C
XT	Greater London C	YF	London C	YY	London C
XU	Greater London C	YG	Leeds	ZV-	See Republic of
XV	Greater London C	YH	London C	ZZ	Ireland below.
XW	Greater London C	YJ	Brighton		

Note: The **SV** and **SY** marks allocated to all VROs for issue to vehicles which require a non-suffix mark on registration.

Since 1 September 2001, registration index marks have been issued with the **first two letters** showing the area in which the vehicle is registered *(see below); the **following two numbers** give the period of registration and, therefore, are the age identifier, e.g., **51** = September to February 2001/2, **02** = March to August 2002, **52** = September to February 2002/3, **03** = March to August 2003 etc.; the **final three letters** are issued at random.

*The **first two letters** are issued as follows:

First Letter	Area	Second Letter	Local Offices
A	Anglia	A-N	Peterborough
		O-U	Norwich
		V-Y	Ipswich
B	Birming- ham	A-Y	Birmingham
C	Cymru	A-O	Cardiff
		P-V	Swansea
		W-Y	Bangor
D	Deeside to Shrews- bury	A-K	Chester
		L-Y	Shrewsbury
E	Essex	A-Y	Chelmsford
F	Forest and Fens	A-P	Nottingham
		R-Y	Lincoln
G	Garden of England	A-O	Maidstone
		P-Y	Brighton
H	Hampshire & Dorset	A-J	Bournemouth
		K-Y	Portsmouth
K		A-L	Luton
		M-Y	Northampton
L	London	A-J	Wimbledon
		K-T	Stanmore

First Letter	Area	Second Letter	Local Offices
		U-Y	Sidcup
M	Manchester & Mersey- side	A-Y	Manchester
N	North	A-O	Newcastle
		P-Y	Stockton
O	Oxford	A-Y	Oxford
P	Preston	A-T	Preston
		U-Y	Carlisle
R	Reading	A-Y	Reading
S	Scotland	A-J	Glasgow
		K-O	Edinburgh
		P-T	Dundee
		U-W	Aberdeen
		X-Y	Inverness
V	Severn Valley	A-Y	Worcester
W	West of England	A-J	Exeter
		K-L	Truro
		M-Y	Bristol
Y	Yorkshire	A-K	Leeds
		L-U	Sheffield
		V-Y	Beverley

NORTHERN IRELAND

Index Mark	Office				
AAZ	Belfast	AJZ	Downpatrick	AJZ	Downpatrick
ABZ	Downpatrick	AIA	Ballymena	AKZ	Ballymena
ACZ	Belfast	AIB	Armagh	ALZ	Armagh
ADZ	Ballymena	AIJ	Downpatrick	ANZ	Coleraine
AHZ	Omagh	AIL	Enniskillen	AOI	Belfast
		AIW	Coleraine	AUI	Londonderry
		AJI	Omagh	AXI	Belfast

AZ	Belfast (also suffix)
BAZ	Belfast
BBZ	Downpatrick
BCZ	Belfast
BDZ	Ballymena
BHZ	Omagh
BIA	Ballymena
BIB	Armagh
BIJ	Downpatrick
BIL	Enniskillen
BIW	Coleraine
BJI	Omagh
BJZ	Downpatrick
BKZ	Ballymena
BLZ	Armagh
BNZ	Coleraine
BOI	Belfast
BUI	Londonderry
BXI	Belfast
BZ	Downpatrick (also suffix)
CAZ	Belfast
CBZ	Downpatrick
CCZ	Belfast
CDZ	Ballymena
CHZ	Omagh
CIA	Ballymena
CIB	Armagh
CIJ	Downpatrick
CIL	Enniskillen
CIW	Coleraine
CJI	Omagh
CJZ	Downpatrick
CKZ	Ballymena
CLZ	Armagh
CNZ	Coleraine
COI	Belfast
CUI	Londonderry
CXI	Belfast
CZ	Belfast (also suffix)
DAZ	Belfast
DBZ	Downpatrick
DCZ	Belfast
DDZ	Ballymena
DHZ	Omagh
DIA	Ballymena
DIB	Armagh
DIJ	Downpatrick
DIL	Enniskillen
DIW	Coleraine
DJI	Omagh
DJZ	Downpatrick
DKZ	Ballymena
DLZ	Armagh
DNZ	Coleraine
DOI	Belfast
DUI	Londonderry
DXI	Belfast
DZ	Ballymena (also suffix)
EAZ	Belfast
EBZ	Downpatrick

ECZ	Belfast
EDZ	Ballymena
EIA	Ballymena
EIB	Armagh
EIJ	Downpatrick
EIL	Enniskillen
EIW	Coleraine
EJI	Omagh
EJZ	Downpatrick
EKZ	Ballymena
ELZ	Armagh
EOI	Belfast
EUI	Londonderry
EXI	Belfast
EZ	Belfast (also suffix)
FAZ	Belfast
FBZ	Downpatrick
FCZ	Belfast
FDZ	Ballymena
FIA	Ballymena
FIB	Armagh
FIJ	Downpatrick
FIL	Enniskillen
FIW	Coleraine
FJI	Omagh
FKZ	Ballmena
FLZ	Armagh
FOI	Belfast
FXI	Belfast
FZ	Belfast (also suffix)
GAZ	Belfast
GBZ	Downpatrick
GCZ	Belfast
GDZ	Ballymena
GIA	Ballymena
GIB	Armagh
GIJ	Downpatrick
GIL	Enniskillen
GIW	Coleraine
GJI	Omagh
GKZ	Ballymena
GLZ	Armagh
GOI	Belfast
GUI	Londonderry
GXI	Belfast
GZ	Belfast (also suffix)
HAZ	Belfast
HBZ	Downpatrick
HCZ	Belfast
HDZ	Ballymena
HIA	Ballymena
HIB	Armagh
HIJ	Downpatrick
HIL	Enniskillen
HIW	Coleraine
HKZ	Ballymena
HLZ	Armagh
HOI	Omagh
HOI	Belfast
HUI	Londonderry
HXI	Belfast
HZ	Omagh (also suffix)

IA	Ballymena (also suffix)
IB	Armagh (also suffix)
IAZ	Belfast
IBZ	Downpatrick
ICZ	Belfast
IDZ	Ballymena
IIB	Armagh
IJ	Downpatrick (also suffix)
IIA	Ballymena
IIL	Enniskillen
IIJ	Downpatrick
IIW	Coleraine
IJI	Omagh
IKZ	Ballymena
ILZ	Armagh
IUI	Londonderry
IXI	Belfast
IL	Enniskillen (also suffix)
IW	Coleraine (also suffix)
JI	Omagh (also suffix)
JAZ	Belfast
JBZ	Downpatrick
JCZ	Belfast
JDZ	Ballymena
JIA	Ballymena
JIL	Enniskillen
JIJ	Downpatrick
JJI	Omagh
JIB	Armagh
JIW	Coleraine
JLZ	Armagh
JOI	Belfast
JUI	Londonderry
JZ	Downpatrick (also suffix)
JXI	Belfast
KAZ	Belfast
KBZ	Downpatrick
KCZ	Belfast
KDZ	Ballymena
KIA	Ballymena
KIB	Armagh
KIJ	Downpatrick
KIW	Coleraine
KJI	Omagh
KLZ	Armagh
KOI	Belfast
KUI	Londonderry
KXI	Belfast
KZ	Ballymena (also suffix)
LAZ	Belfast
LBZ	Downpatrick
LCZ	Belfast
LDZ	Ballymena
LIA	Ballymena
LIB	Armagh

LIJ	Downpatrick	PIL	Enniskillen	UJI	Omagh
LIL	Enniskillen	PIW	Coleraine	UOI	Belfast
LIW	Coleraine	PJI	Omagh	UXI	Belfast
LJI	Omagh	POI	Belfast	UZ	Belfast (also suffix)
LOI	Belfast	PXI	Belfast		
LUI	Londonderry	PZ	Belfast (also suffix)	VAZ	Belfast
LXI	Belfast			VBZ	Downpatrick
LZ	Armagh (also suffix)	RAZ	Belfast	VDZ	Ballymena
		RBZ	Downpatrick	VIA	Ballymena
		RDZ	Ballymena	VIB	Armagh
MAZ	Belfast	RIA	Ballymena	VIJ	Downpatrick
MBZ	Downpatrick	RIB	Armagh	VIL	Enniskillen
MCZ	Belfast	RIJ	Downpatrick	VIW	Coleraine
MDZ	Ballymena	RIL	Enniskillen	VJI	Omagh
MIA	Ballymena	RIW	Coleraine	VOI	Belfast
MIB	Armagh	RJI	Omagh	VXI	Belfast
MIJ	Downpatrick	ROI	Belfast	VZ	Omagh (also suffix)
MIL	Enniskillen	RXI	Belfast		
MIW	Coleraine	RZ	Ballymena (also suffix)	WAZ	Belfast
MJI	Omagh			WBZ	Downpatrick
MOI	Belfast			WDZ	Ballymena
MUI	Londonderry	SAZ	Belfast	WIA	Ballymena
MXI	Belfast	SBZ	Downpatrick	WIB	Armagh
MZ	Belfast (also suffix)	SDZ	Ballymena	WIJ	Downpatrick
		SIA	Ballymena	WIW	Coleraine
NBZ	Downpatrick	SIB	Armagh	WJI	Omagh
NCZ	Belfast	SIJ	Downpatrick	WOI	Belfast
NDZ	Ballymena	SIL	Eniskillen	WXI	Belfast
NIA	Ballymena	SIW	Coleraine	WZ	Belfast (also suffix)
NIB	Armagh	SJI	Omagh		
NIJ	Downpatrick	SOI	Belfast	XI	Belfast (also suffix)
NIL	Enniskillen	SXI	Belfast	XAZ	Belfast
NIW	Coleraine	SZ	Downpatrick (also suffix)	XBZ	Downpatrick
NJI	Omagh			XDZ	Ballymena
NXI	Belfast			XIA	Ballymena
NZ	Coleraine (also suffix)	TAZ	Belfast	XIB	Armagh
		TBZ	Downpatrick	XIJ	Downpatrick
		TDZ	Ballymena	XIW	Coleraine
OI	Belfast (also suffix)	TIA	Ballymena	XJI	Omagh
OAZ	Belfast	TIB	Armagh	XOI	Belfast
OBZ	Downpatrick	TIJ	Downpatrick	XXI	Belfast
OCZ	Belfast	TIL	Eniskillen	XZ	Armagh (also suffix)
ODZ	Ballymena	TIW	Coleraine		
OIA	Ballymena	TJI	Omagh		
OIB	Armagh	TOI	Belfast	YAZ	Belfast
OIJ	Downpatrick	TXI	Belfast	YBZ	Downpatrick
OIL	Enniskillen	TZ	Belfast (also suffix)	YDZ	Ballymena
OIW	Coleraine			YIA	Ballymena
OJI	Omagh	UI	Londonderry (also suffix)	YIB	Armagh
OXI	Belfast			YIJ	Downpatrick
OZ	Belfast (also suffix)	UAZ	Belfast	YIW	Coleraine
		UBZ	Downpatrick	YJI	Omagh
PAZ	Belfast	UDZ	Ballymena	YOI	Belfast
PBZ	Downpatrick	UIA	Ballymena	YXI	Belfast
PDZ	Ballymena	UIB	Armagh	YZ	Coleraine (also suffix)
PIA	Ballymena	UIJ	Downpatrick		
PIB	Armagh	UIL	Enniskillen		
PIJ	Downpatrick	UIW	Coleraine		

REPUBLIC OF IRELAND*

Index Mark	Office	D	Dublin	L	Limerick
C	Cork	DL	Donegal	LD	Longford
CE	Clare	G	Galway	LH	Louth
CN	Cavan	KE	Kildare	LK	Limerick
CW	Carlow	KK	Kilkenny	LM	Leitrim
		KY	Kerry	LS	Laois

MH	Meath	**TN**	Tipperary North	**WX**	Wexford
MN	Monaghan	**TS**	Tipperary South	**ZV**	30 + years'
MO	Mayo	**W**	Waterford City		registration
OY	Offaly	**WD**	Waterford	**ZZ**	Temporary
RN	Roscommon	**WH**	Westmeath		registration
SO	Sligo	**WW**	Wicklow		

* In the Republic of Ireland, from 1 January 1987 vehicle index marks consist of the last two numbers of the year of first entry into use, followed by one or two letters denoting the area of the licensing authority, followed by a unique number from 1 to 99,999. Only two of the old style index marks remain: ZZ denotes temporary registration; and ZV, followed by a unique four or five digit number, is an optional alternative to the conventional numbering system for vehicles of 30+ years' registration.

HM INSPECTORATE OF PRISONS

First Floor, Ashley House, 2 Monck Street, London SW1P 2BQ.
Tel: 020 7035 2136. Fax: 030 7035 2141. Email:
hmiprisons.enquiries@hmiprisons.gsi.gov.uk Website:
www.justice.gov.uk/about/hmi-prisons

Chief Inspector of Prisons: Nick Hardwick CBE.
Deputy Chief Inspector of Prisons: Martin Lomas.
HM Chief Inspector of Prisons is appointed for a term of five years. The Chief Inspector reports directly to the government on the treatment and conditions for prisoners in England and Wales and other matters. The Prisons Inspectorate also has statutory responsibility to inspect all immigration removal centres and holding facilities on behalf of the Immigration and Nationality Directorate. The Chief Inspector is invited to inspect prisons in Northern Ireland, the Channel Islands, the Isle of Man and some Commonwealth dependent territories.

YOUTH JUSTICE BOARD FOR ENGLAND AND WALES

102 Petty France, London SW1H 9AJ.
Tel: 020 3334 5300. Fax: 020 3334 2250. Website: www.justice.gov.uk/about/yjb/

Chair: Frances Done.
The Youth Justice Board for England and Wales (YJB) is an executive non-departmental public body. Board members are appointed by the Secretary of State for Justice. The YJB: oversees the youth justice system in England and Wales; works to prevent offending and reoffending by children and young people under the age of 18; ensures that custody for young people is safe, secure, and addresses the causes of their offending behaviour.

NATIONAL OFFENDER MANAGEMENT SERVICE

Clive House, 70 Petty France, London, SW1H 9EX.
Email: public.enquiries@noms.gsi.gov.uk Website:
www.justice.gov.uk/about/noms/index

Provides prison and probation services in England and Wales.

Chief Executive Officer: Michael Spurr. Tel: 0300 047 5163.
Director of Finance & Analysis: Andrew Emmett. Tel: 0300 047 6730.
Director of HR: Carol Carpenter. Tel: 0300 047 5161.
Director of Offender Health: Richard Bradshaw. Tel: 020 7972 4767.
Director of NOMS ICT & Change: Martin Bellamy. Tel: 0300 047 5165.
Director of Commissioning & Commercial (Interim): Ian Blakeman. Tel: 0300 047 5318.
Director of Public Sector Prisons: Phil Copple. Tel: 0300 047 5152.
Director of Probation & Contracted Services: Colin Allars. Tel: 0300 047 5157
Director of National Operational Services: Digby Griffith. Tel: 0300 047 5868

EAST MIDLANDS
Public Sector Prisons (NOMS), HMP Wellingborough (Training Centre), Millers Park, Doddington Road, Wellingborough, Northampton NN8 2NH, Tel: 01933 232796. Fax: 01933 2332929.
Deputy Director of Custody: Andrew Cross.
Secretary: Antoinette Steel. Tel: 01933 232946.
Operations Manager: Alan Wallace. Tel: 01933 232910.
Prisons: Foston Hall; Gartree; Glen Parva; Leicester; Lincoln; Morton Hall; North Sea Camp; Nottingham; Onley; Ranby; Stocken; Sudbury; Wellingborough; Whatton.

EAST OF ENGLAND
Stirling House, Bury Road, Stradishall, Suffolk CB8 9YL. Tel: 01440 743277.
Deputy Director of Custody: Adrian Smith.
Prisons: Bedford; Blundeston; Bure; Chelmsford; Highpoint North; Highpoint South; Hollesley Bay; Littlehey; The Mount; Norwich; Warren Hill; Wayland.

GREATER LONDON
Second Floor, Clive House, 70 Petty France, London SW1H 9EX. Tel: 0300 047 5887.
Deputy Director of Custody: Nick Pascoe.
Secretary: Jackie Wright. Tel: 0300 047 5887.
Prisons: Brixton; Coldingley; Downview; Feltham; Highdown; Holloway; Isis; Latchmere House; Pentonville; Send; Wandsworth; Wormwood Scrubs.

KENT & SUSSEX
80 Sir Evelyn Road, Rochester, Kent ME1 3NF. Fax: 01634 673029.
Deputy Director of Custody: Michelle Jarman-Howe. Tel: 01634 673011.
Secretary: Pauline Kidney. Tel: 01634 673010.
Operations Manager: Leisa Staples. Tel: 01634 673022.
Prisons: Blantyre House; Cookham Wood; Dover; East Sutton Park; Ford; Lewes; Maidstone; Rochester; Sheppey Cluster.

NORTH EAST
Forest House, Aykley Heads Business Park, Aykley Heads, Durham DH1 5TS. Tel: 0191 378 6054. Fax: 0191 378 6001.
Deputy Director of Custody: Alan Tallentire. Tel: 0191 376 6811. Mob: 07968 908472.
Secretary: Gillian Beeston. Tel: 0191 376 6803.
Operations Manager: Clair Hutchings-Budd. Tel: 0191 376 6825.
Prisons: Deerbolt; Durham; Holme House; Kirklevington Grange; Low Newton; Northumberland.

NORTH WEST
Wymott Conference Centre, Ulnes Walton Lane, Leyland PR26 8LT. Postal address: PO Box 368, Leyland PR25 9EJ. Tel: 01772 442442.
Deputy Director of Custody: Alan Scott. Tel: 01772 442442.
Secretary: Kathryn Bullock. Tel: 01772 442442.
Operations Managers: Nick Foulds; Joanne Wood. Tel: 01257 344603/344608.
Prisons: Buckley Hall; Garth; Haverigg; Hindley; Kennet; Kirkham; Lancaster Farms; Liverpool; Preston; Risley; Styal; Thorn Cross; Wymott.

SOUTH CENTRAL
South Central Office HMP Winchester, Romsey Road, Winchester SO22 5DF.
Deputy Director of Custody: Claudia Sturt. Tel: 0754 573 2731.
Secretary: Rachel Hardy. Tel: 01962 723090.
Operations Manager: Neil Howard. Tel: 07973 457492.
Area Estates Manager: Phil Harle. Tel: 01296 442706.
Prisons: Aylesbury; Bullingdon; Grendon/Spring Hill; Haslar; Huntercombe; Isle of Wight; Reading; Winchester.

SOUTH WEST
1 Tortworth Road, Leyhill, Wotton-under-Edge, Gloucestershire GL12 8BQ.
Deputy Director of Custody: Ferdie Parker. Tel: 01454 264271.
Secretary: Vacant. Tel: 01454 264271.
Operations Manager: Sharon Moss. Tel: 01454 264272.
Prisons: Bristol; Channings Wood; Dartmoor; Eastwood Park; Erlestoke; Exeter; Guys Marsh; Leyhill; Portland; The Verne.

WEST MIDLANDS
West Midlands DDC Team, Regional Office, c/o HMP Stafford, 54 Gaol Road, Stafford ST16 3AW. Tel: 01785 773185.
Deputy Director of Custody: Luke Serjeant.
Secretary: Jamies Elsmore. Tel: 01785 773077.
Operations Manager: Debbie Lewis. Tel: 01785 773148.
Prisons: Brinsford; Drake Hall; Featherstone; Hewell; Stafford; Stoke Heath; Swinfen Hall; Werrington.

YORKSHIRE & HUMBERSIDE
DDC Office, HMP Askham Grange, Main Street, Askham Richard, York YO23 3FT. Tel: 01904 772000. Fax: 01904 772001.
Deputy Director of Custody: Amy Rice. Tel: 01904 772056.
Secretary: Clare Burton. Tel: 01904 772056.
Operations Manager: Christopher Dyer.
Prisons: Askham Grange; Everthorpe; Hull; Leeds; Lindholme; Moorland & Hatfield; New Hall; Northallerton; Wealstun; Wetherby.

WALES
NOMS Cymru, Directorate of Public Sector Prisons, 2nd Floor, Churchill House, Churchill Way, Cardiff CF10 2HH. Fax: 029 2067 8338.
Deputy Director of Custody: Ian Mulholland. Tel: 029 2067 8312. Mob: 07968 907607.
Secretary: Elaine Eliot. Tel: 029 2067 8383.
Prisons: Cardiff; Swansea; Usk/Prescoed.

HIGH SECURITY
Clive House, 70 Petty France, London SW1H 9EX.
Deputy Director of Custody: Richard Vince. Tel: 0300 047 6104.
Secretary: Denise Gayle. Tel: 0300 047 5152.

Prisons: Belmarsh; Frankland; Full Sutton; Long Lartin; Manchester; Wakefield; Whitemoor; Woodhill.

DIRECTORATE OF PROBATION AND CONTRACTED SERVICES
Room 7.07, Seventh Floor, Clive House, 70 Petty France, London SW1H 9EX. Tel: 0300 047 5157. Fax: 0300 047 6819.
Director of Probation & Contracted Services: Colin Allars. Tel: 0300 047 5157.
Secretary: Robert Palmer. Tel: 0300 047 6270.
Contracted Prisons: Altcourse; Ashfield; Birmingham; Bronzefield; Doncaster; Dorchester; Dovegate; Forest Bank; Lowdham Grange; Oakwood; Parc; Peterborough; Rye Hill; Thameside; Wolds.

PENAL ESTABLISHMENTS ENGLAND AND WALES

Key: * – contracted out prison; ABCD – prisoner categories (see Prison Service Order 0900 Categorisation); CL – closed; F – females; HC – holding centre; IRC – immigration removal centre; J – juveniles; L – local; M – males; O – open; RC – remand centre; RES – resettlement; S-O – semi-open; YOI – young offenders.
Further information can be found on the prison service website www.justice.gov.uk/about/hmps

Establishment	*Contact details & (categories)*
HMP Altcourse*	Higher Lane, Fazakerley, Liverpool L9 7LH. Tel: 0151 522 2000. Fax: 0151 522 2121. (M, L)
HMP/YOI Ashfield*	Shortwood Road, Pucklechurch, Bristol BS16 9QJ. Tel: 0117 303 8000. Fax: 0117 303 8001. (CL, J, RC, YOI)
HMP/YOI Askham Grange	Askham Richard, York YO23 3FT. Tel: 01904 772000. Fax: 01904 772001. (F, O)
HMYOI Aylesbury	Bierton Road, Aylesbury HP20 1EH. Tel: 01296 444000. Fax: 01296 444001. (YOI(M), A, CL, RES)
HMP Bedford	St Loyes Street, Bedford MK40 1HG. Tel: 01234 373000. Fax: 01234 273568. (M, L)
HMP Belmarsh	Western Way, Thamesmead, London SE28 0EB. Tel: 020 8331 4400. Fax: 020 8331 4401. (M, A, CL)
HMP Birmingham*	Winson Green Road, Birmingham B18 4AS. Tel: 0121 345 2500. Fax: 0121 345 2501. (M, L)
HMP Blantyre House	Goudhurst, Cranbrook, Kent TN17 2NH. Tel: 01580 213200. Fax: 01580 213201. (M, C, S-O)
HMP Blundeston	Lowestoft NR32 5BG. Tel: 01502 734500. Fax: 01502 734501. (M, C, CL)
HMP/YOI Brinsford	New Road, Featherstone, Wolverhampton WV10 7PY. Tel: 01902 533450. Fax: 01902 533451. (YOI, J, CL, RC)
HMP Bristol	19 Cambridge Road, Bristol BS7 8PS. Tel: 0117 372 3100. Fax: 0117 372 3113. (M, L)
HMP Brixton	PO Box 269, Jebb Avenue, Brixton, London SW2 5XF. Tel: 020 8588 6000. Fax: 020 8588 6191. (M, B, L)
HMP Bronzefield*	Woodthorpe Road, Ashford, Middlesex TW15 3JZ. Tel: 01784 425690. Fax: 01784 425691. (F)
HMP Buckley Hall	Buckley Road, Rochdale OL12 9DP. Tel: 01706 514300. Fax: 01706 514399. (M, C)
HMP Bullingdon	PO Box 50, Bicester, Oxon OX25 1PZ. Tel: 01869 353100. Fax: 01869 353101. (M, C, CL, L)
HMP Bure	Jaguar Drive, Scottow, Norwich NR10 5GB. Tel: 01603 326000. Fax: 01603 326001. (M, C)
HMP/RC Cardiff	Knox Road, Cardiff, CF2 0UG. Tel: 029 2092 3100. Fax: 029 2092 3318. (M, L, RC)
HMP Channings Wood	Denbury, Newton Abbot, Devon TQ12 6DW. Tel: 01803 814600. Fax: 01803 814601. (M, C, CL)
HMP/YOI Chelmsford	200 Springfield Road, Chelmsford CM2 6LQ. Tel: 01245 552000. Fax: 01245 552001. (M, L, RC)
HMP Coldingley	Shaftesbury Road, Bisley, Woking GU24 9EX. Tel: 01483 344300. Fax: 01483 344427. (M, C, CL)
HMP Cookham Wood	Sir Evelyn Road, Rochester ME1 3LU. Tel: 01634 202500. Fax: 01634 202501. (F, CL)
HMP Dartmoor	Princetown, Yelverton, Devon PL20 6RR. Tel: 01822 322000. Fax: 01822 322001. (M, C, CL)
HMYOI Deerbolt	Bowes Road, Barnard Castle, Co Durham DL12 9BG. Tel: 01833 633200. Fax: 01833 633201. (YOI, CL)

HMP/YOI Doncaster*	Off North Bridge Road, Marshgate, Doncaster DN5 8UX. Tel: 01302 760870. Fax: 01302 760851. (M, L)
HMP Dorchester*	North Square, Dorchester DT1 1JD. Tel: 01305 714500. Fax: 01305 714501. (M, L, RC)
HMP Dovegate*	Uttoxeter, Staffordshire ST14 8XR. Tel: 01283 829400. Fax: 01283 820066. (M, B, CL)
IRC Dover	The Citadel, Western Heights, Dover CT17 9DR. Tel: 01304 246400. Fax: 01304 246401. (CL, IR, C)
HMP Downview	Sutton Lane, Sutton SM2 5PD. Tel: 020 8196 6300. Fax: 020 8196 6301. (F, C, CL)
HMP/YOI Drake Hall	Eccleshall, Staffordshire ST21 6LQ. Tel: 01785 774100. Fax: 01785 774010. (F, S-O, YOI)
HMP Durham	Old Elvet, Durham DH1 3HU. Tel: 0191 332 3400. Fax: 0191 332 3401. (M, RES)
HMP/YOI East Sutton Park	Sutton Valance, Maidstone ME17 3DF. Tel: 01622 785000. Fax: 01622 785001. (F, O)
HMP Edmunds Hill	Stradishall, Newmarket CB8 9YN. Tel: 01440 743500. Fax: 01440 743560. (M, C)
HMP Elmley (Sheppey Cluster)	Church Road, Eastchurch, Sheerness ME12 4DZ. Tel: 01795 882000. Fax: 01795 882001. (M, B, CL, L)
HMP Erlestoke	Devizes SN10 5TU. Tel: 01380 814250. Fax: 01380 814273. (M, C, CL)
HMP Everthorpe	1a Beck Road, Brough, East Yorkshire HU15 1RB. Tel: 01430 426500. Fax: 01430 426501. (M, C, CL)
HMP/YOI Exeter	New North Road, Exeter EX4 4EX. Tel: 01392 415650. Fax: 01392 415691. (M, L, RC)
HMP Featherstone	New Road, Featherstone, Wolverhampton WV10 7PU. Tel: 01902 703000. Fax: 01902 703001. (M, C, CL)
HMP/YOI Feltham	Bedfont Road, Feltham, Middlesex TW13 4ND. Tel: 020 8844 5000. Fax: 020 8844 5001. (M, CL, RC)
HMP Ford	Arundel, West Sussex BN18 0BX. Tel: 01903 663000. Fax: 01903 663001. (M, D, O)
HMP/YOI Forest Bank*	Agecroft Road, Pendlebury, Salford M27 8FB. Tel: 0161 925 7000. Fax: 0161 925 7001. (M, L, YOI)
HMP/YOI Foston Hall	Foston, Derbyshire DE65 5DN. Tel: 01283 584300. Fax: 01283 584301. (F, CL)
HMP Frankland	Brasside, Durham DH1 5YD. Tel: 0191 376 5000. Fax: 0191 376 5001. (M, A, CL)
HMP Full Sutton	Full Sutton, York YO41 1PS. Tel: 01759 475100. Fax: 01759 371206. (M, A, CL)
HMP Garth	Ulnes Walton Lane, Leyland PR26 8NE. Tel: 01772 443300. Fax: 01772 443301. (M, B, CL)
HMP Gartree	Gallow Field Road, Market Harborough LE16 7RP. Tel: 01858 426600. Fax: 01858 426601. (M, B, CL)
HMYOI & RC Glen Parva	Tigers Road, Wigston, Leicestershire LE18 4TN. Tel: 0116 228 4100. Fax: 0116 228 4000. (CL, RC, YOI)
HMP Grendon	Grendon Underwood, Aylesbury HP18 0TL. Tel: 01296 445000. Fax: 01296 445001. (M, B, CL)
HMP/YOI Guys Marsh	Shaftesbury, Dorset SP7 0AH. Tel: 01747 856400. Fax: 01747 856401. (M, C, CL, YOI)
IRC Haslar	2 Dolphin Way, Gosport PO12 2AW. Tel: 023 9260 4000. Fax: 023 9260 4001. (HC)
HMP Haverigg	Millom, Cumbria LA18 4NA. Tel: 01229 713000. Fax: 01229 713001. (M, C, CL)
HMP Hewell	Hewell Lane, Redditch, Worcestershire B97 6QS. Tel: 01527 785000. Fax: 01527 785001. (M, B, C, D)
HMP High Down	Sutton Lane, Sutton SM2 5PJ. Tel: 020 7147 6300. Fax: 020 7147 6301. (M, L)
HMP Highpoint North & HMP Highpoint South	Stradishall, Newmarket CB8 9YG. Tel: 01440 743100. Fax: 01440 743092. (M, C, CL)
HMYOI Hindley	Gibson Street, Bickershaw, Wigan WN2 5TH. Tel: 01942 663000. Fax: 01942 663101. (RC, CL, YOI)
HMP Hollesley Bay	Woodbridge, Suffolk IP12 3JW. Tel: 01394 412400. Fax: 01394 410115. (M, D, O, YOI(CL))

HMP/YOI Holloway	Parkhurst Road, Holloway, London N7 0NU. Tel: 020 7979 4400. Fax: 020 7979 4401. (F, L)
HMP Holme House	Holme House Road, Stockton-on-Tees, Cleveland TS18 2QU. Tel: 01642 744000. Fax: 01642 744001. (M, B, CL, L)
HMP Hull	Hedon Road, Hull HU9 5LS. Tel: 01482 282200. Fax: 01482 282400. (M, L, YOI(CL))
HMP Huntercombe	Huntercombe Place, Nuffield, Henley-on-Thames RG9 5SB. Tel: 01491 643100. Fax: 01491 643101. (CL)
HMP Isis	Western Way, Thamesmead, London SE28 0NZ. Tel: 020 3356 4000. Fax: 020 3356 4001. (C, YOI)
HMP Isle of Wight	Clissold Road, Newport, Isle of Wight PO30 5RS. Tel: 01983 556300. Fax: 01983 556362. (M, B, C)
HMP Kennet	Parkbourn, Maghull, Liverpool L31 1HX. Tel: 0151 213 3000. Fax: 0151 213 3103. (M, C)
HMP Kirkham	Freckleton Road, Kirkham, Preston PR4 2RN. Tel: 01772 675400. Fax: 01772 675401. (M, D, O)
HMP Kirklevington Grange	Yarm, Cleveland TS15 9PA. Tel: 01642 792600. Fax: 01642 792601. (M, C, D, RES)
HMP/YOI Lancaster Farms	Stone Row Head, off Quernmore Road, Lancaster LA1 3QZ. Tel: 01524 563450. Fax: 01542 563451. (J, YOI, RC, CL)
HMP Latchmere House	Church Road, Ham Common, Richmond TW10 5HH. Tel: 020 8588 6650. Fax: 020 8588 6698. (M, D, RES)
HMP Leeds	Gloucester Terrace, Armley, Leeds LS12 2TJ. Tel: 0113 203 2600. Fax: 0113 203 2601. (M, L)
HMP Leicester	116 Welford Road, Leicester LE2 7AJ. Tel: 0116 228 3000. Fax: 0116 228 3001. (M, L)
HMP/YOI Lewes	1 Brighton Road, Lewes, East Sussex BN7 1EA. Tel: 01273 785100. Fax: 01273 785101. (M, L, YOI(CL))
HMP Leyhill	Wotton-under-Edge, Gloucestershire GL12 8BT. Tel: 01454 264000. Fax: 01454 264001. (M, D, O)
HMP Lincoln	Greetwell Road, Lincoln LN2 4BD. Tel: 01522 663000. Fax: 01522 663001. (M, L)
HMP IRC Lindholme	Bawtry Road, Hatfield Woodhouse, Doncaster DN7 6EE. Tel: 01302 524700. Fax: 01302 524750. (M, C, CL, O, IRC)
HMP Littlehey	Perry, Huntingdon, Cambridgeshire PE28 0SR. Tel: 01480 333000. Fax: 01480 333070. (M, C, CL)
HMP Liverpool	68 Hornby Road, Liverpool L9 3DF. Tel: 0151 530 4000. Fax: 0151 530 4001. (M, C, CL).
HMP Long Lartin	South Littleton, Evesham, Worcestershire WR11 8TZ. Tel: 01386 295100. Fax: 01386 295101. (M, A, CL)
HMYOI Low Newton	Brasside, Durham DH1 5YA. Tel: 0191 376 4000. Fax: 0191 376 4001. (F, L, CL)
HMP Lowdham Grange*	Old Epperstone Road, Lowdham, Nottingham NG14 7DA. Tel: 0115 966 9200. Fax: 0115 966 9220. (M, B, CL)
HMP Maidstone	36 County Road, Maidstone ME14 1UZ. Tel: 01622 775300. Fax: 01622 775301. (M, C, CL)
HMP Manchester	Southall Street, Manchester M60 9AH. Tel: 0161 817 5600. Fax: 0161 817 5601. (M, A, CL)
HMPYOI Moorland & Hatfield	Bawtry Road, Hatfield Woodhouse, Doncaster DN7 6BW. Tel: 01302 523000. Fax: 01302 523001. (M, C, CL, YOI) Thorne Road, Hatfield, Doncaster DN7 6EL. Tel: 01405 746500. Fax: 01405 746501. (M, D, O, YOI)
HMP Morton Hall	Swinderby, Lincoln LN6 9PT. Tel: 01522 666700. Fax: 01522 666750. (F, O, IRC)
HMP The Mount	Molyneaux Avenue, Bovingdon, Hemel Hempstead HP3 0NZ. Tel: 01442 836300. Fax: 01442 836301. (M, C, CL)
HMP/YOI New Hall	Dial Wood, Flockton, Wakefield WF4 4XX. Tel: 01924 803000. Fax: 01924 803001. (F, CL, YOI(CL))
HMP North Sea Camp	Freiston, Boston, Lincolnshire PE22 0QX. Tel: 01205 769300. Fax: 01205 769301. (M, D, O)
HMYOI Northallerton	15a East Road, Northallerton, North Yorkshire DL6 1NW. Tel: 01609 785100. Fax: 01609 785101. (YOI CL)
HMP/YOI Northumberland	Morpeth, Northumberland NE65 9XG. Tel: 01670 382100. Fax: 01670 382101. (YOI, J, CL)

HMP/YOI Norwich	Knox Road, Norwich NR1 4LU. Tel: 01603 708600. Fax: 01603 708601. (M, L, YOI(CL))
HMP Nottingham	Perry Road, Sherwood, Nottingham NG5 3AG. Tel: 0115 872 4000. Fax: 0115 872 4001. (M, L)
HMP Oakwood*	Oak Road, Featherstone WV10 7PU. Tel: 01902 799700. Fax: 01902 703001.
HMP Onley	Willoughby, Rugby, Warwickshire CV23 8AP. Tel: 01788 523400. Fax: 01788 523401. (J, CL)
HMP/YOI Parc*	Heol Hopcyn John, Bridgend, Mid Glamorgan CF35 6AP. Tel: 01656 300200. Fax: 01656 300201. (M, B, L, YOI(CL, RC))
HMP Pentonville	Caledonian Road, London N7 8TT. Tel: 020 7023 7000. Fax: 020 7023 7001. (M, L)
HMP Peterborough*	Saville Road, Westwood, Peterborough PE3 7PD. Tel: 01733 217500. Fax: 01733 217501. (M, F, L, RC)
HMYOI Portland	104 The Grove, Easton, Portland, Dorset DT5 1DL. Tel: 01305 715600. Fax: 01305 715601. (YOI CL)
HMP/YOI Prescoed	Coed-y-Paen, Pontypool, Gwent NP4 0TB. Tel: 01291 675000. Fax: 01291 675158. (M, C, CL, D, O, YOI(O)).
HMP Preston	2 Ribbleton Lane, Preston PR1 5AB. Tel: 01772 444550. Fax: 01772 444551. (M, L)
HMP Ranby	Retford, Nottinghamshire DN22 8EU. Tel: 01777 862000. Fax: 01777 862001. (M, C, CL)
HMP/YOI Reading	Forbury Road, Reading RG1 3HY. Tel: 0118 908 5000. Fax: 0118 908 5001. (YOI RC)
HMP Risley	Warrington Road, Risley, Warrington WA3 6BP. Tel: 01925 733000. Fax: 01925 733001. (M, C, CL)
HMYOI Rochester	1 Fort Road. Rochester ME1 3QS. Tel: 01634 803100. Fax: 01634 803101. (YOI)
HMP Rye Hill*	Willoughby, Rugby CV23 8SZ. Tel: 01788 523300. Fax: 01788 523311. (M, B)
HMP Send	Ripley Road, Send, Woking GU23 7LJ. Tel: 01483 471000. Fax: 01483 471001. (F, CL)
HMP Spring Hill	Grendon Underwood, Aylesbury HP18 OTL. Tel: 01296 445000. Fax: 01296 445001. (M, D, O)
HMP Stafford	54 Gaol Road, Stafford ST16 3AW. Tel: 01785 773000. Fax: 01785 773001. (M, C, CL)
HMP Standford Hill (Sheppey Cluster)	Church Road, Eastchurch, Sheerness ME12 4AA. Tel: 01795 884500. Fax: 01795 884638. (M, D, O)
HMP Stocken	Stocken Hall Road, Stretton, Oakham, Rutland LE15 7RD. Tel: 01780 795100. Fax: 01780 410767. (M, C, CL)
HMYOI Stoke Heath	Market Drayton, Shropshire TF9 2JL. Tel: 01630 636000. Fax: 01630 636001. (J, YOI, CL)
HMP/YOI Styal	Wilmslow SK9 4HR. Tel: 01625 553000. Fax: 01625 553001. (F, CL, L)
HMP Sudbury	Ashbourne, Derbyshire DE6 5HW. Tel: 01283 584000. Fax: 01283 584001.
HMP Swaleside (Sheppey Cluster)	Brabazon Road, Eastchurch, Isle of Sheppey ME12 4AX. Tel: 01795 804100. Fax: 01795 804200. (M, B, CL)
HMP Swansea	200 Oystermouth Road, Swansea SA1 3SR. Tel: 01792 485300. Fax: 01792 485430. (M, L, RC(YOI))
HMYOI Swinfen Hall	Swinfen, Lichfield WS14 9QS. Tel: 01543 484000. Fax: 01543 484001. (YOI CL)
HMP Thameside*	Griffin Manor Way, Thamesmead, London SE28 0FJ. Tel: 020 8317 9777.
HMYOI Thorn Cross	Arley Road, Appleton Thorn, Warrington WA4 4RL. Tel: 01925 805100. Fax: 01925 805101. (J, YOI, O)
HMP Usk	47 Maryport Street, Usk, Monmouthshire NP15 1XP. Tel: 01291 671600. Fax: 01291 671752. (M, C, CL)
HMP The Verne	The Verne, Portland, Dorset DT5 1EQ. Tel: 01305 825000. Fax: 01305 825001. (M, C, CL)
HMP Wakefield	5 Love Lane, Wakefield WF2 9AG. Tel: 01924 612000. Fax: 01924 612001. (M, A)
HMP Wandsworth	PO Box 757, Heathfield Road, Wandsworth, London SW18 3HS. Tel: 020 8588 4000. Fax: 020 8588 4001. (M, L)
HMYOI Warren Hill	Hollesley, Woodbridge, Suffolk IP12 3JW. Tel: 01394 633400. Fax: 01394 633401. (YOI CL)

HMP Wayland	Griston, Thetford, Norfolk IP25 6RL. Tel: 01953 804100. Fax: 01953 804220. (M, C, CL)
HMP Wealstun	Church Causeway, Thorp Arch, Wetherby LS23 7AZ. Tel: 01937 444400. Fax: 01937 444401. (M, C, CL, D, O)
HMP Wellingborough	Millers Park, Doddington Road, Wellingborough NN8 2NH. Tel: 01933 232700. Fax: 01933 232701. (M, C, CL)
HMYOI Werrington	Ash Bank Road, Stoke-on-Trent ST9 0DX. Tel: 01782 463300. Fax: 01782 463301. (J)
HMYOI Wetherby	York Road, Wetherby LS22 5ED. Tel: 01937 544200. Fax: 01937 544201. (J, CL)
HMP Whatton	New Lane, Whatton, Nottinghamshire NG13 9FQ. Tel: 01949 803200. Fax: 01949 803201. (M, C, CL)
HMP Whitemoor	Longhill Road, March, Cambridgeshire PE15 0PR. Tel: 01354 602350. Fax: 01354 602351. (M, A)
HMP Winchester	Romsey Road, Winchester SO22 5DF. Tel: 01962 723000. Fax: 01962 723001. (M, B, L)
HMP Wolds*	Everthorpe, Brough, East Yorkshire HU15 2JZ. Tel: 01430 428000. Fax: 01430 428001. (M, L)
HMP Woodhill	Tattenhoe Street, Milton Keynes MK4 4DA. Tel: 01908 722000. Fax: 01908 867063. (M, A, L)
HMP Wormwood Scrubs	PO Box 757, Du Cane Road, London W12 0AE. Tel: 020 8588 3200. Fax: 020 8588 3201. (M, L)
HMP Wymott	Ulnes Walton Lane, Leyland, Preston PR26 8LW. Tel: 01772 442000. Fax: 01772 442001.

SPECIAL HOSPITALS

Ashworth	Ashworth Hospital, Parkbourn, Maghull, Liverpool L31 1HW. Tel: 0151 473 0303.
Broadmoor	Broadmoor Hospital, Crowthorne, Berkshire RG11 7EG. Tel: 01344 773111.
Rampton	Rampton Hospital, Retford, Nottinghamshire DN22 0PD. Tel: 01777 248321.

SCOTLAND

SCOTTISH PRISON SERVICE

Calton House, 5 Redheughs Rigg, Edinburgh EH12 9HW. Tel: 0131 244 8745. Email: gaolinfo@sps.pnn.gov.uk Website: www.sps.gov.uk

Chief Executive, Scottish Prison Service: Colin McConnell.
Director of Operations: Dan Gunn (interim).
Director of Human Resources: Stephen Swan.
Director of Partnerships & Commissioning: Eric Murch.
Director of Finance & Business Services: Willie Pretswell.

PENAL ESTABLISHMENTS

Establishment	*Contact details*
HMP Aberdeen	Craiginches, 4 Grampian Place, Aberdeen AB11 8FN. Tel: 01224 238300. Fax: 01224 896209.
HMP Addiewell (Sodexo Justice Services)	9 Station Road, Addiewell, West Lothian EH55 8QF. Tel: 01506 874500. Fax: 01506 874501.
HMP Barlinnie	81 Lee Avenue, Glasgow G33 2QX. Tel: 0141 770 2000. Fax: 0141 770 2060.
HMP Open Estate –Castle Huntly	Open Estate – Castle Huntly, Longforgan, Nr Dundee DD2 5HL. Tel: 01382 319333. Fax: 01382 319350.
HMP/HMYOI Cornton Vale	Cornton Road, Stirling FK9 5NU. Tel: 01786 832591. Fax: 01786 833597.
HMP Dumfries	Terregles Street, Dumfries DG2 9AX. Tel: 01387 261218. Fax: 01387 264144.
HMP Edinburgh	33 Stenhouse Road, Edinburgh EH11 3LN. Tel: 0131 444 3000. Fax: 0131 444 3045.
HMP Glenochil	King O'Muir Road, Tullibody, Clackmannanshire FK10 3AD. Tel: 01259 760471. Fax: 01259 762003.
HMP Greenock	Gateside, Greenock, Renfrewshire PA16 9AH. Tel: 01475 787801. Fax: 01475 783154.
HMP Inverness	Duffy Drive, Inverness IV2 3HH. Tel: 01463 229000. Fax: 01463 229010.
HMP Kilmarnock (Serco)	Mauchline Road, Kilmarnock KA1 5AA. Tel: 01563 548800. Fax: 01563 548845.
HMP Low Moss	Crosshill Road, Bishopbriggs, Glasgow G64 2PZ. Tel: 0141 762 9500.

HMP Perth	3 Edinburgh Road, Perth PH2 8AT. Tel: 01738 458100. Fax: 01738 630545.
HMP Peterhead	Peterhead, Aberdeenshire AB42 2YY. Tel: 01779 479101. Fax: 01779 470529.
HMYOI Polmont	Brightons, Falkirk, Stirlingshire FK2 0AB. Tel: 01324 711558. Fax: 01324 714919.
HMP Shotts	Shotts, Lanarkshire ML7 4LE. Tel: 01501 824000. Fax: 01501 824022.

STATE HOSPITAL

The State Hospital	Carstairs, Lanark ML11 8RP. Tel: 01555 840293. Fax: 01555 840024. Email: tsh.info@nhs.net Website: www.tsh.scot.nhs.uk

SECURE UNITS

Website: www.sanscotland.org

Establishment	*Contact details: independent secure centres*
Good Shepherd Centre	Good Shepherd Secure/Close Support Unit, Greenock Road, Bishopton PA7 5PW. Tel: 01505 864500. Email: enquiries@goodshepherdcentre.org.uk Website: www.goodshepherdcentre.org.uk
Kibble Education and Care Centre	Goudie Street, Paisley, Renfrewshire PA2 3LG. Tel: 0141 889 0044. Fax: 0141 887 6694. Email: info@kibble.org Website: www.kibble.org
Rossie Secure Accommoda-tion Services	Montrose, Angus DD10 9TW. Tel: 01674 820204. Fax: 01674 820249. Website: www.rossie.org.uk
St Mary's	Kenmure, Bishopbriggs, Glasgow G64 2EH. Tel: 0141 586 1200. Fax: 0141 586 1224. Email: administrator@stmaryskenmure.org.uk
	Contact details: local authority secure centres
Edinburgh Secure Services	39 Howdenhall Road, Edinbugh EH16 6PG. Tel: 0131 664 8488.
The Elms School	Oak House, 317 South Road, Dundee DD2 2RT. Tel: 01382 436791.

NORTHERN IRELAND

PRISON SERVICE

Dundonald House, Upper Newtownards Road, Belfast BT4 3SU. Tel: 028 9186 3028/3063. Email: info@niprisonservice.gov.uk Website: www.dojni.gov.uk/index/ni-prison-service.htm

PENAL ESTABLISHMENTS

Establishment	*Contact details*
Hydebank Wood Young Offenders' Centre & Prison	Hospital Road, Belfast BT8 8NA. Tel: 028 9025 3666. Fax: 028 9025 3668.
Maghaberry Prison	Old Road, Ballinderry Upper, Lisburn, Co Antrim BT28 2PT. Tel: 028 9261 1888. Fax: 028 9261 9516.
Magilligan Prison	Point Road, Limavady, Co Londonderry BT49 0LR. Tel: 028 7776 3311. Fax: 028 7772 0307.

CHANNEL ISLANDS AND THE ISLE OF MAN

States of Jersey: HM Prison La Moye, La Rue Baal, St Brelade, Jersey JE3 8HQ. Tel: 01534 441800. *Prison Governor:* Mr Bill Millar.

Guernsey: Guernsey Prison, Les Nicolles, St Samsons, Guernsey GY2 4YF. Tel: 01481 248376. *A/Prison Governor (Acting):* Mr D Matthews.

Isle of Man Prison Service: Isle of Man Prison, St Patrick's Close, Coast Road, Jurby, Isle of Man IM7 3JP. Tel: 891000. Email: prison@gov.im *Governor:* Mrs Alison Gomme. *Deputy Governors:* Mr Colin Ring; Mr Nigel Fisher; Mr Paul Skillicorn.

COURTS IN THE UNITED KINGDOM

HER MAJESTY'S COURTS AND TRIBUNALS SERVICE (HMCTS)
ENGLAND AND WALES
Website: www.justice.gov.uk

Her Majesty's Courts and Tribunals Service (HMCTS) was launched on 1 April 2011, bringing Her Majesty's Courts Service and the Tribunals Service together into one integrated agency to provide support for the administration of justice in courts and tribunals.

LONDON REGION
3rd Floor, Rose Court, 2 Southwark Bridge, London SE1 9HS. DX: 154261 Southwark 12.
Delivery Director: Sheila Proudlock. Tel: 020 7921 2010. Fax: 0870 739 4469.
Head of Crime: Dave Weston. Tel: 020 7921 2196.
Head of Civil, Family & Tribunals: Martin Jones. Tel: 020 7921 2171. Fax: 020 7921 2004.
Director of the Royal Courts of Justice: David Thompson. Director's Office, Room E331, Royal Courts of Justice, Strand, London WC2A 2LL. Tel: 020 7947 6534. Fax: 020 7947 6666. DX: 44450 Strand.

CROWN COURTS
Blackfriars. 1–15 Pocock Street, London SE1 0BJ. Tel: 020 7922 5800
Central Criminal. Old Bailey, London EC4M 7EH. Tel: 020 7248 3277.
Croydon. The Law Courts, Altyre Road, Croydon CR9 5AB. Tel: 020 8410 4700.
Harrow. Hailsham Drive, off Headstone Drive, Harrow HA1 4TU. Tel: 020 8424 2294.
Inner London Crown Court. Sessions House, Newington Causeway, London SE1 6AZ. Tel: 020 7234 3100.
Isleworth. 36 Ridgeway Road, Isleworth, London TW7 5LP. Tel: 020 8380 4500.
Kingston-upon-Thames. 6–8 Penryhn Road, Kingston-upon-Thames KT1 2BB. Tel: 020 8240 2500.
Snaresbrook. 75 Hollybush Hill, Snaresbrook, London E11 1QW. Tel: 020 8530 0000.
Southwark. 1 English Grounds (off Battlebridge Lane), Southwark, London SE1 2HU. Tel: 020 7522 7200.
Wood Green. Woodall House, Lordship Lane, Wood Green, London N22 5LF. Tel: 020 8826 4100.
Woolwich. 2 Belmarsh Road, London SE28 0EY. Tel: 020 8312 7000.

MAGISTRATES' COURTS
Barkingside. 850 Cranbrook Road, Barkingside, Ilford, Essex IG6 1HW. Tel: 020 8437 6525.
Belmarsh. South East London Administration Centre, The Court House, London Road, Bromley, Kent BR1 1RA. Tel: 020 8437 3522.
Bexley. South East London Administration Centre, The Court House, London Road, Bromley, Kent BR1 1RA. Tel: 020 8437 3522.
Bromley. South East London Administration Centre, The Court House, London Road, Bromley, Kent BR1 1RA. Tel: 020 8437 3522.
Camberwell Green. 15 D'Eynsford Road, Camberwell Green, London SE5 7UP. Tel: 020 7805 9851.
City of London. 181 Marylebone Road, London NW1 5BR. Tel: 020 3126 33355.
Croydon. The Magistrates' Court, Barclay Road, Croydon, Surrey CR9 3NG. Tel: 020 8686 8680.
Ealing. North West and West London Administration Centre, Willesden Magistrates' Court, 448 High Road, Willesden, London NW10 2DZ. Tel: 020 8437 4707.
Enfield. North London Administration Centre, PO Box 52693, London N7 1AF. Tel: 020 7506 3146.
Feltham. North West and West London Administration Centre, Willesden Magistrates' Court, 448 High Road, Willesden, London NW10 2DZ. Tel: 020 8955 0679.
Greenwich. South East London Administration Centre, The Court House, London Road, Bromley, Kent BR1 1RA. Tel: 020 8437 3522.
Hammersmith. 181 Talgarth Road, Hammersmith, London W6 8DN. Tel: 020 8700 9360.
Haringey. North London Administration Centre, PO Box 52693, London N7 1AF. Tel: 020 7506 3100.
Havering. 850 Cranbrook Road, Barkingside, Ilford, Essex IG6 1HW. Tel: 020 8437 6525.
Hendon. North West and West London Administration Centre, Willesden Magistrates' Court, 448 High Road, Willesden, London NW10 2DZ. Tel: 020 8511 1200.
Highbury Corner. North London Administration Centre, PO Box 52693, London N7 1AF. Tel: 020 7506 3146.
Highgate. North London Administration Centre, PO Box 52693, London N7 1AF. Tel: 020 7506 3146.
Inner London Family Proceedings Court. 59–65 Wells Street, London W1A 3AF. Tel: 020 7805 3400.
Lavender Hill. South West Administration Centre, 176a Lavender Hill, Battersea, London SW11 1JU. Tel: 020 7805 1445.
Redbridge. North East London Administration Centre, 850 Cranbrook Road, Barkingside, Ilford, Essex IG6 1HW. Tel: 020 8437 6525.

Richmond-upon-Thames. South West Administration Centre, 176a Lavender Hill, Battersea, London SW11 1JU. Tel: 020 7805 1445.
Romford. North East London Administration Centre, 850 Cranbrook Road, Barkingside, Ilford, Essex IG6 1HW. Tel: 020 8437 6525.
South Western. South West Administration Centre, 176a Lavender Hill, Battersea, London SW11 1JU. Tel: 020 7805 1445.
Stratford. 389–397 High Street, London E15 4SB. Tel: 020 8437 6066.
Thames. 58 Bow Road, London E3 4DJ. Tel: 020 8271 1530.
Tottenham. North London Administration Centre, PO Box 52693, London N7 1AF. Tel: 020 8808 5411.
Tower Bridge. South London Administration Centre, 15 D'Eynsford Road, Camberwell Green, London SE5 7UP. Tel: 020 7805 9851.
Uxbridge. North West and West London Administration Centre, Willesden Magistrates' Court, 448 High Road, Willesden, London NW10 2DZ. Tel: 020 8955 0679.
Waltham Forest. The Court House, 1 Farnan Avenue, Walthamstow, London E17 4NX. Tel: 020 8272 4113.
Westminster. Central London Administration Centre, 181 Marylebone Road, London NW1 5BR. Tel: 020 3126 3050.
Willesden. North West and West London Administration Centre, 448 High Road, London NW10 2DZ. Tel: 020 8955 0679.
Wimbledon. South West London Administration Centre, 176a Lavender Hill, Battersea, London SW11 1JU. Tel: 020 7805 1445.

MIDLANDS REGION
Midlands Regional Office, 6th Floor, Temple Court, Birmingham. DX: 701993 Birmingham 7.
Delivery Director: Lucy Garrod.

CROWN COURTS
Birmingham. Queen Elizabeth II Law Courts, 1 Newton Street, Birmingham B4 7NA. Tel: 0121 681 3300.
Coventry. Coventry Combined Court Centre, 140 Much Park Street, Coventry CV1 2SN. Tel: 0300 123 5557.
Derby. Derby Combined Court Centre, Morledge, Derby DE1 2XE. Tel: 01332 622600.
Hereford. The Shirehall, St Peter's Square, Hereford HR1 2HY. Tel: 01432 276118.
Leicester. 90 Wellington Street, Leicester LE1 6HG. Tel: 0116 222 5800.
Lincoln. The Castle, Castle Hill, Lincoln LN1 3GA. Tel: 01522 525222.
Northampton. Northampton Combined Court Centre, 85/87 Lady's Lane, Northampton NN1 3HQ. Tel: 01604 470400.
Nottingham. The Law Courts, 60 Canal Street, Nottingham NG1 7EL. Tel: 0115 910 3551.
Shrewsbury. The Shire Hall, Abbey Foregate, Shrewsbury SY2 6LU. Tel: 01743 260820.
Stafford. Stafford Combined Court Centre, Victoria Square, Stafford ST16 2QQ. Tel: 01785 610730.
Stoke-on-Trent. Stoke-on-Trent Combined Court Centre, Bethesda Street, Hanley, Stoke-on-Trent ST1 3BP. Tel: 01782 854000.
Warwick. Warwickshire Justice Centre, Newbold Terrace, Leamington Spa CV32 4EL. Tel: 01926 682100.
Wolverhampton. Wolverhampton Combined Court Centre, Pipers Row, Wolverhampton WV1 3LQ. Tel: 01902 481000.
Worcester. Worcester Combined Court Centre, Shire Hall, Foregate Street, Worcester WR1 1EQ. Tel: 01905 730823.

MAGISTRATES' COURTS
Aldridge. Stafford Street, Walsall, West Midlands WS2 8HA. Tel: 01922 638222.
Birmingham. Victoria Law Courts, Corporation Street, Birmingham B4 6QA. Tel: 0121 212 6600.
Boston. The Court House, Park Avenue, Skegness PE25 1BH. Tel: 01754 898848.
Bromsgrove and Redditch. The Magistrates' Courts, Comberton Place, Kidderminster DY10 1QQ. Tel: 01562 514000.
Burton-upon-Trent. Southern Courts and Administration Centre, South Walls, Stafford ST16 3DW. Tel: 01785 223144.
Buxton. Peak Buildings, Terrace Road, Buxton SK17 6DY. Tel: 01298 23951.
Cannock. Southern Courts and Administration Centre, South Walls, Stafford ST16 3DW. Tel: 01785 223144.
Corby. Regent's Pavilion, Summerhouse Road, Moulton Park, Northampton NN3 6AS. Tel: 01604 497000.
Coventry District. Magistrates' Court, Little Park Street, Coventry CV1 2SQ. Tel: 024 7663 0666.
Derby. The Court House, St Mary's Gate, Derby DE1 3JR. Tel: 01332 362000.
Dudley and Halesowen. Magistrates' Court, The Inhedge, Dudley DY1 1RY. Tel: 01384 211411.

Grantham. The Court House, Harlaxton Road, Grantham NG31 7SB. Tel: 01476 563438.
Hereford. The Magistrates' Court, Bath Street, Hereford HR1 2HE. Tel: 01562 514000.
High Peak. Peak Buildings, Terrace Road, Buxton SK17 6DY. Tel: 01298 23951.
Hinckley. The Court House, 60 Pinfold Gate, Loughborough LE11 1AZ. Tel: 01509 215715.
Kettering. Regent's Pavilion, Summerhouse Road, Moulton Park, Northampton NN3 6AS. Tel: 01604 497000.
Kidderminster. The Magistrates' Courts, Comberton Place, Kidderminster DY10 1QQ. Tel: 01562 514000.
Leamington Spa. Warwickshire Justice Centre, Newbold Terrace, Leamington Spa CV32 4EL. Tel: 01926 682100.
Leicester. 15 Pocklingtons Walk, Leicester LE1 6BT. Tel: 0116 255 3666.
Lincoln. The Court House, 358 High Street, Lincoln LN5 7QA. Tel: 01522 528218.
Loughborough. The Court House, 60 Pinfold Gate, Loughborough LE11 1AZ. Tel: 01509 215715.
Mansfield. Mansfield Magistrates' Court, Rosemary Street, Mansfield NG19 6EE. Tel: 01623 451500.
Newcastle-under-Lyme. Baker Street, Fenton, Stoke-on-Trent ST4 3BX. Tel: 01782 418300.
North East Derbyshire and Dales. Court House, Tapton Lane, Chesterfield S41 7TW. Tel: 01246 224040.
Northampton. Regent's Pavilion, Summerhouse Road, Moulton Park, Northampton NN3 6AS. Tel: 01604 497000.
Nottingham. Carrington Street, Nottingham NG2 1EE. Tel: 0115 955 8111.
Nuneaton. Warwickshire Justice Centre, Vicarage Street, Nuneaton CV11 4JU. Tel: 01926 429133.
Redditch. Grove Street, Redditch B98 8DB. Tel: 01562 514000.
Sandwell. The Court House, Oldbury Ringway, Oldbury, West Midlands B69 4JN. Tel: 0121 511 2222.
Shrewsbury. Court Office, Preston Street, Shrewsbury SY2 5NX. Tel: 01743 458500.
Skegness. The Court House, Park Avenue, Skegness PE25 1BH. Tel: 01754 898848.
Solihull. The Court House, Homer Road, Solihull B91 3RD. Tel: 0121 705 8101.
South Worcestershire. Magistrates' Court, Castle Street, Worcester WR1 3QZ. Tel: 01905 743200.
Southern Derbyshire. The Court House, St Mary's Gate, Derby DE1 3JR. Tel: 01332 362000.
Spalding. The Court House, Harlaxton Road, Grantham NG31 7SB. Tel: 01476 563438.
Stafford. The Court House, South Walls, Stafford ST16 3DW. Tel: 01785 223144.
Stoke-on-Trent. The Court House, Baker Street, Fenton, Stoke-on-Trent ST4 3BX. Tel: 01782 845353.
Telford and South Shropshire. Telford Square, Malinsgate, Telford TF3 4HX. Tel: 01952 204500.
Walsall. Magistrates' Court, Stafford Street, Walsall, West Midlands WS2 8HA. Tel: 01922 638222.
Wellingborough. Regent's Pavilion, Summerhouse Road, Moulton Park, Northampton NN3 6AS. Tel: 01604 497000.
Wolverhampton. The Law Courts, North Street, Wolverhampton WV1 1RA. Tel: 01902 773151.
Worcester. Castle Street, Worcester WR1 3QZ. Tel: 01905 743200.
Worksop and Retford. The Court House, 30 Potter Street, Worksop S80 2AJ. Tel: 01909 486111.

NORTH EAST REGION

Civil and Family Justice Centre, Green Lane, Old Elvet, Durham DH1 3RG. Tel: 0191 375 1815.
Fax: 0191 375 1833.

A/Delivery Director: Dave Foley.

CROWN COURTS

Bradford. Bradford Combined Court Centre, Bradford Law Courts, Exchange Square, Drake Street, Bradford BD1 1JA. Tel: 01274 840274.
Doncaster. Crown Court, College Road, Doncaster DN1 3HS. Tel: 01302 322211.
Durham. The Law Courts, Old Elvet, Durham DH1 3HW. Tel: 0191 386 6/14.
Great Grimsby. Great Grimsby Combined Court Centre, Town Hall Square, Grimsby DN31 1HX. Tel: 01472 265250.
Kingston-upon-Hull. Kingston-upon-Hull Combined Court Centre, Lowgate, Hull HU1 2EZ. Tel: 01482 586161.
Leeds. Leeds Combined Court Centre, The Court House, 1 Oxford Row, Leeds LS1 3BG. Tel: 0113 306 2800.
Newcastle-upon-Tyne. Newcastle-upon-Tyne Combined Court Centre, The Law Courts, Quayside, Newcastle-upon-Tyne NE1 3LA. Tel: 0191 201 2000.
Sheffield. Sheffield Combined Court Centre, The Law Courts, 50 West Bar, Sheffield S3 8PH. Tel: 0114 281 2400.
Teesside. Teesside Combined Court Centre, Russell Street, Middlesbrough TS1 2AE. Tel: 01642 340000.
York. The Castle, York YO1 9WZ. Tel: 01904 645121.

MAGISTRATES' COURTS

Barnsley District. Court House, PO Box 17, Barnsley S70 2DW. Tel: 01226 320000.
Berwick-upon-Tweed. 40 Church Street, Berwick-upon-Tweed TD15 1DX. Tel: 01289 306885.

Beverley. The Court House, Champney Road, Beverley HU17 9EJ. Tel: 01482 861607.
Bradford and Keighley. The Court Office, PO Box 187, The Tyrls, Bradford BD1 1JL. Tel: 01274 390111.
Bridlington. The Court House, Quay Road, Bridlington YO16 4EJ. Tel: 01482 861607.
Chester-le-Street. Newcastle Road, Chester-le-Street, Co Durham DH3 3UA. Tel: 0191 387 0700.
Consett. Newcastle Road, Chester-le-Street, Co Durham DH3 3UA. Tel: 0191 387 0700.
Darlington. Central Avenue, Newton Aycliffe DL5 5RT. Tel: 01325 318114.
Doncaster. PO Box 49, The Law Courts, College Road, Doncaster DN1 3HT. Tel: 01302 366711.
Durham. Newcastle Road, Chester-le-Street, Co Durham DH3 3UA. Tel: 0191 387 0700.
Gateshead. Warwick Street, Gateshead, Tyne and Wear NE8 1DT. Tel: 0191 477 5821.
Grimsby. Victoria Street, Grimsby DN31 1NH. Tel: 01472 320444.
Halifax. PO Box 32, Harrison Road, Halifax HX1 2AN. Tel: 01422 360695.
Harrogate. The Court House, PO Box 72, Victoria Avenue, Harrogate HG1 1LS. Tel: 01423 722000.
Hartlepool. The Law Courts, Victoria Road, Hartlepool TS24 8AG. Tel: 01429 271451.
Huddersfield. PO Box B37, The Court House, Civic Centre, Huddersfield HD1 2NH. Tel: 01484 423552.
Hull and Holderness. PO Box 2, Market Place, Kingston-upon-Hull HU1 2AD. Tel: 01482 328914.
Kingston-upon-Hull. The Law Courts, Market Place, Kingston-upon-Hull HU1 2AD. Tel: 01482 328914.
Leeds. The Court House, PO Box 97, Westgate, Leeds LS1 3JP. Tel: 0113 245 9653.
Newcastle-upon-Tyne. Magistrates' Courts, PO Box 839, Market Street, Newcastle-upon-Tyne NE99 1AU. Tel: 0191 232 7326.
Newton Aycliffe. Central Avenue, Newton Aycliffe DL5 5RT. Tel: 01325 318114.
North Tyneside. The Courthouse, Tynemouth Road, North Shields NE30 1AG. Tel: 0191 296 0099.
Northallerton. 3 Racecourse Lane, Northallerton DL7 8QZ. Tel: 01609 788200.
Peterlee. Newcastle Road, Chester-le-Street, Co Durham DH3 3UA. Tel: 0191 387 0700.
Pontefract. The Court House, 2 Front Street, Pontefract WF8 1BW. Tel: 01977 691600.
Rotherham. The Law Courts, The Statutes, Off Main Street, Rotherham S60 1YW. Tel: 01709 839339.
Scarborough. The Law Courts, Northway, Scarborough YO12 7AE. Tel: 01723 505000.
Scunthorpe. Court Centre Office, Corporation Road, Scunthorpe DN15 6QB. Tel: 01724 281100.
Selby. Law Courts, Clifford Street, York YO1 9RE. Tel: 01904 818300.
Sheffield. Magistrates' Court, Castle Street, Sheffield S3 8LU. Tel: 0114 276 0760.
Skipton. The Court House, PO Box 72, Victoria Avenue, Harrogate HG1 1LS. Tel: 01423 722000.
South East Northumberland. The Law Courts, Bedlington NE22 7LX. Tel: 01670 531100.
South Tyneside. Millbank, Secretan Way, South Shields NE33 1RG. Tel: 0191 455 8800.
Sunderland. Gillbridge Avenue, Sunderland SR1 3AP. Tel: 0191 514 1621.
Teesside. Teesside Law Courts, Victoria Square, Middlesbrough TS1 2AS. Tel: 01642 240301.
Wakefield. The Court Office, Cliff Parade, Wakefield WF1 2TW. Tel: 01924 231100.
York. Law Courts, Clifford Street, York YO1 9RE. Tel: 01904 818300.

NORTH WEST REGION
Manchester Civil Justice Centre, PO Box 4237, 1 Bridge Street West, Manchester M60 1TE. Fax: 0161 240 5846. DX: 724780 Manchester 44.
Delivery Director: Gill Hague. Tel: 0161 240 5800.
Head of Crime: Paul McGladrigan. Tel: 0161 240 5913.
Head of Civil, Family & Tribunals: Simon Vowles. Tel: 0161 240 5901.
Head of Regional Support Unit: Leslie Handford. Tel: 0161 240 5805.

CROWN COURTS
Bolton. Bolton Combined Court Centre, The Law Courts, Blackhorse Street, Bolton BL1 1SU. Tel: 01204 392881.
Burnley. Burnley Combined Court Centre, The Law Courts, Hammerton Street, Burnley BB11 1XD. Tel: 01282 855300.
Carlisle. Carlisle Combined Court Centre, Courts of Justice, Earl Street, Carlisle CA1 1DJ. Tel: 01228 882120.
Chester. The Castle, Chester CH1 2AN. Tel: 01244 317606.
Knutsford. The Castle, Chester CH1 2AN. Tel: 01244 317606.
Lancaster. Preston Combined Court Centre, The Law Courts, Openshaw Place, Ring Way, Preston PR1 2LL. Tel: 01772 844700.
Liverpool. The Queen Elizabeth II Law Courts, Derby Square, Liverpool L2 1XA. Tel: 0151 473 7373.
Manchester (Crown Square). Manchester Crown Court, Crown Square, Manchester M3 3FL. Tel: 0161 954 1800.
Manchester (Minshull Street). The Crown Court at Manchester, Minshull Street, Manchester M1 3FS. Tel: 0161 954 7500.

Preston. Preston Combined Court Centre, The Law Courts, Openshaw Place, Ring Way, Preston PR1 2LL. Tel: 01772 844700.

MAGISTRATES' COURTS

Accrington. The Court House, Northgate, Blackburn BB2 1AF. Tel: 01254 687500.
Barrow-in-Furness. Abbey Road, Barrow-in-Furness, Cumbria LA14 5QX. Tel: 01229 820161.
Blackburn. The Court House, Northgate, Blackburn BB2 1AF. Tel: 01254 687500.
Blackpool. Civic Centre, Chapel Street, Blackpool FY1 5RH. Tel: 01253 757000.
Bolton. The Courts, Civic Centre, Le Mans Crescent, Bolton BL1 1UA. Tel: 01204 558200.
Burnley. The Court House, Parker Lane, Burnley BB11 2BS. Tel: 01282 800100.
Bury and Rochdale. The Courthouse, Tenters Street, Bury BL9 0HX. Tel: 0161 447 8600.
Carlisle. The Court House, Rickergate, Carlisle CA3 8QH. Tel: 01228 518800.
Chester, Ellesmere Port and Neston. Grosvenor Street, Chester CH1 2XA. Tel: 0870 162 6261.
Chorley. Court House, St Thomas's Square, Chorley PR7 1DS. Tel: 01257 240500.
Fleetwood. Civic Centre, Chapel Street, Blackpool FY1 5RH. Tel: 01253 757000.
Furness. Abbey Road, Barrow-in-Furness, Cumbria LA14 5QX. Tel: 01229 820161.
Kendal. The Court House, Burneside Road, Kendal, Cumbria LA9 4TJ. Tel: 01229 820161.
Lancaster. Magistrates' Court, George Street, Lancaster LA1 1XZ. Tel: 01524 597000.
Liverpool and Knowsley. 107 Dale Street, Liverpool L2 2JQ. Tel: 0151 243 5500.
Macclesfield. The Law Courts, Civic Centre, Crewe, Cheshire CW1 2DT. Tel: 0870 162 6261.
Manchester and Salford. Crown Square, Manchester M60 1PR. Tel: 0161 830 4200.
North Liverpool Community Justice Centre. Boundary Street, Kirkdale, Liverpool L5 2QD. Tel: 0151 298 3600.
Oldham. Magistrates' Court, St Domingo Place, West Street, Oldham OL1 1QE. Tel: 0161 620 2331.
Ormskirk. Court House, St Thomas's Square, Chorley PR7 1DS. Tel: 01257 240500.
Preston. Magistrates' Court, PO Box 52, Lawson Street, Preston PR1 2RD. Tel: 01772 208000.
Reedley. The Court House, Parker Lane, Burnley BB11 2BS. Tel: 01282 800100.
Runcorn (Halton). The Court House, Halton Lea, Runcorn, Cheshire WA7 2HA. Tel: 0870 162 6261.
St Helens. The Court House, Corporation Street, St Helens WA10 1SZ. Tel: 01744 620244.
South Cheshire. Law Courts, Civic Centre, Crewe CW1 2DT. Tel: 01270 655927.
South Ribble. Court House, St Thomas's Square, Chorley PR7 1DS. Tel: 01257 240500.
South Sefton. Merton Road, Bootle L20 3XX. Tel: 0151 933 6999.
Southport. Law Courts, Albert Road, Southport, Merseyside PR9 0LJ. Tel: 0151 933 6999.
Stockport. The Courthouse, Edward Street, Stockport SK1 3NF. Tel: 0161 477 2020.
Tameside. Henry Square, Ashton-under-Lyne, Lancashire OL6 7TP. Tel: 0161 330 2023.
Trafford. PO Box 13, Ashton Lane, Sale, Cheshire M33 7NR. Tel: 0161 976 3333.
Warrington. Winmarleigh Street, Warrington WA1 1PB. Tel: 0870 162 6261.
Wigan and Leigh. Magistrates' Court, Darlington Street, Wigan, Greater Manchester WN1 1DW. Tel: 01942 405405.
Wirral. Chester Street, Birkenhead CH41 5HW. Tel: 0151 285 4100.

SOUTH EAST REGION
5rd Floor, Fox Court, 14 Grays Inn Road, London WC1X 8UN. Tel: 020 3206 0688.
Delivery Director: Guy Tompkins.

CROWN COURTS

Aylesbury. County Hall, Market Square, Aylesbury HP20 1XD. Tel: 01296 434401.
Basildon. Basildon Combined Court, The Gore, Basildon SS14 2BU. Tel: 01268 458000.
Bury St Edmunds. The Court House, 1 Russell Road, Ipswich IP1 2AG. Tel: 01473 228585.
Cambridge. 83 East Road, Cambridge CB1 1BT. Tel: 01223 488321.
Canterbury. Canterbury Combined Court Centre, The Law Courts, Chaucer Road, Canterbury CT1 1ZA. Tel: 01227 819200.
Chelmsford. PO Box 9, New Street, Chelmsford CM1 1EL. Tel: 01245 603000.
Chichester. Chichester Combined Court Centre, Southgate, Chichester PO19 1SX. Tel: 01243 520742.
Guildford. Bedford Road, Guildford GU1 4ST Tel: 01483 468500.
Ipswich. The Court House, 1 Russell Road, Ipswich IP1 2AG. Tel: 01473 228585.
King's Lynn. Norwich Combined Court Centre, The Law Courts, Bishopgate, Norwich NR3 1UR. Tel: 01603 728200.
Lewes. Lewes Combined Court Centre, The Law Courts, High Street, Lewes BN7 1YB. Tel: 01273 480400.
Luton. 7 George Street, Luton LU1 2AA. Tel: 01582 522000.
Maidstone. Maidstone Combined Court Centre, The Law Courts, Barker Road, Maidstone ME16 8EQ. Tel: 01622 202000.
Norwich. Norwich Combined Court Centre, The Law Courts, Bishopgate, Norwich NR3 1UR. Tel: 01603 728200.
Oxford. Oxford Combined Court Centre, St Aldate's, Oxford OX1 1TL. Tel: 01865 264200.

Peterborough. Peterborough Combined Court Centre, Crown Buildings, Rivergate, Peterborough PE1 1EJ. Tel: 01733 349161.
Reading. The Old Shire Hall, The Forbury, Reading RG1 3EH. Tel: 0118 967 4400.
St Albans. The Court Building, Bricket Road, St Albans AL1 3JW. Tel: 01727 753220.
Southend. Basildon Combined Court, The Gore, Basildon SS14 2BU. Tel: 01268 458000.

MAGISTRATES' COURTS

Aylesbury. Milton Keynes Magistrates' Court, 301 Silbury Boulevard, Witan Gate East, Milton Keynes MK9 2AJ. Tel: 01908 451145.
Banbury. The Court House, Warwick Road, Banbury OX16 2AW. Tel: 01865 448020.
Basildon. Court Administration Centre, PO Box 10754, Chelmsford CM1 9PZ. Tel: 01245 313300.
Bedford and Mid Bedfordshire. Shire Hall, 3 St Paul's Square, Bedford MK40 1SQ. Tel: 01234 319100.
Bicester. Waverley House, Queen's Avenue, Bicester OX26 1NZ. Tel: 01869 853114.
Brighton. The Law Courts, Edward Street, Brighton BN2 0LG. Tel: 01273 670888.
Bury St Edmunds. Elm Street, Ipswich IP1 2AP. Tel: 01473 217261.
Cambridge. The Court House, Bridge Street, Peterborough PE1 1ED. Tel: 0845 310 0575.
Canterbury. Pencester Road, Dover CT16 1BS. Tel: 01304 218600.
Chatham. The Court House, The Brook, Chatham ME4 4JZ. Tel: 01634 830232.
Chelmsford. Court Administration Centre, PO Box 10754, Chelmsford CM1 9PZ. Tel: 01245 313300.
Chichester. The Law Courts, Christchurch Road, Worthing BN11 1JE. Tel: 01903 210981.
Colchester. Court Administration Centre, PO Box 10754, Chelmsford CM1 9PZ. Tel: 01245 313300.
Crawley. Bolnore Road, Haywards Heath RH16 4BA. Tel: 01273 670888.
Dartford. The Court House, The Brook, Chatham ME4 4JZ. Tel: 01634 830232.
Dover. Pencester Road, Dover CT16 1BS. Tel: 01304 218600.
East Berkshire, Bracknell. The Law Courts, Chalvey Park, off Windsor Road, Slough SL1 2HJ. Tel: 01753 232100.
East Berkshire, Maidenhead. The Law Courts, Chalvey Park, off Windsor Road, Slough SL1 2HJ. Tel: 01753 232100.
East Berkshire, Slough. The Law Courts, Chalvey Park, off Windsor Road, Slough SL1 2HJ. Tel: 01753 232100.
Eastbourne. The Law Courts, Horntye Park, Bohemia Road, Hastings TN34 1ND. Tel: 01424 437644.
Folkestone. Pencester Road, Dover CT16 1BS. Tel: 01304 218600.
Great Yarmouth. Bishopgate, Norwich NR3 1UP. Tel: 01603 679500.
Guildford. Mary Road, Guildford GU1 4PS. Tel: 01483 405300.
Harlow. PO Box 10754, Chelmsford CM1 9PZ. Tel: 01245 313300.
Hastings. The Law Courts, Horntye Park, Bohemia Road, Hastings TN34 1ND. Tel: 01424 437644.
Hatfield. The Court House, Clarendon Road, Watford WD17 1ST. Tel: 01923 297500.
Hertford. Bayley House, Sish Lane, Stevenage SG1 3SS. Tel: 01438 730412.
High Wycombe. Law Courts, Easton Street, High Wycombe HP11 1LR. Tel: 01908 451145.
Horsham. Horsham Family Proceedings Court, Horsham County Court, Hurst Road, Horsham RH12 2EU. Tel: 01403 252474.
Ipswich. Elm Street, Ipswich, Suffolk IP1 2AP. Tel: 01473 217261.
King's Lynn. Bishopgate, Norwich NR3 1UP. Tel: 01603 679500.
Lowestoft. Criminal and Youth Court, Elm Street, Ipswich, Suffolk IP1 2AP. Tel: 01502 501060.
Luton and South Bedfordshire. Stuart Street, Luton LU1 5BL. Tel: 01582 524200.
Maidstone. The Courthouse, Palace Avenue, Maidstone ME15 6LL. Tel: 01622 671041.
Margate. Pencester Road, Dover CT16 1BS. Tel: 01304 218600.
Medway. The Court House, The Brook, Chatham ME4 4JZ. Tel: 01634 830232.
Milton Keynes. 301 Silbury Boulevard, Witan Gate East, Milton Keynes MK9 2AJ. Tel: 01908 451145.
Norwich. Bishopgate, Norwich NR3 1UP. Tel: 01603 679500.
Oxford and Southern Oxfordshire. The Court House, PO Box 37, Speedwell Street, Oxford OX1 1RZ. Tel: 01865 448020.
Peterborough. Magistrates' Court, Bridge Street, Peterborough PE1 1ED. Tel: 0845 310 0575.
Reading. Civic Centre, Reading RG1 7TQ. Tel: 0118 980 1800.
Redhill. The Law Courts, Hatchlands Road, Redhill RH1 6DH. Tel: 01737 765581.
St Albans. The Court House, Clarendon Road, Watford WD17 1ST. Tel: 01923 297500.
Sevenoaks. The Courthouse, Palace Avenue, Maidstone ME15 6LL. Tel: 01622 671041.
Southend. Court Administration Centre, PO Box 10754, Chelmsford CM1 9PZ. Tel: 01245 313300.
Staines. The Law Courts, Knowle Green, Staines, Middlesex TW18 1XH. Tel: 01784 895500.
Stevenage. Bayley House, Sish Lane, Stevenage SG1 3SS. Tel: 01438 730412.
Watford. The Court House, Clarendon Road, Watford WD17 1ST. Tel: 01923 297500.
West Berkshire, Newbury. Civic Centre, Reading RG1 7TQ. Tel: 0118 980 1800.
Worthing. The Law Courts, Christchurch Road, Worthing BN11 1JE. Tel: 01903 210981.

SOUTH WEST REGION

HMCTS, Queensway House, The Hedges, St George's, Weston-super-Mare BS22 7BB. Tel: 01934 528668. Fax: 01934 528520. DX: 152360 Westonsupermare 5. Email: sandra.aston@hmcts.gsi.gov.uk *Delivery Director:* Sandra Aston.

CROWN COURTS

Barnstaple. Exeter Crown and County Court, Southernhay Gardens, Exeter EX1 1UH. Tel: 01392 415300.
Bournemouth. Bournemouth Crown and County Court, Courts of Justice, Deansleigh Road, Bournemouth BH7 7DS. Tel: 01202 502800.
Bristol. The Law Courts, Small Street, Bristol BS1 1DA. Tel: 0117 976 3030.
Dorchester. Dorchester Crown Court, Colliton Park, Dorchester DT1 1XJ. Tel: 01305 265867.
Exeter. Exeter Crown and County Court, Southernhay Gardens, Exeter EX1 1UH. Tel: 01392 415300.
Gloucester. 2nd Floor, Southgate House, Southgate Street, Gloucester GL1 1UB. Tel: 01452 420100.
Hereford. Worcester Combined Court Centre, The Shirehall, Foregate Street, Worcester WR1 1EQ. Tel: 01905 730823.
Plymouth. Plymouth Combined Court Centre, The Law Courts, Armada Way, Plymouth PL1 2ER. Tel: 01752 677400.
Portsmouth. Portsmouth Combined Court Centre, The Courts of Justice, Winston Churchill Avenue, Portsmouth PO1 2EB. Tel: 023 9289 3000.
Salisbury. The Law Courts, Wilton Road, Salisbury SP2 7EP. Tel: 01722 345200.
Southampton. Southampton Combined Court Centre, The Courts of Justice, London Road, Southampton SO15 2XQ. Tel: 023 8021 3200.
Swindon. Swindon Combined Court Centre, The Law Courts, Islington Street, Swindon SN1 2HG. Tel: 01793 690500.
Taunton. Shire Hall, Taunton TA1 4EU. Tel: 01823 281100.
Truro. Courts of Justice, Edward Street, Truro TR1 2PB. Tel: 01872 267420.
Winchester. Winchester Combined Court Centre, The Law Courts, Winchester SO23 9EL. Tel: 01962 814100.

MAGISTRATES' COURTS

Aldershot. The Court House, Civic Centre, Aldershot GU11 1NY. Tel: 01252 366000.
Alton. The Court House, Civic Centre, Aldershot GU11 1NY. Tel: 01252 366000.
Andover. The Court House, Civic Centre, Aldershot GU11 1NY. Tel: 01252 366000. *Note: this court is expected to close in April 2013.*
Basingstoke. The Court House, London Road, Basingstoke RG21 4AB. Tel: 01252 366000.
Bath. The Law Courts, North Parade Road, Bath BA1 5AF. Tel: 01225 463281.
Bodmin (East Cornwall). PO Box 2, Launceston Road, Bodmin PL31 1XQ. Tel: 01208 262700.
Bournemouth. The Law Courts, Stafford Road, Bournemouth BH1 1LA. Tel: 01202 745309.
Bristol. Magistrates' Court, Marlborough Street, Bristol BS1 3NU. Tel: 0117 930 2400.
Cheltenham. HMCTS, PO Box 9051, Gloucester GL1 2XG. Tel: 01452 420100.
Chippenham. North West Wiltshire Magistrates' Court, The Court House, Pewsham Way, Chippenham SN15 3BF. Tel: 01249 463473.
Fareham. The Court House, Trinity Street, Fareham PO16 7SB. Tel: 023 9281 9421.
Gloucester. HMCTS, PO Box 9051, Gloucester GL1 2XG. Tel: 01452 420100.
Isle of Wight. The Law Courts, Quay Street, Newport, Isle of Wight PO30 5YT. Tel: 01983 535100.
Isles of Scilly. Cornwall (Truro) Magistrates' Court, PO Box 60, Truro TR1 1HZ. Tel: 01872 321900.
Newton Abbot. HMCTS South Devon, Nicholson Road, Torquay TQ2 7AZ. Tel: 01803 612211.
North and East Devon – Barnstaple. The Law Courts, Civic Centre, Barnstaple EX31 1DX. Tel: 01271 340410.
North and East Devon – Exeter. Southernhay Gardens, Exeter EX1 1HU. Tel: 01392 415300.
North Avon. Kennedy Way, Yate, Bristol BS37 4PY. Tel: 01454 310505.
North Somerset. The Hedges, St George's, Weston-super-Mare BS22 7BB. Tel: 01934 528700.
Plymouth. St Andrew's Street, Plymouth PL1 2DP. Tel: 01752 206200.
Poole. The Law Courts, Park Road, Poole BH15 2NS. Tel: 01202 745309.
Portsmouth. The Law Courts, Winston Churchill Avenue, Portsmouth PO1 2DQ. Tel: 023 9281 9421.
Salisbury. The Law Courts, Wilton Road, Salisbury SP2 7EP. Tel: 01722 345200.
South Somerset and Mendip. The Law Courts, Petters Way, Yeovil BA20 1SW. Tel: 01935 426281.
Southampton. 100 The Avenue, Southampton SO17 1EY. Tel: 023 8038 4200.
Swindon. Princes Street, Swindon SN1 2JB. Tel: 01793 699800
Taunton Deane. St John's Road, Taunton TA1 4AX. Tel: 01823 257084.
Torquay. HMCTS South Devon, Nicholson Road, Torquay TQ2 7AZ. Tel: 01803 612211.
Truro. Cornwall (Truro) Magistrates' Court, PO Box 60, Truro TR1 1HZ. Tel: 01872 321900.
West Somerset. St John's Road, Taunton TA1 4AX. Tel: 01823 257084.
Weymouth. The Law Courts, Westwey Road, Weymouth DT4 8BS. Tel: 01305 783891.

HMCTS WALES
Wales Support Unit, Churchill House, Churchill Way, Cardiff CF10 2HH. Tel: 029 2067 8300. Fax: 029 2067 8406. DX: 121723 Cardiff 9.
Delivery Director: Mark Swales. Email: mark.swales2@hmcts.gsi.gov.uk
Head of Crime: Luigi Strinati. Email: luigi.strinati@hmcts.gsi.gov.uk

CROWN COURTS
Caernarfon. The Law Courts, County Civic Centre, Mold CH7 1AE. Tel: 01352 707340.
Cardiff. The Law Courts, Cathays Park, Cardiff CF10 3PG. Tel: 029 2067 8730.
Carmarthen. The Law Courts, St Helen's Road, Swansea SA1 4PF. Tel: 01792 637000.
Dolgellau. The Law Courts, County Civic Centre, Mold CH7 1AE. Tel: 01352 707340.
Haverfordwest. The Law Courts, St Helen's Road, Swansea SA1 4PF. Tel: 01792 637000.
Merthyr Tydfil. Merthyr Tydfil Combined Court Centre, The Law Courts, Glebeland Place, Merthyr Tydfil CF47 8BH. Tel: 01685 727600.
Mold. The Law Courts, County Civic Centre, Mold CH7 1AE. Tel: 01352 707340.
Newport (South Wales). Crown Court, Faulkner Road, Newport NP20 4PR. Tel: 01633 266211.
Swansea. The Law Courts, St Helen's Road, Swansea SA1 4PF. Tel: 01792 637000.

MAGISTRATES' COURTS
Abergavenny. HMCTS Gwent, PO Box 85, Cwmbran Torfaen NP44 1WY. Tel: 01633 645000.
Aberystwyth. Aberaeron Magistrates' Court Office, 21 Alban Square, Aberaeron, Cardiganshire SA46 0DB. Tel: 01545 570886.
Bridgend. The Law Courts, Sunnyside, Bridgend CF31 4AJ. Tel: 01656 673800.
Caernarfon. Criminal Justice Centre, Llanberis Road, Caernarfon, Gwynedd LL55 2DF. Tel: 01286 669700.
Caerphilly. HMCTS Gwent, PO Box 83, Cwmbran, Torfaen NP44 1ZW. Tel: 01633 645000.
Cardiff LJA. Fitzalan Place, Cardiff CF24 0RZ. Tel: 029 2046 3040.
Carmarthen. Town Hall Square, Llanelli, Carmarthenshire SA15 3AW. Tel: 01554 757201.
Cwmbran. HMCTS Gwent, PO Box 83, Cwmbran, Torfaen NP44 1ZW. Tel: 01633 645000.
Denbigh. The Courthouse, Conwy Road, Llandudno LL30 1GA. Tel: 01492 871333.
Dolgellau. Criminal Justice Centre, Llanberis Road, Caernarfon, Gwynedd LL55 2DF. Tel: 01286 669700.
Haverfordwest. Penffynnon (Rackhill Terrace), Hawthorn Rise, Haverfordwest SA61 2AX. Tel: 01437 772090.
Holyhead. Criminal Justice Centre, Llanberis Road, Caernarfon, Gwynedd LL55 2DF. Tel: 01286 669700.
Llandrindod Wells. Brecon Law Courts, Cambrian Way, Brecon, Powys LD3 7HR. Tel: 01874 622993.
Llandudno. The Courthouse, Conwy Road, Llandudno LL30 1GA. Tel: 01492 871333.
Llanelli. Town Hall Square, Llanelli, Carmarthenshire SA15 3AW. Tel: 01554 757201.
Merthyr Tydfil. Law Courts, Glebeland Place, Merthyr Tydfil CF47 8BU. Tel: 01685 727600.
Mold. The Law Courts, Mold, Flintshire CH7 1AE. Tel: 01352 7073330.
Neath. Fairfield Way, Neath SA11 1RF. Tel: 01639 765900.
Newport. HMCTS Gwent, PO Box 83, Cwmbran, Torfaen NP44 1ZW. Tel: 01633 645000.
Pontypridd. Union Street, Pontypridd Rhonda Cynon Taf CF37 1SD. Tel: 01443 480750.
Port Talbot. Fairfield Way, Neath SA11 1RF. Tel: 01639 765900.
Prestatyn. Victoria Road, Prestatyn, Denbighshire LL19 7TE. Tel: 01745 851916.
Swansea. Grove Place, Swansea SA1 5DB. Tel: 01792 478300.
Vale of Glamorgan. Thompson Street, Barry, Glamorgan CF63 4SX. Tel: 029 2046 3040.
Welshpool. Mansion House, 24 Severn Street, Welshpool SY21 7UX. Tel: 01938 555968.
Wrexham. The Law Courts, Mold, Flintshire CH7 1AE. Tel: 01352 707330.

SCOTLAND
COURT OF SESSION
Supreme Courts, Parliament House, 11 Parliament Square, Edinburgh EH1 1RQ. Tel: 0131 225 2595. Fax: 0131 240 6755. DX: 549306 Edinburgh 36. Website: www.scotcourts.gov.uk

HIGH COURT OF JUSTICIARY
Supreme Courts, Parliament House, as above. Tel: 0131 225 2595. Fax: 0131 240 6915. DX: 549307 Edinburgh 36.
The Lord President and Lord Justice General: The Rt Hon Lord Gill.
Scottish Court Service
Saughton House, Broomhouse Drive, Edinburgh EH11 3XD. Tel: 0131 444 3300. Fax: 0131 444 2610. DX: 545309. Website: www.scotcourts.gov.uk

SHERIFF AND JUSTICE OF THE PEACE COURTS
SHERIFFDOM OF GLASGOW AND STRATHKELVIN

Glasgow and Strathkelvin Sheriff Court. Sheriff Court House, PO Box 23, 1 Carlton Place, Glasgow G5 9DA. Tel: 0141 429 8888.

Glasgow Justice of the Peace and Stipendiary Magistrates' Court. 21 St Andrew's Street, Glasgow G1 5PW. Tel: 0141 429 8888.

SHERIFFDOM OF GRAMPIAN, HIGHLAND AND ISLANDS

Aberdeen Sheriff Court and Justice of the Peace Court. Sheriff Court House, Castle Street, Aberdeen AB10 1WP. Tel: 01224 657200.

Banff Sheriff Court and Justice of the Peace Court. Sheriff Court House, Banff AB45 1AU. Tel: 01261 812140.

Dingwall Sheriff Court and Justice of the Peace Court. Sheriff Court House, Dingwall IV15 9QX. Tel: 01349 863153.

Dornoch Sheriff Court and Justice of the Peace Court. Sheriff Court House, Dornoch IV25 3SD. Tel: 01862 810224.

Elgin Sheriff Court and Justice of the Peace Court. Sheriff Court House, Elgin IV30 1BU. Tel: 01343 542505.

Fort William Sheriff Court and Justice of the Peace Court. Sheriff Court House, High Street, Fort William PH33 6EE. Tel: 01397 702087.

Inverness Sheriff Court and Justice of the Peace Court. Sheriff Court House, Inverness IV2 3EG. Tel: 01463 230782.

Kirkwall Sheriff Court. Sheriff Court House, Kirkwall KW15 1PD. Tel: 01856 872110.

Lerwick Sheriff Court. Sheriff Court House, Lerwick ZE1 0HD. Tel: 01595 693914.

Lochmaddy Sheriff Court. Sheriff Court House, Lochmaddy HS6 5AE. Tel: 01478 612191.

Peterhead Sheriff Court and Justice of the Peace Court. Sheriff Court House, Queen Street, Peterhead AB42 1TP. Tel: 01779 476676.

Portree Sheriff Court and Justice of the Peace Court. Sheriff Court House, Portree IV51 9EH. Tel: 01478 612191.

Stonehaven Sheriff Court and Justice of the Peace Court. Sheriff Court House, Stonehaven AB39 2JH. Tel: 01569 762758.

Stornoway Sheriff Court and Justice of the Peace Court. Sheriff Court House, 9 Lewis Street, Stornoway HS1 2JF. Tel: 01851 702231.

Tain Sheriff Court and Justice of the Peace Court. Sheriff Court House, Tain IV19 1AB. Tel: 01862 892518.

Wick Sheriff Court and Justice of the Peace Court. Sheriff Court House, Wick KW1 4AJ. Tel: 01955 602846.

SHERIFFDOM OF LOTHIAN AND BORDERS

Duns Sheriff Court and Justice of the Peace Court. Sheriff Court House, 8 Newtown Street, Duns TD11 3DT. Tel: 01835 863231.

Edinburgh Sheriff Court and Justice of the Peace Court. Sheriff Court House, 27 Chambers Street, Edinburgh EH1 1LB. Tel: 0131 225 2525.

Haddington Sheriff Court and Justice of the Peace Court. Sheriff Court House, Haddington EH41 3HN. Tel: 01620 822325.

Jedburgh Sheriff Court and Justice of the Peace Court. Sheriff and JP Court House, Castlegate, Jedburgh TD8 6AR. Tel: 01835 863231.

Livingston Sheriff Court and Justice of the Peace Court. The Civic Centre, Howden South Road, Livingston EH54 6FF. Tel: 01506 402400.

Peebles Sheriff Court and Justice of the Peace Court. c/o Sheriff Court Selkirk, Ettrick Terrace, Selkirk TD1 1TB. Tel: 01750 721269.

Selkirk Sheriff Court and Justice of the Peace Court. Sheriff Court House, Selkirk TD7 4LE. Tel: 01750 721269.

SHERIFFDOM OF NORTH STRATHCLYDE

Campbeltown Sheriff Court and Justice of the Peace Court. Sheriff Court House, Castlehill, Campbeltown PA28 6AN. Tel: 01586 552503.

Dumbarton Sheriff Court and Justice of the Peace Court. Church Street, Dumbarton G82 1QR. Tel: 01389 763266.

Dunoon Sheriff Court and Justice of the Peace Court. George Street, Dunoon PA23 8BQ. Tel: 0300 790 0049.

Greenock Sheriff Court and Justice of the Peace Court. Sheriff Court House, 1 Nelson Street, Greenock PA15 1TR. Tel: 01475 787073.

Irvine Justice of the Peace Court, Town House, 66 High Street, Irvine KA12 0AZ. Tel: 0300 790 0075.

Kilmarnock Sheriff Court and Justice of the Peace Court. Sheriff Court House, St Marnock Street, Kilmarnock KA1 1ED. Tel: 01563 550024.

Lochgilphead Justice of the Peace Court. Lochnell Street, Lochgilphead PA31 8JJ. (Contact via Dunoon Sheriff Court.)

Oban Sheriff Court and Justice of the Peace Court. Sheriff Court House, Albany Street, Oban PA34 4AL. Tel: 01631 562414.

Paisley Sheriff Court and Justice of the Peace Court. Sheriff Court House, St James' Street, Paisley PA3 2HW. Tel: 0141 887 5291.

Rothesay Sheriff Court. Eaglesham House, Mount Pleasant Road, Rothesay, Isle of Bute PA20 9HQ. Tel: 01700 502982.

SHERIFFDOM OF SOUTH STRATHCLYDE, DUMFRIES AND GALLOWAY

Airdrie Sheriff Court. Sheriff Court House, Graham Street, Airdrie ML6 6EE. Tel: 01236 751121.

Ayr Sheriff Court and Justice of the Peace Court. Sheriff Court House, Wellington Square, Ayr KA7 1EE. Tel: 01292 268474.

Coatbridge Justice of the Peace Court. Sheriff Court House, Graham Street, Airdrie ML6 6EE. Tel: 01236 751121.

Cumbernauld Justice of the Peace Court. Sheriff Court House, Graham Street, Airdrie ML6 6EE. Tel: 01236 439184.

Dumfries Sheriff Court and Justice of the Peace Court. Sheriff Court House, Dumfries DG1 2AN. Tel: 01387 262334.

Hamilton Sheriff Court and Justice of the Peace Court. Sheriff Court House, 4 Beckford Street, Hamilton ML3 0BT. Tel: 01698 282957.

Justice of the Peace Court at Motherwell. Sheriff Court House, 4 Beckford Street, Hamilton ML3 0BT. Tel: 01698 282957.

Kirkcudbright Sheriff Court and Justice of the Peace Court. Sheriff Court House, Kirkcudbright DG6 4JW. Tel: 01557 330574.

Lanark Sheriff Court and Justice of the Peace Court. Sheriff Court House, 24 Hope Street, Lanark ML11 7NE. Tel: 01555 661531.

Stranraer Sheriff Court and Justice of the Peace Court. Sheriff Court House, Stranraer DG9 7AA. Tel: 01776 702138.

SHERIFFDOM OF TAYSIDE, CENTRAL AND FIFE

Alloa Sheriff Court and Justice of the Peace Court. Sheriff Court House, 47 Drysdale Street, Alloa FK10 1JA. Tel: 01259 722734.

Arbroath Sheriff Court and Justice of the Peace Court. Sheriff Court House, 88–92 high Street, Arbroath DD11 1HL. Tel: 01241 876600.

Cupar Sheriff Court and Justice of the Peace Court. Sheriff Court House, Cupar KY15 4LX. Tel: 01334 652121.

Dundee Sheriff Court and Justice of the Peace Court. Sheriff Court House, Dundee DD1 9AD. Tel: 01382 229961.

Dunfermline Sheriff Court and Justice of the Peace Court. Sheriff Court House, 1–6 Carnegie Drive, Dunfermline KY12 7HJ. Tel: 01383 724666.

Falkirk Sheriff Court and Justice of the Peace Court. Sheriff Court House, Camelon, Falkirk FK1 4AR. Tel: 01324 620822.

Forfar Sheriff Court and Justice of the Peace Court. Sheriff Court House, Market Street, Forfar DD8 3LA. Tel: 01307 462186.

Kirkcaldy Sheriff Court and Justice of the Peace Court. Sheriff Court House, Whytescauseway, Kirkcaldy KY1 1XQ. Tel: 01592 260171.

Perth Sheriff Court and Justice of the Peace Court. Sheriff Court House, Perth PH2 8NL. Tel: 01738 620546.

Stirling Sheriff Court and Justice of the Peace Court, Sheriff Court House, Stirling FK8 1NH. Tel: 01786 462191.

NORTHERN IRELAND

ROYAL COURTS OF JUSTICE

Chichester Street, Belfast BT1 3JF. Tel: 028 9023 5111. Fax: 028 9031 3508.
Lord Chief Justice of Northern Ireland: The Rt Hon Sir Declan Morgan.

THE NORTHERN IRELAND COURTS AND TRIBUNALS SERVICE

Laganside House, 23–27 Oxford Street, Belfast BT1 3LA. Tel: 028 9032 8594. Fax: 028 9072 8942.
Director: David A Lavery CB.

CROWN COURTS

Antrim. The Courthouse, 30 Castle Way, Antrim BT41 4AQ. Tel: 028 9446 2661.

Armagh. Armagh Court Office, The Courthouse, The Mall, Armagh BT61 9DJ. Tel: 028 3752 2816.

Ballymena. Ballymena Court Office, The Courthouse, Albert Place, Ballymena BT43 5BS. Tel: 028 2564 9416.
Belfast. Crown Court Office, Laganside Courts, 45 Oxford Street, Belfast BT1 3LL. Tel: 028 9032 8594.
Coleraine. Coleraine Court Office, The Courthouse, 46A Mountsandel Road, Coleraine BT52 1NY.
Craigavon. Craigavon Court Office, The Courthouse, Central Way, Craigavon BT64 1AP. Tel: 028 3834 1324.
Downpatrick. Downpatrick Court Office, The Courthouse, 21 English Street, Downpatrick BT30 6AD. Tel: 028 4461 4621.
Dungannon. The Courthouse, 46 Killyman Road, Dungannon BT71 6DE. Tel: 028 8772 2992.
Enniskillen. Enniskillen Court Office, The Courthouse, East Bridge Street, Enniskillen BT74 7BP. Tel: 028 6632 2356.
Londonderry. Londonderry Court Office, The Courthouse, Bishop Street, Londonderry BT48 6PQ. Tel: 028 7136 3448.
Newry. The Courthouse, 23 New Street, Newry BT35 6JD. Tel: 028 3025 2040.
Newtonards. Newtonards Court Office, The Courthouse, Regent Street, Newtownards BT23 4LP.
Omagh. Omagh Court Office, The Courthouse, High Street, Omagh BT78 1DU. Tel: 028 8224 2056.

MAGISTRATES' COURTS
Antrim. Antrim Court Office, The Courthouse, 30 Castle Way, Antrim BT41 4AQ. Tel: 028 9446 2661.
Ards. Newtownards Court Office, The Courthouse, Regent Street, Newtownards BT23 4LP. Tel: 028 9181 4343.
Armagh. Armagh Court Office, The Courthouse, The Mall, Armagh BT61 9DJ. Tel: 028 3752 2816.
Ballymena. Ballymena Court Office, The Courthouse, Albert Place, Ballymena BT43 5BS. Tel: 028 2564 9416.
Banbridge. Banbridge Court Office, The Courthouse, 23 New Street, Newry BT35 6JD. Tel: 028 4062 3622.
Belfast and Newtownabbey. Laganside Courts, 45 Oxford Street, Belfast BT1 3LL. Tel: 028 9023 2721.
Castlereagh. Newtownards Court Office, The Courthouse, Regent Street, Newtownards BT23 4LP. Tel: 028 9181 4343.
Craigavon. Craigavon Court Office, The Courthouse, Central Way, Craigavon BT64 1AP. Tel: 028 3834 1324.
Down. Downpatrick Court Office, The Courthouse, English Street, Downpatrick BT30 6AB. Tel: 028 4461 4621.
East Tyrone. Dungannon Court Office, The Courthouse, 46 Killyman Road, Dungannon BT71 6FG. Tel: 028 8772 2992.
Fermanagh. Enniskillen Court Office, The Courthouse, East Bridge Street, Enniskillen BT74 7BP. Tel: 028 6632 2356.
Larne. Larne Court Office, The Courthouse, Victoria Road, Larne BT40 1RN. Tel: 028 2827 2927.
Limavady. Limavady Court Office, The Courthouse, Main Street, Limavady BT49 0EY. Tel: 028 7772 2688.
Lisburn. Lisburn Court Office, The Courthouse, Railway Street, Lisburn BT28 1XR. Tel: 028 9267 5336.
Londonderry. Londonderry Court Office, The Courthouse, Bishop Street, Londonderry BT48 6PQ. Tel: 028 7136 3448.
Magherafelt. Magherafelt Court Office, The Courthouse, Hospital Road, Magherafelt BT45 5DG. Tel: 028 7963 2121.
Newry and Mourne. Newry Court Office, The Courthouse, 22 New Street, Newry BT35 6JD. Tel: 028 3025 2040.
North Antrim. Coleraine Court Office, The Courthouse, 46A Mountsandel Road, Coleraine BT52 1NY. Tel: 028 7034 3437.
North Down. Bangor Court Office, The Courthouse, 6 Quay Street, Bangor BT20 5ED. Tel: 028 9147 2626.
Omagh. Omagh Court Office, The Courthouse, High Street, Omagh BT78 1DU. Tel: 028 8224 2056.
Strabane. Strabane Court Office, The Courthouse, Derry Road, Strabane BT82 8DT. Tel: 028 7138 2544.

ISLE OF MAN
ISLE OF MAN COURTS OF JUSTICE
Deemsters Walk, Bucks Road, Douglas, Isle of Man IM1 3AR. Tel: 685265. Fax: 685236. Email: enquiries@courts.im Website: www.courts.im
1st Deemster & Clerk of the Rolls: His Hon David Doyle.
High Bailiff & Coroner of Inquests: His Worship John Needham BSc.
Director of Courts & Tribunal Services: Mr P Coppell.

PROBATION

PROBATION TRUSTS ENGLAND AND WALES

Avon & Somerset: Queensway House, The Hedges, St Georges, Weston-super-Mare BS22 7BB. Tel: 0300 049 2210. Fax: 0300 049 2251. Website: www.avonandsomersetprobation.org.uk
Chief Executive: Sally Lewis OBE.
Bedfordshire: 3 St Peter's Street, Bedford MK40 2PN. Tel: 01234 213541. Fax: 01234 327497. Website: www.bedsprobation.org.uk
Chief Executive: Linda Hennigan.
Cambridgeshire & Peterborough: Second Floor, Godwin House, George Street, Huntingdon PE29 3BD. Tel: 0300 047 7000. Fax: 0300 047 7050. Website: www.cambridgeshireprobation.org.uk
Chief Executive Officer: John Budd.
Cheshire: 11 Hunters Walk, Off Canal Street, Chester CH1 4EB. Tel: 01244 605850. Website: www.cheshireprobation.org.uk
Chief Executive: Angela Cossins.
Cumbria: Magistrates' Court, Rickergate, Carlisle CA3 8XP. Tel: 0300 047 3750. Fax: 0300 047 3751. Website: www.cumbriaprobation.org.uk
Interim Chief Executive: Russell Bruce.
Derbyshire: 18 Brunswood Road, Matlock Bath, Derbyshire DE4 3PA. Tel: 01629 55422. Fax: 01629 580838. Website: www.dpsonline.org.uk
Chief Executive: Jo Mead.
Devon & Cornwall: Queen's House, Little Queen Street, Exeter EX4 3LJ. Tel: 01392 474100. Fax: 01392 413563. Website: www.dcpt.org.uk
Chief Executive: Rob Menary.
Dorset: Poole Probation Centre, 63 Commercial Road, Parkstone, Poole BH14 0JB. Tel: 01202 307200. Fax: 01202 307223. Website: www.dorset-probation.gov.uk
Chief Executive: John Wiseman.
Durham Tees Valley: 6th Floor, Centre North East, 73–75 Albert Road, Middlesbrough TS1 2RU. Tel: 01642 230533. Fax: 01642 220083. Website: www.dtvprobation.org.uk
Chief Executive: Russell Bruce.
Essex: Cullen Mill, 49 Braintree Road, Witham CM8 2DD. Tel: 01376 501626. Fax: 01376 501174. Website: www.essexprobation.org.uk
Chief Executive: Mary Archer OBE.
Gloucestershire: Head Office, Twyver House, Bruton Way, Gloucester GL1 1PB. Tel: 01452 389200. Fax: 01452 389230. Website: www.glosprobation.org.uk
Chief Executive: John Bensted.
Greater Manchester: 5th Floor, Oakland House, Talbot Road, Manchester M16 0PQ. Tel: 0161 872 4802. Fax: 0161 872 3483. Website: www.gm-probation.org.uk
Chief Executive: Roz Hamilton.
Hampshire: 1st Floor, Cromwell House, 15 Andover Road, Winchester SO23 7EZ. Tel: 0300 047 2000. Fax: 01962 865278. Website: www.hampshire-probation.gov.uk
Chief Executive: Barrie Crook.
Hertfordshire: Argyle House, Argyle Way, Stevenage SG1 2AD. Tel: 01438 747074. Fax: 01438 765206. Website: www.hertfordshireprobation.gov.uk
Chief Executive: Tessa Webb.
Humberside: Head Office, Floor One, Liberty House (West), Liberty Lane, Kingston-upon-Hull HU1 1RS. Tel: 01482 480000. Fax: 01482 480007. Website: www.humberside-probation.org.uk
Chief Executive: Peter Wright.
Kent: Chaucer House, 25 Knightrider Street, Maidstone ME15 6ND. Tel: 0300 047 3040. Fax: 01622 751638. Website: www.kentprobation.org
Chief Executive: Sarah Billiald.
Lancashire: Area HQ, 99–101 Garstang Road, Preston PR1 1LD. Tel: 01772 201209. Fax: 01772 884399. Website: www.probation-lancashire.org.uk
Chief Executive: Kevin Robinson.
Leicestershire & Rutland: 2 St John Street, Leicester LE1 3WL. Tel: 0116 251 6008. Fax: 0116 242 3250. Website: www.leicsprobation.co.uk
Chief Executive: Helen West.
Lincolnshire: 8 Corporation Street, Lincoln LN2 1HN. Tel: 01522 510011. Website: www.lincolnshireprobationtrust.org.uk
Chief Executive: Martin Davies.
London: 151 Buckingham Palace Road, London SW1W 9SZ. Tel: 0300 048 0000. Fax: 0300 048 0297. Website: www.london-probation.org.uk

Chief Executive: Heather Munro. *Service Director/Deputy Chief Executive:* Sonia Crozier. *Corporate Director:* Everton Bryan. *Governance Director:* Paul Davies.
Merseyside: Burlington House, Crosby Road North, Waterloo, Liverpool L22 0PJ. Tel: 0151 257 6090. Fax: 0151 257 6154. Website: www.merseysideprobationtrust.gov.uk
Chief Executive: Annette Hennessy.
Norfolk & Suffolk: Norwich Office: Centenary House, 19 Palace Street, Norwich NR3 1RT. Tel: 01603 724000. Fax: 01603 664019. Ipswich Office: 11–13 Lower Brook Street, Ipswich IP4 1AQ. Tel: 01473 408130. Website: www.nsprobation.org.uk
Chief Executive: Martin Graham.
Northamptonshire: Walter Tull House, 43–47 Bridge Street, Northampton NN1 1NS. Tel: 01604 658000. Fax: 01604 658004. Website: www.northants-probation.org.uk
Interim Chief Executive: John Budd.
Northumbria: Lifton House, Eslington Road, Jesmond, Newcastle-upon-Tyne NE2 4SP. Tel: 0191 281 5721. Fax: 0191 281 3548. Website: www.northumbria-probation.co.uk
Chief Executive: Nick Hall.
Nottinghamshire: Marina Road, Castle Marina, Nottingham NG7 1TP. Tel: 0115 840 6500. Fax: 0115 840 6502. Website: www.nottinghamshire-probation.co.uk
Chief Executive: Jane Geraghty.
South Yorkshire: 45 Division Street, Sheffield S1 4GE. Tel: 0300 047 0800. Fax: 0114 276 1967. Website: www.syprobation.gov.uk
Chief Executive: Roz Brown.
Staffordshire & West Midlands: 1 Victoria Square, Birmingham B1 1BD. Tel: 0121 634 1300 Fax: 0121 634 1411. Website: www.swmprobation.gov.uk
Chief Executive: Mike Maiden.
Surrey & Sussex: 4th Floor, Invicta House, Trafalgar Place, Brighton BN1 4FR. Tel: 01273 627800. Fax: 01273 625207. Website: www.surreysussexprobation.gov.uk
Chief Executive: Nick Smart.
Thames Valley: Head Office, Kingsclere Road, Bicester, Oxon OX26 2QD. Tel: 01869 255300. Fax: 01869 255355. Website: www.thamesvalleyprobation.gov.uk
Chief Officer: Paul Gillbard.
Warwickshire: Warwickshire Justice Centre, Newbold Terrace, Leamington Spa CV32 4EL. Tel: 01926 682217. Fax: 01926 682241. Website: www.warwickshireprobation.org.uk
Chief Executive: Liz Stafford.
West Mercia: Stourbank House, 90 Mill Street, Kidderminster DY11 6XA. Tel: 01562 748375. Fax: 01562 748407. Website: www.westmerciaprobation.org.uk
Chief Executive Officer: David Chantler.
West Yorkshire: Cliff Hill House, Sandy Walk, Wakefield WF1 2DJ. Tel: 0300 048 7000. Fax: 0300 048 7152. Website: www.westyorksprobation.org.uk
Chief Executive: Sue Hall.
Wiltshire: 34 Marshfield Road, Chippenham SN15 1JT. Tel: 01249 461577. Fax: 01249 445497. Website: www.wiltshireprobation.org.uk
Chief Executive: Liz Rijnenberg.
York & North Yorkshire: Essex Lodge, 16 South Parade, Northallerton DL7 8SG. Tel: 01609 772271. Fax: 01609 772931. Website: www.ynyprobation.co.uk
Chief Executive: Pete Brown. Pavilion 2000, Amy Johnson Way, Clifton Moor, York YO3 DXT. Tel: 01904 698920.
Wales: 33 Westgate Street, Cardiff CF10 1JE. Tel: 029 2023 2999. Website: www.walesprobationtrust.gov.uk
Chief Executive: Sarah Payne.

SCOTLAND

DIRECTORATE FOR CRIMINAL JUSTICE
Community Justice Services Division: Floor GRW, St Andrew's House, Regent Road, Edinburgh EH1 3DG. Tel: 0131 244 4236. Fax: 0131 244 3548.
Director Criminal Justice: Bridget Campbell.
COMMUNITY JUSTICE AUTHORITIES
Fife & Forth Valley CJA: Glebe Hall, Burgh Mews, Alloa FK10 1HS. Tel: 01259 727435. Website: www.ffvcja.co.uk
Glasgow CJA: Suite 4(a), 4th Floor, 101 Portman Street, Glasgow G41 1EJ. Tel: 0141 287 0916. Fax: 0141 287 5821. Website: www.glasgowcja.org.uk
Lanarkshire CJA: Floor 2, Beckford Street, Hamilton ML3 0AA. Tel: 01698 454234. Website: www.lanarkshirecja.org.uk

Lothian & Borders CJA: Rosetta Road, Peebles EH45 8HL. Tel: 01721 726314. Fax: 01721 726309. Email: cjal&b@scotborders.gov.uk Website: www.cjalb.co.uk
North Strathclyde CJA: Unit 905, Mile End Mill, 12 Seedhill Road, Paisley PA1 1JS. Tel: 0141 887 6133. Website: nscja.co.uk
Northern CJA: Woodhill House Annexe, Westburn Road, Aberdeen AB16 5GB. Tel: 01224 665780. Email: northerncja@aberdeenshire.gov.uk Website: northerncja.org.uk
South West Scotland CJA: Sovereign House, Suite 6, Academy Road, Irvine KA12 8RL. Tel: 01294 277968. Fax: 01294 277968. Email: info@swscja.org.uk Website: swscja.org.uk
Tayside CJA: 5 City Square (Floor 2), City Square, Dundee DD1 3BA. Tel: 01382 435390. Fax: 01382 435393. Website: www.taysidecja.com

NORTHERN IRELAND

Probation Board for Northern Ireland: 80–90 North Street, Belfast BT1 1LD. Tel: 028 9026 2400. Fax: 0300 123 3290. Email: info@pbni.gsi.gov.uk Website: www.pbni.org.uk
Director of Probation: Brian McCaughey.

CHANNEL ISLANDS AND THE ISLE OF MAN

Guernsey Probation Service: The Market Building, Fountain Street, St Peter Port, Guernsey GY1 1BX. Tel: 01481 724337. Fax: 01481 710545. Email: probation@gov.gg
Jersey Probation and After-care Service: PO Box 656, 1 Lemprière Street, St Helier, Jersey JE4 8YT. Tel: 01534 441900. Email: contactus@probation.je Website: www.probation.je
Isle of Man Prison and Probation Service: 27–29 Prospect House, Prospect Hill, Douglas, Isle of Man IM1 1ET. Tel: 01624 687324. Email: probation.dha@gov.im Website: www.gov.im/dha/probation

RETIRED OFFICERS' ASSOCIATIONS

NATIONAL ASSOCIATION OF RETIRED POLICE OFFICERS
38 Bond Street, Wakefield WF1 2QP. Tel: 01924 362166. Fax: 01924 372088.
Email: hq@narpo.org Website: www.narpo.org.uk

NATIONAL EXECUTIVE COMMITTEE

Eastern	Mr L Wright, 130 Ainsdale Drive, Werrington, Peterborough PE4 6RP.
	Mr B Burdus, 1 Stowe Avenue, West Bridgeford, Nottingham NG2 7QH.
London	Mrs J A Cole, Lauradale, Norwich Road, Edgefield NR24 2RL.
	Mr N Hartfree, 87 Lime Grove, New Malden KT13 3TR.
Midlands	Mr N F Taylor, 3 Harrington Court, Jervoise Drive, Birmingham B31 2XU.
	Mr J Carrington, 159 Dovedale Road, Ettingshall Park, Wolverhampton WV4 6R.E
North East	Mr R A Storry, Badgers Gill, 46 Riversdene, Stokesley, North Yorkshire TS9 5DD.
	Mr T W Storey, 34 Fairfield Avenue, Knaresborough HG5 8HB.
North West	Mrs K Rowley QPM, Choma, 19 St Edmunds Park, Carlisle CA2 6TS.
	Mrs S E Wilde Ma, Vice President, 94 Sandringham Road, Bredbury, Stockport SK6 2EL.
South East	Mr I F Potter, 7 North Hill Way, Bridport DT6 4JX.
	Mr G Alexander, 6 Horam Park Close, Horam, East Sussex TN21 0HW.
South West	Miss L Haydon, 17 Birchwood Road, Exmouth EX8 4LH.
	Ms P A Gates, 72 The Nursery, Ashton, Bristol BS3 3EB.
Wales	Mr R E Evans MVO QPM, President, CaeClyd, Wynn Gardens, Old Colwyn, Clwyd LL29 9RB.
	Mrs M Morgan, Marbryn, Greenfield Close, Pontnewydd, Cwmbran NP44 1BY.

Chief Executive Officer: Clint Elliott QPM, NARPO House, 38 Bond Street, Wakefield WF1 2QP. Tel: 01924 362166.
Deputy Chief Executive Officer: Steve Edwards, as above.
Financial Controller: Sue Ward, as above.

BRANCH SECRETARIES

Altrincham	Mr J Forster, 338 Northenden Road, Sale M33 2PW.
Avon & Somerset	Mr D E Leach, BSc, 3 Cherwell Road, Keynsham BS31 1QU.
Barnsley	Mr M O'Hara, 26 Ainsdale Road, Royston, Barnsley S71 4HJ.
Bedfordshire	Mr L Stewart, 15 Loveridge Avenue, Kempston MK42 8SF.
Berkshire	See TVP Berkshire
Birmingham	Mr N F Taylor, 3 Harrington Court, Jervoise Drive, Birmingham B31 2XU.
Blackpool	Mr J Pickard, 97 Norcliffe Road, Blackpool FY2 9EN.
Bolton & District	Mr E Holliday, 9 Barnston Close, Astley Bridge, Bolton BL1 8TF.
Bournemouth	Mrs J Talbot, 654 Castle Lane West, Bournemouth BH8 9UG.
Bradford	Mr D Wright, 9 Sylvan Avenue, Queensbury, Bradford BD13 2HZ.
Brighton & District	Mr P J Burrows, 4 View Road, Peacehaven, Brighton BN10 8DE.
Bristol Avon	Ms P A Gates, 72 The Nursery, Ashton, Bristol BS3 3EB.
Buckinghamshire	See TVP Buckinghamshire
Burnley	Mr R Newton, 471 Newchurch Road, Higher Cloughfold, Rossendale BB4 7TG.
Bury & District	Mr R Laing, 47 Garstang Drive, Bury BL8 2JS.
Cambridgeshire	Mr B Upchurch, 18 Church Way, Little Stukeley, Huntingdon PE28 4BQ.
Cardiff	Mr A Greaves, 11 Clos Cromwell, Rhiwbina, Cardiff CF14 6QN.
Chelmsford	Mr R Good, 78 Lime Walk, Chelmsford CM2 9NH.
Chester	Mr F Hough, 2 Boughton Hall Drive, Great Boughton, Chester CH3 5QQ.
Chichester & District	Mr L Mann, 42 Foxdale Drive, Angmering, Littlehampton BN46 4HF.
Cleveland	Mr R A Storry, Badgers Gill, 46 Riversdene, Stokesley TS9 5DD.
Colchester	Mr R C Bird, Chelsfield, Mill Road, Marks Tey, Colchester C06 1EA.
Cornwall	Mr P V O'Brien, Higher Tresmarrow, St Thomas, Launceston PL15 7EP.
Coventry	Mr S Francis, 17 Pennant Road, Burbage, Leicester LE10 2LA.
Crewe & District	Mr M Holmes, 12 Abbotsbury Close, Wistaston, Crewe CW2 6XD.
Cumberland	Mrs J Lowther, 3 Low Moor Avenue, Blackwell, Carlisle CA2 4SX.
Dartford & District	Mr D L Kiell, 6 Harris Close, Northfleet, Gravesend DA11 8PY.
Denbigh	Mr G Roberts, Colwyn, 32 Maes Brith, Dolgellau, Gwynedd LL40 1LF.
Derbyshire	Mr S Murphy, 34 The Delves, Swanwick, Alfreton DE55 1AR.
Devon, North	Mr P Lambourn, 10 Station Close, Holsworthy EX22 6DE.
Devon, South	Mr J H Ball, 51 Pegasus Court, Torquay Road, Paignton TQ3 2UB.
Dewsbury	Ms K A Bainbridge-Keith, An Searin, Tigh Poilis, 1–2 Uig Portree IV51 9XP.
Doncaster	Mr L Agar, 13 Sycamore Crescent, Bawtry DN10 6LE.
Dorset	Mr C Probin, 4 Old School Lane, Owermoinge, nr Dorchester DT2 8FQ.
Dudley	Mr A Mifsud, Melita, 1 Ibis Gardens, Kingswinford, Dudley DY6 8XS.
Durham County	Mr B C Crawford, 8 Warwick Place, Peterlee SR8 2EZ.
Dyfed Powys	Mr C Cowey, 36 Elder Grove, Llangunnor, Carmarthen SA31 2LQ.
Eastbourne & District	Mr R Diplock, 20 Purbeck Close, Eastbourne BN23 8EX.
Exeter & District	Miss L Haydon, 17 Birchwood Road, Exmouth EX8 4LH.
Flint	Mr J R Jones, 14 Viola Avenue, Rhyl LL18 2NE.

Gateshead	Mr J McCoy, 7 Ashtrees Gardens, Low Fell, Gateshead NE9 5BH.
Glamorgan	Mr A Crocombe, 16 Deri Avenue, Pen Coed, Bridgend CF35 6TU.
Gloucestershire	Mr J Bennett, 1 Peakstile Peace, Woodmancote, Cheltenham GL52 9XA.
Gwent	Miss S Davies, 5 Ross Street, Newport, Gwent NP20 5RD.
Gwynedd	Mr T J Edwards, Pentre Hwfa, Rhostrehwfa, Llangefni LL77 7YP.
Halifax	Mr P Cuthill, 20 Caldercroft, Elland HX5 9AY.
Hampshire, North	Mr M Lloyd, 12 Conholt Road, Andover SP10 2HR.
Hampshire (Southampton)	Mr G J Crowe, 83 Brunswick Road, Fair Oak, Eastleigh SO50 8FF.
Harrogate & Skipton	Mr T Storey, 34 Farfield Avenue, Knaresborough HG5 8HB.
Hastings & District	Mrs J Harper-Watson, Dalkeith, North Lane, Guestling Thorn TN35 4LX.
Hertfordshire	Mr A Wright, Station House, 97 Station Road, Odsey SG7 5RT.
Huddersfield	Mr T Jepson, 21 Hawkroyd Bank Road, Netherton, Huddersfield HD4 7JP.
Humberside	Mr M Le Grove, 2 Willow Gardens, Barrow-upon-Humber DN19 7SW.
Isle of Man	Mr D Newbery, 107 Ballabrooie Way, Douglas, Isle of Man IM1 4HD.
Isle of Wight	Mr A Stovell, Pine Gap, Old Park Road, St Lawrence, Ventnor PO38 1XR.
Keighley	Mr R J Bousfield, 24 Hazelgrove Road, Sutton-in-Craven, Keighley BD20 7QT.
Kent, East	Mr P Eggleton, Primrose Cottage, 74 Swan Lane, Sellidge, Ashford TN25 6HB.
Lancaster & Morecambe	Mr G Richardson, 1 St Michael's Crescent, Bolton-le-Sands, Carnforth LA5 8LD.
Leeds & District	Mrs P E Revill-Johnson, 11 Layton Mount, Rawdon, Leeds LS19 6PQ.
Leicestershire	Mr T Ludlam, Nutwood, 4 Rupert Crescent, Queniborough LE7 3TU.
Lincolnshire	Mr M Holmes, 230 Sleaford Road, Boston PE21 7PG.
London	The Branch Secretary, Global House, 1 Ashley Avenue, Epsom, Surrey KT18 5AD.
London, City of	Mr P Gilbert, 3 Valley Mushroom Farm, Ricketts Hill Road, Tatsfield TN16 2NG.
Macclesfield	Mr G H Allen, 69 Tytherington Drive, Macclesfield SK10 2HN.
Maidstone & District	Mr G Coles, Burnlea, Grove Green Lane, Weavering, Maidstone ME14 5JW.
Manchester & District	Mr R Dunbar, 10 Larch Avenue, Stretford, Manchester M32 8HZ.
Medway & District	Mr B Goldfarb, 7 Saracen Fields, Walderslade, Chatham ME5 9DG.
Merseyside	Mr D Anderton LLB, 15 Childwall Park Avenue, Childwall, Liverpool L16 0JE.
Norfolk	Mr E Bussey, 13 Spixworth Road, Old Catton, Norwich NR6 7NE.
Northamptonshire	Mrs P Kirk, Northamptonshire NARPO, Police HQ, Wootton Hall, Northampton NN4 0JQ.
Northumbria	Mr J A Tailford, 15 Romsey Close, Cramlington NE23 1NQ.
Northwich	Mr G Ilott, 8 Water Street, Northwich CW9 5HP.
Nottinghamshire	Mr J Kennedy, 139 Cavendish Road, Carlton, Nottingham NG4 3ED.
Oldham & District	Mr G W Hale, 29 Fir Tree Avenue, Hathershaw, Oldham OL8 2NG.
Oxfordshire	See TVP Oxfordshire
Plymouth & District	Mr G Stephens, 20 Lester Close, Higher Compton PL3 6PX.
Pontefract	Mr G D Knight, 17 Lynwood Close, Streethouse, Pontefract WF7 6BX.
Portsmouth/Gosport	Mr A N Thompson, 24 Sovereign Crescent, Locksheath, Fareham PO14 4LT.
Preston & District	Mr A I Edwards, 8 Lyndale Avenue,Lostock Hall, Preston PR5 5UU.
Rochdale	Mr J Bamford, 12 Dewhirst Road, Rochdale OL12 0AG.
Rotherham & District	Mr M France, The Willows, Hawthorne Avenue, Maltby, Rotherham S66 8BT.
St Helens	Mr J Russell, 8 Rectory Close, Winwick WA2 8LD.
Salford	Mr D Russell, 296 New Church Road, Stacksteads, Bacup OL13 0UJ.
Scarborough	Mr K Moore, 73 Box Hill, Scarborough YO12 5NQ.
Sheffield	Mr A R Shenton, 14 Linden Court, Ecclesfield, Sheffield S35 9UZ.
South Shields	Mr H Sprouting, 2 Field Terrace, Jarrow NE32 5PH.
Southend-on-Sea	Mr P J Yorke-Wade, 12 Springwater Close, Leigh-on-Sea SS9 5BN.
Southport & District	Mr L E Waltho, 12 Nuthall Road, Southport PR8 6XB.
Staffordshire	Mr D Lockwood, 97 Pirehill Lane, Walton, Stone ST15 0AS.
Suffolk	Mr L C Jolley, 9 Reade Road, Holbrook, Ipswich IP9 2QL.
Sunderland	Mr A Pattison MBE, 10 Cliffe Court, Seaburn, Sunderland SR6 9NT.
Surrey, West	Mr L Milligan, 12 Spring Avenue, Egham TW20 9PL.
Sussex, North	Mr A Christie, 18 Reynard Close, Horsham RH12 4GX.
Swansea	Mr P D Taylor, Beaumont, Bryntawe Road, Ynystawe, Swansea SA6 5AD.
Tameside (Manchester)	Mr F Lee, 32 Hob Hill, Stalybridge SK15 1TP.
Tunbridge Wells	Mr N Govett, 17 Highfield Road, Kemsing, Sevenoaks TN15 6TN.
TVP Berkshire	Mrs A McMahon, Claret House, Mill Lane, Calcot, Reading RG31 7RS.
TVP Buckinghamshire	Mr S W Swann BEM, 2 Crosby Close, Malthouse Square, Beaconsfield HP9 2JU.
TVP Oxfordshire	Mr P M Cusworth, 6 The Spears, Yarnton, Kidlington OX5 1NS.
Tyneside, North	Mr D O'Flanagan, 6 The Haven, Roya Quays, North Shields NE29 6YH.
Wakefield	Mr R Critchley, 8 West Court, Roundhay, Leeds LS8 2JP.
Walsall	Mr S Groves, 72 Walsall Road, Great Wyrley, Walsall WS6 6LA.
Warrington	Mr M S McLoughlin, 200 Liverpool Road, Great Sankey, Warrington WA5 1RB.
Warwickshire	Mr B G Caley, 5 Blandford Road, Leamington Spa CV32 6BH.
West Mercia	Mrs M Case, 22 Marsh Avenue, Worcester WR4 0HJ.
Westmorland-with-Furness	Mr J Hetherington, 2 Town End Court, Natland, Kendal LA9 7PZ.
Wigan	Mr F Woolley, 6 Deanwood Avenue, Orrell, Wigan WN5 8QF.
Wiltshire	Mr B Reed, 2 Wayside Drive, Devizes SN10 3EZ.
Wirral	Mr D E Jones, 17 Bryanston Road, Prenton CH42 8PF.
Wolverhampton	Mr P Snape, 47 Southgate End, Cannock WS11 1PS.

Worthing & District	Mrs L Stevens, 117 Princess Avenue, Worthing BN13 1AS.
York	Mrs C Blain, 31 Heslington Lane, York YO10 4HN.
York East Riding	Miss A Marshall, 9 Kingston Avenue, Hessle, Hull HU13 9LR
York North Riding	Mr A Barr, 48 Brompton Road, Northallerton DL6 1ED.

RETIRED POLICE OFFICERS' SCOTLAND ASSOCIATION
Email: rpoascty@yahoo.co.uk Website: www.rpoas.org.uk

President: Lindsay Lowson, 8 Underwood Place, Balloch, Inverness IV2 7RF.
Vice President: William Coughtrie, Westwinds, 50 Monument Road, Ayr KA7 2UA.
Secretary: David Brown, 7 Alloway Drive, Kirkcaldy KY2 6DX.
Treasurer: Arthur Donaldson MBE, 17 Deanburn Gardens, Seafield, Bathgate, West Lothian EH47 7GB.
Branch Secretaries:
Argyll: John Glass, 235b Alexandra Parade, Kirn, Dunoon PA23 8HD.
Ayrshire: David Seawright, 2 Carson Drive, Irvine KA12 2HR.
Central: Lesley Struth, 186 Alloway Drive, Kirkintilloch G66 2RU.
Dumfries: Andrew McMillan, 112 Oakfield Drive, Georgetown, Dumfries DG1 4UX.
Fife: Brian Steer, 10 Fingask Avenue, Glenrothes KY7 4RR.
Glasgow: Robert Law 25 Galbraith Drive, Milngavie, Glasgow G62 6LZ.
Highlands & Islands: David Conner, 17 MacKenzie Park Gardens, Inverness IV2 3SU. Email: rpoas.highland@gmail.com
Lanarkshire: Christopher Keegan, 60 Muirhead Road, Baillieston G69 7HB.
Lothian & Borders: Glenn Milne, Beech Lodge, 27B Manse Road, Roslin EH25 9LG. Email: landbsec@gmail.com
North East: Ronald (Ron) Findlay, 21 Lochside Drive, Bridge of Don, Aberdeen AB23 8EH. Email: ronfindlay@gmail.com
Renfrew/Dunbarton: David Patterson, 11 Garnie Crescent, Erskine PA8 7BG.
Tayside: Andrew McKay QPM, Janaig, Wolfhill Road, Guildtown, Perth PH2 6DL.

ASSOCIATION OF EX CID OFFICERS OF THE METROPOLITAN POLICE
Website: www.exscotlandyarddetectives.org

President: Mr Peter Crow.
Hon Secretary: Robert Fenton QGM. Tel: 01923 263543. Email: bob.fenton@exscotlandyarddetectives.org
Membership is open to all former members of the CID of the Metropolitan Police on their retirement or resignation from the police service and to any ex-officer who served part of his or her service in the Metropolitan Police as a CID officer. Its objects are to maintain the comradeship formerly enjoyed in the CID. The Association was established in 1950.

THE FLYING SQUAD ASSOCIATION

President: Lord John Stevens QPM LLB.
Chairman: Barry Phillips.
Secretary: Barry Jones MBE. Tel: 01237 474869. Mob: 07776 393538.
Membership is open to all current serving and retired officers and staff of the Metropolitan Police Flying Squad. The aim of the Association is to maintain the contact and comradeship enjoyed by serving members of the Metropolitan Police Flying Squad and to generate funds for charitible purposes.

GROUPS AND ASSOCIATIONS

INTEREST GROUPS

ASSOCIATION OF MUSLIM POLICE (AMP)
Email: muslimpolice@hotmail.com
The Association of Muslim Police (AMP) aims to: assist Muslims in the police service to observe their faith, and to promote understanding of Islam within the police service and the wider community; provide a forum for Muslims in the police, and support their religious and welfare needs, with a view to improving their immediate working environment and retaining them in the service; assist in the recruitment and retention of Muslim staff, and in the creation of a fair and just working environment for all cultural minorities.

BRITISH ASSOCIATION FOR WOMEN IN POLICING
PO Box 999, Bordon, GU35 5AQ. Website: www.bawp.org
National Co-ordinator: Parwinder Dale. Tel: 07790 505204. Email: coord@bawp.org *Secretary:* Carolyn Williamson MBE. Tel/fax: 0844 414 0448. Email: sec@bawp.org
BAWP provides a voice for women in policing, lobbies on their behalf, and is a network of professional contacts within the policing 'family'. Full membership is available to police officers and staff, both men and women, and members of allied policing organisations such as SOCA, NPIA and HMIC.

BRITISH POLICE SYMPHONY ORCHESTRA
Email: info@bpso.org.uk. Website: www.bpso.org.uk
Chair: Mike Cunningham, Chief Constable, Staffordshire Police.
Membership is open to all serving or retired police/civilian personnel. While improving police/public relations, the aims of the Orchestra are to provide an education in the art of music and to raise funds for other charities. Concerts are arranged nationally with leading professional performers. Email info@bpso.org.uk for information. Registered Charity No 1003562.

CATHOLIC POLICE GUILD
CPG Box, 42 Francis Street, London SW1P 1QW. Email: secretary@catholicpoliceguild.org.uk. Website: www.catholicpoliceguild.org.uk
Patrons: The Archbishops and Bishops of England and Wales. *President:* Patrick J Somerville QPM. *Chairman:* Andrew Natrass. *Secretary:* Chris Sloan. *National Chaplain:* Vacant.
Membership is open to all serving and retired police officers, special constables and civilian support staff of recognised police forces in the United Kingdom.

THE GAY POLICE ASSOCIATION (GPA)
GPA, London WC1N 3XX. Action line tel: 07092 700000 (24 hrs). Fax: 07092 700100. Email: info@gpa.police.uk. Website: www.gay.police.uk
Chairman: Paul M Cahill MBE. Email: chair@gpa.police.uk *Deputy Chairman:* Vic Codling. Email: deputy@gpa.police.uk
The GPA exists to: work towards equal opportunities for gay police service employees; offer advice and support to gay police service employees; promote better relations between the police service and the gay community. Membership is free to all serving and retired police officers, special constables and civilian support staff in the United Kingdom.

JEWISH POLICE ASSOCIATION
G97, Block 38, Peel Centre, Aerodrome Road, Hendon, London NW9 5JE. Tel: 07770 492782. Email: info@jewishpoliceassociation.org.uk Website: www.jewishpoliceassociation.org.uk
Chair: Mathew Shaer. *Deputy Chair:* Michael Loebenberg. *Secretary:* Danny Phillips.
The Jewish Police Association's aims and objectives are to: provide a network for support and advice to Jewish personnel within the police service; promote understanding of the Jewish faith within the police service; act as a resource reference for police services regarding religious, cultural and community issues, particularly those that affect front-line policing; actively promote the police service as an employer of choice for the Jewish community.

METROPOLITAN BLACK POLICE ASSOCIATION (MBPA)
The Piazza, Empress State Building, Empress Approach, Lillie Road, London SW6 1TR. Tel: 020 7161 0941/2. Fax: 020 7161 0115. Email: info@metbpa.com. Website: www.metbpa.com
Chair: Bevan Powell MBE.
The Metropolitan Black Police Association (MetBPA) endeavours to improve the working environment of black personnel within the Metropolitan Police Service. The Association is committed to enhancing the quality of service to the black communities of London and thus helping to improve overall police service delivery to the people of London.

METROPOLITAN POLICE SERVICE GREEK STAFF ASSOCIATION (MPSGSA)
Southgate Police Station, 1st Floor, 25 Chase Side, Southgate, London N14 5BW. Tel: 07825 106845. Email: greekstaffassociation@met.police.uk Website: www.greekpolice.co.uk
Chair: Leon Christodoulou. Email: leon.christodoulou@met.police.uk *Vice Chair:* Marc Georghiou. Email: marc.georghiou@met.police.uk *Secretary:* Tom Haji-Savva. Email: thomas.s.haji-savva@met.police.uk *Treasurer:* Phil Panayides. Email: philippos.a.panayides@met.police.uk
The aims of the MPSGSA are to develop and implement strategies to attract and retain Greek and Cypriot recruits to the Metropolitan Police, provide a focus group for Greek and Cypriot issues, provide mentoring for all members, establish a social forum for Greek and Cypriot members of the Metropolitan Police, promote MPS policies and values to its members and its community, act as a first point of contact to Greeks and Cypriots, represent its members' views strategically and review corporate policies as an active member of SAMURAI.

METROPOLITAN POLICE SIKH ASSOCIATION (MPSA)
Empress State Building, 4th Floor, North, Lillie Road, Earl's Court, London SW6 1TR. Tel: 020 7230 0141. Email: admin@sikhpolice.org Website: www.sikhpolice.org
The MPSA seeks to advance the Sikh religion among members of the Metropolitan Police and promote the efficiency of the Metropolitan Police.

METROPOLITAN WOMEN POLICE ASSOCIATION
Website: www.metwpa.org.uk
The Association was formed in 1976 to provide a means of helping Metropolitan women police officers to meet and keep in touch with each other. All serving or former Metropolitan women police officers are eligible to join at any time.

NATIONAL BLACK POLICE ASSOCIATION
PO Box 15690, Tamworth, Staffordshire B77 9HZ. Tel: 07971 162821. Website: www.nbpa.co.uk
President: Charles Crichlow. *General Secretary:* Stafford Brooks.
The National Black Police Association seeks to improve the working environment of black staff by protecting the rights of those employed within the police service and to enhance racial harmony and the quality of service to the black community of the UK.

THE POLICE COMMUNITY CLUBS OF GREAT BRITAIN
PO Box 160, Devon Waters (Level 1), Bideford, Devon EX39 2RL. Tel: 01237 474869. Email: policecc@aol.com. Website: www.policecommunityclubs.org
Patrons: Lord John Stevens QPM LLB; Gerry Sutcliffe MP; Martin Hewitt, Deputy Assistant Commissioner Metropolitan Police. *Secretary:* Barry Jones MBE. Tel: 07776 393538. Email: barryjones@policecommunityclubs.org
Administration of all police community clubs throughout the United Kingdom. Providers of projects to the police service and Home Office, including gun, knife and gang crime; sports clubs in mosques; and other bespoke citizen programmes.

POLICE HISTORY SOCIETY
Email: info@policehistory.co.uk. Website: policehistorysociety.co.uk
Patron: Lord Knights CBE QPM DL. *President:* Sir Denis O'Connor CBE QPM MA. *Chair:* Rob Beckley QPM, Deputy Chief Constable, Avon and Somerset Constabulary. *Secretary:* Steve Bridge. *Membership Secretary:* Leonard Woodley, 37 South Lawne, Bletchley, Milton Keynes MK3 6BU. Email: len.woodley@btopenworld.com
The Police History Society was founded in 1985 and now has over 350 members, including serving and retired members of police forces, academics, librarians, writers, police forces and police related museums and people from many occupations who have an interest in police history. The object of the Society is to advance public education in police history. It holds an annual conference and publishes an annual journal, as well as a newsletter three times a year.

POLICE INSIGNIA COLLECTORS ASSOCIATION OF GREAT BRITAIN (PICA GB)
Website: www.pica.co.uk
Chair: Vic Wilkinson (Chief Supt (Rtd) Metropolitan). 2 The Heights, Bumbles Green Lane, Nazeing, Essex EN9 2SG. *Secretary:* Christian Duckett (Sgt Surrey Police). 7 Ely Close, Frimley, Surrey GU16 9FB. Email: chris.duckett@ntlworld.com. *Treasurer:* Steve Marriott (PC (Rtd) Metropolitan). 8 Betchley Close, East Grinstead, West Sussex RH19 2DA. Email: pica.marriott@tiscali.co.uk *Membership Secretary:* Tony Collman (PC Surrey Police). 8 Foxon Lane, Gardens, Caterham, Surrey CR3 5SN (for all membership enquires). Email: tony@tcollman.freeserve.co.uk
PICA has over 500 members around the world and unlike, many other associations, has matured over the years to support and welcome civilians and police officers alike, although many members are serving or retired police officers. We hold regular Swaps meetings throughout the year, which are spread around the country and all members are encouraged to attend, when and if possible. PICA's aims are: to keep alive the history of the police service through the insignia, photographs and other recorded detailed information; to foster comradeship through a mutual interest in police insignia; and to devote ourselves, individually and collectively, to upholding the best traditions of the police service.

POLICE SPORT UK
Website: www.policesportuk.com
Administration Manager: Mr I E Campbell. 19 Lingwood Park, Cartmel Road, Grange-over-Sands, Cumbria LA11 7QA. Tel: 07976 720156. Email: ianecampbell@hotmail.co.uk
Joint Presidents: The Secretaries of State for the Home Department for Scotland, Wales and Northern Ireland. *Chair:* Steve Finnigan CBE QPM BA MA DipAC&PS, Chief Constable, Lancashire Constabulary.
The Council of Police Sport UK is the governing body for all affiliated sports taking place between UK police forces. The Association is divided into sections covering each sport and deals with the general policy of administering competitions and championships for the benefit of all serving police officers, police cadets, special constables, police staff, PSNI part time reserves, retired police officers and retired police staff, including employees of the Scottish Police Services Authority (SPSA), former police staff now employed by the Serious Organised Crime Agency (SOCA) and personnel affected by the transfer of former police civilian staff through the TUPE process. Police Sport UK is a member of the Union Sportive des Polices d'Europe (UPSE), allowing officers the opportunity to compete abroad with fellow officers from European countries.

SEMPERSCOTLAND (SUPPORTING ETHNIC MINORITY POLICE STAFF FOR EQUALITY IN RACE)
Bishopbriggs Police Office, 113 Kirkintilloch Road, Bishopbriggs G64 2AA. Tel: 0141 207 5809. Fax: 0141 207 5810. Email: info@semperscotland.org.uk Website: www.semperscotland.org.uk
Chair: Baseem Akbar. *Vice-Chair:* Aaron Chadha. *Secretary:* Misheck Muchemwa. *Treasurer:* Carolyn Isong. *Director:* Sandra Deslandes-Clark. *Hon President:* Robin Iffla.
SEMPERscotland was established and publicly inaugurated in 2004, primarily to (a) support and represent minority ethnic employees; and (b) promote equality of opportunity and fairness throughout the police service. The organisation is run by an executive committee made up of members of staff from various ranks and levels within the service, who are committed to promoting wider understanding of the needs of minority ethnic employees and the contribution they make to the overall success of the Police Service of Scotland. Full membership is open to all minority ethnic serving police officers, special constables and civilian staff employed by any of the police services in Scotland. Associate membership is open to individuals and organisations that support the aims of the organisation.

INTERNATIONAL GROUPS

EUROPEAN ASSOCIATION OF AIRPORT & SEAPORT POLICE
Website: www.eaasp.net
President: John Donlon QPM. 10 Victoria Street, London SW1H 0NN. Tel: 020 7084 8550. Email: john.donlon@homeoffice.gsi.gov.uk
Vice President Maritime: Peter van den Berg. Dienst Waterpolitie, tav PR van den Berg, Postbus 867, 3300 AW Dordrecht, Netherlands. Tel: 078 648 2163. Email: peter.van.den.berg@klpd.politie.nl
Vice President Aviation: Eddie Yome. Police Headquarters, New Mole House, Gibraltar. Tel: 350 200 48055. Email: edward.yome@royalgib.police.gi
General Secretary: Paul Campbell. The Old Court House, c/o The Police Station, Library Road, Totton SO40 3ZE. Tel: 023 8067 4446. Email: paul.campbell@hampshire.pnn.police.uk

ICC COMMERCIAL CRIME SERVICES (CCS)
Cinnabar Wharf, 26 Wapping High Street, London E1W 1NG. Tel: 020 7423 6960. Fax: 020 7160 5249. Email: ccs@icc-ccs.org Website: www.icc-ccs.org
Director: Mr P Mukundan.
ICC Commercial Crime Services is the anti-crime arm of the International Chamber of Commerce. Based in London, CCS is a membership organisation tasked with combating all forms of commercial crime.
Counterfeiting Intelligence Bureau (CIB). Email: cib@icc-ccs.org
Assistant Director: Max Vetter.
Established in 1985 to investigate and prevent product counterfeiting on an international basis, the CIB is one of the world's leading organisations dedicating to combating the counterfeiting of products and documents, protecting the integrity of intellectual property and brands, and preventing copyright abuse. CIB hosts the International Hologram Image Register and publishes the annual International Anti-Counterfeiting Directory.
Financial Investigation Bureau (FIB). Email: fib@icc-ccs.org
Divisional Director: Mr P Mukundan.
The FIB conducts enquiries and investigations into matters associated with money laundering, fraud, and suspect documents. Its membership includes international banks and financial institutions, regulatory authorities, and law enforcement agencies. It maintains a confidential database on all aspects of commercial fraud, including reports on suspected fraudsters operating worldwide, as well as providing document authentication and due diligence checks for members.
International Maritime Bureau (IMB). Email: imb@icc-ccs.org
Deputy Director: Michael Howlett.
The IMB is a non-profit-making organisation established in 1981 to act as a focal point in the fight against all types of maritime crime and malpractice. The IMB is supported by a resolution of the International Maritime Organisation which urges governments to co-operate and exchange information with the IMB, which is recognised by the Home Office and has observer status with ICPO-Interpol. It also runs the IMB Piracy Reporting Centre.
FraudNet. Email: fraudnet@icc-ccs.org
FraudNet is a global network of law firms which specialise in tackling business crime.

INTERNATIONAL ASSOCIATION OF WOMEN POLICE
Website: www.iawp.org
President: Chief Insp Jane Townsley.
UK Contact: Julia Jaeger. Region 13 Co-ordinator (Europe), 34 Shaftesbury Crescent, Staines, Middlesex TW18 1QW. Tel: 07963 628465. Email: jaeger_julia@hotmail.com.
The aims of the Association are to increase professionalism in police work, to further the utilisation of women in law enforcement and to provide a forum for sharing developments in police administration. Membership is open to both women and men.

INTERNATIONAL POLICE ASSOCIATION
United Kingdom
British Section Administration Centre, Arthur Troop House, 1 Fox Road, West Bridgford, Nottingham NG2 6AJ. This is the executive office, to which all correspondence should be addressed. Tel: 0115 981 3638 (24-hour answerphone). Fax: 0115 981 3349. Email: mail@ipa-uk.org Website: www.ipa-uk.org
President: Tom Crozier. *Secretary General:* Dave Taylor.

There are over 9000 members in Section UK, organised in 11 regions. Membership is open to serving and retired police officers, PCSOs, scene of crime officers, investigating officers, and members of the special constabulary. Officers who resigned after five years' service or more may also apply.

International
Headquarters: c/o International Secretary General (see below).
President: Pierre-Martin Moulin, 1933 Sembrancher, Switzerland. *International Secretary General:* Georgios Katsaropoulos. International Administration Centre, Arthur Troop House, as above. Tel: 0115 945 5985. Fax: 0115 982 2578. Email: isg@ipa-iac.org. *International Treasurer:* Romain Miny, BP 55, L-7571 Mersch, Luxembourg.
Membership is worldwide.

INTERNATIONAL PROFESSIONAL SECURITY ASSOCIATION
IPSA, Railway House, Railway Road, Chorley, Lancashire PR6 0HW. Tel: 0845 873 8114. Fax: 0845 873 8115. Email: post@ipsamail.org.uk. Website: www.ipsa.org.uk
Chief Executive Officer: Justin P Bentley. *Chairman:* Michael White. *Vice President:* Patrick J Somerville QPM.
The Association is a professional body which offers individual and company membership to those employed at all levels in the manned guarding sector of the security industry and those intending to pursue a career in security, including those currently serving in the armed services or other law enforcement and police services. The Association is represented on various industry bodies, and consults with the Home Office on matters relevant to the security industry and those employed in it. Through training courses delivered in accordance with standards set nationally for the industry, it provides opportunities for career development and the raising of standards across the industry. Member companies are subject to regular inspection for compliance with relevant British Standards, and all members are expected to adhere to the Association Code of Conduct and Ethical Code. Regional activities encourage co-operation, the exchange of information, ideas and experience, and promote best practice at regional, national and international levels.

INTERPORT POLICE
Email: info@interportpolice.org. Website: www.interportpolice.org
President: Chief Ronald J Boyd. *Secretary General:* Jay Grant.

PROFESSIONAL ASSOCIATIONS

ADS GROUP LTD
ADS Show Centre, ETPS Road, Farnborough, Hampshire GU14 6FD. Tel: 020 7091 4500. Fax: 020 7091 4546. Email: enquiries@adsgroup.org.uk. Website: www.adsgroup.org.uk
Director Security: Bob Rose.
ADS is a not for profit trade association providing support and advice to UK companies supplying the police and other public security agencies. It processes enquiries from government departments and identifies supply sources for the widest range of policing equipment requirements. ADS acts as a focal point between the public security sector and industry and organises the annual Security & Policing exhibition on behalf of the Centre for Applied Science and Technology (CAST).

ASSOCIATION OF POLICE AND CRIME COMMISSIONERS (APCC)
Tel: 020 7202 0080. Twitter: @AssocPCCs Website: www.apccs.police.uk
Chief Executive, Transitional Board of the Association of Police and Crime Commissioners: Mark Castle OBE.
The APCC was commissioned by the Home Office to help ensure a smooth transition from police authorities to elected PCCs and to provide an interim support function for all police and crime commissioners (PCCs) and police governance bodies until 31 March 2013. This work has been developed by the Association of Police and Crime Commissioners' Transitional Board and the Home Office. The future of the APCC will be determined by PCCs and policing governance bodies. Should it be commissioned to work beyond April 2013, it will relocate to new office premises. For full details please see www.apccs.police.uk

ASSOCIATION OF POLICE COMMUNICATORS (APCOMM)
Email: info@policecommunicators.org.uk Website: www.policecommunicators.org.uk
Hon President: Chief Constable Andy Trotter, Chair, ACPO Communications Advisory Group. *Chair:* Amanda Coleman, Greater Manchester Police. Email: amanda.coleman@gnp.pnn.police.uk. *Vice-Chairs:* Tony Diggins, Lincolnshire Police. Email: tony.diggins@lincs.pnn.police.uk. Dan Barton, West Midlands Police. Email: daniel.barton@west-midlands.pnn.police.uk. Ed Stearns, Metropolitan Police. Email: ed.stearns@met.police.uk *Treasurer:* Tony Diggins, as above. *Secretary:* Jacqui Hanson, Cheshire Constabulary. Email: jacqui.hanson@cheshire.pnn.police.uk. *Membership Secretary:* Tanya Croft, Devon and Cornwall Police. Email: tanya.croft@devonandcornwall.pnn.police.uk
The Association of Police Communicators represents the hundreds of professional police staff who work in specialist media and corporate communications roles supporting the police service. Membership of APComm provides access to a network of like-minded people who are striving to improve people's knowledge and understanding of modern policing, helping them to access police services.

ASSOCIATION OF POLICE HEALTH AND SAFETY ADVISORS (APHSA)
Email: enquiries@aphsa.org.uk Website: www.aphsa.org.uk
Chair: Nicholas Cornwell-Smith, Lincolnshire Police. Tel: 01522 558043. *Vice Chair:* Nick Kettle, Metropolitan Police. Tel: 020 7161 0850. *Treasurer:* Steven Thorley-Lawson, West Yorkshire Police. Tel: 01924 292567. *Secretary:* Anthony Boswell, Lancashire Constabulary. Tel: 01772 413656.
The Association was formed in 1995 and recognised by ACPO in 1996. Its objectives are: to promote policies which lead to a reduction in accidents, disease, ill health and dangerous occurrences within the police service; to raise the

profile of health and safety, promote knowledge and understanding of effective health and safety management; to promote the appointment and training of professional safety advisors; to promote health and safety training.

ASSOCIATION OF POLICE LAWYERS
Legal Services Department, County Police HQ, No 1 Waterwells, Quedgeley, Gloucestershire GL2 2AN. Tel: 01452 754306. Fax: 01452 721709.
Chair: Vacant. *Vice Chair:* Michelle Buttery, West Mercia Police. *Secretary:* Paul Trott, Gloucestershire Constabulary. *Treasurer:* Lisa-Marie Smith, West Midlands Police.
The Association represents lawyers employed by police forces throughout England, Wales, Scotland and Northern Ireland and is active in promoting the development of police legal services particularly through training and exchange of information.

ASSOCIATION OF POLICE PROCUREMENT PROFESSIONALS
Chair: Sean Lally-Randall, Director of Category Management, Metropolitan Police. *Secretary:* Sheena Evans, Thames Valley Police.
Formed in 1994 with the support of the ACPO Procurement Sub-Committee, the Association is a professional consultative body which aims to support the police service and individual chief officers. It also aims to improve the technical competence and management skills of those responsible for purchasing and contracts in the police service, and to act as a forum for the exchange of information and the facilitation of co-operative procurement arrangements. Since 1996 its activities have come under the auspices of the ACPO Finance Committee.

ASSOCIATION OF POLICING AND CRIME CHIEF EXECUTIVES (APAC²E)
Chair: Fraser Sampson, Chief Executive West Yorkshire OPCC. *Treasurer:* Paul Hammond, Chief Executive Thames Valley OPCC. *Secretary:* Jenni Douglas-Todd, Hampshire OPCC. **Contact:** *Research & Co-ordination Officer:* Mark Sayer. c/o 3 Hoffmanns Way, Chelmsford CM1 1GU. Tel: 01245 291644. Mob: 07595 009713. Email: mark.sayer@essex.pnn.police.uk
All chief executives to police and crime commissioners in England, Wales and Northern Ireland are members of the Association. The objectives of the Association are: to provide professional support and development for its members in their role; to liaise and work closely on behalf of its members with any bodies representing the interests of police and crime commissioners, chief officers and police and crime panels, and any body representing the interests of police and crime commissioners' chief finance officers, government departments and other relevant bodies.

BRITISH POLICE AND SERVICES CANINE ASSOCIATION
Website: www.bpsca.co.uk
Editor of The Service Dog: Keith Long. 42 Greenacres, Gawthorpe, Ossett, West Yorkshire WF5 9RX. Tel: 07712 129984. Email: kdlong@blueyonder.co.uk. *Membership Secretary:* John Warbutton, 6 Meadway Crescent, Selby, North Yorkshire Y08 4FX. Tel: 07841 472542. Email: johnbpsca@aol.com
Membership is composed of serving and retired members of dog sections in UK police forces, HM Prison Service, HM Customs and Excise, HM Immigration Service, the armed services, British Transport Police, the UKAEA Constabulary, Ministry of Defence Police, MOD Guard Services and the fire service. The object of the Association is to promote the friendship and welfare of its members, arrange seminars and competitions, both nationally and internationally, and to encourage an exchange of ideas between service dog handlers both in the United Kingdom and abroad.

CORONERS' OFFICERS AND STAFF ASSOCIATION (COASA)
PO Box 3781, Chester CH1 9YJ. Email: enquiries@coasa.org.uk. Website: www.coronersofficer.org.uk
Chair: Debbie Large. Tel: 01634 799182. Email: chair@coasa.org.uk *Treasurer & Membership Secretary:* Christine Hurst. Email: membership@coasa.org.uk; treasurer@coasa.org.uk *A/Secretary:* Sonia Brooks. Email: secretary@coasa.org.uk
Membership is open to all persons working within or in association with the coroner service. The COASA will liaise with any relevant government department or other organisation or association on behalf of its members in order to promote and develop professional knowledge and interests to enhance the service to coroners, associated professionals and bereaved people. Training enquiries should be directed to debbie.coa@hotmail.co.uk

CORONERS' SOCIETY OF ENGLAND & WALES
HM Coroner's Court, St George's Hall, St George's Place, Liverpool L1 1JJ. Website: www.coroner.org.uk
Hon Secretary: André Rebello, HM Coroner for Liverpool.
Membership is open to coroners, deputy coroners, assistant deputy coroners and retired coroners.

COSLA (THE CONVENTION OF SCOTTISH LOCAL AUTHORITIES)
Verity House, 19 Haymarket Yards, Edinburgh EH12 5BH. Tel: 0131 474 9200. Fax: 0131 474 9292. Email: info@cosla.gov.uk Website: www.cosla.gov.uk
Chief Executive: Rory Mair.

THE FINGERPRINT SOCIETY
Website: www.fpsociety.org.uk
President: Karen Stow. *Chair & A/Editor:* Robert Doak, Humberside Police. Email: robert.doak@humberside.pnn.police.uk *Secretary* Luke McGarr. Email: secretary@fpsociety.org.uk *Membership Secretary:* Allison Power.
The Fingerprint Society was formed in 1974 for the benefit of fingerprint officers and scenes of crime officers employed within the police and military authorities. Membership of the Society is open to personnel employed within these sectors and those with an interest in fingerprints. The Society, an international body with members from most parts of the world, aspires to advance the study and application of fingerprints and allied sciences and facilitate co-operation among persons involved in the fields of personal identification. It publishes a quarterly journal, *Fingerprint Whorld*, which is sent to fellows and members. The Society holds an annual conference each spring where many new techniques and items of equipment are demonstrated. Qualified fingerprint experts within the Society are known as Fellows of the Society (FFS) and non-experts, Members of the Society (MFS).

FORENSIC SCIENCE SOCIETY

Clarke House, 18a Mount Parade, Harrogate HG1 1BX. Tel: 01423 506068/566973. Fax: 01423 566391. Email: info@forensic-science-society.org.uk. Website: www.forensic-science-society.org.uk

The Forensic Science Society was founded in October 1959 with the objects: to advance the study and applications of forensic science and to facilitate co-operation among persons interested in forensic science. Membership is open to scientists, lawyers, pathologists, forensic medical examiners and specialist police officers (e.g. photographers, vehicle examiners, fingerprint experts, CID officers, etc.). The field covered is both civil and criminal, research and applied. The Society offers diplomas (by examination) in specific areas, namely: document examination, identity documents, firearms examination, crime scene examination and fire investigation. The Society is international in scope, and publishes a journal, *Science & Justice*, which is issued free to members. The Society became a professional body in 2004 and now has new membership categories: membership and fellowship. It also offers an accreditation scheme to HEIs and the first accredited courses were awarded on 1 November 2006. Applications for membership should be addressed to the membership administrator at the above address.

NATIONAL ASSOCIATION OF CHAPLAINS TO THE POLICE

National Police Chaplain: Canon David Wilbraham, Thames Valley Police. Tel: 01865 846916. Email: david.wilbraham@thamesvalley.pnn.police.uk. Website: www.police-chaplains.org.uk

The object of the Association is to advance and support the work of chaplaincy to UK police forces by assisting the ministry of mainstream faith communities to the police service, and by promoting the Association of Police Chaplains for mutual assistance and training. Chaplaincy is offered to all people, regardless of faith or belief. Membership, currently 600, is open to all who are appointed to police chaplaincy and authorised by the appropriate police and religious authorities. Associate membership is open to those who, by reason of their occupation, are associated with the work of police chaplains.

NATIONAL ASSOCIATION OF POLICE FLEET MANAGERS (NAPFM)

Chair: Mr K Wilson (Northumbria Police). Tel: 01661 863406. Fax: 01661 863418. Email: keith.wilson.4465@northumbria.pnn.police.uk *Vice Chair:* Mr D Ord (Sussex Police). Tel: 01273 404024. Fax: 01273 404284. Email: dennis.ord@sussex.pnn.police.uk *Secretary:* Mr M Davy (Norfolk Constabulary). Tel: 01953 423695. Fax: 01953 423698. Email: davym@norfolk.pnn.police.uk *Treasurer:* Mr S Sloan (Hertfordshire Constabulary). Tel: 01707 354380. Fax: 01707 354391. Email: sam.sloan@herts.pnn.police.uk **Press & Information:** Mr R Pope (Leicestershire Police). Tel: 0116 248 2130. Fax: 0116 248 2036. Email: robert.pope@leicestershire.pnn.police.uk

The NAPFM aims to support the police service and individual chief officers as a professional consultative body and to improve the technical competence and managerial skills of those responsible for the operation and maintenance of police vehicle fleets.

PORT POLICE CHIEF OFFICERS' ASSOCIATION

Email: info@ppcoa.org Website: www.ppcoa.org

The Association was formed to develop professional contacts between the UK port police forces of Belfast, Bristol, Dover, Felixstowe, Liverpool, Tees & Hartlepool and Tilbury.

TRADE UNION

UNISON

UNISON Centre, 130 Euston Road, London NW1 2AY. Email: b.priestley@unison.co.uk. Website: www.unison.org.uk

General Secretary: Dave Prentis. *National Officer Responsible for Police Staff* (*England & Wales*)*:* Ben Priestley. *Regional Organiser Responsible for Police Staff* (*Scotland*)*:* Gerry Crawley. Email: g.crawley@unison.co.uk

The union deals with police staff pay, conditions of service, pensions and all other matters arising from employment in the police service, and organises its police staff membership in branches within each force area. UNISON also has regional police and justice committees and a UK Police and Justice Executive with representatives from all English regions, plus Scotland and Wales. UNISON police staff undertake a wide range of operational, administrative, clerical, technical, professional and other duties within all police forces in England (not Metropolitan), Scotland and Wales.

SERVICES

AUDIO/VIDEO INTERVIEW RECORDING

AV NICHE (RECORDING SYSTEMS) LIMITED

5 Heron Court, Cranes Farm Road, Basildon SS14 3DF. Tel: 01268 474608. Fax: 01268 531482. Email: avniche@btconnect.com. Website: www.avniche.co.uk

Managing Director: Neil Holmes.

AV Niche provides a complete range of digital audio and audio/video interview recorders, transcription software and workflow management solutions, including network ready and NPIA ISIS programme friendly options, as well as dedicated audio-visual recording systems for numerous applications including training.

DAVID HORN COMMUNICATIONS LIMITED

Comtec House, Bramingham Business Park, Enterprise Way, Luton LU3 4BU. Tel: 01582 490300. Fax: 01582 490700. Email: sales@dhcltd.co.uk. Website: www.davidhorncommunications.com

Managing Director: David Horn. *Directors:* Jeff Horn; Stuart Horn; Maureen Horn. *Business Manager:* Geoff Bwye.

At the forefront of interview recording technologies since 1985, the company is now the world's largest producer of police digital interview equipment. Meeting all national standards, its MultiStream range is modular and upgradeable. Systems are available from the DVD recorder range (including portables) through to solutions compatible with new and existing back-offices. The company is a market leader in the provision of audio/video evidence and intelligence gathering equipment. A wide range of off-the-shelf surveillance products is available together with a large in-house design facility manufacturing innovative and custom-made solutions.

EMPLOYMENT

EPIC – EX POLICE IN INDUSTRY & COMMERCE
65 Poplar Hill, Stowmarket, Suffolk IP14 2AX. Email: secretary@epic-uk.com. Website: www.epic-uk.com
Patron: Don Dovaston OBE QPM. (*Retired*) *Chair:* David Ryan. *Secretary:* Graham H Dooley.
EPIC members are professionals in corporate environments or individual businesses whose police background has helped them develop and provide services, processes, or products across the whole commercial environment.

POLICING SUPPORT SERVICES (PSS)
3–4 Elwick Road, Ashford, Kent TN23 1PF. Tel: 01233 614790. Fax: 01233 646840.
    Email: info@policing-support.com. Website: www.policing-support.com
Directors: Lord Imbert of New Romney CVO QPM JP; Simon Imbert; Gerald Moor.
Policing Support Services contracts experienced former police officers and civilian staff to police forces across the UK. Client forces use PSS operatives for a range of work including helping to cope with operational demand peaks and to provide back-office support in a variety of functions requiring police knowledge. PSS also provides former senior staff for management functions such as planning and review.

SERVOCA RESOURCING SOLUTIONS
41 Whitcomb Street, London WC2H 7DT. Tel: 0845 073 7800. Fax: 0845 073 7801.
    Email: policing@servoca.com. Website: www.servoca-police.com
Servoca Resourcing Solutions provides police-skilled staff and law enforcement personnel, specialising in former police officers, across all areas of investigation, intelligence, enforcement and training. The company's national database also covers specialist civilian and security staff. Servoca Managed Services provides managed and outsourced services covering a wide range of operational policing, civil and criminal justice needs, ranging from independent investigations, case and departmental reviews through to crime scene guarding and tape transcription.

TROY MANAGED SERVICES
Global House, Ashley Avenue, Epsom KT18 5AD. Tel: 01372 253204. Fax: 01372 253201.
    Email: info@troyms.com. Website: www.troyms.com
Supplier of investigative, training and consultancy resources, either on an ad hoc basis or longer term, to the law enforcement and criminal justice sectors. Specialist in providing bespoke solutions to meet clients' resource requirements.

EQUIPMENT

ARKTIS LTD
4a Brookside Industrial Units, Venny Bridge, Exeter EX4 8JN. Tel: 01392 201614. Fax: 01392 461993. Email (sales): debbie@arktisltd.co.uk; jo@arktisltd.co.uk; (design) william@arktisltd.co.uk Website: www.arktisltd.co.uk
Arktis Ltd is a UK manufacturer of equipment vests and waterproof clothing.

FINANCE

POLICE MUTUAL ASSURANCE SOCIETY LTD
Alexandra House, Queen Street, Lichfield, Staffordshire WS13 6QS. Tel: 0845 882 2999. Fax: 01543 305349.
    Website: www.policemutual.co.uk
Police Mutual was set up by the police in 1922 and today is a leading provider of financial services and welfare support for members of the police service and their families. With over 200,000 members, it is the UK's largest friendly society of its kind, offering a full range of financial planning help and services. Police Mutual collaborates with forces across the UK to promote financial health and personal wellbeing. It is overseen by a committee of management which includes some of its members as well as senior representatives of the police service, to ensure that it is run in the interests of both the police service and its membership.

FORENSIC

CELLMARK FORENSIC SERVICES
PO Box 265, Abingdon, Oxfordshire OX14 1YX. Tel: 01235 528609. Email: info@cellmark.co.uk. Website: www.orchidcellmark.co.uk
Cellmark provides a comprehensive analytical service for a range of forensic casework, including specialist services for the investigation of sexual offences and the review of cold cases. Cellmark's reputation is built on the quality of its DNA analysis, its success rates and the speed and responsiveness of its service. It combines traditional forensic expertise with an innovative approach.

ENVIRONMENTAL SCIENTIFICS GROUP LTD
Derwent House, Bretby Business Park, Ashby Road, Bretby, Burton-upon-Trent DE15 0YZ. Tel: 01283 554400. Fax: 01283 554549. Email: sales@esg.co.uk. Website: www.esg.co.uk
Managing Director: Norman Sleeth. Tel: 01283 554313.
Environmental Scientifics Group is a multi-disciplinary organisation providing forensic analysis and technical support services, including the examination of glass, paint, shoe marks and tool marks from bulk crime investigation. The laboratory specialises in the analysis of controlled drug substances, providing rapid analyses of street purchase deals and scene examiners to assist with the collection and preservation of evidence.

FORENSIC TELECOMMUNICATIONS SERVICES LTD
PO Box 242, Sevenoaks, Kent TN15 6ZT. Tel: 01732 459811 (24/7 advice & call-out line). Email: info@forensicts.co.uk. Website: www.forensicts.co.uk
Managing Director: Ray Clethro.
Sevenoaks Laboratory. Tel: 01732 459811. Fax: 01732 741261. *Forensic Manager:* Chris Tomlin.
Warrington Laboratory. PO Box 143, Warrington WA3 6ZB. Tel: 07919 050945. *Exhibits Officer:* Robin Preece.
Specialist Telecoms Advisors: Eastern England, Scotland & NI STA – Police & Cell Site: Ray Chappell. Tel: 07876 591823. *Wales & Western England STA – Police & Cell Site:* Ray Jones. Tel: 07876 136642.
Forensic Telecommunications Services Ltd (FTS) specialises in extracting, analysing and presenting data from mobile phones, cellular networks and all forms of computing and mobile telecommunications technology. It provides technical services and data extraction tools to a wide range of security services, police forces, legal services and corporate clients. It supports the activities of law enforcement and internal security agencies worldwide through providing specialised software, hardware and training solutions. FTS is an accredited ISO9001:2008 and ISO17025:2009 company.

LGC FORENSICS
Head office: Queens Road, Teddington, Middlesex TW11 0LY. Tel: 0844 2641 999. Email: forensic@lgcforensics.com. Email (staff): firstname.lastname@lgcforensics.com. Website: www.lgcforensics.com
Managing Director: Steve Allen. *Director of Finance:* Francis King. *Operations Director:* Jennifer Pratt. *Head of Service Delivery Analytical:* Martin Hanly. *Head of Service Delivery Case Work:* Guy Shorley. *Commercial Director:* Paul Harding. *Forensic Services Manager:* Mark Pearse. *Chief Scientist:* Brian McKeown.
UK Laboratories: Bromsgrove (Worcestershire); Culham (Oxfordshire); Leeds (specialist firearms facility); Runcorn and Risley (Cheshire); St Neots (Cambridgeshire); Tamworth (Staffordshire); Teddington (Middlesex).
LGC Forensics provides casework and analytical services in DNA techniques, controlled drugs, toxicology, ecology, questioned documents, digital crime, firearms and ballistics and forensic pathology. With eight UK and two German forensic laboratories, it provides bespoke services at a local level to customers including police forces, other law enforcement agencies, coroners, and government departments. It has access to other specialist teams across the LGC Group including pathologists, forensic pathology services and a victim identification and mass fatalities team.

HELICOPTERS

EUROCOPTER UK LTD
Oxford Airport, Kidlington, Oxfordshire OX5 1QZ. Tel: 01865 852400. Email: sales@eurocopter.co.uk
Website: www.eurocopter.co.uk
Eurocopter UK's helicopters create bespoke solutions for all kinds of missions including police. Eurocopter UK was established in November 2007 through the purchase of McAlpine Helicopters Ltd. Its headquarters are in Oxford, and it also has bases in Dublin, Belfast, Wales and Aberdeen. It has over 450 helicopters in service in the British Isles.

TRAFFIC

TELE-TRAFFIC (UK) LTD
LaserTec Centre, C2 Harris Road, Warwick CV34 5JU. Tel: 01926 407272. Fax: 01926 407977. Email: tt@teletraffic.co.uk. Website: www.teletrafficuk.com
Managing Director: Paul Garratt. *Customer Services & Business Development Manager:* Mike Ricketts.
Tele-Traffic UK Ltd pioneers LASER speed measurement and traffic data collection systems. The company provides road traffic enforcement solutions to more than 98 per cent of the UK's police forces and the whole of Ireland. It also offers courses relating to specific Tele-Traffic products, and on the legislation and signage associated with highway speed enforcement and management.

CHARITIES

POLICE CHARITIES

CHRISTIAN POLICE ASSOCIATION (CPA)
Bedford Heights, Manton Lane, Bedford MK41 7PH. Tel: 01234 272865. Email: info@cpauk.net. Website: www.cpauk.net
Executive Director: Don Axcell.
Founded in 1883, the CPA promotes the fellowship of Christians in the police service and encourages them in their faith. The CPA also seeks to build bridges between the police service and the Christian community. Registered Charity No 220482.

GURNEY FUND FOR POLICE ORPHANS
9 Bath Road, Worthing, Sussex BN11 3NU. Tel: 01903 237256. Website: www.gurneyfund.org
Patron: HM The Queen.
For the care and education of the children of deceased or incapacitated police officers from subscribing forces in England and Wales. Registered Charity No 261319.

METROPOLITAN & CITY POLICE ORPHANS FUND
30 Hazlewell Road, Putney, London SW15 6LH. Tel: 020 8788 5140. Fax: 020 8789 7047. Website: www.met-cityorphans.org.uk
Patron: HM The Queen. *President:* Sir Bernard Hogan-Howe QPM. *Vice-President:* A Leppard. *Chairman:* Bob Broadhurst QPM. *Deputy Chairman:* N Basu. *Chief Executive Officer:* Phillip Cronin. *Deputy Chief Executive Officer:* Peter Smyth.
Registered Charity No 234787.

THE NATIONAL POLICE COMMUNITY TRUST
PO Box 160, Devon Waters (Level 1), Bideford, Devon EX39 2RL. Tel: 01237 474869. Email: nationalpolicect@aol.com
Patrons: Lord John Stevens QPM LLB; Gerry Sutcliffe MP; Martin Hewitt, Deputy Assistant Commissioner, Metropolitan Police. *Secretary:* Barry Jones MBE. Tel: 07776 393538.
For the support of police community projects throughout England and Wales. Registered Charity No 1079612.

NATIONAL POLICE FUND
3 Mount Mews, High Street, Hampton, Middlesex TW12 2SH. Tel: 020 8941 7661. Fax: 020 8979 4323. Email: office@nationalpolicefund.org.uk Website: www.pdtrust.org
The National Police Fund came into being after the General Strike of 1926, when *The Times* newspaper organised a fund open to public subscription in recognition of the good services of the police. The Fund is incorporated by Royal Charter which regulates its charitable activities. It concentrates on supporting police benevolent funds, on giving assistance for the education of children of police officers and supporting recreational activities. Registered Charity No 207608.

NATIONAL POLICE MEMORIAL DAY
Federation House, Highbury Road, Leatherhead, Surrey KT22 7UY. Tel: 07843 293958. email: nationalpolicememorialday@polfed.org Website: www.nationalpolicememorialday.org
Patron: HRH The Prince of Wales. *Founder:* Joe Holness QPM.
The National Police Memorial Day aims to: remember police officers who have been killed or died on duty; demonstrate to relatives, friends, and colleagues of fallen officers that their sacrifice is not forgotten; recognise annually the dedication to duty and courage displayed by police officers. Registered Charity No 1103000.

POLICE DEPENDANTS' TRUST
3 Mount Mews, High Street, Hampton, Middlesex TW12 2SH. Tel: 020 8941 6907. Fax: 020 8979 4323. Email: office@pdtrust.org Website: www.pdtrust.org
Patron: HM The Queen. *Chief Executive Officer:* Richard Moule. *Chairman:* Terry Spence.
The object of the Trust as stated in the Deed dated 21 December 1966 is 'to assist in cases of need a) dependants of police officers or former police officers who die or have died, whether before, on or after the date hereof, as a result of an injury received in the execution of duty; b) police officers or former police officers who are, or have been, whether before, on or after the date hereof, incapacitated as a result of an injury received in the execution of duty or dependants of such officers'. Registered Charity No 251021.

THE POLICE FOUNDATION
First Floor, Park Place, 12 Lawn Lane, London SW8 1UD. Tel: 020 7582 3744. Fax: 020 7587 0671. Website: www.police-foundation.org.uk
President: The Rt Hon Sir John Chilcot GCB. *Chairman:* Sir William Jeffrey. *Director:* John Graham. Email: john.graham@police-foundation.org.uk. *PA to the Director:* Sue Roberts. Email: sue.roberts@police-foundation.org.uk
The Police Foundation aims to improve policing and promote the safety and security of every citizen by providing an independent, evidence-led perspective on policing and related matters. It is the only charity focused entirely on developing people's knowledge and understanding of policing, challenging the police service and the government to improve policing and acting as a bridge between the public, the police service and the government, while being owned by none of them. A full list of publications and other information about the Foundation can be found on its website www.police-foundation.org.uk. Registered Charity No 278257.

THE POLICE MEMORIAL TRUST
Police Roll of Honour Trust, PO Box 999, Preston PR4 5WW. Tel: 07775 633655. Fax: 020 7602 9217. Email: enquiries@policememorial.org.uk Website: www.policememorial.org.uk

Manager & Vice-Chairman: Steve Lloyd.
The aims and objects of the Trust are the promotion of good citizenship through the provision and maintenance of memorials to police officers killed in the execution of their hazardous duty and through these memorials also to honour the police service in general and subject thereto to relieve the need of police officers or their dependants arising from the special hazards of police duty. The Trust erected the National Police Memorial in the Mall, unveiled by HM The Queen in April 2005. Registered Charity No 289371.

POLICE PENSIONERS' HOUSING ASSOCIATION LTD
Registered office: c/o Green Wright Chalton Annis (Solicitors), 1 Tarrant Street, Arundel, West Sussex BN18 9AZ. Website: policepensionershousingassn.co.uk
Patron: Lord Mackenzie of Framwellgate OBE LLB(Hons). *President:* Mr D J Milburn MBE. *Chairman:* Ian Eady. *Treasurer:* Graham Hill. *Secretary:* Robert Davies. Pine Garth, 21 West Close, Middleton-on-Sea, West Sussex PO22 7RP. Tel/fax: 01243 586643. Email: ppha.secretary@btinternet.com
The PPHA was founded in 1968 to establish sheltered warden assisted accommodation for police pensioners and their spouses, widows, or widowers, from any police area, who are over 60 years old, provided they are able to look after themselves. Registered Charity No XN23781A. Industrial & Provident Society No 19085R.

POLICE REHABILITATION CENTRE
Flint House, Reading Road, Goring-on-Thames, Oxfordshire RG8 0LL. Tel: 01491 874499. Fax: 01491 875002 (24 hrs). Email: enquiries@flinthouse.co.uk Website: www.flinthouse.co.uk
Patron: HM The Queen. *Chief Executive:* Commander Tom McAuslin RN.
Flint House offers convalescence and rehabilitation to all ranks of serving police officers and pensioners. Facilities include physiotherapy and hydrotherapy treatment with fully equipped gymnasium; 24-hour nursing cover; individual counselling if requested. Application forms available on the website or from force welfare officers, occupational health departments, etc. Further particulars available on request. Registered Charity No 1146913.

POLICE REHABILITATION TRUST
2nd Floor West, Edinburgh House, 170 Kennington Lane, London SE11 5DP. Tel: 020 7091 5108/5112. Email: info@polrehab.co.uk Website: www. polrehab.co.uk
Chairman of the Trustees: The Lord Dear QPM DL. *Director:* Mr C M Mann.
During the last 25 years, the Trust has contributed more than £5 million towards the conversion and expansion of Flint House in the Thames Valley as the Police Rehabilitation Centre. Its support continues to be needed for capital development and refurbishment, for the provision of equipment and comforts to help police officers recovering from physical injury and mental stress. Pledges, donations and legacies are urgently needed for the Trust to continue this important work. Registered Charity No 292941.

POLICE ROLL OF HONOUR TRUST
PO Box 999, Preston PR4 5WW. Tel: 07775 633655. Email: enquiries@policememorial.org.uk Website: www.policememorial.org.uk
Patron: Sir Denis O'Connor CBE QPM. *Hon President:* Sir Hugh Orde OBE QPM, President of ACPO. *Chairman:* Sidney MacKay. *Treasurer:* Peter Olphert. *Manager & Vice-Chairman:* Steve Lloyd. *Secretary:* David Acheson.
The Trust researches and maintains the National Police Officers' Roll of Honour for the UK police service. The Roll is an ongoing historical record of officers who have lost their lives in the line of duty, by any means. The Trust maintains a comprehensive archive of information relating to some 4000 line of duty deaths over three centuries of professional law enforcement. It is able to provide support, advice and information and particularly welcomes contact from relatives of officers killed on duty. Registered Charity No 1081637.

THE POLICE TREATMENT CENTRES
St Andrew's, Harlow Moor Road, Harrogate, North Yorkshire HG2 0AD; Castlebrae, Castleton Road, Auchterarder, Perthshire PH3 1AG. Tel: 01423 504448 (all enquiries). Fax: 01423 527543. Email: chiefexecutive@thepolicetreatmentcentres.org. Website: Www.thepolicetreatmentcentres.org
Patron: HRH The Prince Andrew, Duke of York. *Chief Executive:* Michael Baxter QPM BA(Hons) MCIPD.
Intensive physiotherapy and treatment facilities for serving and retired officers from forces in the north of England, North Wales, Scotland and Northern Ireland. Registered Charity No 220956. OSCR No SC039749.

PRRT (POLICE REHABILITATION AND RETRAINING TRUST)
Maryfield Complex, 100 Belfast Road, Holywood, Co Down BT18 9QY. Tel: 028 9042 7788. Fax: 028 9042 3566. Email: info@prrt.org Website: www.prrt.org
The PRRT, a non-profit making arm's length body of the Department of Justice Northern Ireland, was established in 1999 to support former and retiring police officers with personal development and employment transition assistance; training, education and employment support; physiotherapy and psychological therapies. PRRT helps its clients to achieve and enjoy optimum mental and physical well-being beyond policing.

ROYAL ULSTER CONSTABULARY GEORGE CROSS FOUNDATION
Brooklyn, 65 Knock Road, Belfast BT5 6LE. Tel: 028 9070 0116. Fax: 028 9056 1516. Email: rucgcfoundation@nics.gov.uk Website: www.rucgcfoundation.org
Patron: HRH The Prince of Wales. *Chairman:* Jim McDonald CBE LVO KCSG GCHS JP DL.
The Foundation was established by virtue of the Police (Northern Ireland) Act 2000 for the purpose of 'marking the sacrifices and honouring the achievements of the Royal Ulster Constabulary'.

THE ST GEORGE'S POLICE CHILDREN TRUST
St Andrew's, Harlow Moor Road, Harrogate, North Yorkshire HG2 0AD. Tel: 01423 504448. Fax: 01423 527543. Email: chiefexecutive@thepolicetreatmentcentres.org
Chief Executive: Michael Baxter QPM BA(Hons) MCIPD.
The Trust provides financial support for the children of officers who have died or been incapacitated from earning a living on or off duty. Registered Charity No 220955. OSCR No SC038769.

GENERAL CHARITIES

BRITISH RED CROSS SOCIETY
44 Moorfields, London EC2Y 9AL. Tel: 0844 871 1111. Fax: 020 7562 2000. Website: www.redcross.org.uk
Patron: HM The Queen. *Chairman:* Sir Charles Allen CBE. *CEO:* Sir Nicholas Young.
The British Red Cross is a volunteer-led humanitarian organisation that helps people in crisis, whoever and wherever they are. It enables vulnerable people at home and overseas to prepare for and respond to emergencies in their own communities. When the crisis is over, it helps people recover and move on with their lives.

CARNEGIE HERO FUND TRUST (FOUNDED 1908)
Andrew Carnegie House, Pittencrieff Street, Dunfermline, Fife KY12 8AW. Tel: 01383 723638. Fax: 01383 749799. Email: herofund@carnegietrust.com. Website: www.carnegiehero.org.uk
Chief Executive: Nora T C Rundell BA MBA MCMI.
The aim of the Carnegie Hero Fund Trust is to recognise heroism and give financial assistance, if necessary, to people who have been injured and have, therefore, incurred appreciable financial loss; or to dependants of people who have died performing acts of heroism in peaceful pursuits. The act of heroism must have occurred in Great Britain, Ireland, the Channel Islands, or surrounding territorial waters. The Trust would welcome reports on acts of heroism which fall within the above criteria. Please send details to the office at the above address. Scottish Charity No SCO 00729.

CHILD VICTIMS OF CRIME
Staff Office, Child Victims of Crime, City of London Police, Wood Street Police Station, 37 Wood Street, London EC2P 2NQ. Tel: 01785 227325. Email: info@cvoc.org.uk. Website: www.cvoc.org.uk
President: Sir Ronnie Flanagan GBE QPM MA. *Patron:* Ben Richards.
Child Victims of Crime (CVOC) is the only national police children's charity. It was founded by the British Police Rugby Section in response to the aftermath of the 1993 terrorist bomb explosion in Warrington that killed two young boys. CVOC seeks to provide practical and emotional support for any child up to the age of 16 years who has been a victim of or traumatised by any crime committed in the UK, as well as personal safety education to help prevent children becoming victims of crime. Registered Charity No 1043101.

CHILDREN 1ST (ROYAL SCOTTISH SOCIETY FOR PREVENTION OF CRUELTY TO CHILDREN)
83 Whitehouse Loan, Edinburgh EH9 1AT. Tel: 0131 446 2300. Fax: 0131 446 2339.
Email: info@children1st.org.uk Website: www.children1st.org.uk
ParentLine Scotland (free helpline for parents and carers). Tel: 0800 028 2233. Confidential email: parentlinescotland@children1st.org.uk
Safeguarders Panel. Tel: 0131 319 8066. Email: safeguarderspanel@children1st.org.uk
CHILDREN 1ST supports families under stress, protects children from harm and neglect, helps children recover from abuse and promotes children's rights and interests. For more information about specific services offered by our projects, phone or visit our website. Registered Charity No SC 016092.

CRIMESTOPPERS TRUST
Tel: 020 8835 3700. Fax: 020 8835 3701. Email: cst@crimestoppers-uk.org Website: www.crimestoppers-uk. org
Chief Executive: Michael Laurie CBE. *Director of Operations:* Roger Critchell. *Director of Finance:* Bob Booker FCCA. *Director of Business Development:* Rodger Holden.
Crimestoppers works in partnership with law enforcement agencies, the media and the community. It runs the 0800 555 111 number, which allows members of the public to call anonymously with information about criminals and criminal activity. In addition, the Crimestoppers Most Wanted Website (www.mostwanted-uk.org) allows police forces to appeal for information on a national basis. If the information leads to an arrest and charge, the caller may be eligible to receive a cash reward, provided by Crimestoppers. Crimestoppers also provides call-handling services to the police through its 24/7 bureau based in Surrey. Registered Charity No 1108687.

INSTITUTE OF ADVANCED MOTORISTS
Headquarters: IAM House, 510 Chiswick High Road, London W4 5RG. Tel: 020 8996 9600. Fax: 020 8996 9601. Website: www.iam.org.uk
President: Nigel Mansell CBE. *Chief Executive:* Simon Best.
The Institute of Advanced Motorists (IAM) supports the raising of driving and riding standards and campaigns for increased on-road skills. Its commercial business, IAM Drive & Survive, promotes occupational driver improvement through the fleet/business community. Registered Charity No 249002.

MISSING PEOPLE
284 Upper Richmond Road West, London SW14 7JE. Tel: 020 8392 4590; 0871 222 5055 (all police enquiries). Fax: 020 8878 7752. Email: services@missingpeople.org.uk Website: www.missingpeople.org.uk
Missing People provides support for missing children, vulnerable adults and families left in limbo. It offers the families of the missing specialist advice and practical support, as well as searching and securing publicity that could end years of heartache.

NSPCC
Weston House, 42 Curtain Road, London EC2A 3NH. Tel: 020 7825 2500. Fax: 020 7825 2525. 24-hour Child Protection Helpline: 0808 800 5000. ChildLine: 0800 1111. Email: info@nspcc.org.uk. Website: www.nspcc.org.uk
Chair, Board of Trustees: Mark Wood. *Director & Chief Executive:* Andrew Flanagan (until June 2013); Peter Wanless (from June 2013).
The NSPCC works to prevent cruelty to children. The NSPCC Helpline is for anyone who has concerns about the welfare of a child, and is free, and confidential. The NSPCC also has divisional offices across England, Wales and Northern Ireland which can be contacted via the National Centre. Registered Charity No 216401.

ROYAL HUMANE SOCIETY
50/51 Temple Chambers, 3–7 Temple Avenue, London EC4Y 0HP. Tel/fax: 020 7936 2942. Email: info@royalhumanesociety.org.uk. Website: www.royalhumanesociety.org.uk
Patron: HM The Queen. *President:* HRH Princess Alexandra KG GCVO. *Chairman & Treasurer:* Richard Titley. *Secretary:* Dick Wilkinson TD.
Founded in 1774, the Society gives awards to those who put their lives into danger, or perform a praiseworthy action, in saving or attempting to save someone. It also gives awards to those who have effected a successful resuscitation. Registered Charity No 231469.

THE ROYAL LIFE SAVING SOCIETY UK (RLSS UK)
River House, High Street, Broom, Alcester, Warwickshire B50 4HN. Tel: 01789 773994. Fax: 01789 773995. Email: lifesavers@rlss.org.uk Website: www.lifesavers.org.uk
Patron: HM The Queen. *Commonwealth President:* HRH Prince Michael of Kent GCVO. *President:* Stuart Bailey. *CEO:* Di Standley.
RLSS UK is a charity, governing body and lead provider of training and education in lifesaving, lifeguarding, water safety and life support skills in the UK. Registered Charity No 3033781.

ROYAL SOCIETY FOR THE PREVENTION OF ACCIDENTS (ROSPA)
Head Office: RoSPA House, 28 Calthorpe Road, Edgbaston, Birmingham B15 1RP. Tel: 0121 248 2000. Fax: 0121 248 2001. Email: help@rospa.com Website: www.rospa.com
Patron: HM the Queen. *President:* Lord Jordan of Bournville CBE. *Chief Executive:* Tom Mullarkey MBE. *Deputy Chief Executive:* Errol Taylor.
Road Safety Regional Organisation: England: 28 Calthorpe Road, as above. Tel: 0121 248 2000. **Scotland:** *Regional Manager.* Livingston House, 43 Discovery Terrace, Heriot-Watt University Research Park, Edinburgh EH14 4AP. Tel: 0131 449 9378. **Wales:** *Regional Manager.* 2nd Floor, 2 Cwrt-y-Parc, Parc Ty Glas, Cardiff Business Park, Llanishen, Cardiff CF14 5GH. **Northern Ireland:** *Regional Manager.* Nella House, Dargan Crescent, Belfast BT3 9JP. Tel: 028 9050 1160.
RoSPA National Road Safety Committee, RoSPA National Safe Driving Awards, RoSPA Advanced Drivers' Association, RoSPA dvd/video library, RoSPA professional training courses, RoSPA defensive driving courses, RoSPA publications and posters, RoSPA health and safety consultancy, RoSPA auditing services, RoSPA Occupational Safety & Health awards.

RSPB
The Lodge, Sandy, Bedfordshire SG19 2DL. Tel: 01767 680551. Fax: 01767 692365. Website: www.rspb.org.uk
Chief Executive: Dr Mike Clarke. *Head of Investigations:* Bob Elliot. *Investigations Officers:* Duncan McNiven; Guy Shorrock; Mark Thomas; James Leonard (North East Office). *Head of Investigations (Scotland):* Ian Thomson. *Investigations Officer (Scotland):* Elsie Ashworth. Tel: 0131 317 4100. *Data Intelligence Manager:* Helen Mason. *Investigations Co-ordinator:* Vicki Blair. Email: vicki.blair@rspb.org.uk
The RSPB has regional offices throughout England, Scotland, Wales and Northern Ireland.

RSPCA
Wilberforce Way, Southwater, Horsham, Sussex RH13 9RS. Tel: 0300 1234 555. 24-hour national cruelty and advice line: 0300 1234 999. Fax: 0303 123 0100. Website: www.rspca.org.uk
Chief Executive: Gavin Grant.
The RSPCA has five regional offices throughout England and Wales.

ST ANDREW'S FIRST AID
48 Milton Street, Glasgow G4 0HR. Tel: 0141 332 4031. Fax: 0141 332 6582. Website: www.firstaid.org.uk
Patron: HRH The Princess Royal.
St Andrew's First Aid is Scotland's premier provider of first aid training and services and is one of the country's leading charities. Every year it teaches vital life-saving skills to over 20,000 people. St Andrew's Ambulance Corps volunteers provide first-aid cover at events throughout Scotland. Registered Charity No SC006750.

ST JOHN AMBULANCE
27 St John's Lane, Clerkenwell, London EC1M 4BU. Tel: 08700 104950. Fax: 08700 104065. Website: www.sja.org.uk
Sovereign Head: HM The Queen.
A voluntary organisation of The Order of St John. Registered Charity No 1077265.

VICTIM SUPPORT
Hallam House, 50–60 Hallam Street, London W1W 6JL. Tel: 020 7268 0200. Victim support line tel: 0845 303 0900. Fax: 020 7268 0210. Website: www.victimsupport.org.uk
President: HRH The Princess Royal. *Chair:* Enid Rowlands. *Chief Executive:* Javed Khan. *Assistant Chief Executives:* Susannah Hancock; Adam Pemberton.
Victim Support (VS) is the independent national charity for people affected by crime. Victims do not have to report a crime to the police to get help, and can ask for support at any time, regardless of when the crime happened. VS has a network of offices across England and Wales which run and co-ordinate local services. It also runs the Witness Service in every criminal court to help those called as witnesses. The Victim Support line (0845 30 30 900) gives immediate help and puts people in touch with local teams. VS is not a government agency or part of the police. VS also campaigns for greater awareness of the effects of crime and to increase the rights of victims and witnesses. Registered Charity No 298028.

WRVS
WRVS Cardiff Gate, Beck Court, Cardiff Gate Business Park, Cardiff CF23 8RP. Tel: 0845 600 5885. Website: www.wrvs.org.uk

Patron: HM The Queen. *President:* The Duchess of Cornwall. *Chairman:* Richard Greenhalgh. *Chief Executive:* David McCullough.

WRVS' network of over 45,000 volunteers provides a regular visitor and practical services, including Meals on Wheels, home library services, social centres and community transport to thousands of people in local communities throughout England, Wales and Scotland every day. Teams of trained and equipped WRVS emergency services volunteers are on call 24 hours a day, 365 days a year, and are able to assist in rest centres for evacuees and provide refreshments for the fire, police and ambulance services on site. WRVS works with local emergency response teams and is included in 98 per cent of local authority emergency plans.

GAZETTEER

LOCATIONS IN THE UNITED KINGDOM

This is not a complete gazetteer of place names in the United Kingdom. Some force entries contain locations which are not included here and, therefore, reference should also be made to the appropriate force entry. Police stations designated under s35 PACE Act 1984 are indicated in each entry in England and Wales by a dagger †, or are listed separately.

Ab-Kettleby *Leicestershire*
Abbey Hey *Gtr Manchester*
Abbey Hulton *Staffordshire*
Abbeyhills *Gtr Manchester*
Abbeytown *Cumbria*
Abbey Village *Lancashire*
Abbots Bromley *Staffordshire*
Abbotsbury *Dorset*
Abbots Langley *Hertfordshire*
Abbots Leigh *Avon & Somerset*
Abbotsley *Cambridgeshire*
Abbots Ripton *Cambridgeshire*
Aberaeron *Dyfed-Powys*
Aberavon *South Wales*
Aberbargoed *Gwent*
Aberbeeg *Gwent*
Abercarn *Gwent*
Aberchirder *Police Scotland*
Abercrave *South Wales*
Abercynon *South Wales*
Aberdare *South Wales*
Aberdaron *North Wales*
Aberdeen *Police Scotland*
Aberdour *Police Scotland*
Aberdovey *North Wales*
Aberdulais *South Wales*
Aberfeldy *Police Scotland*
Aberffraw *North Wales*
Aberffrwd *Gwent*
Aberford *West Yorkshire*
Aberfoyle *Police Scotland*
Abergavenny *Gwent*
Abergele *North Wales*
Abergwili *Dyfed-Powys*
Abergwynfi *South Wales*
Abergynolwyn *North Wales*
Aberkenfig *South Wales*
Aberlour *Police Scotland*
Abernethy *Police Scotland*
Aberporth *Dyfed-Powys*
Abersoch *North Wales*
Abersychan *Gwent*
Aberthaw *South Wales*
Abertillery *Gwent*
Abertridwr *Gwent*
Abertysswg *Gwent*
Aberystwyth *Dyfed-Powys*
Abingdon *Thames Valley*
Abington *Police Scotland*
Abington Pigotts *Cambridgeshire*
Abinger *Surrey*
Abinger Hammer *Surrey*
Abney *Derby*
Aboyne *Police Scotland*
Abram *Gtr Manchester*
Abrahams Chair *Gtr Manchester*
Abridge *Essex*
Abthorpe *Northampton*
Acaster Malbis *North Yorkshire*
Acaster Selby *North Yorkshire*
Accrington *Lancashire*
Achurch *Northamptonshire*
Acklam (Malton) *North Yorkshire*
Acklington *Northumbria*
Ackton *West Yorkshire*
Ackworth Moor Top *West Yorkshire*
Acle *Norfolk*
Acocks Green *West Midlands*
Acomb *Northumbria*

Acrefair *North Wales*
Acres Wood *Staffordshire*
Acton *Metropolitan*
Acton (Crewe) *Cheshire*
Acton (Vale Royal) *Cheshire*
Acton Turville *Avon & Somerset*
Adamsdown *South Wales*
Adderbury *Thames Valley*
Adderley Green *Staffordshire*
Addingham *West Yorkshire*
Addlestone *Surrey*
Adel *West Yorkshire*
Adelaide *Cambridgeshire*
Adisham *Kent*
Adlington *Lancashire*
Adstone *Northampton*
Adswood *Gtr Manchester*
Adwick-le-Street *South Yorkshire*
Adwy *North Wales*
Affpuddle *Dorset*
Aghalee *PSNI*
Agden (Macc) *Cheshire*
Agden (Chester) *Cheshire*
Agglethorpe *North Yorkshire*
Ainderby Mires with Holtby
  North Yorks
Ainderby Quernhow *North Yorks*
Ainderby Steeple *North Yorkshire*
Ainsdale *Merseyside*
Ainsworth *Gtr Manchester*
Airdrie *Police Scotland*
Airedale *West Yorkshire*
Airlie *Police Scotland*
Airmyn *Humberside*
Airth *Police Scotland*
Airton *North Yorkshire*
Albany Street *Metropolitan*
Albert Park *Gtr Manchester*
Albert Dock *Police Scotland*
Albert Village *Leicestershire*
Albourne *Sussex*
Albrighton *West Mercia*
Albury *Hertfordshire*
Albury *Surrey*
Alcester *Warwickshire*
Alconbury *Cambridgeshire*
Alconbury Weston
  Cambridgeshire
Aldbourne *Wiltshire*
Aldbrough *Humberside*
Aldbury *Hertfordshire*
Aldeburgh *Suffolk*
Aldenham *Hertfordshire*
Aldecar *Derby*
Alderbury *Wiltshire*
Alderholt *Dorset*
Alderley Edge *Cheshire*
Aldermaston *Thames Valley*
Alderminster *Warwickshire*
Aldersey *Cheshire*
Aldershot *Hampshire*
Alderton *Suffolk*
Alderwasley *Derby*
Aldfield *North Yorkshire*
Aldford *Cheshire*
Aldingbourne *Sussex*
Aldington *Kent*
Aldreth *Cambridgeshire*
Aldridge *West Midlands*
Aldwark *Derby*

Aldwincle *Northamptonshire*
Aldworth *Thames Valley*
Alexandra Park *Gtr Manchester*
Alexandria *Police Scotland*
Alfold *Surrey*
Alford *Lincolnshire*
Alford *Police Scotland*
Alfreton *Derbyshire*
Alfrick *West Mercia*
Alfriston *Sussex*
Alkmonton *Derbyshire*
Alkrington Gdn Vill *Gtr Manchester*
Allanton *Police Scotland*
Allendale *Northumbria*
Allensford *Durham*
Allenton *Derbyshire*
Allerton *West Yorkshire*
Allerton Bywater *West Yorks*
Allesley *Warwickshire*
Allestree *Derby*
Allexton *Leicestershire*
Allington *Dorset*
Alloa *Police Scotland*
Allonby *Cumbria*
Allostock *Cheshire*
Alltwalis *Dyfed-Powys*
All Hallows *Kent*
Almondsbury *Avon & Somerset*
Alness *Police Scotland*
Alnmouth *Northumbria*
Alnwick *Northumbria*
Alport *Derbyshire*
Alpraham *Cheshire*
Alresford *Hampshire*
Alsager *Cheshire*
Alsop-le-Dale *Derbyshire*
Alston *Cumbria*
Alswear *Devon & Cornwall*
Alt *Gtr Manchester*
Althorp *Northamptonshire*
Altofts *West Yorkshire*
Alton *Hampshire*
Alton (Alfreton) *Derbyshire*
Alton (Buxton) *Derbyshire*
Alton Pancras *Dorset*
Altrincham *Gtr Manchester*
Alva *Police Scotland*
Alvanley *Cheshire*
Alvaston *Derbyshire*
Alvechurch *West Mercia*
Alveley *West Mercia*
Alveston *Avon & Somerset*
Alveston *Warwickshire*
Alwalton *Cambridgeshire*
Alway *Gwent*
Alwoodley *West Yorkshire*
Alyth *Police Scotland*
Amber Hill *Lincolnshire*
Ambergate *Derbyshire*
Amberley *Sussex*
Amble *Northumbria*
Ambleside *Cumbria*
Amersham *Thames Valley*
Amersham Common *Thames*
Amesbury *Wiltshire*
Amlwch *North Wales*
Amlwch Port *North Wales*
Ammanford *Dyfed-Powys*
Ampfield *Hampshire*

Ampleforth *North Yorkshire*
Ampthill *Bedfordshire*
Amwell *Hertfordshire*
Ancoats *Gtr Manchester*
Anderson *Dorset*
Anderston *Police Scotland*
Andersonstown *PSNI*
Anderton *Lancashire*
Andover *Hampshire*
Andoversford *Glos*
Andreas *Isle of Man*
Angmering *Sussex*
Angrim *PSNI*
Angus House *Police Scotland*
Anlaby *Humberside*
Annalong *PSNI*
Annan *Police Scotland*
Annesley *Nottinghamshire*
Annesley Woodhouse *Notts*
Annfield Plain *Durham*
Ansley *Warwickshire*
Anstey *Hertfordshire*
Anstey *Leicestershire*
Anston North *South Yorks*
Anston South *South Yorks*
Anstruther *Police Scotland*
Antony *Devon & Cornwall*
Antrim *PSNI*
Antrobus *Cheshire*
Apethorpe *Northants*
Apperknowle *Derbyshire*
Apperley Bridge *West Yorks*
Appin *Police Scotland*
Appleby *Cumbria*
Appleby Magna *Leics*
Appledore *Kent*
Appleford *Thames Valley*
Appleton *Cheshire*
Appleton *Thames Valley*
Appleton East & West *North
Yorks*
Appleton-Le-Moors *North Yorks*
Appleton-Le-Street *North Yorks*
Appleton Wiske *North Yorkshire*
Appleton Roebuck *North Yorks*
Appletreewick *North Yorkshire*
Apsley End *Hertfordshire*
Apsley Guise *Bedfordshire*
Arborfield *Thames Valley*
Arbour Square *Metropolitan*
Arclid *Cheshire*
Arbroath *Police Scotland*
Ardeley *Hertfordshire*
Ardersier *Police Scotland*
Ardgass *PSNI*
Ardington *Thames Valley*
Ardleigh *Essex*
Ardrishaig *Police Scotland*
Ardsley East *West Yorkshire*
Ardsley West *West Yorkshire*
Ardvasar *Police Scotland*
Ardwick *Gtr Manchester*
Areley Kings *West Mercia*
Argoed *Gwent*
Arisaig *Police Scotland*
Arkholme *Lancashire*
Arksey *South Yorkshire*
Arkwright *Derbyshire*
Arlecdon *Cumbria*
Arlesey *Bedfordshire*
Arleston *Derbyshire*
Arley *Warwickshire*
Armadale *Police Scotland*
Armagh *PSNI*
Armley *West Yorkshire*
Armthorpe *South Yorks*
Arncliffe *North Yorkshire*
Arne *Dorset*
Arnesby *Leicestershire*

Arnold *Nottinghamshire*
Arnside *Cumbria*
Arrington *Cambridgeshire*
Arrochar *Police Scotland*
Arrowe *Merseyside*
Arthingworth *Northants*
Artington *Surrey*
Arundel *Sussex*
Ascot *Thames Valley*
Asfordby *Leicestershire*
Ash *Derbyshire*
Ash *Surrey*
Ash *Kent*
Ashampstead *Thames Valley*
Ashbocking *Suffolk*
Asbourne *Derbyshire*
Ashburton *Devon & Cornwall*
Ashbury *Thames Valley*
Ashby-de-la-Zouch *Leics*
Ashby St Ledgers *Northants*
Ashby Folville *Leicestershire*
Ashby Magna *Leicestershire*
Ashby Parva *Leicestershire*
Ashby Woulds *Leicestershire*
Ashchurch *Glos*
Ashford *Derbyshire*
Ashford *Kent*
Ashington *Northumbria*
Ashley *Cheshire*
Ashley *Cambridgeshire*
Ashley *Northamptonshire*
Ashley *Gtr Manchester*
Ashley Heath *Gtr Manchester*
Ashley-cum-Silverley *Cambs*
Ashleyhay *Derbyshire*
Ashmore *Dorset*
Ashopton *Derbyshire*
Ashover *Derbyshire*
Ashperton *West Mercia*
Ashtead *Surrey*
Ashton *Cambridgeshire*
Ashton *Cheshire*
Ashton *Devon & Cornwall*
Ashton (Nr Oundle) *Northants*
Ashton (Nr Roade) *Northants*
Ashton-in-Makerfield *Gtr
Manchester*
Ashton-under-Lyne *Gtr
Manchester*
Ashton-upon-Mersey *Gtr
Manchester*
Ashton Keynes *Wiltshire*
Ashurst *Hampshire*
Ashvale *Gwent*
Ash Vale *Surrey*
Ashway Gap *Gtr Manchester*
Ashwell *Hertfordshire*
Ashwell *Leicestershire*
Ashwellthorpe *Norfolk*
Ashwood *Staffordshire*
Askam *Cumbria*
Askern *South Yorkshire*
Askerwell *Dorset*
Askrigg *North Yorkshire*
Aspatria *Cumbria*
Aspenden *Hertfordshire*
Aspley *Nottinghamshire*
Aspley Heath *Bedfordshire*
Aspull *Gtr Manchester*
Aspull Common *Gtr Manchester*
Astley *West Mercia*
Astley Bridge *Gtr Manchester*
Astley Green *Gtr Manchester*
Aston *Cheshire*
Aston *Derbyshire*
Aston Abbotts *Thames Valley*
Aston-by-Budworth *Cheshire*
Aston Clinton *Thames Valley*
Aston Fields *West Mercia*

Aston Flamville *Leicestershire*
Aston Juxta Mondrum *Cheshire*
Aston-on-Trent *Derbyshire*
Aston-le-Walls *Northants*
Aston Tirrold *Thames Valley*
Astwood Bank *West Mercia*
Atcham *West Mercia*
Athelhampton *Dorset*
Atherstone *Warwickshire*
Atherton *Gtr Manchester*
Atherton Hall *Gtr Manchester*
Atlow *Derbyshire*
Attleborough *Norfolk*
Atworth *Wiltshire*
Auchinleck *Police Scotland*
Auchterarder *Police Scotland*
Auchterhouse *Police Scotland*
Auchtermuchty *Police Scotland*
Auckland Park *Durham*
Audlem *Cheshire*
Audley *Staffordshire*
Audonshaw *Gtr Manchester*
Aughton *Lancashire*
Aughton *South Yorkshire*
Ault Hucknall *Derbyshire*
Austerfield *South Yorkshire*
Austerlands *Gtr Manchester*
Austerton *Cheshire*
Austhorpe *West Yorkshire*
Austwick *North Yorkshire*
Averham *Nottinghamshire*
Aveton Gifford *Devon & Cornwall*
Aviemore *Police Scotland*
Avonbridge *Police Scotland*
Awbridge *Hampshire*
Awsworth *Nottinghamshire*
Axbridge *Avon & Somerset*
Axminster *Devon & Cornwall*
Aycliff *Durham*
Aylesbury *Thames Valley*
Aylesford *Kent*
Aylesham *Kent*
Aylestone *Leicestershire*
Aylsham *Norfolk*
Aynho *Northants*
Ayot St Lawrence *Herts*
Ayot St Peter *Hertfordshire*
Ayr *Police Scotland*
Aysgarth *North Yorkshire*
Ayston *Leicestershire*
Ayton *Police Scotland*
Babraham *Cambridgeshire*
Bache *Cheshire*
Backbower *Gtr Manchester*
Back-O'th-Moor *Gtr Manchester*
Backford *Cheshire*
Bacton *Norfolk*
Bacton *Suffolk*
Bacup *Lancashire*
Badby *Northamptonshire*
Baddeley Green *Staffordshire*
Baddesley *Hampshire*
Baddesley Ensor *Warwickshire*
Baddiley *Cheshire*
Baddington *Cheshire*
Badsey *West Mercia*
Badshot Lea *Surrey*
Badsworth *West Yorkshire*
Bagby *North Yorkshire*
Baggrave *Leicestershire*
Bagillt *North Wales*
Baginton *Warwickshire*
Bagshot *Surrey*
Bagslate Moor *Gtr Manchester*
Baguley *Gtr Manchester*
Bagworth *Leicestershire*
Baildon *West Yorkshire*
Bailiff Bridge *West Yorks*
Baillieston *Police Scotland*

Bainsford *Police Scotland*
Bainton *Cambridgeshire*
Baird Street *Police Scotland*
Bakestone Moor *Derbyshire*
Bakewell *Derbyshire*
Bala *North Wales*
Balgan *South Wales*
Balbeggie *Police Scotland*
Balby *South Yorkshire*
Balcombe *Sussex*
Baldersdale *Durham*
Balderstone *Gtr Manchester*
Balderton *Nottinghamshire*
Baldingstone *Gtr Manchester*
Baldock *Hertfordshire*
Baldwins Hill *Surrey*
Balfron *Police Scotland*
Ball Green *Staffordshire*
Ballantrae *Police Scotland*
Ballasalla *Isle of Man*
Ballater *Police Scotland*
Ballidon *Derbyshire*
Ballinamallard *PSNI*
Ballingry *Police Scotland*
Ballinluig *Police Scotland*
Ballycastle *PSNI*
Ballyclare *PSNI*
Ballygawley *PSNI*
Ballymena *PSNI*
Ballymoney *PSNI*
Ballynafeigh *PSNI*
Ballynahinch *PSNI*
Balsham *Cambridgeshire*
Bamber Bridge *Lancashire*
Bamburgh *Northumbria*
Bamford *Gtr Manchester*
Bamford *Derbyshire*
Bamfurlong *Gloucestershire*
Bamfurlong *Gtr Manchester*
Bampton *Devon & Cornwall*
Bampton *Thames Valley*
Banbridge *PSNI*
Banbury *Thames Valley*
Banchory *Police Scotland*
Banff *Police Scotland*
Bangor *North Wales*
Bangor *PSNI*
Bangor-on-Dee *North Wales*
Bank Toll *Gtr Manchester*
Bankfoot *West Yorkshire*
Bankfoot *Police Scotland*
Banks *Lancashire*
Bannockburn *Police Scotland*
Banstead *Surrey*
Banwell *Avon & Somerset*
Bapchild *Kent*
Barbon *Cumbria*
Barby *Northamptonshire*
Barcombe *Sussex*
Bardney *Lincolnshire*
Bardon *Leicestershire*
Bardsea *Cumbria*
Bardsey *West Yorkshire*
Bardsley *Gtr Manchester*
Barford *Warwickshire*
Barford-St-Martin *Wiltshire*
Bargoed *Gwent*
Barham *Cambridgeshire*
Barham *Kent*
Bar Hill *Cambridgeshire*
Bark Hill *West Mercia*
Barkby *Leicestershire*
Barkby Thorpe *Leics*
Barkestone *Leicestershire*
Barkham *Thames Valley*
Barking *Metropolitan*
Barking *Suffolk*
Barkingside *Metropolitan*
Barkisland *West Yorkshire*

Barkston Ash *North Yorkshire*
Barkway *Hertfordshire*
Barlanark *Police Scotland*
Barlaston *Staffordshire*
Barlborough *Derbyshire*
Barlby *North Yorkshire*
Barlestone *Leicestershire*
Barley *Hertfordshire*
Barleythorpe *Leicestershire*
Barlow *Derbyshire*
Barlow *North Yorkshire*
Barmouth *North Wales*
Barnack *Cambridgeshire*
Barnard Castle *Durham*
Barnards Green *West Mercia*
Barnburgh *South Yorkshire*
Barnby Dun *South Yorkshire*
Barnby Moor *Nottinghamshire*
Barnes *Metropolitan*
Barnes Green *Gtr Manchester*
Barnet *Metropolitan*
Barnetby *Humberside*
Barnham *Sussex*
Barnham Broom *Norfolk*
Barningham *Durham*
Barningham *Suffolk*
Barnoldswick *Lancashire*
Barnsley *South Yorkshire*
Barnstaple *Devon & Cornwall*
Barnston *Merseyside*
Barnstone *Nottinghamshire*
Barnt Green *West Mercia*
Barnton *Cheshire*
Barnwell *Northamptonshire*
Barra *Police Scotland*
Barrhead *Police Scotland*
Barrington *Cambridgeshire*
Barrow *Cheshire*
Barrow *Cumbria*
Barrow *Leicestershire*
Barrow *Suffolk*
Barrow Bridge *Gtr Manchester*
Barrow Hill *Derbyshire*
Barrow-in-Furness *Cumbria*
Barrow-on-Soar *Leicestershire*
Barrow-on-Trent *Derbyshire*
Barrowden *Leicestershire*
Barry *South Wales*
Barry *Police Scotland*
Barry Island *South Wales*
Barsby *Leicestershire*
Bartestree *West Mercia*
Barthomley *Cheshire*
Bartlow *Cambridgeshire*
Barton *Bedfordshire*
Barton *Cambridgeshire*
Barton *Cheshire*
Barton *North Yorkshire*
Barton Blount *Derbyshire*
Barton Grane *Gtr Manchester*
Barton-on-Humber *Humberside*
Barton Lock *Gtr Manchester*
Barton Mills *Suffolk*
Barton-in-the-Beans *Leicestershire*
Barton-under-Needwood *Staffs*
Barton-upon-Irwell *Gtr Manchester*
Barton Stacey *Hampshire*
Barvas *Police Scotland*
Barway *Cambridgeshire*
Barwell *Leicestershire*
Barwick *Hertfordshire*
Barwick-in-Elmet *West Yorks*
Baschurch *West Mercia*
Basford *Cheshire*
Basford *Nottinghamshire*
Basford *Staffordshire*
Basildon *Essex*
Basing *Hampshire*

Basingstoke *Hampshire*
Baslow *Derbyshire*
Bassaleg *Gwent*
Bassenthwaite *Cumbria*
Bassingbourn *Cambridgeshire*
Bassingham *Lincolnshire*
Baston *Lincolnshire*
Batchley *West Mercia*
Batchworth Heath *Herts*
Batcombe *Dorset*
Batford *Hertfordshire*
Bath *Avon & Somerset*
Bath Street *Nottinghamshire*
Batheaston *Avon & Somerset*
Batherton *Cheshire*
Bathgate *Police Scotland*
Batley *West Yorkshire*
Batley Carr *West Yorkshire*
Battersea *Metropolitan*
Battle *Sussex*
Batts Corner *Surrey*
Battyeford *West Yorkshire*
Baughurst *Hampshire*
Baumber *Lincolnshire*
Bawburgh *Norfolk*
Bawdeswell *Norfolk*
Bawdrip *Avon & Somerset*
Bawtry *South Yorkshire*
Baxterley *Warwickshire*
Bayford *Hertfordshire*
Baylham *Suffolk*
Baynards *Surrey*
Bayston Hill *West Mercia*
Beaconsfield *Thames Valley*
Beal *North Yorkshire*
Bealings *Suffolk*
Beaminster *Dorset*
Beamish *Durham*
Beard *Derbyshire*
Beare Green *Surrey*
Bearpark *Durham*
Bearsted *Kent*
Bearwardcote *Derbyshire*
Beaufort *Gwent*
Beaulieu & East Boldre *Hants*
Beauly *Police Scotland*
Beaumanor *Leicestershire*
Beaumaris *North Wales*
Beaumont Leys *Leicestershire*
Babington *Merseyside*
Beccles *Suffolk*
Beck Row *Suffolk*
Beckenham *Metropolitan*
Beckford *West Mercia*
Beckhampton *Wiltshire*
Beckingham *Nottinghamshire*
Beckington *Avon & Somerset*
Beckley *Sussex*
Bedale *North Yorkshire*
Beddau *South Wales*
Beddgelert *North Wales*
Bedgrove *Thames Valley*
Bedlington *Northumbria*
Bedlinog *South Wales*
Bedminster *Avon & Somerset*
Bedminster Down *Avon & Somerset*
Bedmond *Hertfordshire*
Bedwas *Gwent*
Bedwellty *Gwent*
Bedwellty Pits *Gwent*
Bedworth *Warwickshire*
Beeby *Leicestershire*
Beech Hill *Gtr Manchester*
Beeding *Sussex*
Beedon *Thames Valley*
Beeford *Humberside*
Beeley *Derbyshire*
Beenham *Thames Valley*

Beer *Devon & Cornwall*
Beer Hackett *Dorset*
Beeston *Cheshire*
Beeston *Nottinghamshire*
Beeston *West Yorkshire*
Beguildy *Dyfed-Powys*
Beith *Police Scotland*
Belasis *Cleveland*
Belbroughton *West Mercia*
Belchamp St Paul *Essex*
Belcoo *PSNI*
Belfield *Gtr Manchester*
Belford *Northumbria*
Belgrave Road *West Midlands*
Bell Green *West Midlands*
Bellingham *Northumbria*
Bellshill *Police Scotland*
Belmisthorpe *Leicestershire*
Belmont *Gtr Manchester*
Belmont *Lancashire*
Belleek *PSNI*
Belper *Derbyshire*
Belph *Derbyshire*
Belsay *Northumbria*
Beltinge *Kent*
Belton *Leicestershire*
Belton *Lincolnshire*
Belton *Norfolk*
Belton-in-Rutland *Leics*
Belvedere *Metropolitan*
Belvoir *Leicestershire*
Bembridge *Hampshire*
Ben Rhydding *West Yorks*
Benburb *PSNI*
Benchill *Gtr Manchester*
Bendish *Hertfordshire*
Benefield *Northamptonshire*
Benenden *Kent*
Benfleet *Essex*
Bengeo *Hertfordshire*
Benhall *Suffolk*
Benington *Hertfordshire*
Benington *Lincolnshire*
Benllech *North Wales*
Benson *Thames Valley*
Bent Lanes *Gtr Manchester*
Bentham *North Yorkshire*
Bentley *Hampshire*
Bentley *South Yorkshire*
Benwick *Cambridgeshire*
Beragh *PSNI*
Bere Regis *Dorset*
Berinsfield *Thames Valley*
Berkeley *Gloucestershire*
Berkhamsted *Hertfordshire*
Berkswell *West Midlands*
Berriew *Dyfed-Powys*
Berry Pomeroy *Devon & Cornwall*
Berwick *Northumbria*
Bescaby *Leicestershire*
Besom Hill *Gtr Manchester*
Bessacarr *South Yorkshire*
Bessbrook *PSNI*
Besselsleigh *Thames Valley*
Besses O'th Barn *Gtr Manchester*
Bestwood *Nottinghamshire*
Bestwood Park *Nottinghamshire*
Beswick *Gtr Manchester*
Betchton *Cheshire*
Betchworth *Surrey*
Bethel *North Wales*
Bethersden *Kent*
Bethesda *North Wales*
Bethnal Green *Metropolitan*
Bettiscombe *Dorset*
Bettws *Gwent*
Bettws *South Wales*
Bettws Newydd *Gwent*
Bettyhill *Police Scotland*

Betws-y-Coed *North Wales*
Beverley *Humberside*
Bewdley *West Mercia*
Bewerley *North Yorkshire*
Bexhill *Sussex*
Bexleyheath *Metropolitan*
Bexton *Cheshire*
Beyton *Suffolk*
Bib Knows *Gtr Manchester*
Bibury *Gloucestershire*
Bicester *Thames Valley*
Bicker *Lincolnshire*
Bickerton *Cheshire*
Bickerton *North Yorkshire*
Bickley *Cheshire*
Bickershaw *Gtr Manchester*
Bickerstaffe *Lancashire*
Bickington *Devon & Cornwall*
Bickington (Fremington) *Devon & Cornwall*
Bickleigh *Devon & Cornwall*
Bidborough *Kent*
Biddenden *Kent*
Biddulph *Staffordshire*
Bideford *Devon & Cornwall*
Bidford-on-Avon *Warwickshire*
Bidston *Merseyside*
Bierley *West Yorkshire*
Bierton *Thames Valley*
Bigbury-on-Sea *Devon & Cornwall*
Biggar *Police Scotland*
Biggin *Derbyshire*
Biggin *North Yorkshire*
Biggleswade *Bedfordshire*
Bigrigg *Cumbria*
Bildeston *Suffolk*
Billericay *Essex*
Billesdon *Leicestershire*
Billesley *West Midlands*
Billing *Northampton*
Billingborough *Lincolnshire*
Billinge *Gtr Manchester*
Billingham *Cleveland*
Billinghay *Lincolnshire*
Billinghurst *Sussex*
Billington *Lancashire*
Bilsdale *North Yorkshire*
Bilsthorpe *Nottinghamshire*
Bilston *West Midlands*
Bilstone *Leicestershire*
Bilton *Humberside*
Bilton-in-Ainsty *North Yorks*
Binbrook *Lincolnshire*
Binchester *Durham*
Bincombe *Dorset*
Binfield *Thames Valley*
Bingham *Nottinghamshire*
Bingley *West Yorkshire*
Binley Wood *Warwickshire*
Binscombe *Surrey*
Binstead *Hampshire*
Binton *Warwickshire*
Birch *Essex*
Birch *Gtr Manchester*
Birches *Gtr Manchester*
Birches *PSNI*
Birches Head *Staffordshire*
Birch Green *Hertfordshire*
Birchgrove (Cardiff) *South Wales*
Birchgrove (Swansea) *South Wales*
Birchover *Derbyshire*
Birchvale *Derbyshire*
Birdham *Sussex*
Birdlip *Gloucestershire*
Birdsall *North Yorkshire*
Birdwell *South Yorkshire*
Birkenhead *Merseyside*
Birkenshaw *West Yorkshire*
Birkhill *Police Scotland*

Birling *Kent*
Birlingham *West Mercia*
Birmingham *West Midlands*
Birmingham Road *West Midlands*
Birstall *Leicestershire*
Birstall *West Yorkshire*
Birtle *Gtr Manchester*
Bisbrooke *Leicestershire*
Bisham *Thames Valley*
Bishop Auckland *Durham*
Bishop Middleham *Durham*
Bishopbriggs *Police Scotland*
Bishopsgate *City of London*
Bishopston *South Wales*
Bishopthorpe *North Yorkshire*
Bishopton *Durham*
Bishopton *Police Scotland*
Bishop Burton *Humberside*
Bishop Monkton *North Yorkshire*
Bishops *Essex*
Bishops Castle *West Mercia*
Bishops Caundle *Dorset*
Bishop's Cleeve *Gloucestershire*
Bishops Frome *West Mercia*
Bishops Itchington *Warwickshire*
Bishops Lydeard *Avon & Somerset*
Bishops Stortford *Hertfordshire*
Bishops Tachbrook *Warwickshire*
Bishops Tawton *Devon & Cornwall*
Bishops Waltham *Hampshire*
Bisley *Gloucestershire*
Bisley *Surrey*
Bisley Old Road *Gloucestershire*
Bispham *Lancashire*
Bitterne *Hampshire*
Bittesby *Leicestershire*
Bitteswell *Leicestershire*
Blaby *Leicestershire*
Blackburn *Lancashire*
Blackburn *Police Scotland*
Blackdown *Surrey*
Blackford *Police Scotland*
Blackford Bridge *Gtr Manchester*
Blackfordby *Leicestershire*
Blackhall *Durham*
Blackheath *Surrey*
Blackheath *West Midlands*
Blackhill *Police Scotland*
Black Horse Drove *Cambridgeshire*
Black Lane *Gtr Manchester*
Blackley *Gtr Manchester*
Blackmill *South Wales*
Blackmoor *Gtr Manchester*
Blackmore *Essex*
Black Notley *Essex*
Blackpool *Lancashire*
Blackpool South *Lancashire*
Blackthorn *Thames Valley*
Blackwall *Metropolitan*
Blackwater *Hampshire*
Blackwell *West Mercia*
Blackwell (Alfreton) *Derbyshire*
Blackwell-in-the-Peak (Buxton) *Derbys*
Blackwood *Gwent*
Blackwood *Police Scotland*
Blaenau Ffestiniog *North Wales*
Blaenau Gwent *Gwent*
Blaenavon *Gwent*
Blaenclydach *South Wales*
Blaendare *Gwent*
Blaengarw *South Wales*
Blaenrhondda *South Wales*
Blaenymaes *South Wales*
Blagdon *Avon & Somerset*
Blagdon Hill *Avon & Somerset*
Blaina *Gwent*

Blair Atholl *Police Scotland*
Blairgowrie *Police Scotland*
Blairhall *Police Scotland*
Blakedown *West Mercia*
Blakeney *Gloucestershire*
Blakeney *Norfolk*
Blakenhall *Cheshire*
Blakesley *Northamptonshire*
Blanchland *Northumbria*
Blandford *Dorset*
Blandford St Mary *Dorset*
Blanefield *Police Scotland*
Blatherwycke *Northamptonshire*
Blantyre *Police Scotland*
Blaxton *South Yorkshire*
Bleadon *Avon & Somerset*
Bleakgate Moor *Gtr Manchester*
Bleak Hey Nook *Gtr Manchester*
Blean *Kent*
Bleasby *Nottinghamshire*
Bledlow Ridge *Thames Valley*
Bletchingley *Surrey*
Bletchley *Thames Valley*
Blewbury *Thames Valley*
Blidworth *Nottinghamshire*
Blindley Heath *Surrey*
Blisland *Devon & Cornwall*
Blisworth *Northamptonshire*
Blockley *Gloucestershire*
Bloemfontein *Durham*
Blofield *Norfolk*
Bloxham *Thames Valley*
Bloxwich *West Midlands*
Bloxworth *Dorset*
Bluebell Hill *Kent*
Bluesil *Gtr Manchester*
Blundeston *Suffolk*
Blunham *Bedfordshire*
Blunsdon *Wiltshire*
Bluntisham *Cambridgeshire*
Blurton *Staffordshire*
Blyth *Northumbria*
Blyth *Nottinghamshire*
Blythburgh *Suffolk*
Blythe Bridge *Staffordshire*
Boat of Garten *Police Scotland*
Bobbing *Kent*
Bocking *Essex*
Boddam *Police Scotland*
Boddington *Northamptonshire*
Bodedern *North Wales*
Bodelwyddan *North Wales*
Bodenham *West Mercia*
Bodmin *Devon & Cornwall*
Bodorgan *North Wales*
Bog Road *Police Scotland*
Boggart-hole-Clough *Cheshire*
Bognor Regis *Sussex*
Bolam *Durham*
Bold *Merseyside*
Bolehill *Derbyshire*
Bollington *Cheshire*
Bollington (Bucklow) *Cheshire*
Bolsover *Derbyshire*
Bolton *Gtr Manchester*
Bolton *West Yorkshire*
Bolton Abbey *North Yorkshire*
Bolton Percy *North Yorkshire*
Bolton-by-Bowland *Lancashire*
Bolton-le-Sands *Lancashire*
Bolton-on-Swale *North Yorkshire*
Bolton Woods *West Yorkshire*
Bomere Heath *West Mercia*
Bonar Bridge *Police Scotland*
Bo'ness *Police Scotland*
Bonnybridge *Police Scotland*
Bonnyrigg *Police Scotland*
Bonsall *Derbyshire*
Bontnewydd *North Wales*

Bonton-on-Dearne *South Yorkshire*
Bonvilston *South Wales*
Bonymaen *South Wales*
Booker *Thames Valley*
Bookham *Surrey*
Boothen *Staffordshire*
Boothroyden *Gtr Manchester*
Bootle *Cumbria*
Bootle *Merseyside*
Bordelsey Green *West Midlands*
Boreham *Essex*
Borehamwood *Hertfordshire*
Boroughbridge *North Yorkshire*
Borough Fen *Cambridgeshire*
Borough Green *Kent*
Borrowash *Derbyshire*
Borrowby (N'allerton) *North Yorks*
Borrowby (Whitby) *North Yorks*
Borth *Dyfed-Powys*
Boscastle *Devon & Cornwall*
Boscombe *Dorset*
Bosham *Sussex*
Bosley *Cheshire*
Bostock *Cheshire*
Boston *Lincolnshire*
Boston Spa *West Yorkshire*
Botany Bay *Staffordshire*
Botany Bay Wood *Gtr Manchester*
Botcheston *Leicestershire*
Botesdale *Suffolk*
Bothel *Cumbria*
Bothenhampton *Dorset*
Bothwell *Police Scotland*
Botley *Hampshire*
Botley *Thames Valley*
Bottesford *Leicestershire*
Bottisham *Cambridgeshire*
Bottisham Lode *Cambridgeshire*
Botton O'th Moor *Gtr Manchester*
Boughton *Kent*
Boughton *Northamptonshire*
Boughton Monchelsea *Kent*
Boulton *Derbyshire*
Boundstone *Surrey*
Bourn *Cambridgeshire*
Bourne *Lincolnshire*
Bourne *Surrey*
Bourne End *Hertfordshire*
Bourne End *Thames Valley*
Bournemouth *Dorset*
Bourneville *Gwent*
Bournville Lane *West Midlands*
Bourton *Dorset*
Bourton-on-the-Water *Glos*
Dovey Tracey *Devon & Cornwall*
Bovingdon *Hertfordshire*
Bow *Devon & Cornwall*
Bow *Metropolitan*
Bow Street *Metropolitan*
Bowburn *Durham*
Bowden Edge *Derbyshire*
Bowdon *Gtr Manchester*
Bowers Heath *Hertfordshire*
Bowes *Durham*
Bowgreen *Gtr Manchester*
Bowling *West Yorkshire*
Bowmore *Police Scotland*
Box *Wiltshire*
Boxford *Suffolk*
Boxford *Thames Valley*
Boxgrove *Sussex*
Boxhill *Surrey*
Boxley *Kent*
Boxmoor *Hertfordshire*
Boxworth *Cambridgeshire*
Boylestone *Derbyshire*

Bozeat *Northamptonshire*
Bracebridge Heath *Lincolnshire*
Brackenfield *Derbyshire*
Brackley *Northamptonshire*
Bracknell *Thames Valley*
Braco *Police Scotland*
Bradbourne *Derbyshire*
Bradden *Northamptonshire*
Bradeley *Staffordshire*
Bradfield *South Yorkshire*
Bradfield *Thames Valley*
Bradford *West Yorkshire*
Bradford Abbas *Dorset*
Bradford-on-Avon *Wiltshire*
Bradford-on-Tone *Avon & Somerset*
Bradford Moor *West Yorkshire*
Bradford Peverill *Dorset*
Bradford Street *West Midlands*
Brading *Hampshire*
Bradley *Derbyshire*
Bradley (Chester) *Cheshire*
Bradley (Malpas) *Cheshire*
Bradley Folk *Gtr Manchester*
Bradninch *Devon & Cornwall*
Bradpole *Dorset*
Bradshaw *Gtr Manchester*
Bradshaw Edge *Derbyshire*
Bradwall *Cheshire*
Bradwell *Derbyshire*
Bradwell *Norfolk*
Braemar *Police Scotland*
Brafield-on-the-Green *Northants*
Brailes *Warwickshire*
Brailsford *Derbyshire*
Braintree *Essex*
Braithwaite *Cumbria*
Braithwell *South Yorkshire*
Bramcote *Nottinghamshire*
Bramdean *Hampshire*
Bramford *Hertfordshire*
Bramford *Suffolk*
Bramhall *Gtr Manchester*
Bramhall Moor *Gtr Manchester*
Bramhall Park *Gtr Manchester*
Bramham *West Yorkshire*
Bramhope *West Yorkshire*
Bramley *South Yorkshire*
Bramley *Surrey*
Bramley *West Yorkshire*
Brampton *Cambridgeshire*
Brampton *Cumbria*
Brampton *Derbyshire*
Brampton *South Yorkshire*
Brampton Ash *Northants*
Brancaster *Norfolk*
Brancepeth *Durham*
Brandon *Durham*
Brandon *Suffolk*
Brands Hatch *Kent*
Branksome *Dorset*
Bransgore *Hampshire*
Branston *Leicestershire*
Brantham *Suffolk*
Brassington *Derbyshire*
Brasted *Kent*
Bratton *Wiltshire*
Bratton-Fleming *Devon & Cornwall*
Braughing *Hertfordshire*
Braunston *Leicestershire*
Braunston *Northampton*
Braunstone *Leicestershire*
Braunton *Devon & Cornwall*
Bray *Thames Valley*
Braybrooke *Northampton*
Brayton *North Yorkshire*
Breachwood Green *Hertfordshire*
Breadsall *Derbyshire*

Bream *Gloucestershire*
Breamore *Hampshire*
Brearley *West Yorkshire*
Breaston *Derbyshire*
Brechfa *Dyfed-Powys*
Brechin *Police Scotland*
Brecon *Dyfed-Powys*
Bredbury & Romiley *Gtr Manchester*
Brede *Sussex*
Bredenbury *West Mercia*
Bredgar *Kent*
Bredhurst *Kent*
Bredon *West Mercia*
Breedon-on-the-Hill *Leicestershire*
Breightmet *Gtr Manchester*
Brenchley *Kent*
Brent Pelham *Hertfordshire*
Brentford *Metropolitan*
Brentingby *Leicestershire*
Brentwood *Essex*
Brereton *Cheshire*
Bretby *Derbyshire*
Bretforton *West Mercia*
Bretherton *Lancashire*
Bretton West *West Yorkshire*
Brewood *Staffordshire*
Brickendon *Hertfordshire*
Bricket Wood *Hertfordshire*
Brickhill *Thames Valley*
Bridens Camp *Hertfordshire*
Bridestowe *Devon & Cornwall*
Bridge *Kent*
Bridge of Allan *Police Scotland*
Bridge of Don *Police Scotland*
Bridge of Earn *Police Scotland*
Bridge Street West *West Midlands*
Bridge Trafford *Cheshire*
Bridgemere *Cheshire*
Bridgemont *Derbyshire*
Bridgend *South Wales*
Bridgnorth *West Mercia*
Bridlington *Humberside*
Bridport *Dorset*
Briercliffe *Lancashire*
Brierley *South Yorkshire*
Brierley Hill *West Midlands*
Brigg *Humberside*
Brigham *Cumbria*
Brighouse *West Yorkshire*
Brightlingsea *Essex*
Brighton *Sussex*
Brightons *Police Scotland*
Brightwalton *Thames Valley*
Brightwell *Thames Valley*
Brigstock *Northampton*
Brill *Thames Valley*
Brimington *Derby*
Brimstage *Merseyside*
Brindlehath *Gtr Manchester*
Brindley *Cheshire*
Brindley Ford *Staffordshire*
Bringhurst *Leicestershire*
Bringsty *West Mercia*
Brington *Northampton*
Brington and Molesworth *Cambs*
Brinkley *Cambridgeshire*
Brinklow *Warwickshire*
Brinkworth *Wiltshire*
Brinnington *Gtr Manchester*
Brinscall *Lancashire*
Brinsley *Nottinghamshire*
Brinsworth *South Yorkshire*
Bristol *Avon & Somerset*
Briston *Norfolk*
Brithdir *South Wales*
British *Gwent*
Briton Ferry *South Wales*
Britwell *Thames Valley*

Brixham *Devon & Cornwall*
Brixton *Metropolitan*
Brixworth *Northamptonshire*
Broadbottom *Gtr Manchester*
Broadchalke *Wiltshire*
Broadclyst *Devon & Cornwall*
Broadfield *Gtr Manchester*
Broadford *Police Scotland*
Broad Haven *Dyfed-Powys*
Broadhalgh *Gtr Manchester*
Broadheath *Gtr Manchester*
Broadheath *West Mercia*
Broadley *Gtr Manchester*
Broadmayne *Dorset*
Broadoak Park *Gtr Manchester*
Broadstairs *Kent*
Broadstone *Dorset*
Broadwas *West Mercia*
Broadwaters *West Mercia*
Broadway *West Mercia*
Broadwey *Dorset*
Broadwindsor *Dorset*
Brock *Lancashire*
Brockenhurst *Hampshire*
Brockhall *Northamptonshire*
Brockham *Surrey*
Brockholes *West Yorkshire*
Brockley *Metropolitan*
Brodick *Police Scotland*
Bromborough *Merseyside*
Bromfield *West Mercia*
Bromfield Lane *West Midlands*
Bromham *Bedfordshire*
Bromham *Wiltshire*
Bromley *Metropolitan*
Bromley *South Yorkshire*
Bromley Cross *Gtr Manchester*
Brompton (London) *Metropolitan*
Brompton (Northallerton) *North Yorks*
Brompton (Scarborough) *North Yorks*
Brompton Regis *Avon & Somerset*
Brompton-on-Swale *North Yorks*
Bromsgrove *West Mercia*
Bromyard *West Mercia*
Bronllwyn *South Wales*
Brook *Surrey*
Brook Bottom *Gtr Manchester*
Brooke *Leicestershire*
Brooke *Norfolk*
Brookhouse *Gtr Manchester*
Brookhouse Green & Bemersley *Staffordshire*
Brookland *Kent*
Brooklands *Gtr Manchester*
Brooklands *Surrey*
Brookmans Park *Hertfordshire*
Brooks Bar *Gtr Manchester*
Brooksby *Leicestershire*
Brookwood *Surrey*
Broomfield *Essex*
Broomfield *Gtr Manchester*
Broomhall *Cheshire*
Broompark *Durham*
Brora *Police Scotland*
Broseley *West Mercia*
Brothertoft *Lincolnshire*
Brotherton *North Yorkshire*
Brotton *Cleveland*
Brough *Cumbria*
Brough *Humberside*
Brough & Shatton *Derbyshire*
Broughton *Cambridgeshire*
Broughton *Cumbria*
Broughton *Hampshire*
Broughton *Humberside*
Broughton *Lancashire*
Broughton *Northamptonshire*

Broughton *North Wales*
Broughton Astley *Leicestershire*
Broughton-in-Furness *Cumbria*
Broughton Moor *Cumbria*
Broughton Park *Gtr Manchester*
Broughty Ferry *Police Scotland*
Brownhill *West Yorkshire*
Brownhills *West Midlands*
Brown Law *Gtr Manchester*
Brownside *Derbyshire*
Brownsover *Warwickshire*
Broxbourne *Hertfordshire*
Broxburn *Police Scotland*
Broxton *Cheshire*
Bruen Stapleford *Cheshire*
Bruntcliffe *West Yorkshire*
Bruntingthorpe *Leicestershire*
Brunton *Northumbria*
Brushes *Gtr Manchester*
Brushfield *Derbyshire*
Bruton *Avon*
Bryanston *Dorset*
Brymbo *North Wales*
Brynamman *Dyfed-Powys*
Brynamman *South Wales*
Brynbryddan *South Wales*
Bryncethin *South Wales*
Bryncoch *South Wales*
Brynford *North Wales*
Bryn Gates *Gtr Manchester*
Brynhoffnant *Dyfed-Powys*
Brynithel *Gwent*
Brynmawr *Gwent*
Brynmill *South Wales*
Brynsiencyn *North Wales*
Bubnell *Derbyshire*
Bubwith *Humberside*
Buchlyvie *Police Scotland*
Buckall *Gtr Manchester*
Buckden *Cambridgeshire*
Buckfastleigh *Devon & Cornwall*
Buckhaven *Police Scotland*
Buckhorn Weston *Dorset*
Buckie *Police Scotland*
Buckingham *Thames Valley*
Buckland *Hertfordshire*
Buckland *Surrey*
Buckland (Berks) *Thames Valley*
Buckland (Bucks) *Thames Valley*
Buckland Newton *Dorset*
Bucklebury *Thames Valley*
Buckley *Gtr Manchester*
Buckley *North Wales*
Buckminster *Leicestershire*
Bucknall *Staffordshire*
Bucks Hill *Hertfordshire*
Bucksburn *Police Scotland*
Buckshorn Oak *Hampshire*
Buckton Vale *Gtr Manchester*
Buckworth *Cambridgeshire*
Bude *Devon & Cornwall*
Budleigh Salterton *Devon & Cornwall*
Buersil Head *Gtr Manchester*
Buerton *Cheshire*
Bugbrooke *Northamptonshire*
Buglawton *Cheshire*
Bugle *Devon & Cornwall*
Builth Wells *Dyfed-Powys*
Bulford Camp *Wiltshire*
Bulford Village *Wiltshire*
Bulkeley *Cheshire*
Bulkington *Warwickshire*
Bulls Green *Hertfordshire*
Bulwell *Nottinghamshire*
Bulwick *Northampton*
Bunbury *Cheshire*
Bunessan *Police Scotland*
Bungay *Suffolk*

Bunkers Hill *Gtr Manchester*
Bunny *Nottinghamshire*
Buntingford *Hertfordshire*
Bunwell *Norfolk*
Burbage *Derbyshire*
Burbage *Leicestershire*
Burbage *Wiltshire*
Bures *Essex*
Bures-St-Mary *Suffolk*
Burford *Thames Valley*
Burgess Hill *Sussex*
Burgh Castle *Norfolk*
Burgh-le-Marsh *Lincolnshire*
Burgh-by-Sands *Cumbria*
Burghead *Police Scotland*
Burghfield *Thames Valley*
Burghwallis *South Yorkshire*
Burham *Kent*
Burland *Cheshire*
Burleston *Dorset*
Burley *Hampshire*
Burley *Leicestershire*
Burley-in-Wharfedale *West Yorks*
Burleygate *West Mercia*
Burmantofts *West Yorkshire*
Burnage *Gtr Manchester*
Burnaston *Derbyshire*
Burncross *South Yorkshire*
Burnden *Gtr Manchester*
Burnedge *Gtr Manchester*
Burnham *Thames Valley*
Burnham-on-Crouch *Essex*
Burnham Green *Hertfordshire*
Burnham Market *Norfolk*
Burnham-on-Sea *Avon & Somerset*
Burnley *Lancashire*
Burnopfield *Durham*
Burnsall *North Yorkshire*
Burnside *Cumbria*
Burnt Fen *Cambridgeshire*
Burntisland *Police Scotland*
Burpham *Surrey*
Burrelton *Police Scotland*
Burrough Green *Cambridgeshire*
Burrough-on-the-Hill
  Leicestershire
Burrs *Gtr Manchester*
Burry Port *Dyfed-Powys*
Burscough *Lancashire*
Burslem *Staffordshire*
Burstock *Dorset*
Burstow *Surrey*
Burton Agnes *Humberside*
Burton Joyce *Nottinghamshire*
Burton-in-Kendal *Cumbria*
Burton Latimer *Northamptonshire*
Durton Lazars *Leicestershire*
Burton Leonard *North Yorkshire*
Burton Overy *Leicestershire*
Burton-in-Lonsdale *North Yorks*
Burton-on-the-Wolds
  Leicestershire
Burton Salmon *North Yorkshire*
Burton (Chester) *Cheshire*
Burton (Ellesmere Port) *Cheshire*
Burton-cum-Waldon *North Yorks*
Burton-on-Stather *Lincolnshire*
Burton-on-Yore *North Yorkshire*
Burton-on-Trent *Staffordshire*
Burtonwood *Cheshire*
Burwardsley *Cheshire*
Burwash *Sussex*
Burwell *Cambridgeshire*
Burwood Park *Surrey*
Bury *Cambridgeshire*
Bury *Gtr Manchester*
Bury Green *Hertfordshire*
Bury-St-Edmunds *Suffolk*
Busby *Police Scotland*

Buscot *Thames Valley*
Bushby *Leicestershire*
Bushey *Hertfordshire*
Bushmills *PSNI*
Busk *Gtr Manchester*
Butler Green *Gtr Manchester*
Butlers Cross *Thames Valley*
Butterknowle *Durham*
Butterley *Derbyshire*
Buttershaw *West Yorkshire*
Butterwick *Lincolnshire*
Buttington *Dyfed-Powys*
Buxted *Sussex*
Buxton *Derbyshire*
Buxton-with-Lammas *Norfolk*
Buxworth *Derbyshire*
B. Winning *Derbyshire*
Bwlchgwyn *North Wales*
Byers Green *Durham*
Byfield *Northamptonshire*
Byfleet *Surrey*
Bygrave *Hertfordshire*
Byley *Cheshire*
Byram-cum-Poole *North Yorkshire*
Byram-cum-Sutton *North Yorks*
Bythorn & Keyston
  Cambridgeshire
Caddington *Bedfordshire*
Cadeby *Leicestershire*
Cadeby *South Yorkshire*
Cadishead *Gtr Manchester*
Cadnam *Hampshire*
Cadoxton (Barry) *South Wales*
Cadoxton (Neath) *South Wales*
Caerau *South Wales*
Caergwrle *North Wales*
Caerleon *Gwent*
Caernarfon *North Wales*
Caerphilly *Gwent*
Caersws *Dyfed-Powys*
Caerwent *Gwent*
Caerwys *North Wales*
Caister-on-Sea *Norfolk*
Caistor *Lincolnshire*
Caistor St Edmunds *Norfolk*
Calbourne *Hampshire*
Calcot *Thames Valley*
Caldbeck *Cumbria*
Caldecote *Cambridgeshire*
Caldecote *Hertfordshire*
Caldecote & Denton
  Cambridgeshire
Caldecott *Cheshire*
Caldecott *Leicestershire*
Calder Vale *Lancashire*
Calderbrook *Gtr Manchester*
Caldercruix *Police Scotland*
Caldermoor *Gtr Manchester*
Caldicot *Gwent*
Caldwell *Derbyshire*
Caldwell *North Yorkshire*
Caldy *Merseyside*
Caledon *PSNI*
Caledonian Road *Metropolitan*
Cale Green *Gtr Manchester*
Calke *Derbyshire*
Callander *Police Scotland*
Callington *Devon & Cornwall*
Callow *Derbyshire*
Calne *Wiltshire*
Calow *Derbyshire*
Calshot *Hampshire*
Calveley *Cheshire*
Calver *Derbyshire*
Calverley *West Yorkshire*
Calverton *Nottinghamshire*
Calvine *Police Scotland*
Cam *Gloucestershire*
Camber *Sussex*

Camberley *Surrey*
Camborne *Devon & Cornwall*
Cambridge *Cambridgeshire*
Cambusbarron *Police Scotland*
Cambuslang *Police Scotland*
Camelford *Devon & Cornwall*
Camelon *Police Scotland*
Camerton *Avon & Somerset*
Cammachmore *Police Scotland*
Campbeltown *Police Scotland*
Campden *Gloucestershire*
Campsall *South Yorkshire*
Canewdon *Essex*
Canford Heath *Dorset*
Canford Magna *Dorset*
Cann *Dorset*
Cannich *Police Scotland*
Canning Circus *Nottinghamshire*
Cannington *Avon & Somerset*
Cannock *Staffordshire*
Canon Row *Metropolitan*
Canonbie *Police Scotland*
Canons Ashby *Northants*
Canterbury *Kent*
Canterbury Road *West Midlands*
Cantley *South Yorkshire*
Canton *South Wales*
Canvey Island *Essex*
Capcoch *South Wales*
Capel *Surrey*
Capel Curig *North Wales*
Capel-le-Ferne *Kent*
Capel St Mary *Suffolk*
Capenhurst *Cheshire*
Capstones *Gtr Manchester*
Captain Fold *Gtr Manchester*
Carbis Bay *Devon & Cornwall*
Carcroft *South Yorkshire*
Carden *Cheshire*
Cardenden *Police Scotland*
Cardiff *South Wales*
Cardigan *Dyfed-Powys*
Cardington *Bedfordshire*
Cardington *West Mercia*
Cardross *Police Scotland*
Carisbrook *Hampshire*
Carlecotes *South Yorkshire*
Carleton *West Yorkshire*
Carleton *North Yorkshire*
Carlinghow *West Yorkshire*
Carlisle *Cumbria*
Carloway *Police Scotland*
Carlton *Cambridgeshire*
Carlton *Leicestershire*
Carlton *Nottinghamshire*
Carlton (Selby) *North Yorkshire*
Carlton (Stokesley) *North Yorks*
Carlton (Wakefield) *West Yorks*
Carlton Curlieu *Leicestershire*
Carlton-in-Lindrick
  Nottinghamshire
Carlton Colville *Suffolk*
Carlton Highdale *North Yorkshire*
Carlton Husthwaite *North Yorks*
Carlton Miniott *North Yorkshire*
Carlton Town *North Yorkshire*
Carlton-cum-Willingham *Cambs*
Carluke *Police Scotland*
Carmarthen *Dyfed-Powys*
Carmunnock *Police Scotland*
Carnforth *Lancashire*
Carnoustie *Police Scotland*
Carnwath *Police Scotland*
Carpenders Park *Hertfordshire*
Carr *Gtr Manchester*
Carr Vale *Derbyshire*
Carradale *Police Scotland*
Carrbridge *Police Scotland*
Carrbrook *Gtr Manchester*

Carrgreen *Gtr Manchester*
Carrickfergus *PSNI*
Carrington *Gtr Manchester*
Carrington *Nottinghamshire*
Carronshore *Police Scotland*
Carrville *Durham*
Carryduff *PSNI*
Carsington *Derbyshire*
Carstairs *Police Scotland*
Carter Street *Metropolitan*
Carterton *Thames Valley*
Cartmel *Cumbria*
Cassington *Thames Valley*
Cassop *Durham*
Castle Ashby *Northamptonshire*
Castle Camps *Cambridgeshire*
Castle Carrock *Cumbria*
Castle Cary *Avon & Somerset*
Castle Combe *Wiltshire*
Castle Donington *Leicestershire*
Castle Douglas *Police Scotland*
Castle Eden *Durham*
Castle Gresley *Derbyshire*
Castle Hedingham *Essex*
Castle Hill *Gtr Manchester*
Castle Hill (Astley Bdge) *Gtr Manchester*
Castle Hill (Bradbury) *Gtr Manchester*
Castle Howard *North Yorkshire*
Castle Milk *Police Scotland*
Castle Shaw *Gtr Manchester*
Castleacre *Norfolk*
Castledawson *PSNI*
Castlederg *PSNI*
Castleford *West Yorkshire*
Castlereagh *PSNI*
Castlerock *PSNI*
Castleside *Durham*
Castleton *Derbyshire*
Castleton *Dorset*
Castleton *Gtr Manchester*
Castleton *Gwent*
Castleton *North Yorkshire*
Castletown *Police Scotland*
Castlewellan *PSNI*
Castor *Cambridgeshire*
Caswell *South Wales*
Catchgate *Durham*
Catcliffe *South Yorkshire*
Caterham *Surrey*
Catesby *Northamptonshire*
Catford *Metropolitan*
Cathays *South Wales*
Cathays Park *South Wales*
Catherston *Dorset*
Catley Lane Head *Gtr Manchester*
Caton *Lancashire*
Catsash *Gwent*
Catshill *West Mercia*
Catterick Village *North Yorkshire*
Catthorpe *Leicestershire*
Cattistock *Dorset*
Catton *Derbyshire*
Catworth *Cambridgeshire*
Caughall *Cheshire*
Caundle Marsh *Dorset*
Caunton *Nottinghamshire*
Causwayhead *Police Scotland*
Cavendish *Suffolk*
Cavendish Road *Metropolitan*
Caversham *Thames Valley*
Cawood *North Yorkshire*
Cawston *Norfolk*
Cawthorne *North Yorkshire*
Cawthorne *South Yorkshire*
Caxton *Cambridgeshire*
Caythorpe *Lincolnshire*
Cayton *North Yorkshire*

Cefn Coed *South Wales*
Cefn Cribbwr *South Wales*
Cefn Fforest *Gwent*
Cefn Hengoed *South Wales*
Cefn Mawr *North Wales*
Cemaes Bay *North Wales*
Cemmaes Road *Dyfed-Powys*
Ceres *Police Scotland*
Cerne Abbas *Dorset*
Cerrigydrudion *North Wales*
Chacewater *Devon & Cornwall*
Chacombe *Northamptonshire*
Chadderton *Gtr Manchester*
Chadderton Fold *Gtr Manchester*
Chadderton Heights *Gtr Manchester*
Chaddesden *Derbyshire*
Chaddesley Corbett *West Mercia*
Chaddleworth *Thames Valley*
Chadwell *Leicestershire*
Chadwell Health *Metropolitan*
Chadwick End *Warwickshire*
Chagford *Devon & Cornwall*
Chailey *Sussex*
Chain Bar *Gtr Manchester*
Chalbury *Dorset*
Chaldon *Surrey*
Chaldon Herring *Dorset*
Chalfont St Giles *Thames Valley*
Chalfont St Peter *Thames Valley*
Chalford *Gloucestershire*
Chalgrove *Thames Valley*
Challock *Kent*
Chandlers Cross *Hertfordshire*
Chapel Allerton *West Yorkshire*
Chapel Brampton *Northants*
Chapel-en-le-Frith *Derbyshire*
Chapel Field *Gtr Manchester*
Chapel-St-Leonard's *Lincolnshire*
Chapelhall *Police Scotland*
Chapelthorpe *West Yorkshire*
Chapeltown *West Yorkshire*
Chapeltown *South Yorkshire*
Chapmore End *Hertfordshire*
Chapel Haddlesey *North Yorks*
Chard *Avon & Somerset*
Charfield *Avon & Somerset*
Charford *West Mercia*
Charing *Kent*
Charlbury *Thames Valley*
Charlestown *Gtr Manchester*
Charlesworth *Derbyshire*
Charley *Leicestershire*
Charlton *Hertfordshire*
Charlton *Northamptonshire*
Charlton Marshall *Dorset*
Charwelton *Northamptonshire*
Charlwood *Surrey*
Charminster *Dorset*
Charmouth *Dorset*
Charnock Richard *Lancashire*
Chart Sutton *Kent*
Chartham *Kent*
Chatburn *Lancashire*
Chatham *Kent*
Chatmos *Gtr Manchester*
Chatsworth *Derbyshire*
Chatteris *Cambridgeshire*
Chauntry Brow *Gtr Manchester*
Cheadle *Gtr Manchester*
Cheadle *Staffordshire*
Cheadle Heath *Gtr Manchester*
Cheadle Hulme *Gtr Manchester*
Checkheaton *West Yorkshire*
Checkley *Cheshire*
Chedburgh *Suffolk*
Cheddar *Avon & Somerset*
Cheddington *Thames Valley*
Chedington *Dorset*

Chedworth *Gloucestershire*
Cheesden *Gtr Manchester*
Cheetham *Gtr Manchester*
Cheetham Hill *Gtr Manchester*
Cheetwood *Gtr Manchester*
Chelburn Moor *Gtr Manchester*
Chelford *Cheshire*
Chell *Staffordshire*
Chellaston *Derbyshire*
Chelmorton *Derbyshire*
Chelmsford *Essex*
Chelmsley Wood *West Midlands*
Chelsea *Metropolitan*
Chelsham *Surrey*
Cheltenham *Gloucestershire*
Chelveston-cum-Caldecott *Northamptonshire*
Chepstow *Gwent*
Chequerbent *Gtr Manchester*
Cherhill *Wiltshire*
Chertsey *Surrey*
Chesham *Gtr Manchester*
Chesham *Thames Valley*
Cheshunt *Hertfordshire*
Chesilbourne *Dorset*
Chester *Cheshire*
Chesterfield *Derbyshire*
Chester-le-Street *Durham*
Chesterton *Cambridgeshire*
Chetnole *Dorset*
Chettisham *Cambridgeshire*
Chettle *Dorset*
Cheveley *Cambridgeshire*
Cheveralls Green *Hertfordshire*
Chevening *Kent*
Chew Moor *Gtr Manchester*
Chew Stoke *Avon & Somerset*
Chewton Mendip *Avon & Somerset*
Chichester *Sussex*
Chichester Road *PSNI*
Chickerell *Dorset*
Chiddingfold *Surrey*
Chiddingly *Sussex*
Chiddingstone *Kent*
Chideock *Dorset*
Chidlow *Cheshire*
Chieveley *Thames Valley*
Chigwell *Essex*
Chilcombe *Dorset*
Chilcote *Leicestershire*
Childe Okeford *Dorset*
Childerley *Cambridgeshire*
Childerley Gate *Cambridgeshire*
Childrey *Thames Valley*
Childwickbury *Hertfordshire*
Chilfrome *Dorset*
Chilham *Kent*
Chilmark *Wiltshire*
Chilton *Durham*
Chilworth *Hampshire*
Chilworth *Surrey*
Chingford *Metropolitan*
Chinley *Derbyshire*
Chinnor *Thames Valley*
Chippenham *Cambridgeshire*
Chippenham *Wiltshire*
Chipperfield *Hertfordshire*
Chipping *Hertfordshire*
Chipping *Lancashire*
Chipping Norton *Thames Valley*
Chipping Sodbury & Yate *Avon & Somerset*
Chipping Warden *Northants*
Chirbury *West Mercia*
Chirk *North Wales*
Chirnside *Police Scotland*
Chislehurst *Metropolitan*
Chislet *Kent*

Chiswell Green *Hertfordshire*
Chiswick *Metropolitan*
Chisworth *Derbyshire*
Chittering *Cambridgeshire*
Chobham *Surrey*
Cholmondeley *Cheshire*
Cholmondeston *Cheshire*
Cholsey *Thames Valley*
Chorley *Lancashire*
Chorley (Crewe) *Cheshire*
Chorley (Macclesfield) *Cheshire*
Chorley Wood *Hertfordshire*
Chorley Wood *Thames Valley*
Chorlton *Cheshire*
Chorlton by Backford *Cheshire*
Chorlton-cum-Hardy *Gtr Manchester*
Chorlton (Nantwich) *Cheshire*
Chorlton-on-Medlock *Gtr Manchester*
Chorltonville *Gtr Manchester*
Chowley *Cheshire*
Christchurch *Cambridgeshire*
Christchurch *Dorset*
Christchurch *Gwent*
Christleton *Cheshire*
Chudleigh *Devon & Cornwall*
Chudleigh Knighton *Devon & Cornwall*
Chulmleigh *Devon & Cornwall*
Chunal *Derbyshire*
Church Brampton *Northants*
Church Broughton *Derbyshire*
Church Fenton *North Yorkshire*
Church Gresley *Derbyshire*
Church Hulme *Cheshire*
Church Knowle *Dorset*
Church Lawton *Cheshire*
Church Minshull *Cheshire*
Church Shocklach *Cheshire*
Church Stretton *West Mercia*
Church Village *South Wales*
Church Wilne *Derbyshire*
Churchill *Avon & Somerset*
Churchill *Thames Valley*
Churchstoke *Dyfed-Powys*
Churt *Surrey*
Churton-by-Aldford *Cheshire*
Churton-by-Fardon *Cheshire*
Churton Heath *Cheshire*
Churwell *West Yorkshire*
Cifynydd *South Wales*
Cilycwm *Dyfed-Powys*
Cirencester *Gloucestershire*
City Road *Metropolitan*
Clackmannan *Police Scotland*
Clacton *Essex*
Clandon *Surrey*
Clanfield *Hampshire*
Clapham *Bedfordshire*
Clapham *Metropolitan*
Clapham-cum-Newby *North Yorks*
Clare *Suffolk*
Clarkston *Police Scotland*
Clase *South Wales*
Clatford *Hampshire*
Claudy *PSNI*
Claverdon *Warwickshire*
Claverton *Cheshire*
Clawddnewydd *North Wales*
Claybrooke Magna *Leicestershire*
Claybrooke Parva *Leicestershire*
Claybury *Metropolitan*
Clay Coton *Northamptonshire*
Clay Cross *Derbyshire*
Claydon *Suffolk*
Clayhithe *Cambridgeshire*
Clay Lane *Derbyshire*

Clayton *Gtr Manchester*
Clayton *West Yorkshire*
Clayton Bridge *Gtr Manchester*
Clayton Heights *West Yorkshire*
Clayton West *West Yorkshire*
Clayton-with-Frickley *South Yorks*
Cleator Moor *Cumbria*
Cleckheaton *West Yorkshire*
Clee Hill *West Mercia*
Cleethorpes *Humberside*
Cleeve *Avon & Somerset*
Clegg Moor *Gtr Manchester*
Cleggswood Hill *Gtr Manchester*
Clenchwarton *Norfolk*
Clent *West Mercia*
Cleobury Mortimer *West Mercia*
Clevedon *Avon & Somerset*
Cliff Vale *Staffordshire*
Cliffe *Kent*
Clifford *West Mercia*
Clifton *Bedfordshire*
Clifton *Derbyshire*
Clifton *Gtr Manchester*
Clifton *Lancashire*
Clifton Maybank *Dorset*
Clifton-on-Dunsmore *Warwickshire*
Clifton-on-Teme *West Mercia*
Clifton-on-Yore *North Yorkshire*
Clifton Without *North Yorkshire*
Clipsham *Leicestershire*
Clipston *Northamptonshire*
Clipstone *Nottinghamshire*
Clitheroe *Lancashire*
Cliviger *Lancashire*
Clogher *PSNI*
Clophill *Bedfordshire*
Clopton *Northampton*
Clothall *Hertfordshire*
Clotton Hoofield *Cheshire*
Clough (Crompton) *Gtr Manchester*
Clough (Loughborough) *Gtr Manchester*
Cloughmills *PSNI*
Cloughton *North Yorkshire*
Clovelly *Devon & Cornwall*
Clowbridge *Lancashire*
Clowne *Derbyshire*
Clows Top *West Mercia*
Clun *West Mercia*
Clutton *Cheshire*
Clydach *Gwent*
Clydach *South Wales*
Clydach Vale *South Wales*
Clydebank *Police Scotland*
Clyro *Dyfed-Powys*
Clyst Honiton *Devon & Cornwall*
Clytha *Gwent*
Coads Green *Devon & Cornwall*
Coagh *PSNI*
Coal Aston *Derbyshire*
Coaley *Gtr Manchester*
Coalisland *PSNI*
Coaltown of Wemyss *Police Scotland*
Coalville *Leicestershire*
Coatbridge *Police Scotland*
Coates *Cambridgeshire*
Cobham *Kent*
Cobham *Metropolitan*
Cobridge *Staffordshire*
Cockburnspath *Police Scotland*
Cockerham *Lancashire*
Cockermouth *Cumbria*
Cokernhoe *Hertfordshire*
Cockett *South Wales*
Cockfield *Durham*

Cockfield *Suffolk*
Cocking *Sussex*
Cocknage *Staffordshire*
Coddenham *Suffolk*
Coddington *Cheshire*
Coddington *Nottinghamshire*
Codford *Wiltshire*
Codicote *Hertfordshire*
Codnor *Derbyshire*
Codsall *Staffordshire*
Coed Talon *North Wales*
Coedpoeth *North Wales*
Cofton Hackett *West Mercia*
Cogenhoe *Northamptonshire*
Coggeshall *Essex*
Colburn *North Yorkshire*
Colchester *Essex*
Colcot *South Wales*
Cold Ash *Thames Valley*
Cold Ashby *Northamptonshire*
Cold Cotes *North Yorkshire*
Cold Kirby *North Yorkshire*
Coldbrook *Gwent*
Colden Common *Hampshire*
Coldham *Cambridgeshire*
Coldharbour *Hertfordshire*
Coldharbour *Surrey*
Cold Higham *Northamptonshire*
Cold Newton *Leicestershire*
Cold Overton *Leicestershire*
Coldingham *Police Scotland*
Coldra *Gwent*
Coldstream *Police Scotland*
Cole Green *Hertfordshire*
Coleford *Gloucestershire*
Coleford *Avon & Somerset*
Colehill *Dorset*
Coleman Green *Hertfordshire*
Coleorton *Leicestershire*
Coleraine *PSNI*
Colerne *Wiltshire*
Coleshill *Thames Valley*
Coleshill *Warwickshire*
Colinsburgh *Police Scotland*
Colintraive *Police Scotland*
Colley Gate *West Midlands*
Collier Row *Metropolitan*
Collier Street *Kent*
Colliers End *Hertfordshire*
Collingham *Nottinghamshire*
Collingham *West Yorkshire*
Collingtree *Northamptonshire*
Collyhurst *Gtr Manchester*
Collyweston *Northamptonshire*
Colmworth *Bedfordshire*
Colne *Cambridgeshire*
Colne *Lancashire*
Colney Heath *Hertfordshire*
Colney Street *Hertfordshire*
Colsterdale *North Yorkshire*
Colsterworth *Lincolnshire*
Coltishall *Norfolk*
Colton *North Yorkshire*
Colwall *West Mercia*
Colwyn Bay *North Wales*
Colyton *Devon & Cornwall*
Combe Down *Avon & Somerset*
Combe Keynes *Dorset*
Combe Martin *Devon & Cornwall*
Combe-St-Nicholas *Avon & Somerset*
Comberbach *Cheshire*
Comberton *Cambridgeshire*
Comberton *West Mercia*
Combs *Derbyshire*
Compstall *Gtr Manchester*
Compton *Surrey*
Compton *Thames Valley*
Compton Abbas *Dorset*

Compton Martin *Avon & Somerset*
Compton Valence *Dorset*
Comrie *Police Scotland*
Congerstone *Leicestershire*
Congleton *Cheshire*
Congresbury *Avon & Somerset*
Coningsby *Lincolnshire*
Conington *Cambridgeshire*
Conisbrough *South Yorkshire*
Coniston *Cumbria*
Coniston Cold *North Yorkshire*
Connel *Police Scotland*
Coniston-with-Kilnsey *North Yorks*
Connell *Police Scotland*
Cononley *North Yorkshire*
Consett *Durham*
Constantine *Devon & Cornwall*
Conwil *Dyfed-Powys*
Conwy *North Wales*
Cookham *Thames Valley*
Cookley *West Yorkshire*
Cookstown *PSNI*
Coole Pilate *Cheshire*
Coombe Hill *Gloucestershire*
Cooper Turning *Gtr Manchester*
Copdock *Suffolk*
Copford *Essex*
Cople *Bedfordshire*
Copley *Gtr Manchester*
Copley *Durham*
Copmanthorpe *North Yorkshire*
Coppingford and Upton *Cambs*
Copplestone *Devon & Cornwall*
Coppull *Lancashire*
Copsterhill *Gtr Manchester*
Copt Hewick *North Yorkshire*
Copt Oak *Leicestershire*
Copthorne *Surrey*
Copthorne *Sussex*
Corbridge *Northumbria*
Corby *Northamptonshire*
Corby Hill *Cumbria*
Corfe Castle *Dorset*
Corfe Mullen *Dorset*
Cornelly *South Wales*
Cornhill *Northumbria*
Cornholme *West Yorkshire*
Cornsay *Durham*
Cornwood *Devon & Cornwall*
Corpusty *Norfolk*
Corringham *Essex*
Corringham *Lincolnshire*
Corris *North Wales*
Corscombe *Dorset*
Corsham *Wiltshire*
Corston *Avon & Somerset*
Corstorphine *Police Scotland*
Corton *Suffolk*
Corwen *North Wales*
Cosby *Leicestershire*
Cosford *West Mercia*
Cosgrove *Northamptonshire*
Cosham *Hampshire*
Cossington *Leicestershire*
Coston *Leicestershire*
Cotehill *Cumbria*
Cotes *Leicestershire*
Cotesbach *Leicestershire*
Cotes-de-Val *Leicestershire*
Cotgrave *Nottinghamshire*
Cotherstone *Durham*
Cotmanhay *Derbyshire*
Coton *Cambridgeshire*
Coton-in-the-Elms *Derbyshire*
Cottenham *Cambridgeshire*
Cottered *Hertfordshire*
Cotteridge *West Midlands*

Cotterstock *Northamptonshire*
Cottesbrooke *Northamptonshire*
Cottesmore *Leicestershire*
Cottesthorpe *Leicestershire*
Cottingham *Humberside*
Cottingham *Northamptonshire*
Cottingley *West Yorkshire*
Cotton Abbots *Cheshire*
Cotton Edmunds *Cheshire*
Cotton End *Bedfordshire*
Coundon *Durham*
Countersthorpe *Leicestershire*
Coupar Angus *Police Scotland*
Courteenhall *Northamptonshire*
Cove & Kilcreggan *Police Scotland*
Coveney *Cambridgeshire*
Coventry *West Midlands*
Coventry Road *West Midlands*
Covington *Cambridgeshire*
Cowan Bridge *Lancashire*
Cowbit *Lincolnshire*
Cowbridge *South Wales*
Cowden *Kent*
Cowdenbeath *Police Scotland*
Cowes *Hampshire*
Cowfold *Sussex*
Cowie *Police Scotland*
Cowley *Thames Valley*
Cowling *North Yorkshire*
Cowling (Skipton) *North Yorkshire*
Cowlishaw *Gtr Manchester*
Cowplain *Hampshire*
Cowshill *Durham*
Coxbench *Derbyshire*
Coxhoe *Durham*
Coxley *Avon & Somerset*
Coxwold *North Yorkshire*
Coychurch *South Wales*
Cracoe *North Yorkshire*
Cradley, Ledbury *West Mercia*
Craghead *Durham*
Craigcefnparc *South Wales*
Craigie Street *Police Scotland*
Craigmillar *Police Scotland*
Craigneuk *Police Scotland*
Craignure (Mull) *Police Scotland*
Crail *Police Scotland*
Crakehall *North Yorkshire*
Cramlington *Northumbria*
Cranage *Cheshire*
Cranborne *Dorset*
Cranbrook *Kent*
Cranfield *Bedfordshire*
Cranford *Northamptonshire*
Crankwood *Gtr Manchester*
Cranleigh *Surrey*
Cranoe *Leicestershire*
Cransley *Northamptonshire*
Cranwell *Lincolnshire*
Crathorne *North Yorkshire*
Craven Arms *West Mercia*
Crawford *Police Scotland*
Crawley *Sussex*
Crawshowbooth *Lancashire*
Cray *North Yorkshire*
Crayke *North Yorkshire*
Crays Hill *Essex*
Crays Pond *Thames Valley*
Creaton *Northamptonshire*
Crediton *Devon & Cornwall*
Creech St Michael *Avon & Somerset*
Cregganside *PSNI*
Cressage *West Mercia*
Cressbank *Derbyshire*
Creswell *Derbyshire*
Crewe *Cheshire*

Crewe (Tarvin) *Cheshire*
Crewkerne *Avon & Somerset*
Crianlarich *Police Scotland*
Cribbs Causeway *Avon & Somerset*
Criccieth *North Wales*
Crich *Derbyshire*
Crick *Gwent*
Crick *Northamptonshire*
Crickhowell *Dyfed-Powys*
Cricklade *Wiltshire*
Crieff *Police Scotland*
Crigglestone *West Yorkshire*
Crimble *Gtr Manchester*
Cringleford *Norfolk*
Crockenhill *Kent*
Crocketford *Police Scotland*
Crockham Hill *Kent*
Croescrw *South Wales*
Croesyceiliog *Gwent*
Croft *Cheshire*
Croft *Leicestershire*
Croft Spa *Durham*
Croft-on-Tees *North Yorkshire*
Crofton *West Yorkshire*
Crofts Bank *Gtr Manchester*
Cromarty *Police Scotland*
Cromer *Hertfordshire*
Cromer *Norfolk*
Cromford *Derbyshire*
Crompton Fold *Gtr Manchester*
Crondall *Hampshire*
Crook *Durham*
Crook of Devon *Police Scotland*
Crooksbury *Surrey*
Cropston *Leicestershire*
Cropthorne *West Mercia*
Cropwell Butler *Nottinghamshire*
Crosby *Cumbria*
Crosby *Isle of Man*
Crosby *Merseyside*
Crosby *North Yorkshire*
Crosby-on-Eden *Cumbria*
Crossacres *Gtr Manchester*
Cross Ash *Gwent*
Cross Bank *Gtr Manchester*
Cross-in-Hand *Sussex*
Cross Roads *West Yorkshire*
Crossflatts *West Yorkshire*
Crossford *Police Scotland*
Crossgar *PSNI*
Crossgates *West Yorkshire*
Crossgates *Police Scotland*
Crosshands (Carms) *Dyfed-Powys*
Crosshands (Pembs) *Dyfed-Powys*
Crosshills *North Yorkshire*
Crosskeys *Gwent*
Crossmaglen *PSNI*
Croston *Lancashire*
Croughton *Cheshire*
Croughton *Northampton*
Crowborough *Sussex*
Crowdecote *Derbyshire*
Crowhurst *Surrey*
Crowland *Lincolnshire*
Crowlas *Devon & Cornwall*
Crowle *Humberside*
Crowle *West Mercia*
Crowmarsh *Thames Valley*
Crowthorne *Thames Valley*
Crowton *Cheshire*
Croxdale *Durham*
Croxley Green *Hertfordshire*
Croxton *Cambridgeshire*
Croxton Kerrial *Leicestershire*
Croyde *Devon & Cornwall*
Croydon *Cambridgeshire*
Croydon *Metropolitan*
Cruden Bay *Police Scotland*

Crudwell *Wiltshire*
Crumlin *Gwent*
Crumlin *PSNI*
Crumpsall *Gtr Manchester*
Crymmych *Dyfed-Powys*
Crynant *South Wales*
Cubbington *Warwickshire*
Cubley *Derbyshire*
Cuckney *Nottinghamshire*
Cuddington *Cheshire*
Cudworth *South Yorkshire*
Cuerdley *Cheshire*
Cuffley *Hertfordshire*
Culcheth *Cheshire*
Culham *Thames Valley*
Cullen *Police Scotland*
Cullingworth *West Yorkshire*
Cullivoe *Police Scotland*
Culloden *Police Scotland*
Cullompton *Devon & Cornwall*
Cullybackey *PSNI*
Culross *Police Scotland*
Culter *Police Scotland*
Cults *Police Scotland*
Culworth *Northamptonshire*
Cumberlow Green *Hertfordshire*
Cumbernauld *Police Scotland*
Cumberworth *West Yorkshire*
Cuminestown *Police Scotland*
Cummersdale *Cumbria*
Cumnock *Police Scotland*
Cumnor *Thames Valley*
Cupar *Police Scotland*
Cupid Green *Hertfordshire*
Curbar *Derbyshire*
Curdworth *Warwickshire*
Currie *Police Scotland*
Curry Rivel *Avon & Somerset*
Cushendall *PSNI*
Cusworth *South Yorkshire*
Cutgate *Gtr Manchester*
Cut Mill *Surrey*
Cutnall Green *West Mercia*
Cutsyke *West Yorkshire*
Cutthorpe *Derbyshire*
Cuxton *Kent*
Cwym *Gwent*
Cwmaman *South Wales*
Cwmavon *Gwent*
Cwmavon *South Wales*
Cwmbach *South Wales*
Cwmbran *Gwent*
Cwmbwrla *South Wales*
Cwmcarn *Gwent*
Cwmdare *South Wales*
Cwmdu *South Wales*
Cwmfelinfach *Gwent*
Cwmffrwdoer *Gwent*
Cwmgwrach *South Wales*
Cwmllynfell *South Wales*
Cwmparch *South Wales*
Cwmrhydyceirw *South Wales*
Cwmsyfiog *South Wales*
Cwmtillery *Gwent*
Cwmyoy *Gwent*
Cymmau *North Wales*
Cymmer (Afan) *South Wales*
Cymmer (Pontypridd) *South Wales*
Cyncoed *South Wales*
Dadlington *Leicestershire*
Dafen *Dyfed-Powys*
Dagenham *Metropolitan*
Dailly *Police Scotland*
Dairy *Police Scotland*
Daisy Hill *West Yorkshire*
Daisy Nook *Gtr Manchester*
Dalbeattie *Police Scotland*
Dalbury-Lees *Derbyshire*

Dalby *North Yorkshire*
Dale *Gtr Manchester*
Dale Abbey *Derbyshire*
Dale Head *North Yorkshire*
Dalehall *Staffordshire*
Dales Brow *Gtr Manchester*
Dalkeith *Police Scotland*
Dalmally *Police Scotland*
Dalmellington *Police Scotland*
Dalnaspidal *Police Scotland*
Dalry *Police Scotland*
Dalston *Cumbria*
Dalston *Metropolitan*
Dalton *Cumbria*
Dalton (Thirsk) *North Yorkshire*
Dalton (Richmond) *North Yorks*
Dalton *South Yorkshire*
Dalton-on-Tees *North Yorkshire*
Damerham *Hampshire*
Danbury *Essex*
Danby (Richmond) *North Yorks*
Danby (Whitby) *North Yorkshire*
Danby Wiske *North Yorkshire*
Dane Bank *Gtr Manchester*
Dane End *Hertfordshire*
Danehill *Sussex*
Danesmoor *Derbyshire*
Darcy Lever *Gtr Manchester*
Darenth *Kent*
Daresbury *Cheshire*
Darfield *South Yorkshire*
Darlaston *West Midlands*
Darley *Derbyshire*
Darley *North Yorkshire*
Darley *West Yorkshire*
Darley Abbey *Derbyshire*
Darley Dale *Derbyshire*
Darlington *Durham*
Darnhall *Cheshire*
Darrington *West Yorkshire*
Darnhill *Gtr Manchester*
Dartford *Kent*
Dartmouth *Devon & Cornwall*
Darton *South Yorkshire*
Darvel *Police Scotland*
Darwen *Lancashire*
Datchet *Thames Valley*
Datchworth *Hertfordshire*
Daubhill *Gtr Manchester*
Davenham *Cheshire*
Davenport *Cheshire*
Davenport Green *Cheshire*
Davenport Park *Gtr Manchester*
Daventry *Northamptonshire*
Davington *Kent*
Daviot *Police Scotland*
Davyhulme *Gtr Manchester*
Dawes Green *Surrey*
Dawley *West Mercia*
Dawlish *Devon & Cornwall*
Dawlish Warren *Devon & Cornwall*
Deal *Kent*
Dean *Bedfordshire*
Deane *Gtr Manchester*
Deans *Gtr Manchester*
Deanshanger *Northamptonshire*
Deanwater *Cheshire*
Dearham *Cumbria*
Dearnley *Gtr Manchester*
Debenham *Suffolk*
Dedham *Essex*
Deddington *Thames Valley*
Deene *Northamptonshire*
Deenethorpe *Northamptonshire*
Deepcar *South Yorkshire*
Deepcut *Surrey*
Deepdene *Surrey*
Deeping Gate *Cambridgeshire*

Deeping-St-James *Lincolnshire*
Deeping-St-Nicholas *Lincolnshire*
Deeside *North Wales*
Deganwy *North Wales*
Deiniolen *North Wales*
Delamere *Cheshire*
Delph *Gtr Manchester*
Delph Hill *Gtr Manchester*
Denaby *South Yorkshire*
Denbigh *North Wales*
Denby *Derbyshire*
Denby *West Yorkshire*
Denby Dale *West Yorkshire*
Denchworth *Thames Valley*
Denford *Northamptonshire*
Denham *Thames Valley*
Denholm *Police Scotland*
Denholm *West Yorkshire*
Denholme Gate *West Yorkshire*
Denmead *Hampshire*
Denny *Police Scotland*
Denshaw *Gtr Manchester*
Dent *Cumbria*
Denton *Great Manchester*
Denton *North Yorkshire*
Denton *Northamptonshire*
Deptford *Metropolitan*
Derby Hills *Derbyshire*
Dereham *Norfolk*
Deri *Gwent*
Derker *Gtr Manchester*
Derrygonnelly *PSNI*
Dersingham *Norfolk*
Derwent *Derbyshire*
Desborough *Northamptonshire*
Desford *Leicestershire*
Dethick *Derbyshire*
Detling *Kent*
Devauden *Gwent*
Devil's Bridge *Dyfed-Powys*
Devizes *Wiltshire*
Dewlish *Dorset*
Dewsbury *West Yorkshire*
Dickleburgh *Norfolk*
Didcot *Thames Valley*
Diddington *Cambridgeshire*
Disbury *Gtr Manchester*
Digbeth *West Midlands*
Diggle *Gtr Manchester*
Digswell *Hertfordshire*
Dinas *South Wales*
Dinas Mawddwy *North Wales*
Dinas Powis *South Wales*
Dingestow *Gwent*
Dingley *Northamptonshire*
Dingwall *Police Scotland*
Dinham *Gwent*
Dinnington *Northumbria*
Dinnington *South Yorkshire*
Dinsdale *Durham*
Dinton *Wiltshire*
Dippenhall *Surrey*
Dipton *Durham*
Diseworth *Leicestershire*
Dishforth *North Yorkshire*
Dishley *Leicestershire*
Disley *Cheshire*
Diss *Norfolk*
Distington *Cumbria*
Ditchingham *Norfolk*
Ditton *Kent*
Dixton *Gwent*
Dobcross *Gtr Manchester*
Dobwalls *Devon & Cornwall*
Dockenfield *Surrey*
Docking *Norfolk*
Dodcott-cum-Wilkesley *Cheshire*
Doddington *Cheshire*
Doddington *Cambridgeshire*

Dodford *Northamptonshire*
Dodleston *Cheshire*
Dodworth *South Yorkshire*
Doe Lea *Derbyshire*
Doffcocker *Gtr Manchester*
Dog Hill *Gtr Manchester*
Dolgarrog *North Wales*
Dolgellau *North Wales*
Dollar *Police Scotland*
Dolphinholme *Lancashire*
Dolwyddelan *North Wales*
Donaghadee *PSNI*
Doncaster *South Yorkshire*
Donegall Pass *PSNI*
Donemagh *PSNI*
Donhead *Wiltshire*
Donington *Lincolnshire*
Donnington *West Mercia*
Donington-le-Heath *Leicestershire*
Donisthorpe *Leicestershire*
Dooley Lane *Gtr Manchester*
Dorchester *Dorset*
Dorchester *Thames Valley*
Dordon *Warwickshire*
Dorking *Surrey*
Dormansland *Surrey*
Dornoch *Police Scotland*
Dorridge *West Midlands*
Douglas *Police Scotland*
Doune *Police Scotland*
Dove Holes *Derbyshire*
Dover *Gtr Manchester*
Dover *Kent*
Doveridge *Derbyshire*
Dowlais *South Wales*
Downham Market *Norfolk*
Downpatrick *PSNI*
Downton *Wiltshire*
Draethen *Gwent*
Drakelow *Derbyshire*
Drakes Broughton *West Mercia*
Draperstown *PSNI*
Draughton *Northamptonshire*
Draughton *North Yorkshire*
Drax *North Yorkshire*
Draycott *Derbyshire*
Drayton *Leicestershire*
Dresden *Staffordshire*
Driffield *Humberside*
Drighlington *West Yorkshire*
Droitwich *West Mercia*
Dromara *PSNI*
Dromore (Down) *PSNI*
Dromore (Tyrone) *PSNI*
Dronfield *Derbyshire*
Dronfield Woodhouse *Derbyshire*
Drongan *Police Scotland*
Droxford *Hampshire*
Droylesden *Gtr Manchester*
Drumnadrochit *Police Scotland*
Drybrook *Gloucestershire*
Dry Drayton *Cambridgeshire*
Drylaw Mains *Police Scotland*
Drymen *Police Scotland*
Duckington *Cheshire*
Duckmanton *Derbyshire*
Duddington *Northamptonshire*
Duddon *Cheshire*
Dudley *West Midlands*
Dudley Hill *West Yorkshire*
Dudley Road *West Midlands*
Dudswell *Hertfordshire*
Duffield *Derbyshire*
Dufftown *Police Scotland*
Dukestown *Gwent*
Dukinfield *Gtr Manchester*
Dulverton *Avon & Somerset*
Dullingham *Cambridgeshire*
Dumbarton *Police Scotland*

Dumfries *Police Scotland*
Dumplington *Gtr Manchester*
Dunbar *Police Scotland*
Dunbeath *Police Scotland*
Dunblane *Police Scotland*
Dunchurch *Warwickshire*
Duncton *Sussex*
Dundee *Police Scotland*
Dundonald *PSNI*
Dundrum *PSNI*
Dunfermline *Police Scotland*
Dungannon *PSNI*
Dungiven *PSNI*
Dunham Massey *Gtr Manchester*
Dunham-on-the Hill *Cheshire*
Dunham-on-Trent
    Nottinghamshire
Dunham Town *Gtr Manchester*
Dunham Woodhouses *Gtr
    Manchester*
Dunkeld *Police Scotland*
Dunmow *Essex*
Dunmurry *PSNI*
Dunning *Police Scotland*
Dunoon *Police Scotland*
Duns *Police Scotland*
Dunscar *Gtr Manchester*
Dunscroft *South Yorkshire*
Dunsfold *Surrey*
Dunsop Bridge *Lancashire*
Dunstall Road *West Midlands*
Dunster *Avon & Somerset*
Dunsville *South Yorkshire*
Dunswell *Humberside*
Dunton Bassett *Leicestershire*
Dunton Green *Kent*
Dunvant *South Wales*
Dunvegan *Police Scotland*
Durbar *Cumbria*
Durham City *Durham*
Durkar *West Yorkshire*
Durn *Gtr Manchester*
Durrington *Wiltshire*
Dursley *Gloucestershire*
Durweston *Dorset*
Dutton *Cheshire*
Duxford *Cambridgeshire*
Duxhurst *Surrey*
Dyffryn *North Wales*
Dyffryn Ardudwy *North Wales*
Dymchurch *Kent*
Dymock *Gloucestershire*
Dyserth *North Wales*
Eaglescliffe *Cleveland*
Eaglesham *Police Scotland*
Eagley *Gtr Manchester*
Ealing *Metropolitan*
Earby *Lancashire*
Eardisley *West Mercia*
Earith *Cambridgeshire*
Earl Shilton *Leicestershire*
Earls Barton *Northamptonshire*
Earls Colne *Essex*
Earlsfield *Metropolitan*
Earl Soham *Suffolk*
Earl Sterndale *Derbyshire*
Earlston *Police Scotland*
Earlswood *Surrey*
Earlswood *Warwickshire*
Earsham *Norfolk*
Easby (Richmond) *North
    Yorkshire*
Easby (Stokesley) *North Yorkshire*
Eashing *Surrey*
Easington Colliery *Durham*
Easington Village *Durham*
Easingwold *North Yorkshire*
East Bergholt *Suffolk*
East Bierley *West Yorkshire*

Eastbourne *Sussex*
East Bridgeford *Nottinghamshire*
East Carlton *Northamptonshire*
East Clandon *Surrey*
East Challow *Thames Valley*
East Chelborough *Dorset*
Eastchurch *Kent*
East Cowes *Hampshire*
East Dean *Sussex*
East Disbury *Gtr Manchester*
East Dulwich *Metropolitan*
East End Green *Hertfordshire*
East End/Pilley *Hampshire*
Easterhouse *Police Scotland*
East Farleigh *Kent*
East Farndon *Northamptonshire*
Eastgate *Durham*
East Goscote *Leicestershire*
East Grinstead *Sussex*
East Haddon *Northamptonshire*
East Hagbourne *Thames Valley*
Eastham *Merseyside*
East Ham *Metropolitan*
East Hanningfield *Essex*
East Harling *Norfolk*
East Hatley *Cambridgeshire*
East Hendred *Thames Valley*
East Holme *Dorset*
East Horsley *Surrey*
East Ilsley *Thames Valley*
East Kilbride *Police Scotland*
East Knoyle *Wiltshire*
East Langton *Leicestershire*
East Leake *Nottinghamshire*
Eastleigh *Hampshire*
Eastling *Kent*
East Lulworth *Dorset*
East Malling *Kent*
East Markam *Nottinghamshire*
East Marton *North Yorkshire*
East Meon *Hampshire*
East Molesey *Metropolitan*
East Moors *South Wales*
East Norton *Leicestershire*
Easton *Cambridgeshire*
Easton Maudit *Northamptonshire*
Easton Neston *Northamptonshire*
Easton-on-the-Hill *Northants*
East Orchard *Dorset*
East Peckham *Kent*
East Preston *Sussex*
Eastrea *Cambridgeshire*
East Rudham *Norfolk*
Eastry *Kent*
East Stoke *Dorset*
East Stoke *Nottinghamshire*
East Stour *Dorset*
East Vale *Staffordshire*
East Wemyss *Police Scotland*
Eastwell *Leicestershire*
Eastwick *Hertfordshire*
Eastwood *Nottinghamshire*
Eastwood (Todmorden) *West
    Yorks*
Eastwood (Keighley) *West Yorks*
Eaton *Derbyshire*
Eaton Bray *Bedfordshire*
Eaton-by-Tarporley *Cheshire*
Eaton (Chester) *Cheshire*
Eaton *Leicestershire*
Eaton Hastings *Thames Valley*
Eaton Socon *Cambridgeshire*
Ebbw Vale *Gwent*
Ebchester *Durham*
Eccles *Kent*
Eccles *Gtr Manchester*
Ecclesfield *South Yorkshire*
Eccleshall *Staffordshire*
Eccleston *Cheshire*

Eccleston *Lancashire*
Eccup *West Yorkshire*
Echt *Police Scotland*
Eckington *Derbyshire*
Ecton *Northamptonshire*
Edale *Derbyshire*
Edenbridge *Kent*
Edenfield *Lancs*
Edensor *Derbyshire*
Edgcote *Northamptonshire*
Edge *Cheshire*
Edge Fold *Gtr Manchester*
Edge Green *Gtr Manchester*
Edgeley *Cheshire*
Edgerley *Gtr Manchester*
Edgeworth *Lancashire*
Edgeworth *Lancashire*
Edgware *Metropolitan*
Edinburgh *Police Scotland*
Edith Weston *Leicestershire*
Edlaston *Derbyshire*
Edlesborough *Thames Valley*
Edleston *Cheshire*
Edlington *South Yorkshire*
Edmondsham *Dorset*
Edmondthorpe *Leicestershire*
Edmonton *Metropolitan*
Edmundbyers *Durham*
Ednaston *Derbyshire*
Edwalton *Nottinghamshire*
Edward Road *West Midlands*
Edwinstowe *Nottinghamshire*
Edzell *Police Scotland*
Effingham *Surrey*
Egerton *Cheshire*
Egerton *Gtr Manchester*
Eggborough *North Yorkshire*
Egginton *Derbyshire*
Eggleston *Durham*
Egham *Surrey*
Egham Hythe *Surrey*
Egleton *Leicestershire*
Eglinton *PSNI*
Eglwysbach *North Wales*
Eglwyswrw *Dyfed-Powys*
Egmond *West Mercia*
Egremont *Merseyside*
Egremont *Cumbria*
Egstow *Derbyshire*
Elburton *Devon & Cornwall*
Elderslie *Police Scotland*
Eldon *Durham*
Eldwick *West Yorkshire*
Elgin *Police Scotland*
Elham *Kent*
Elie *Police Scotland*
Elkesley *Nottinghamshire*
Elkington *Northamptonshire*
Elland *West Yorkshire*
Ellenbrook *Gtr Manchester*
Ellens Green *Surrey*
Ellesborough *Thames Valley*
Ellesmere *West Mercia*
Ellesmere Park *Gtr Manchester*
Ellesmere Port *Cheshire*
Ellington *Cambridgeshire*
Ellington *Northumbria*
Ellistown *Leicestershire*
Ellon *Police Scotland*
Elm *Cambridgeshire*
Elmbridge *Surrey*
Elmdon *Essex*
Elmdon (airport) *West Midlands*
Elmstead *Essex*
Elmsthorpe *Leicestershire*
Elmswell *Suffolk*
Elmton *Derbyshire*
Elsecar *South Yorkshire*
Elsenham *Essex*

Elstead *Surrey*
Elstree *Hertfordshire*
Elsworth *Cambridgeshire*
Eltan *Gtr Manchester*
Eltham *Metropolitan*
Eltisley *Cambridgeshire*
Elton *Cambridgeshire*
Elton (Chester) *Cheshire*
Elton (Congleton) *Cheshire*
Elton *Derbyshire*
Elvaston *Derbyshire*
Elveden *Suffolk*
Elvington *North Yorkshire*
Elworth *Cheshire*
Ely *Cambridgeshire*
Ely *South Wales*
Embleton *Northumbria*
Embsay *North Yorkshire*
Emley *West Yorkshire*
Emneth *Norfolk*
Empingham *Leicestershire*
Emsworth *Hampshire*
Enderby *Leicestershire*
Endmoor *Cumbria*
Endon *Staffordshire*
Enfield *Metropolitan*
Englefield *Thames Valley*
Englefield Green *Surrey*
Enham Alamein *Hampshire*
Enniskillen *PSNI*
Ensbury Park *Dorset*
Enstone *Thames Valley*
Enton *Surrey*
Epping *Essex*
Epping Green *Hertfordshire*
Eppleby *North Yorkshire*
Epsom *Surrey*
Epworth *Humberside*
Erdington *West Midlands*
Eridge *Sussex*
Erith *Metropolitan*
Erlestroke *Wiltshire*
Ermington *Devon & Cornwall*
Errol *Police Scotland*
Erskine *Police Scotland*
Escombe *Durham*
Escrick *North Yorkshire*
Esh *Durham*
Esher *Surrey*
Esholt *Bradford*
Eskdale *Cumbria*
Essendine *Leicestershire*
Essendon *Hertfordshire*
Eston *Cleveland*
Eton *Thames Valley*
Etrop Green *Gtr Manchester*
Etruria *Staffordshire*
Ettington *Warwickshire*
Etton *Cambridgeshire*
Etwall *Derbyshire*
Euston Street *Leicestershire*
Euxton *Lancashire*
Evenley *Northampton*
Evenwood *Durham*
Evercreech *Avon & Somerset*
Everdon *Northamptonshire*
Eversholt *Bedfordshire*
Evershot *Dorset*
Eversley *Hampshire*
Everton *Nottinghamshire*
Evesham *West Mercia*
Evington *Leicestershire*
Ewell *Surrey*
Ewenny *South Wales*
Ewhurst *Surrey*
Ewood Bridge *Lancashire*
Ewyas Harold *West Mercia*
Exchange *Gtr Manchester*
Exeter *Devon & Cornwall*

Exford *Avon & Somerset*
Exhall *Warwickshire*
Exminster *Devon & Cornwall*
Exmouth *Devon & Cornwall*
Exton *Leicestershire*
Eyam *Derbyshire*
Eyam Woodlands *Derbyshire*
Eydon *Northamptonshire*
Eye *Cambridgeshire*
Eye *Suffolk*
Eye Kettleby *Leicestershire*
Eyemouth *Police Scotland*
Eynesbury *Cambridgeshire*
Eynesbury Hardwicke *Cambs*
Eynsford *Kent*
Eynsham *Thames Valley*
Eyres Monsell *Leicestershire*
Eythorne *Kent*
Faddily *Cheshire*
Fagley *Gtr Manchester*
Failsworth *Gtr Manchester*
Fairburn *North Yorkshire*
Fairfield *Derbyshire*
Fairfield *Gtr Manchester*
Fairfield *West Mercia*
Fairford *Gloucestershire*
Fairlands *Surrey*
Fairlight *Sussex*
Fair Oak *Hampshire*
Fairwater *Gwent*
Fairwater *South Wales*
Fairweather Green *West Yorkshire*
Fairwood *South Wales*
Fakenham *Norfolk*
Falfield *Avon & Somerset*
Falkirk *Police Scotland*
Falkland *Police Scotland*
Fallin *Police Scotland*
Fallowfield *Gtr Manchester*
Falmouth *Devon & Cornwall*
Farcet *Cambridgeshire*
Far Green *Staffordshire*
Far Moor *Gtr Manchester*
Fareham *Hampshire*
Faringdon *Thames Valley*
Farley Green *Surrey*
Farley Hill *Bedfordshire*
Farm Town *Leicestershire*
Farnborough *Hampshire*
Farnborough *Metropolitan*
Farncombe *Surrey*
Farndon *Cheshire*
Farnham *Surrey*
Farnhill *North Yorkshire*
Farningham *Kent*
Farnley *West Yorkshire*
Farnley Tyas *West Yorkshire*
Farnsfield *Nottinghamshire*
Farnworth *Gtr Manchester*
Farringdon *Hampshire*
Farsley *West Yorkshire*
Farthinghoe *Northamptonshire*
Farthingstone *Northamptonshire*
Faversham *Kent*
Fawley *Hampshire*
Fawsley *Northamptonshire*
Faygate *Sussex*
Feckenham *West Mercia*
Fegg Hayes *Staffordshire*
Felbridge *Surrey*
Felinfach *Dyfed-Powys*
Felinfoel *Dyfed-Powys*
Felixstowe *Suffolk*
Felpham *Essex*
Felsted *Essex*
Feltham *Metropolitan*
Felton *Northumbria*
Feltwell *Norfolk*
Fen Ditton *Cambridgeshire*

Fen Drayton *Cambridgeshire*
Fence & Newchurch *Lancashire*
Fencehouses *Durham*
Fenny Bentley *Derbyshire*
Fenny Compton *Warwickshire*
Fenny Drayton *Leicestershire*
Fenstanton *Cambridgeshire*
Fenton *Staffordshire*
Ferndale *South Wales*
Ferndown *Dorset*
Ferngrove *Gtr Manchester*
Fernhill *Gtr Manchester*
Fernhill Gate *Gtr Manchester*
Fernhill Heath *West Mercia*
Fernhurst *Sussex*
Ferring *Sussex*
Ferrybridge *West Yorkshire*
Ferryden *Police Scotland*
Ferryhill *Durham*
Ferryside *Dyfed-Powys*
Fetcham *Surrey*
Fettercairn *Police Scotland*
Fewston *North Yorkshire*
Ffestiniog *North Wales*
Fforestfach *South Wales*
Ffostrasol *Dyfed-Powys*
Ffynnongroew *North Wales*
Fielden Park *Gtr Manchester*
Fifehead Magdalen *Dorset*
Fifehead Neville *Dorset*
Filby *Norfolk*
Filey *North Yorkshire*
Fillongley *Warwickshire*
Filton *Avon & Somerset*
Fincham *Norfolk*
Finchampstead *Thames Valley*
Finchingfield *Essex*
Finchley *Metropolitan*
Findern *Derbyshire*
Findon *Sussex*
Finedon *Northamptonshire*
Fineshade *Northamptonshire*
Finmere *Thames Valley*
Fintona *PSNI*
Fintry *Police Scotland*
Firbeck *South Yorkshire*
Firgrove *Gtr Manchester*
Firs Lane *Gtr Manchester*
Firswood *Gtr Manchester*
Fishbourne *Sussex*
Fishburn *Durham*
Fishguard *Dyfed-Powys*
Fishlake *South Yorkshire*
Fishponds *Bristol*
Fishpool *Gtr Manchester*
Fishtoft *Lincolnshire*
Fittleworth *Sussex*
Fitton Hill *Gtr Manchester*
Fitzwilliam *West Yorkshire*
Five Lanes *Devon & Cornwall*
Fivemiletown *PSNI*
Five Oak Green *Kent*
Flackwell Heath *Thames Valley*
Flagg *Derbyshire*
Flamborough *Humberside*
Flamstead *Hertfordshire*
Flaunden *Hertfordshire*
Fleckney *Leicestershire*
Fleet *Dorset*
Fleet *Hampshire*
Fleet *Lincolnshire*
Fleetwood *Lancashire*
Fleggburgh *Norfolk*
Fletchampstead *West Midlands*
Fleur-de-Lys *Gwent*
Flimby *Cumbria*
Flint *North Wales*
Flintham *Nottinghamshire*
Flitwick *Bedfordshire*

Flixton *Gtr Manchester*
Flockton *West Yorkshire*
Flore *Northamptonshire*
Florence *Staffordshire*
Flowery Field *Gtr Manchester*
Flushdyke *West Yorkshire*
Flyford Flavell *West Mercia*
Fochabers *Police Scotland*
Fochriw *Gwent*
Foggprook *Gtr Manchester*
Fold *Gtr Manchester*
Foley Park *West Mercia*
Folke *Dorset*
Folkestone *Kent*
Folksworth and Washingley *Cambs*
Fontmell Magnus *Dorset*
Foolow *Derbyshire*
Ford *Merseyside*
Ford *West Mercia*
Ford Green *Staffordshire*
Fordham *Cambridgeshire*
Fordingbridge *Hampshire*
Foremark *Derbyshire*
Forest Coal Pit *Gwent*
Forest Gate *Metropolitan*
Forest Green *Surrey*
Forest Row *Sussex*
Forest Town *Nottinghamshire*
Forfar *Police Scotland*
Forhill *West Mercia*
Forkhill *PSNI*
Fromby *Merseyside*
Forres *Police Scotland*
Forth *Police Scotland*
Fort Augustus *Police Scotland*
Forton *Lancashire*
Fortrose *Police Scotland*
Fort William *Police Scotland*
Fosdyke *Lincolnshire*
Fossoway *Police Scotland*
Foston *Derbyshire*
Foston *Leicestershire*
Fotheringhay *Northamptonshire*
Foul Anchor *Cambridgeshire*
Foulk Stapleford *Cheshire*
Foulridge *Lancashire*
Fourcrosses *North Wales*
Four Gates *Gtr Manchester*
Four Gotes *Cambridgeshire*
Four Lane Ends *Gtr Manchester*
Four Marks *Hampshire*
Fovant *Wiltshire*
Fowey *Devon & Cornwall*
Fowlmere *Cambridgeshire*
Fox Corner *Surrey*
Fox Platt *Gtr Manchester*
Foxhall *Suffolk*
Foxton *Cambridgeshire*
Foxton *Leicestershire*
Foyers *Police Scotland*
Framlingham *Suffolk*
Frampton *Dorset*
Frampton *Lincolnshire*
Frampton-on-Severn *Gloucestershire*
Framsden *Suffolk*
Franche *West Mercia*
Frankby *Merseyside*
Frant *Sussex*
Fraserburgh *Police Scotland*
Freckleton *Lancashire*
Free Town *Gtr Manchester*
Freeby *Leicestershire*
Freiston *Lincolnshire*
Frensham *Surrey*
Freshford *Avon & Somerset*
Freshwater *Hampshire*
Freshwater Bay *Hampshire*

Freuchie *Police Scotland*
Frickley *West Yorkshire*
Fridaybridge *Cambridgeshire*
Frimley *Surrey*
Frimley Green *Surrey*
Frindsbury Extra *Kent*
Frinsted *Kent*
Frinton *Essex*
Friockheim *Police Scotland*
Frisby-on-the-Wreake *Leicestershire*
Frisby-by-Gaulby *Leicestershire*
Friskney *Lincolnshire*
Frithesden *Hertfordshire*
Frittenden *Kent*
Fritton *Norfolk*
Frizinghall *West Yorkshire*
Frodsham *Cheshire*
Froggatt *Derbyshire*
Frogmore *Devon & Cornwall*
Frolesworth *Leicestershire*
Frome *Avon & Somerset*
Frome St Quinton *Dorset*
Frome Vauchurch *Dorset*
Froncysyllte *North Wales*
Frosterley *Durham*
Froxfield *Wiltshire*
Fulbourn *Cambridgeshire*
Fulford *North Yorkshire*
Fulham *Metropolitan*
Fulmer *Thames Valley*
Fulwood *Gtr Manchester*
Fulwood *Lancashire*
Furnace End *Warwickshire*
Furneaux Pelham *Hertfordshire*
Furness Vale *Derbyshire*
Fyfield *Essex*
Fyfield *Thames Valley*
Fynnongroew *North Wales*
Fyvie *Police Scotland*
Gabalfa *South Wales*
Gaddesby *Leicestershire*
Gaddesden Row *Hertfordshire*
Gaerwen *North Wales*
Gainford *Durham*
Gainsborough *Lincolnshire*
Gairloch *Police Scotland*
Galashiels *Police Scotland*
Gale *Gtr Manchester*
Galgate *Lancashire*
Galston *Police Scotland*
Gamesley *Derbyshire*
Gamlingay *Cambridgeshire*
Gamston (Bassetlaw) *Notts*
Gamston (Trent) *Nottinghamshire*
Garboldisham *Norfolk*
Garden Village *South Wales*
Garelochhead *Police Scotland*
Garendon *Leicestershire*
Garforth *West Yorkshire*
Gargrave *North Yorkshire*
Garn Dolbenmaen *North Wales*
Garn-yr-Erw *Gwent*
Garnant *Dyfed-Powys*
Garndiffaith *Gwent*
Garsdale *Cumbria*
Garsington *Thames Valley*
Garstang *Lancashire*
Garston *Hertfordshire*
Gartcosh *Police Scotland*
Garth *South Wales*
Garthorpe *Leicestershire*
Gartocharn *Police Scotland*
Garvagh *PSNI*
Gatehouse *Police Scotland*
Gateshead *Northumbria*
Gathurst *Gtr Manchester*
Gatley *Gtr Manchester*
Gatley Hill *Gtr Manchester*

Gatton *Surrey*
Gatwick *Sussex*
Gaulby *Leicestershire*
Gawsworth *Cheshire*
Gaydon *Warwickshire*
Gaythorne *Gtr Manchester*
Gayton *Merseyside*
Gayton *Norfolk*
Gayton *Northamptonshire*
Geddington *Northamptonshire*
Gedney *Lincolnshire*
Gedney Hill *Lincolnshire*
Gee Cross *Gtr Manchester*
Gelligaer *Gwent*
Gerald Road *Metropolitan*
Gerrards Cross *Thames Valley*
Giants Grave *South Wales*
Giffnock *Police Scotland*
Gilbent *Gtr Manchester*
Gildersome *West Yorkshire*
Gileston *South Wales*
Gilfach *Gwent*
Gilfach Goch *South Wales*
Gilford *PSNI*
Gilling West *North Yorkshire*
Gillingham *Dorset*
Gillingham *Kent*
Gillingham *Norfolk*
Gilmorton *Leicestershire*
Gilstead *West Yorkshire*
Gilwern *Gwent*
Gipsy Hill *Metropolitan*
Gipton *West Yorkshire*
Girlington *West Yorkshire*
Girton *Cambridgeshire*
Girvan *Police Scotland*
Gisburn *Lancashire*
Glais *South Wales*
Glaisdale *North Yorkshire*
Glamis *Police Scotland*
Glan Conway *North Wales*
Glanadda *North Wales*
Glanamman *Dyfed-Powys*
Glanrhyd *Dyfed-Powys*
Glapthorn *Northamptonshire*
Glapwell *Derbyshire*
Glasbury *Dyfed-Powys*
Glascoed *Gwent*
Glasgow *Police Scotland*
Glasshoughton *West Yorkshire*
Glaston *Leicestershire*
Glastonbury *Avon & Somerset*
Glatton *Cambridgeshire*
Glazebury *Cheshire*
Gledhow *West Yorkshire*
Glemsford *Suffolk*
Glen Parva *Leicestershire*
Glenarm *PSNI*
Glencarse *Police Scotland*
Glendevon *Police Scotland*
Gleneagles *Police Scotland*
Glenfarg *Police Scotland*
Glenfield *Leicestershire*
Glengormley *PSNI*
Glenisla *Police Scotland*
Glenluce *Police Scotland*
Glenmavis *Police Scotland*
Glenravel Street *PSNI*
Glenrothes *Police Scotland*
Glenshee *Police Scotland*
Glentham *Lincolnshire*
Glinton *Cambridgeshire*
Glodwick *Gtr Manchester*
Glooston *Leicestershire*
Glossop *Derbyshire*
Gloucester *Gloucestershire*
Glusburn *North Yorkshire*
Glynceiriog *North Wales*
Glyncorrwg *South Wales*

Glyndyfrdwy *North Wales*
Glynneath *South Wales*
Goadby *Leicestershire*
Goadby Marwood *Leicestershire*
Goathill *Dorset*
Gobowen *West Mercia*
Godalming *Surrey*
Godmanchester *Cambridge*
Godmanstone *Dorset*
Godregraigh *South Wales*
Godshill *Hampshire*
Godstone *Surrey*
Goffs Oak *Hertfordshire*
Goginan *Dyfed-Powys*
Golborne *Gtr Manchester*
Golbourne Bellow *Cheshire*
Golbourne David *Cheshire*
Golcar *West Yorkshire*
Goldcliffe *Gwent*
Goldenhill *Staffordshire*
Golders Green *Metropolitan*
Goldsithney *Devon & Cornwall*
Goldthorpe *South Yorkshire*
Golspie *Police Scotland*
Gomersal *West Yorkshire*
Gomshall *Surrey*
Gooderstone *Norfolk*
Goole *Humberside*
Goose Green *Gtr Manchester*
Goosnargh *Lancashire*
Goostrey *Cheshire*
Gopsall *Leicestershire*
Gorbals *Police Scotland*
Gorebridge *Police Scotland*
Gorefield *Cambridgeshire*
Goring-on-Thames *Thames Valley*
Gorleston *Norfolk*
Gorley *Hampshire*
Gorseinon *South Wales*
Gorslas *Dyfed-Powys*
Gorton *Gtr Manchester*
Gosberton *Lincolnshire*
Gosberton Risegate *Lincolnshire*
Gosfield *Essex*
Gosforth *Cumbria*
Gosforth *Northumbria*
Gosport *Hampshire*
Gotham *Nottinghamshire*
Goudhurst *Kent*
Gourock *Police Scotland*
Govilon *Gwent*
Gowerton *South Wales*
Goytre *Gwent*
Gracedieu *Leicestershire*
Grafham *Cambridgeshire*
Grafham *Surrey*
Grafton *Cheshire*
Grafton Regis *Northamptonshire*
Grafton Underwood *Northampton*
Grain *Kent*
Grains Bar *Gtr Manchester*
Grandtully *Police Scotland*
Grange *Cheshire*
Grange *Cumbria*
Grange Mill *Derbyshire*
Grange-over-Sands *Cumbria*
Grangemouth *Police Scotland*
Grangetown *South Wales*
Grantchester *Cambridgeshire*
Grantham *Lincolnshire*
Grantown-on-Spey *Police Scotland*
Grappenhall *Cheshire*
Grasmere *Cumbria*
Grasscroft *Gtr Manchester*
Grassington *North Yorkshire*
Grassmoor *Derbyshire*
Gratton *Derbyshire*
Gravel Hole *Gtr Manchester*

Graveley *Hertfordshire*
Graveley *Cambridgeshire*
Graveney *Kent*
Gravesend *Kent*
Grayrigg *Cumbria*
Grays *Essex*
Grayshott *Hampshire*
Grayswood *Surrey*
Greasby *Merseyside*
Great Abington *Cambridgeshire*
Great Addington *Northants*
Great Alne *Warwickshire*
Great Amwell *Hertfordshire*
Great Ayton *North Yorkshire*
Great Barford *Bedfordshire*
Great Barton *Suffolk*
Great Bentley *Essex*
Great Bookham *Surrey*
Great Boughton *Cheshire*
Great Bowden *Leicestershire*
Great Bromley *Essex*
Great Broughton *Cumbria*
Great & Little Broughton *North Yorks*
Great Budworth *Cheshire*
Great Casterton *Leicestershire*
Great Chart *Kent*
Great Chishill *Cambridgeshire*
Great Clifton *Cumbria*
Great Coates *Humberside*
Great Cressingham *Norfolk*
Great Dalby *Leicestershire*
Great Doddington *Northants*
Great Easton *Leicestershire*
Great Eccleston *Lancashire*
Great Eversden *Cambridgeshire*
Great Gaddesden *Hertfordshire*
Great Gidding *Cambridgeshire*
Great Glen *Leicestershire*
Great Gonerby *Lincolnshire*
Great Gransden *Cambridgeshire*
Great Harrowden *Northants*
Great Harwood *Lancashire*
Great Haywood *Staffordshire*
Great Horkesley *Essex*
Great Hormead *Hertfordshire*
Great Horrocks *Gtr Manchester*
Great Horton *West Yorkshire*
Great Houghton *Northamptonshire*
Great Howarth *Gtr Manchester*
Great Hucklow *Derbyshire*
Great Kingshill *Thames Valley*
Great Leighs *Essex*
Great Lever *Gtr Manchester*
Great Longstone *Derbyshire*
Great Massingham *Norfolk*
Great Missenden *Thames Valley*
Great Moor *Gtr Manchester*
Great Moss *Gtr Manchester*
Great Munden *Hertfordshire*
Great Oak *Gwent*
Great Oxendon *Northamptonshire*
Great Paxton *Cambridgeshire*
Great Ryburgh *Norfolk*
Great Sankey *Cheshire*
Great Shelford *Cambridgeshire*
Great Smeaton *North Yorkshire*
Great Somerford *Wiltshire*
Great Stainton *Durham*
Great Staughton *Cambridgeshire*
Great Stretton *Leicestershire*
Great Stukeley *Cambridgeshire*
Great Sutton *Cheshire*
Great Torrington *Devon & Cornwall*
Great Wakering *Essex*
Great Waltham *Essex*
Great Warford *Cheshire*

Great Wilbraham *Cambridgeshire*
Great Witley *West Mercia*
Greatworth *Northamptonshire*
Great Wymondley *Hertfordshire*
Great Yarmouth *Norfolk*
Great Yeldham *Essex*
Greatham *Hampshire*
Greave *Gtr Manchester*
Green End *Gtr Manchester*
Green Fairfield *Derbyshire*
Green Hammerton *North Yorks*
Green Tye *Hertfordshire*
Greenacres *Gtr Manchester*
Greencastle *PSNI*
Greenfield *Gtr Manchester*
Greenfield *North Wales*
Greenford *Metropolitan*
Greengairs *Police Scotland*
Greengate *Gtr Manchester*
Greengates *West Yorkshire*
Greenheys (Manchester) *Gtr Manchester*
Greenhithe *Kent*
Greenlands *West Mercia*
Greenlaw *Police Scotland*
Greenmount *Gtr Manchester*
Greenock *Police Scotland*
Greenodd *Cumbria*
Greens Norton *Northamptonshire*
Greenside *Gtr Manchester*
Greenwich *Metropolitan*
Greetham *Leicestershire*
Greetland *West Yorkshire*
Grendon *Northamptonshire*
Grendon Underwood *Thames Valley*
Grenoside *South Yorkshire*
Gresford *North Wales*
Gresham *Norfolk*
Gresty *Cheshire*
Greta Bridge *Durham*
Gretna *Police Scotland*
Gretton *Northamptonshire*
Greyabbey *PSNI*
Greyrigg *Cumbria*
Griffithstown *Gwent*
Griffydam *Leicestershire*
Grimethorpe *South Yorkshire*
Grimoldby *Lincolnshire*
Grimsargh *Lancashire*
Grimsby *Humberside*
Grimston *Norfolk*
Grimston *Leicestershire*
Grindleford *Derbyshire*
Grindlow *Derbyshire*
Gringley-on-the-Hill *Notts*
Groby *Leicestershire*
Groes *South Wales*
Groesfaen *South Wales*
Groeslon *North Wales*
Gronant *North Wales*
Groombridge *Sussex*
Grosmont *Gwent*
Groton *Suffolk*
Grotton *Gtr Manchester*
Grove *Thames Valley*
The Grove, Queen Square *Avon & Somerset*
Grovesend *South Wales*
Grundisburgh *Suffolk*
Guardbridge *Police Scotland*
Guide Bridge *Gtr Manchester*
Guide Post *Northumbria*
Guiden Morden *Cambridgeshire*
Guilden Sutton *Cheshire*
Guildford *Surrey*
Guilsborough *Northamptonshire*
Guilesfield *Dyfed Powys*
Guisborough *Cleveland*

Guiseley *West Yorkshire*
Guist *Norfolk*
Guiting *Gloucestershire*
Gumley *Leicestershire*
Gunness *Humberside*
Gunnislake *Devon & Cornwall*
Gunthorpe *Leicestershire*
Gurnard *Hampshire*
Gurnos *South Wales*
Gussage-All-Saints *Dorset*
Gussage-St-Michael *Dorset*
Gustard Wood *Hertfordshire*
Guston *Kent*
Guyhirne *Cambridgeshire*
Gwalchmai *North Wales*
Gwauncaegurwen *South Wales*
Gwehelog *Gwent*
Gwernesney *Gwent*
Gwernymynydd *North Wales*
Gwersyllt *North Wales*
Hackleton *Northamptonshire*
Hackney *Metropolitan*
Hackthorpe *Cumbria*
Haddenham *Cambridgeshire*
Haddenham *Thames Valley*
Haddington *Police Scotland*
Haddiscoe *Norfolk*
Haddon *Cambridgeshire*
Hades *Gtr Manchester*
Hadfield *Derbyshire*
Hadleigh *Essex*
Hadleigh *Suffolk*
Hadley *West Mercia*
Hadlow *Kent*
Hady *Derbyshire*
Hafodyrynys *Gwent*
Hagley *West Mercia*
Haigh *Gtr Manchester*
Hailey *Thames Valley*
Hailsham *Sussex*
Hail Weston *Cambridgeshire*
Hainton *Lincolnshire*
Halberton *Devon & Cornwall*
Hale *Cheshire*
Hale *Gtr Manchester*
Hale *Surrey*
Hale Green *Gtr Manchester*
Hale Moss *Gtr Manchester*
Hale Top *Gtr Manchester*
Halebarns *Gtr Manchester*
Halesowen *West Midlands*
Halesworth *Suffolk*
Halewood *Merseyside*
Half Acre *Gtr Manchester*
Halifax *West Yorkshire*
Halkyn *North Wales*
Hallam Fields *Derbyshire*
Hallaton *Leicestershire*
Hallbankgate *Cumbria*
Halling *Kent*
Halliwell *Gtr Manchester*
Hallow *West Mercia*
Halls Green *Hertfordshire*
Halsall *Lancashire*
Halstead *Essex*
Halstead *Leicestershire*
Halstead *Kent*
Halstock *Dorset*
Haltemprice *Humberside*
Halton *Cheshire*
Halton (East, West & Gill) *North Yorks*
Halton *Lancashire*
Halton *West Yorkshire*
Halton Camp *Thames Valley*
Haltwhistle *Northumbria*
Halwell *Devon & Cornwall*
Halwill *Devon & Cornwall*
Ham Street *Kent*

Hamble *Hampshire*
Hambledon *Surrey*
Hambledon *Thames Valley*
Hambleton *Lancashire*
Hambleton *Leicestershire*
Hambleton *North Yorkshire*
Hamerton *Cambridgeshire*
Hamil *Staffordshire*
Hamilton *Police Scotland*
Hammersmith *Metropolitan*
Hamoon *Dorset*
Hampreston *Dorset*
Hampstead *Metropolitan*
Hampsthwaite *North Yorkshire*
Hampton *Metropolitan*
Hampton *Cheshire*
Hampton *West Mercia*
Hampton-in-Arden *West Midlands*
Hamworthy *Dorset*
Hanborough *Thames Valley*
Hanbury *West Mercia*
Handcross *Sussex*
Handforth *Cheshire*
Handley *Cheshire*
Handley *Derbyshire*
Handley *Dorset*
Handsworth *West Midlands*
Hanford *Dorset*
Hanford *Staffordshire*
Hanging Heaton *West Yorkshire*
Hankelow *Cheshire*
Hankley Common *Surrey*
Hanley *Staffordshire*
Hammer *North Wales*
Hanningfield *Essex*
Hannington *Northamptonshire*
Hanslope *Thames Valley*
Happisburgh *Norfolk*
Hapsford *Cheshire*
Hapton *Lancashire*
Harberton *Devon & Cornwall*
Harborne *West Midlands*
Harbury *Warwickshire*
Harby *Leicestershire*
Harden *West Yorkshire*
Hardingstone *Northamptonshire*
Hardley *Hampshire*
Hardmans Green *Gtr Manchester*
Hardwick *Cambridgeshire*
Hardwick *Northamptonshire*
Hare Street *Hertfordshire*
Harehills *West Yorkshire*
Harewood *West Yorkshire*
Hargate Manor *Derbyshire*
Hargrave *Cheshire*
Hargrave *Northamptonshire*
Harlaxton *Lincolnshire*
Harlech *North Wales*
Harlesden *Metropolitan*
Harleston *Norfolk*
Harlestone *Northamptonshire*
Harlow *Essex*
Harlow Hill *North Yorkshire*
Harlton *Cambridgeshire*
Harmer Green *Hertfordshire*
Harold Hill *Metropolitan*
Harpenden *Hertfordshire*
Harper Green *Gtr Manchester*
Harpfields *Staffordshire*
Harpole *Northamptonshire*
Harpur Hill *Derbyshire*
Harpurhey *Gtr Manchester*
Harridge *Gtr Manchester*
Harrietsham *Kent*
Harrington *Northamptonshire*
Harringworth *Northamptonshire*
Harrogate *North Yorkshire*
Harrold *Bedfordshire*

Harrold Bridge *Cambridgeshire*
Harrop Dale *Gtr Manchester*
Harrow *Metropolitan*
Harrow Road *Metropolitan*
Harston *Cambridgeshire*
Harston *Leicestershire*
Hart Common *Gtr Manchester*
Hartford *Cambridgeshire*
Hartford *Cheshire*
Hartford *Sussex*
Harthill *Cheshire*
Harthill *Derbyshire*
Harthill *South Yorkshire*
Harthill *Police Scotland*
Harting *Sussex*
Hartington Middle Qtr *Derbyshire*
Hartington Nether Qtr *Derbyshire*
Hartington Town Qtr *Derbyshire*
Hartington Upper Qtr *Derbyshire*
Hartland *Devon & Cornwall*
Hartlebury *West Mercia*
Hartlepool *Cleveland*
Hartley Wintney *Hampshire*
Hartshead Green *Gtr Manchester*
Hartshill *Staffordshire*
Hartshill *Warwickshire*
Hartshorne *Derbyshire*
Hartwell *Northampton*
Harvel *Kent*
Harvington *West Mercia*
Harwell *Thames Valley*
Harwich *Essex*
Harwood Lee *Gtr Manchester*
Harworth *Nottinghamshire*
Hascombe *Surrey*
Haselbech *Northamptonshire*
Hasland *Derbyshire*
Haslemere *Surrey*
Haslingden *Lancashire*
Haslingfield *Cambridgeshire*
Haslington *Cheshire*
Hassall *Cheshire*
Hassopp *Derbyshire*
Hastings *Sussex*
Hastings Street *PSNI*
Haswell *Durham*
Hatfield *Hertfordshire*
Hatfield *South Yorkshire*
Hatfield Heath *Essex*
Hatfield Peverel *Essex*
Hatherlow *Gtr Manchester*
Hathern *Leicestershire*
Hathersage *Derbyshire*
Hathershaw *Gtr Manchester*
Hatherton *Cheshire*
Hatley *Cambridgeshire*
Hatley East *Cambridgeshire*
Hatley-St-George *Cambridgeshire*
Hattersley *Gtr Manchester*
Hatton *Derbyshire*
Hatton *Warwickshire*
Hatton (Runcorn) *Cheshire*
Hatton (Tarvin) *Cheshire*
Haugh *Gtr Manchester*
Haughley *Suffolk*
Haughton *Cheshire*
Haughton *Gtr Manchester*
Haughton Green *Gtr Manchester*
Hauxton *Cambridgeshire*
Havant *Hampshire*
Havercroft *West Yorkshire*
Haverfordwest *Dyfed-Powys*
Haverhill *Suffolk*
Hawarden *North Wales*
Hawes *North Yorkshire*
Hawick *Police Scotland*
Hawk Green *Gtr Manchester*
Hawkesbury *Gloucestershire*
Hawkhurst *Kent*

Hawkinge *Kent*
Hawkshaw Lane *Gtr Manchester*
Hawkshead *Cumbria*
Hawksworth *West Yorkshire*
Haworth *West Yorkshire*
Haxey *Humberside*
Hay-on-Wye *Dyfed-Powys*
Haydon *Dorset*
Haydon Bridge *Northumbria*
Hayes *Metropolitan*
Hayfield *Derbyshire*
Hayle *Devon & Cornwall*
Hayling Island *Hampshire*
Haynes *Bedfordshire*
Haywards Heath *Sussex*
Hazel Grove *Gtr Manchester*
Hazelbadge *Derbyshire*
Hazelbury Bryan *Dorset*
Hazelhurst (*Gtr Manchester*
Hazelmere *Thames Valley*
Hazelwood *Derbyshire*
Heacham *Norfolk*
Headcorn *Kent*
Headingley *West Yorkshire*
Headless Cross *West Mercia*
Headley (Alton) *Hampshire*
Headley (Whitchurch) *Hampshire*
Headley *Surrey*
Headyhill *Gtr Manchester*
Heage *Derbyshire*
Heald Green *Gtr Manchester*
Healey Stones *Gtr Manchester*
Heanor *Derbyshire*
Heap Bridge *Gtr Manchester*
Heath *Derbyshire*
Heath *West Yorkshire*
Heath End *Surrey*
Heath & Reach *Bedfordshire*
Heather *Leicestershire*
Heathfield *Sussex*
Heaton *West Yorkshire*
Heaton Chapel *Gtr Manchester*
Heaton Mersey *Gtr Manchester*
Heaton Moor *Gtr Manchester*
Heaton Norris *Gtr Manchester*
Heaton Park *Gtr Manchester*
Heaviley *Gtr Manchester*
Hebden Bridge *West Yorkshire*
Heckington *Lincolnshire*
Heckmondwike *West Yorkshire*
Heddon *Northumbria*
Hedge End *Hampshire*
Hedgerly *Thames Valley*
Hedon *Humberside*
Heighington *Durham*
Heighington *Lincolnshire*
Helen's Bay *PSNI*
Helensburgh *Police Scotland*
Hellidon *Northamptonshire*
Hellifield *North Yorkshire*
Helmdon *Northamptonshire*
Helmsdale *Police Scotland*
Helmshore *Lancashire*
Helmsley *North Yorkshire*
Helpringham *Lincolnshire*
Helpston *Cambridgeshire*
Helsby *Cheshire*
Helston *Devon & Cornwall*
Hem Heath *Staffordshire*
Hemel Hempstead *Hertfordshire*
Hemingfield *South Yorkshire*
Hemingford Abbots
    Cambridgeshire
Hemingford Grey *Cambridgeshire*
Hemington *Leicestershire*
Hemlington *Cleveland*
Hemington *Northamptonshire*
Hempnall *Norfolk*
Hemsby *Norfolk*

Hemswell *Lincolnshire*
Hemsworth *West Yorkshire*
Hemyock *Devon & Cornwall*
Henbury *Cheshire*
Hendon *Metropolitan*
Hendre *Gwent*
Hendy *Dyfed-Powys*
Henfield *Sussex*
Hengoed *Gwent*
Henhull *Cheshire*
Henley-in-Arden *Warwickshire*
Henley-on-Thames *Thames Valley*
Henllan *North Wales*
Henllys *Gwent*
Henlow Camp *Bedfordshire*
Henlow Village *Bedfordshire*
Hensall *North Yorkshire*
Heolgerrig *South Wales*
Heolycyw *South Wales*
Hepstonstal *West Yorkshire*
Hereford *West Mercia*
Hermitage *Dorset*
Hermitage *Thames Valley*
Herne *Kent*
Herne Bay *Kent*
Hernhill *Kent*
Heron Cross *Staffordshire*
Heronsgate *Hertfordshire*
Herriard *Hampshire*
Hersham *Surrey*
Hertford *Hertfordshire*
Hertford Heath *Hertfordshire*
Hertingfordbury *Hertfordshire*
Hesketh Bank *Lancashire*
Hesleden *Durham*
Hessle *Humberside*
Heswall *Merseyside*
Hethersett *Norfolk*
Hever *Kent*
Hexham *Northumbria*
Hextable *Kent*
Hexthorpe *South Yorkshire*
Hexton *Hertfordshire*
Heydon *Cambridgeshire*
Heyhead *Gtr Manchester*
Heyheads *Gtr Manchester*
Heyrod *Gtr Manchester*
Heysham *Lancashire*
Heyside *Gtr Manchester*
Heytesbury *Wiltshire*
Heywood *Gtr Manchester*
Hibaldstow *Lincolnshire*
Higginshaw *Gtr Manchester*
High Blantyre *Police Scotland*
High Catton *North Yorkshire*
High Crompton *Gtr Manchester*
High Cross *Gwent*
High Ercall *West Mercia*
High Force *Durham*
High Green *South Yorkshire*
High Halden *Kent*
High Halstow *Kent*
High Lane *Gtr Manchester*
High Legh *Cheshire*
High Street Green *Hertfordshire*
High Wych *Hertfordshire*
High Wycombe *Thames Valley*
Higham *Derbyshire*
Higham *Kent*
Higham *Lancashire*
Higham *South Yorkshire*
Higham Ferrers *Northamptonshire*
Higham-on-the-Hill *Leicestershire*
Highbridge *Avon & Somerset*
Highbury Vale *Metropolitan*
Highclere *Hampshire*
Highcliffe (Christchurch) *Dorset*
Highcliffe (Winchester) *Hampshire*
Higher Blackley *Gtr Manchester*

Higher Broughton *Gtr Manchester*
Higher Green *Gtr Manchester*
Higher Hurst *Gtr Manchester*
Higher Irlam *Gtr Manchester*
Higher Ogden *Gtr Manchester*
Higher Woodhill *Gtr Manchester*
Highfield *Gtr Manchester*
Highfields *South Yorkshire*
Highgate *Metropolitan*
Highgate *South Yorkshire*
Highley *West Mercia*
Highlow *Derbyshire*
Hightown *Merseyside*
Hightown *West Yorkshire*
Highweek *Devon & Cornwall*
Highworth *Wiltshire*
Hilcote *Derbyshire*
Hildenborough *Kent*
Hildersham *Cambridgeshire*
Hilgay *Norfolk*
Hill Head *Hampshire*
Hill Top *Gtr Manchester*
Hillend *Gtr Manchester*
Hillfield *Dorset*
Hillington *Police Scotland*
Hillmorton *Warwickshire*
Hillsborough *PSNI*
Hillsborough *South Yorkshire*
Hillstown *Derbyshire*
Hilltop *West Yorkshire*
Hilperton *Wiltshire*
Hilton *Cambridgeshire*
Hilton *Derbyshire*
Hilton *Dorset*
Hilton Park *Gtr Manchester*
Hinchliffe Mill *West Yorkshire*
Hinckley *Leicestershire*
Hinderwell *North Yorkshire*
Hindhead *Surrey*
Hindley *Gtr Manchester*
Hindley Green *Gtr Manchester*
Hindon *Wiltshire*
Hingham *Norfolk*
Hinstock *West Mercia*
Hintlesham *Suffolk*
Hinton-in-the-Hedges *Northants*
Hinton Martell *Dorset*
Hinton Parva *Dorset*
Hinton-St-Mary *Dorset*
Hinxton *Cambridgeshire*
Hinxworth *Hertfordshire*
Hipperholme *West Yorkshire*
Hirwaun *South Wales*
Histon *Cambridgeshire*
Hitcham *Suffolk*
Hitchin *Hertfordshire*
Hoath *Kent*
Hobson Moor *Gtr Manchester*
Hoby *Leicestershire*
Hookcliffe *Bedfordshire*
Hockenhull *Cheshire*
Hockering *Norfolk*
Hockering *Surrey*
Hockley *Essex*
Hockley Heath *West Midlands*
Hockwold *Norfolk*
Hoddesdon *Hertfordshire*
Hodgefield *Gtr Manchester*
Hodnet *West Mercia*
Hodthorpe *Derbyshire*
Hoghton *Lancashire*
Hognaston *Derbyshire*
Hogsthorpe *Lincolnshire*
Holbeach *Lincolnshire*
Holbeach Bank *Lincolnshire*
Holbeck *West Yorkshire*
Holborn *Metropolitan*
Holbrook *Derbyshire*

Holbrook *Norfolk*
Holcombe *Gtr Manchester*
Holcombe Brook *Gtr Manchester*
Holcombe Rogus *Devon & Cornwall*
Holcot *Northamptonshire*
Holdenby *Northamptonshire*
Holland *Surrey*
Hollesley *Suffolk*
Hollin *Gtr Manchester*
Hollingbourne *Kent*
Hollington *Derbyshire*
Hollingwood *Derbyshire*
Hollingworth *Gtr Manchester*
Hollins *Gtr Manchester*
Hollinwood *Gtr Manchester*
Holloway *Derbyshire*
Holloway *Metropolitan*
Hollowell *Northamptonshire*
Hollybush *Gwent*
Hollywood *West Mercia*
Holmbury-St-Mary *Surrey*
Holme *Derbyshire*
Holme *Cambridgeshire*
Holme *North Yorkshire*
Holme-on-Spalding Moor *Humberside*
Holmer Green *Thames Valley*
Holmes Chapel *Cheshire*
Holmesfield *Derbyshire*
Holme Woods *West Yorkshire*
Holmewood *Derbyshire*
Holmfirth *West Yorkshire*
Holnest *Dorset*
Holsworthy *Devon & Cornwall*
Holt *Dorset*
Holt *North Wales*
Holt *Norfolk*
Holt *West Mercia*
Holt *Wiltshire*
Holt Lane End *Gtr Manchester*
Holton-le-Clay *Lincolnshire*
Holt Town *Gtr Manchester*
Holts *Gtr Manchester*
Holwell *Dorset*
Holwell *Hertfordshire*
Holwell *Leicestershire*
Holywell-cum-Needingworth *Cambs*
Holyhead *North Wales*
Holyhead Road *West Midlands*
Holymoorside *Derbyshire*
Holyport *Thames Valley*
Holywell Green *West Yorkshire*
Holywell *North Wales*
Holywood *PSNI*
Honington *Suffolk*
Honiton *Devon & Cornwall*
Honley *West Yorkshire*
Hoo *Kent*
Hook *Hampshire*
Hook Heath *Surrey*
Hook Norton *Thames Valley*
Hooke *Dorset*
Hookwood *Surrey*
Hoole *Lancashire*
Hoole Village *Cheshire*
Hooley Bridge *Gtr Manchester*
Hooley Brow *Gtr Manchester*
Hooley Hill *Gtr Manchester*
Hoon *Derbyshire*
Hooton Park *Merseyside*
Hope *Derbyshire*
Hopeman *Police Scotland*
Hope Woodlands *Derbyshire*
Hopkinstown *South Wales*
Hopton *Derbyshire*
Hopton *Norfolk*
Hopwell *Derbyshire*

Hopwood *Gtr Manchester*
Hopwood *West Mercia*
Horbury *West Yorkshire*
Horbury Bridge *West Yorkshire*
Horbury Junction *West Yorkshire*
Horden *Durham*
Hordle *Hampshire*
Horley *Surrey*
Hornby *Lancashire*
Hornby (Leyburn) *North Yorkshire*
Hornby (Northallerton) *North Yorks*
Horncastle *Lincolnshire*
Hornchurch *Metropolitan*
Horndean *Hampshire*
Horne *Surrey*
Horning *Norfolk*
Horninghold *Leicestershire*
Horningsea *Cambridgeshire*
Horningsham *Wiltshire*
Hornmill *Leicestershire*
Hornsea *Humberside*
Hornsey *Metropolitan*
Horrocks Fold *Gtr Manchester*
Horseheath *Cambridgeshire*
Horsell *Surrey*
Horsford *Norfolk*
Horsforth *West Yorkshire*
Horsley *Derbyshire*
Horsley *Gloucestershire*
Horsley Woodhouse *Derbyshire*
Horsham *Sussex*
Horsham-St-Faith *Norfolk*
Horsmonden *Kent*
Horstead-with-Stanninghall *Norfolk*
Horsted Keynes *Sussex*
Horton *Dorset*
Horton *Avon & Somerset*
Horton-by-Malpas *Cheshire*
Horton Bank Top *West Yorkshire*
Horton-cum-Peel *Cheshire*
Horton Kirby *Kent*
Horton-in-Ribblesdale *North Yorks*
Horwich *Gtr Manchester*
Horwich End *Derbyshire*
Hose *Leicestershire*
Hothfield *Kent*
Hoton *Leicestershire*
Hough *Cheshire*
Houghton *Gtr Manchester*
Houghton *South Yorkshire*
Houghton Conquest *Bedfordshire*
Houghton Regis *Bedfordshire*
Houghton & Wyton *Cambridgeshire*
Houghton-le-Spring *Northumbria*
Houghton-on-the-Hill *Leicestershire*
Hounslow *Metropolitan*
Houston *Police Scotland*
Hove *Sussex*
Hove Eage *West Yorkshire*
Hoveton *Norfolk*
Hovingham *North Yorkshire*
Howarth Cross *Gtr Manchester*
Howbridge *Gtr Manchester*
Howden *Humberside*
Howden-le-Wear *Durham*
How Green *Hertfordshire*
Howe *North Yorkshire*
Howwood *Police Scotland*
Hoxne *Suffolk*
Hoyland *South Yorkshire*
Hoyland Common *South Yorkshire*
Hoylandswaine *South Yorkshire*

Hoylake *Merseyside*
Hubberholme *North Yorkshire*
Hubbert's Bridge *Lincolnshire*
Huby (Harrogate) *North Yorkshire*
Huby (Tadcaster) *North Yorkshire*
Hucklow (Gtr & Little) *Derby*
Hucknall *Nottinghamshire*
Huddersfield *West Yorkshire*
Hudnall *Hertfordshire*
Hugglescote *Leicestershire*
Hull *Humberside*
Hulland *Derbyshire*
Hulland Ward *Derbyshire*
Hullavington *Wiltshire*
Hullbridge *Essex*
Hulme *Gtr Manchester*
Hulme Walfield *Cheshire*
Hulton Lane Ends *Gtr Manchester*
Hulton Park *Gtr Manchester*
Humberston *Humberside*
Humberstone *Leicestershire*
Humberton *North Yorkshire*
Huncote *Leicestershire*
Hundall *Derbyshire*
Hundred House *Dyfed-Powys*
Hungarton *Leicestershire*
Hunger Hill *Gtr Manchester*
Hungerford *Thames Valley*
Hungry Bentley *Derbyshire*
Hunmanby *North Yorkshire*
Hunsdon *Hertfordshire*
Hunslet *West Yorkshire*
Hunstanton *Norfolk*
Hunsterson *Cheshire*
Huntingdon *Cambridgeshire*
Huntington *Cheshire*
Huntington *North Yorkshire*
Huntley *Gloucestershire*
Huntly *Police Scotland*
Hunton *Kent*
Hunton *North Yorkshire*
Hunton Bridge *Hertfordshire*
Hunwick *Durham*
Hurdsfield *Cheshire*
Hurleston *Cheshire*
Hurley *Warwickshire*
Hurn *Dorset*
Hursley *Hampshire*
Hurst *Gtr Manchester*
Hurst *North Yorkshire*
Hurst *Thames Valley*
Hurstbourne Tarrant *Hampshire*
Hurst Green *Lancashire*
Hurst Green *Surrey*
Hurst Green *Sussex*
Hursthead *Gtr Manchester*
Hurstpierpoint *Sussex*
Hurtmore *Surrey*
Husbands Bosworth *Leicestershire*
Husthwaite *North Yorkshire*
Huthwaite *Nottinghamshire*
Hutton *Essex*
Hutton Bonville *North Yorkshire*
Hutton Buscel *North Yorkshire*
Hutton Conyers *North Yorkshire*
Hutton Cranswick *Humberside*
Hutton Hang *North Yorkshire*
Hutton-le-Hole *North Yorkshire*
Hutton Mulgrave *North Yorkshire*
Hutton Rudby *North Yorkshire*
Hutton Sessay *North Yorkshire*
Hutton Wandesley *North Yorkshire*
Huttons Ambo *North Yorkshire*
Huxley *Cheshire*
Huyton *Merseyside*
Hyde *Bedfordshire*
Hyde *Gtr Manchester*

Hyde Green *Gtr Manchester*
Hyde Park *Metropolitan*
Hyde Park *South Yorkshire*
Hydestile *Surrey*
Hyson Green *Nottinghamshire*
Hythe (Section) *Hampshire*
Hythe *Kent*
Ibberton *Dorset*
Ible *Derbyshire*
Ibsley *Hampshire*
Ibstock *Leicestershire*
Ickleford *Hertfordshire*
Icklesham *Sussex*
Ickleton *Cambridgeshire*
Iddenshall *Cheshire*
Ide *Devon & Cornwall*
Ide Hill *Kent*
Idle *West Yorkshire*
Idridgehry *Derbyshire*
Ightham *Kent*
Ilchester *Avon & Somerset*
Ilford *Metropolitan*
Ilfracombe *Devon & Cornwall*
Ilkeston *Derbyshire*
Ilkley *West Yorkshire*
Illston-on-the-Hill *Leicestershire*
Ilmington *Warwickshire*
Ilminster *Avon & Somerset*
Immingham *Humberside*
Impington *Cambridgeshire*
Ince-in-Makerfield *Gtr Manchester*
Inchinnan *Police Scotland*
Inchture *Police Scotland*
Indian Queens *Devon & Cornwall*
Infirmary *Gtr Manchester*
Ingarsby *Leicestershire*
Ingatestone *Essex*
Ingelby *Derbyshire*
Ingham *Lincolnshire*
Ingham *Suffolk*
Ingleton *North Yorkshire*
Inkberrow *West Mercia*
Inkersall Greer *Derbyshire*
Innellan *Police Scotland*
Innerleithen *Police Scotland*
Insch *Police Scotland*
Intake *South Yorkshire*
Interleithen *Police Scotland*
Inveraray *Police Scotland*
Inverbervie *Police Scotland*
Invergordon *Police Scotland*
Invergowrie *Police Scotland*
Inverkeilor *Police Scotland*
Inverkeithing *Police Scotland*
Inverkip *Police Scotland*
Inverness *Police Scotland*
Inverurie *Police Scotland*
Ipplepen *Devon & Cornwall*
Ipsley *West Mercia*
Ipswich *Suffolk*
Irby *Merseyside*
Irchester *Northamptonshire*
Ireby *Cumbria*
Ireland Wood *West Yorkshire*
Ireton Wood *Derbyshire*
Irlam *Gtr Manchester*
Irlam O'th Height *Gtr Manchester*
Iron Acton *Avon & Somerset*
Ironbridge *West Mercia*
Irons Bottom *Surrey*
Ironville *Derbyshire*
Irthington *Cumbria*
Irthlingborough *Northamptonshire*
Irvine *Police Scotland*
Irvinestown *PSNI*
Irwell Vale *Lancashire*
Isham *Northamptonshire*
Isle of Dogs *Metropolitan*

Isleham *Cambridgeshire*
Isles of Scilly *Devon & Cornwall*
Isley-cum-Langley *Leicestershire*
Isley Walton *Leicestershire*
Islington *Metropolitan*
Islip *Northamptonshire*
Itchen Abbas *Hampshire*
Itton *Gwent*
Iver *Thames Valley*
Iver Heath *Thames Valley*
Ivinghoe *Thames Valley*
Ivonbrook Grange *Derbyshire*
Ivybridge *Devon & Cornwall*
Iwerne Courtney *Dorset*
Iwerne Minster *Dorset*
Ixworth *Suffolk*
Jacksdale *Nottinghamshire*
Jacobs Well *Surrey*
Jedburgh *Police Scotland*
Jenny Cross *Gtr Manchester*
Jericho *Gtr Manchester*
Jersey Marine *South Wales*
John-o-Gaunt *Leicestershire*
Johnston *Dyfed-Powys*
Johnstone *Police Scotland*
Johnstonebridge *Police Scotland*
Johnstown *North Wales*
Jubilee *Gtr Manchester*
Jump *South Yorkshire*
Jumpers & Fairmile *Dorset*
Junction *Gtr Manchester*
Jurby *Isle of Man*
Kames *Police Scotland*
Keady *PSNI*
Kearsley *Gtr Manchester*
Kedington *Suffolk*
Kedleston *Derbyshire*
Keevil *Wiltshire*
Kegworth *Leicestershire*
Keighley *West Yorkshire*
Keith *Police Scotland*
Kelbrook *Lancashire*
Kelling *Norfolk*
Kelloe *Durham*
Kelmarsh *Northamptonshire*
Kelsall *Cheshire*
Kelsall *Hertfordshire*
Kelso *Police Scotland*
Kelty *Police Scotland*
Kelvedon *Essex*
Kelvedon Hatch *Essex*
Kemnay *Police Scotland*
Kempsey *West Merica*
Kempsing *Kent*
Kempston *Bedfordshire*
Kempston (Box End) *Bedfordshire*
Kemys Commander *Gwent*
Kencot *Thames Valley*
Kendal *Cumbria*
Kendon *Gwent*
Kenfig Hill *South Wales*
Kenilworth *Warwickshire*
Kenley *Metropolitan*
Kenmore *Police Scotland*
Kennett *Cambridgeshire*
Kennford *Devon & Cornwall*
Kennington *Thames Valley*
Kennington Road *Metropolitan*
Kennoway *Police Scotland*
Kensington *Metropolitan*
Kensworth *Bedfordshire*
Kentford *Suffolk*
Kentish Town *Metropolitan*
Kenton *Devon & Cornwall*
Kenworthy *Gtr Manchester*
Kenyon *Gtr Manchester*
Keresley *West Midlands*
Kerridge *Cheshire*
Kersal Dale *Gtr Manchester*

Kesgrave *Suffolk*
Kesh *PSNI*
Kessingland *Suffolk*
Keswick *Cumbria*
Kettering *Northamptonshire*
Kettleshulme *Cheshire*
Kettlewell *North Yorkshire*
Ketton *Leicestershire*
Kexborough *South Yorkshire*
Keyham *Leicestershire*
Keyingham *Humberside*
Keysoe *Bedfordshire*
Keythorpe *Leicestershire*
Keyworth *Nottinghamshire*
Kibworth *Leicestershire*
Kibworth Beauchamp
  Leicestershire
Kibworth Harcourt *Leicestershire*
Kidderminster *West Mercia*
Kidlington *Thames Valley*
Kidsgrove *Staffordshire*
Kidwelly *Dyfed-Powys*
Kilbarchan *Police Scotland*
Kilbirnie *Police Scotland*
Kilburn *Derbyshire*
Kilburn *Metropolitan*
Kilburn (High & Low) *North Yorks*
Kilby *Leicestershire*
Kilcreggan *Police Scotland*
Kilgetty *Dyfed-Powys*
Kilkeel *PSNI*
Kilkhampton *Devon & Cornwall*
Killamarsh *Derbyshire*
Killay *South Wales*
Killearn *Police Scotland*
Killiecrankie *Police Scotland*
Killin *Police Scotland*
Killinghall *North Yorkshire*
Killyleagh *PSNI*
Kilmacolm *Police Scotland*
Kilmarnock *Police Scotland*
Kilmington *Devon & Cornwall*
Kilmun *Police Scotland*
Kiln Green *Gtr Manchester*
Kilndown *Kent*
Kilnhurst *South Yorkshire*
Kilnsey *North Yorkshire*
Kilrea *PSNI*
Kilsby *Northamptonshire*
Kilsyth *Police Scotland*
Kilwinning *Police Scotland*
Kilve *Avon & Somerset*
Kimberley *Nottinghamshire*
Kimble *Thames Valley*
Kimbolton *Cambridgeshire*
Kimcote *Leicestershire*
Kimmeridge *Dorset*
Kimpton *Hampshire*
Kimpton *Hertfordshire*
Kimpton Bottom *Hertfordshire*
Kinawley *PSNI*
Kincardine-on-Forth *Police Scotland*
Kineton *Warwickshire*
King Cross *West Yorkshire*
King Sterndale *Derbyshire*
Kingfield *Surrey*
Kinghorn *Police Scotland*
Kinglassie *Police Scotland*
King's Cliffe *Northamptonshire*
King's Cross Road *Metropolitan*
Kings Heath *West Midlands*
Kings Langley *Hertfordshire*
King's Lynn *Norfolk*
Kings Marsh *Cheshire*
Kings Moss *Gtr Manchester*
Kings Newton *Derbyshire*
Kings Norton *Leicestershire*

Kings Norton *West Midlands*
Kings Ripton *Cambridgeshire*
Kings Somborne *Hampshire*
Kings Stanley *Gloucestershire*
King's Sutton *Northamptonshire*
Kings Thorn *West Mercia*
Kings Walden *Hertfordshire*
Kings Weston *Avon & Somerset*
Kings Worthy *Hampshire*
Kingsand *Devon & Cornwall*
Kingsbarns *Police Scotland*
Kingsbridge *Devon & Cornwall*
Kingsbury *Warwickshire*
Kingsbury Episcopi *Avon & Somerset*
Kingsdown *Kent*
Kingserswell *Devon & Cornwall*
Kingskettle *Police Scotland*
Kingsland *West Mercia*
Kingsley *Cheshire*
Kingsnorth *Kent*
Kingsnympton *Devon & Cornwall*
Kingstanding *West Midlands*
Kingsteignton *Devon & Cornwall*
Kingsthorne *West Mercia*
Kingston *Cambridgeshire*
Kingston *Gtr Manchester*
Kingston Bagpuize *Thames Valley*
Kingston Lisle *Thames Valley*
Kingston Russel *Dorset*
Kingston upon Hull *Humberside*
Kingston-on-Thames
  Metropolitan
Kingstone *West Mercia*
Kingstreet *Gtr Manchester*
Kingswinford *West Midlands*
Kingswood *Avon & Somerset*
Kingswood *Thames Valley*
Kington *West Mercia*
Kington Magna *Dorset*
Kingussie *Police Scotland*
Kinlet *West Mercia*
Kinloch Rannoch *Police Scotland*
Kinlochleven *Police Scotland*
Kinnerton *Cheshire*
Kinnesswood *Police Scotland*
Kinouton *Nottinghamshire*
Kinross *Police Scotland*
Kinsbourne Green *Hertfordshire*
Kinsley *West Yorkshire*
Kinson *Dorset*
Kintbury *Thames Valley*
Kintore *Police Scotland*
Kinver *Staffordshire*
Kippax *West Yorkshire*
Kippen *Police Scotland*
Kirby *Essex*
Kirby Bellars *Leicestershire*
Kirby Muxloe *Leicestershire*
Kirk Deighton *North Yorkshire*
Kirk Ella *Humberside*
Kirk Merrington *Durham*
Kirkbride *Cumbria*
Kirkburton *West Yorkshire*
Kirkby *Merseyside*
Kirkby-in-Ashfield
  Nottinghamshire
Kirkby-in-Furness *Cumbria*
Kirkby Lonsdale *Cumbria*
Kirkby Malzeard *North Yorkshire*
Kirkby Mallory *Leicestershire*
Kirkby Steven *Cumbria*
Kirkby Overblow *North Yorkshire*
Kirkbymoorside *North Yorkshire*
Kirkcaldy *Police Scotland*
Kirkconnel *Police Scotland*
Kirkcudbright *Police Scotland*
Kirkella *Humberside*
Kirkham *Lancashire*

Kirkhams *Gtr Manchester*
Kirkhamgate *West Yorkshire*
Kirkheaton *West Yorkshire*
Kirkhill *Police Scotland*
Kirkintilloch *Police Scotland*
Kirklees *Gtr Manchester*
Kirklevington *Cleveland*
Kirklington *North Yorkshire*
Kirklington *Nottinghamshire*
Kirk Merrington *Durham*
Kirkmichael *Police Scotland*
Kirkoswald *Cumbria*
Kirk Sandall *South Yorkshire*
Kirkstall *West Yorkshire*
Kirkwall *Police Scotland*
Kirkwhelpington *Northumbria*
Kirriemuir *Police Scotland*
Kirtling *Cambridgeshire*
Kirton *Lincolnshire*
Kirton *Suffolk*
Kirton Lindsey *Humberside*
Kislingbury *Northamptonshire*
Kirk Ireton *Derbyshire*
Kirk Langley *Derbyshire*
Kirkhallam *Derbyshire*
Kitt Green *Gtr Manchester*
Kitts Moss *Gtr Manchester*
Kiveton Park *South Yorkshire*
Knaphill *Surrey*
Knaptoft *Leicestershire*
Knapwell *Cambridgeshire*
Knaresborough *North Yorkshire*
Knebworth *Hertfordshire*
Kneesworth *Cambridgeshire*
Knighton *Dyfed-Powys*
Knighton *Leicestershire*
Knipton *Leicestershire*
Kniveton *Derbyshire*
Knock *PSNI*
Knockholt *Kent*
Knook *Wiltshire*
Knossington *Leicestershire*
Knott End *Lancs*
Knott Lanes *Gtr Manchester*
Knottingley *West Yorkshire*
Knowl Moor *Gtr Manchester*
Knowle West *Avon & Somerset*
Knutsford *Cheshire*
Kyle of Lochalsh *Police Scotland*
Laceby *Humberside*
Lacey Green *Thames Valley*
Lach Dennis *Cheshire*
Lacock *Wiltshire*
Lady House *Gtr Manchester*
Ladybank *Police Scotland*
Ladybarn *Gtr Manchester*
Ladycross *Devon & Cornwall*
Ladywood *West Midlands*
Laindon *Essex*
Lairg *Police Scotland*
Laisterdyke *West Yorkshire*
Lake *Hampshire*
Lakenheath *Suffolk*
Laleston *South Wales*
Lamberhead Green *Gtr Manchester*
Lamberhurst *Kent*
Lambhill *Police Scotland*
Lambley *Nottinghamshire*
Lambourn *Thames Valley*
Lamlash *Police Scotland*
Lampeter *Dyfed-Powys*
Lamport *Northamptonshire*
Lanark *Police Scotland*
Lancaster *Durham*
Lancaster *Lancashire*
Lancaster Hill *Gtr Manchester*
Lancing *Sussex*
Land Gate *Gtr Manchester*

Landbeach *Cambridgeshire*
Landican *Merseyside*
Landore *South Wales*
Landwade *Cambridgeshire*
Lane End *Thames Valley*
Lane End (Rochdale) *Gtr Manchester*
Lane End (Manchester) *Gtr Manchester*
Lane Ends (Marple) *Gtr Manchester*
Lane Herd *Gtr Manchester*
Laneshawbridge *Lancashire*
Langbank *Police Scotland*
Langdale *Cumbria*
Langford *Bedfordshire*
Langham *Leicestershire*
Langholm *Police Scotland*
Langland *South Wales*
Langley *Cheshire*
Langley *Gtr Manchester*
Langley *Hertfordshire*
Langley *Thames Valley*
Langley Mill *Derbyshire*
Langley Moor *Durham*
Langley Park *Durham*
Langold *Nottinghamshire*
Langport *Avon & Somerset*
Langshaw Common *Gtr Manchester*
Langstone *Gwent*
Langton *Kent*
Langton Herring *Dorset*
Langton Long *Dorset*
Langton Matravers *Dorset*
Langwathby *Cumbria*
Langwith *Derbyshire*
Langwith Junction *Derbyshire*
Langwith Upper *Derbyshire*
Lanivet *Devon & Cornwall*
Lapal *West Midlands*
Lapworth *Warwickshire*
Larbert *Police Scotland*
Larch Farm *Nottinghamshire*
Largoward *Police Scotland*
Largs *Police Scotland*
Larkhall *Police Scotland*
Larhill *Wiltshire*
Larkton *Cheshire*
Larne *PSNI*
Lasham *Hampshire*
Lastingham *North Yorkshire*
Latchingdon *Essex*
Latebrook *Staffordshire*
Lauder *Police Scotland*
Laugharne *Dyfed-Powys*
Laughton *Leicestershire*
Laughton *South Yorkshire*
Laughton Common *South Yorks*
Launceston *Devon & Cornwall*
Launde *Leicestershire*
Laurencekirk *Police Scotland*
Laurieston *Police Scotland*
Lavant *Sussex*
Lavender Hill *Metropolitan*
Lavendon *Thames Valley*
Lavenham *Suffolk*
Laverton *North Yorkshire*
Law *Police Scotland*
Laxey *Isle of Man*
Laxfield *Suffolk*
Laxton *Northamptonshire*
Lazenby *North Yorkshire*
Lazonby *Cumbria*
Lea *Derbyshire*
Lea *Lancashire*
Lea-by-Backford *Cheshire*
Lea Hall *Derbyshire*
Lea Newbold *Cheshire*

Leabrooks *Derbyshire*
Leaden Roding *Essex*
Leadgate *Durham*
Leadhills *Police Scotland*
Leafield *Thames Valley*
Leamington Spa *Warwickshire*
Leasowe *Merseyside*
Leatherhead *Surrey*
Leavesden Green *Hertfordshire*
Lechlade *Gloucestershire*
Leconfield *Humberside*
Ledbury *West Mercia*
Ledsham *Cheshire*
Ledston *West Yorkshire*
Lee Brigg *West Yorkshire*
Lee Moor *West Yorkshire*
Lee-on-Solent *Hampshire*
Lee Road *Metropolitan*
Leeds *Kent*
Leeds *West Yorkshire*
Leek *Staffordshire*
Leek Wootton *Warwickshire*
Leeming *North Yorkshire*
Lees *Gtr Manchester*
Leesthorpe *Leicestershire*
Legbourne *Lincolnshire*
Leicester Forest East *Leicestershire*
Leigh *Dorset*
Leigh *Essex*
Leigh *Gtr Manchester*
Leigh *Kent*
Leigh *Surrey*
Leigh Park *Hampshire*
Leigh Sinton *West Mercia*
Leighfield *Leicestershire*
Leighs *Essex*
Leighton *Cheshire*
Leighton Bromswold *Cambridgeshire*
Leighton Buzzard *Bedfordshire*
Leintwardine *West Mercia*
Leire *Leicestershire*
Leiston *Suffolk*
Leith Hill *Surrey*
Leman Street *Metropolitan*
Lemington *Northumbria*
Lemsford *Hertfordshire*
Lenham *Kent*
Lennoxtown *Police Scotland*
Lenzie *Police Scotland*
Leominster *West Mercia*
Lepton *West Yorkshire*
Lerryn *Devon & Cornwall*
Lerwick *Police Scotland*
Leslie *Police Scotland*
Lesmahagow *Police Scotland*
Letchworth *Hertfordshire*
Letcombe Bassett *Thames Valley*
Letcombe Regis *Thames Valley*
Letham (Angus) *Police Scotland*
Letham (Fife) *Police Scotland*
Letterston *Dyfed-Powys*
Leuchars *Police Scotland*
Levanshulme *Gtr Manchester*
Leven *Police Scotland*
Leven *Humberside*
Levens *Cumbria*
Lever Edge *Gtr Manchester*
Leverington *Cambridgeshire*
Leverstock *Hertfordshire*
Leverton *Lincolnshire*
Levisham *North Yorkshire*
Lewdown *Devon & Cornwall*
Lewes *Sussex*
Leweston *Dorset*
Lewick *Cumbria*
Lewisham *Metropolitan*
Lewknor *Thames Valley*

Lewstock *Gtr Manchester*
Ley Green *Hertfordshire*
Ley Hey Park *Gtr Manchester*
Leyburn *North Yorkshire*
Leyland *Lancashire*
Leysdown *Kent*
Leyton *Metropolitan*
Leytonstone *Metropolitan*
Llanbryde *Police Scotland*
Lichfield *Staffordshire*
Lickey End *West Mercia*
Lidget Green *West Yorkshire*
Lidlington *Bedfordshire*
Lifton *Devon & Cornwall*
Ligatbowne *Gtr Manchester*
Lightwater *Surrey*
Lightwood *Staffordshire*
Ligoniel *PSNI*
Lilbourne *Northamptonshire*
Lilford-cum-Wigsthorpe *Northants*
Lilley *Hertfordshire*
Lillington *Dorset*
Lily Hill *Gtr Manchester*
Limavady *PSNI*
Lime Gate *Gtr Manchester*
Lime Side *Gtr Manchester*
Limefield *Gtr Manchester*
Limehouse *Metropolitan*
Limehurst *Gtr Manchester*
Limekilns *Police Scotland*
Limpsfield *Surrey*
Linchmere *Sussex*
Lincoln *Lincolnshire*
Lindale *Cumbria*
Lindley *Leicestershire*
Linehouses *Staffordshire*
Linfitts *Gtr Manchester*
Lingdale *Cleveland*
Lingfield *Surrey*
Lingwood *Norfolk*
Linlithgow *Police Scotland*
Linslade *Bedfordshire*
Linthwaite *West Yorkshire*
Linton *Cambridgeshire*
Linton *Derbyshire*
Linton *Kent*
Linton *North Yorkshire*
Linton Falls *North Yorkshire*
Linton-on-Ouse *North Yorkshire*
Linwood *Police Scotland*
Liphook *Hampshire*
Lisbellaw *PSNI*
Lisburn *PSNI*
Lisburn Road *PSNI*
Liscard *Merseyside*
Liskeard *Devon & Cornwall*
Lisnaskea *PSNI*
Liss *Hampshire*
Listerhills *West Yorkshire*
Lisvane *South Wales*
Litcham *Norfolk*
Litchborough *Northamptonshire*
Litlington *Cambridgeshire*
Little Abington *Cambridgeshire*
Little Addington *Northamptonshire*
Little Amwell *Hertfordshire*
Little Berkhampstead *Hertfordshire*
Little Bolton *Gtr Manchester*
Little Bowden *Leicestershire*
Little Bookham *Surrey*
Little Bredy *Dorset*
Little Budworth *Cheshire*
Little Casterton *Leicestershire*
Little Chishill *Cambridgeshire*
Little Clacton *Essex*
Little Clegg *Gtr Manchester*

Little Comberton *West Mercia*
Little Dalby *Leicestershire*
Little Downham *Cambridgeshire*
Little Eaton *Derbyshire*
Little Eversden *Cambridgeshire*
Little Gaddesden *Hertfordshire*
Little Gidding *Cambridgeshire*
Little Gransden *Cambridgeshire*
Little Hadham *Hertfordshire*
Little Hallam *Derbyshire*
Little Harrowden *Northants*
Little Heath *Hertfordshire*
Little Hormead *Hertfordshire*
Little Horton *West Yorkshire*
Little Houghton
  Northamptonshire
Little Hucklow *Derbyshire*
Little Hulton *Gtr Manchester*
Little Irchester *Northamptonshire*
Little Leigh *Cheshire*
Little Lever *Gtr Manchester*
Little Longstone *Derbyshire*
Little Mill *Gwent*
Little Moor *Gtr Manchester*
Little Moss *Gtr Manchester*
Little Munden *Hertfordshire*
Little Ouse *Cambridgeshire*
Little Ouseburn *North Yorkshire*
Little Paxton *Cambridgeshire*
Little Plumstead *Norfolk*
Little Shelford *Cambridgeshire*
Little Stanney *Cheshire*
Little Stretton *Leicestershire*
Little Stukeley *Cambridgeshire*
Little Sutton *Cheshire*
Little Thetford *Cambridgeshire*
Little Warford *Cheshire*
Little Weighton *Humberside*
Little Wilbraham *Cambridgeshire*
Little Wymondley *Hertfordshire*
Littleborough *Gtr Manchester*
Littlebourne *Kent*
Littlebury *Essex*
Littledean *Gloucestershire*
Littlehampton *Sussex*
Littleover *Derbyshire*
Littleport *Cambridgeshire*
Littlethorpe *Leicestershire*
Littleton *Cheshire*
Littleton *Surrey*
Littleton *West Mercia*
Littlewick *Thames Valley*
Littleworth *Thames Valley*
Litton *Derbyshire*
Litton *North Yorkshire*
Litton Cheney *Dorset*
Liverpool *Merseyside*
Livington *Police Scotland*
Llanarth *Dyfed-Powys*
Llanarth *Gwent*
Llanaelhaiarn *North Wales*
Llanarthney *Dyfed-Powys*
Llanbadoc *Gwent*
Llanbedrog *North Wales*
Llanberis *North Wales*
Llanbister *Dyfed-Powys*
Llanbradach *Gwent*
Llanbrynmair *Dyfed-Powys*
Llandaff *South Wales*
Llanddewi Brefi *Dyfed-Powys*
Llanddewi Rhydderch *Gwent*
Llanddewi Skirrid *Gwent*
Llanddewi Velfrey *Dyfed-Powys*
Llandegla *North Wales*
Llandegveth *Gwent*
Llandeilo *Dyfed-Powys*
Llandenny *Gwent*
Llandevaud *Gwent*
Llandogo *Gwent*

Llandough *South Wales*
Llandovery *Dyfed-Powys*
Llandrillo *North Wales*
Llandrindod Wells *Dyfed-Powys*
Llandudno *North Wales*
Llandudno Jn *North Wales*
Llanddulas *North Wales*
Llandybie *Dyfed-Powys*
Llandyrnog *North Wales*
Llandysilio *Dyfed-Powys*
Llandyssul *Dyfed-Powys*
Llanedeyrn *South Wales*
Llanegryn *North Wales*
Llanellen *Gwent*
Llanelli *Dyfed-Powys*
Llanelli Docks *Dyfed-Powys*
Llanelly Hill *Gwent*
Llanerchymedd *North Wales*
Llanfaethlu *North Wales*
Llanfair-Caereinion *Dyfed-Powys*
Lanfair DC *North Wales*
Llanfair TH *North Wales*
Llanfairfechan *North Wales*
Llanfairpwll *North Wales*
Llanferres *North Wales*
Llanfoist *Gwent*
Llanfrechfa *Gwent*
Llanfyllin *Dyfed-Powys*
Llangadfan *Dyfed-Powys*
Llangadog *Dyfed-Powys*
Llangattock-Nigh-Usk *Gwent*
Llangattock Lingoed *Gwent*
Llangattock-Vibon-Avel *Gwent*
Llangefni *North Wales*
Llangeinor *South Wales*
Llangeitho *Dyfed-Powys*
Llandgendeirne *Dyfed-Powys*
Llangennech *Dyfed-Powys*
Llangennith *South Wales*
Llangernyw *North Wales*
Llangeview *Gwent*
Llangibby *Gwent*
Llangoed *North Wales*
Llangollen *North Wales*
Llangovan *Gwent*
Llangua *Gwent*
Llangunllo *Dyfed-Powys*
Llangurig *Dyfed-Powys*
Llangwm *Dyfed-Powys*
Llangwm *Gwent*
Llangyfelach *South Wales*
Llanharan *South Wales*
Llanharry *South Wales*
Llanhennock *Gwent*
Llanhilleth *Gwent*
Llanidloes *Dyfed-Powys*
Llanilar *Dyfed-Powys*
Llanishen *Gwent*
Llanishen *South Wales*
Llanllyfni *North Wales*
Llanmartin *Gwent*
Llanon *Dyfed-Powys*
Llanover *Gwent*
Llanrhaeadr Y.C. *North Wales*
Llanrhaeadr Y.M. *Dyfed-Powys*
Llanrhidian *South Wales*
Llanrug *North Wales*
Llanrumney *South Wales*
Llanrwst *North Wales*
Llansamlet *South Wales*
Llansannan *North Wales*
Llansantffraed *Gwent*
Llansantffraid *Dyfed-Powys*
Llansawel *Dyfed-Powys*
Llansilin *North Wales*
Llansoy *Gwent*
Llanstephan *Dyfed-Powys*
Llantarnam *Gwent*
Llanthony *Gwent*

Llantilio Crossenny *Gwent*
Llantilio Pertholey *Gwent*
Llantrisant *South Wales*
Llantrissant *Gwent*
Llantwit Major *South Wales*
Llantysilio *North Wales*
Llanuwchllyn *North Wales*
Llanvaches *Gwent*
Llanvair Discoed *Gwent*
Llanvapley *Gwent*
Llanvetherine *Gwent*
Llanvihangel Crucorney *Gwent*
Llanvihangel Gobion *Gwent*
Llanvihangel-Ystern-Llewern
  Gwent
Llanwenarth Citra *Gwent*
Llanwern *Gwent*
Llanwrda *Dyfed-Powys*
Llanwrtyd Wells *Dyfed-Powys*
Llanybyther *Dyfed-Powys*
Llay (Nantygaer Road) *North
  Wales*
Llay (1st Ave.) *North Wales*
Lloc *North Wales*
Llwydcoed *South Wales*
Llwyngwril *North Wales*
Llwynhendy *Dyfed-Powys*
Llynclys *West Mercia*
Llysfaen *North Wales*
Loanhead *Police Scotland*
Locharbriggs *Police Scotland*
Lochboisdale *Police Scotland*
Lochcarron *Police Scotland*
Lochearnhead *Police Scotland*
Lochee *Police Scotland*
Lochgelly *Police Scotland*
Lochgilphead *Police Scotland*
Lochgoilhead *Police Scotland*
Lochinver *Police Scotland*
Lochmaben *Police Scotland*
Lochmaddy *Police Scotland*
Lochwinnoch *Police Scotland*
Lockerbie *Police Scotland*
Lockerley *Hampshire*
Lockington *Leicestershire*
Lockleaze *Avon & Somerset*
Loddington *Leicestershire*
Loddington *Northamptonshire*
Loddon *Norfolk*
Lode *Cambridgeshire*
Loders *Dorset*
Lodsworth *Sussex*
Lofthouse *North Yorkshire*
Lofthouse *West Yorkshire*
Lofthouse Gate *West Yorkshire*
Loftus *Cleveland*
Lolham *Cambridgeshire*
Lolworth *Cambridgeshire*
London Colney *Hertfordshire*
London Road *Police Scotland*
Long Ashton *Avon & Somerset*
Long Bennington *Lincolnshire*
Long Bredy *Dorset*
Long Buckby *Northamptonshire*
Long Burton *Dorset*
Long Clawson *Leicestershire*
Long Compton *Warwickshire*
Long Crendon *Thames Valley*
Long Crichel *Dorset*
Long Eaton *Derbyshire*
Long Itchington *Warwickshire*
Long Lawford *Warwickshire*
Long Marston *Hertfordshire*
Long Marston *North Yorkshire*
Long Marston *Warwickshire*
Long Preston *North Yorkshire*
Long Stratton *Norfolk*
Long Sutton *Lincolnshire*
Long Whatton *Leicestershire*

Long Wittenham *Thames Valley*
Longbenton *Northumbria*
Longbridge *West Midlands*
Longbridge Deveril *Wiltshire*
Longcot *Thames Valley*
Longcroft *Police Scotland*
Longcross *Surrey*
Longden *West Mercia*
Longdendale *Gtr Manchester*
Longdon *West Mercia*
Longford *Derbyshire*
Longford Park *Gtr Manchester*
Longforgan *Police Scotland*
Longframlington *Northumbria*
Longgope *Gloucestershire*
Longhohe *Police Scotland*
Longhorsley *Northumbria*
Longhoughton *Northumbria*
Longmeadow *Cambridgeshire*
Longnor *West Mercia*
Longparish *Hampshire*
Longport *Staffordshire*
Longridge *Lancashire*
Longsight (Manchester) *Gtr Manchester*
Longsight (Royton) *Gtr Manchester*
Longstanton *Cambridgeshire*
Longstanton-All-Saints *Cambs*
Longstanton-St-Michael's *Cambs*
Longstowe *Cambridgeshire*
Longton *Lancashire*
Longton *Staffordshire*
Longtown *Cumbria*
Longtown *West Mercia*
Longworth *Thames Valley*
Lonsdale *Cumbria*
Looe *Devon & Cornwall*
Lords Bridge *Cambridgeshire*
Lorton *Cumbria*
Loscoe *Derbyshire*
Lossiemouth *Police Scotland*
Lostock Gralam *Cheshire*
Lostock Hall *Lancashire*
Lostock Hall Fold *Gtr Manchester*
Lostwithiel *Devon & Cornwall*
Lothersdale *North Yorkshire*
Loudwater *Thames Valley*
Loughborough *Leicestershire*
Loughgall *PSNI*
Loughor *South Wales*
Loughton *Essex*
Loughton *Thames Valley*
Louth *Lincolnshire*
Lovetts End *Hertfordshire*
Low Catton *North Yorkshire*
Low Green *Gtr Manchester*
Low Hesket *Cumbria*
Low Moor *West Yorkshire*
Low Row *Cumbria*
Low Row *North Yorkshire*
Low Side *Gtr Manchester*
Low Valley *South Yorkshire*
Lowdham *Nottinghamshire*
Lower Basildon *Thames Valley*
Lower Bredbury *Gtr Manchester*
Lower Bourne *Surrey*
Lower Broughton *Gtr Manchester*
Lower Cliff *Gtr Manchester*
Lower Crumpsall *Gtr Manchester*
Lower Fold *Gtr Manchester*
Lower Green *Gtr Manchester*
Lower Healey *Gtr Manchester*
Lower Higham *Gtr Manchester*
Lower Irlam *Gtr Manchester*
Lower Kersal *Gtr Manchester*
Lower Kinnerton *Cheshire*
Lower Knaphill *Surrey*

Lower Moor *West Mercia*
Lower Penarth *South Wales*
Lower Place *Gtr Manchester*
Lowesby *Leicestershire*
Lowestoft *Suffolk*
Lowfield Heath *Surrey*
Lowgates *Derbyshire*
Lowhouse Fold *Gtr Manchester*
Lowick *Cumbria*
Lowick *Northamptonshire*
Lowton *Gtr Manchester*
Lowton Common *Gtr Manchester*
Lowtown-St-Mary's *Gtr Manchester*
Lowhill *Surrey*
Loxhill *Surrey*
Loxley *South Yorkshire*
Loxwood *Sussex*
Lubbesthorpe *Leicestershire*
Lubenham *Leicestershire*
Lucas Green *Surrey*
Luddendenfoot *West Yorkshire*
Luddesdown *Kent*
Luddington *Northamptonshire*
Ludgershall *Wiltshire*
Ludham *Norfolk*
Ludlow *West Mercia*
Luffenhall *Hertfordshire*
Lullington *Derbyshire*
Lumb *Lancashire*
Lumsden *Police Scotland*
Luncarty *Police Scotland*
Lundin Links *Police Scotland*
Lurgan *PSNI*
Luss *Police Scotland*
Luton *Bedfordshire*
Lutterworth *Leicestershire*
Lutton *Northamptonshire*
Luttons (East & West) *North Yorks*
Luzley *Gtr Manchester*
Luzley Brook *Gtr Manchester*
Lybster *Police Scotland*
Lydart *Gwent*
Lydbrook *Gloucestershire*
Lydd *Kent*
Lydden *Kent*
Lyddington *Leicestershire*
Lydford *Avon & Somerset*
Lydgate *Gtr Manchester*
Lydgate (Saddleworth) *Gtr Manchester*
Lydlinch *Dorset*
Lydney *Gloucestershire*
Lydstep *Dyfed-Powys*
Lyme Handley *Cheshire*
Lyme Regis *Dorset*
Lyminge *Kent*
Lymington *Hampshire*
Lyminster *Sussex*
Lymm *Cheshire*
Lympne *Kent*
Lympstone *Devon & Cornwall*
Lynden *Leicestershire*
Lyndhurst *Hampshire*
Lyne *Surrey*
Lyneham *Wiltshire*
Lynemouth *Northumbria*
Lynsted *Kent*
Lynton *Devon & Cornwall*
Lytchett Matravers *Dorset*
Lytchett Minster *Dorset*
Lytham *Lancashire*
Lythe *North Yorkshire*
Mablethorpe *Lincolnshire*
Macclesfield *Cheshire*
Macclesfield Forest *Cheshire*
Macduff *Police Scotland*
Macefan *Cheshire*

Machen *Gwent*
Machynlleth *Dyfed-Powys*
Mackerye End *Hertfordshire*
Mackworth *Derbyshire*
Maddiston *Police Scotland*
Madeley *Staffordshire*
Madeley *West Mercia*
Maenclochog *Dyfed-Powys*
Maentwrog *North Wales*
Maerdy *South Wales*
Maesgeirchen *North Wales*
Maesglas *Gwent*
Maesteg *South Wales*
Maescyoed *South Wales*
Maesycwmmer *Gwent*
Maghera *PSNI*
Madingley *Cambridgeshire*
Magherafelt *PSNI*
Maghull *Merseyside*
Magor *Gwent*
Maiden Newton *Dorset*
Maidenhead *Thames Valley*
Maidford *Northamptonshire*
Maids Moreton *Thames Valley*
Maidstone *Kent*
Maidwell *Northamptonshire*
Maindee *Gwent*
Mainsforth *Durham*
Makants *Gtr Manchester*
Malborough *Devon & Cornwall*
Maldon *Essex*
Malham *North Yorkshire*
Mallaig *Police Scotland*
Malmesbury *Wiltshire*
Malpas *Cheshire*
Malpas *Gwent*
Maltby *South Yorkshire*
Maltby-le-Marsh *Lincolnshire*
Malton *North Yorkshire*
Malvern *West Mercia*
Malvern Link *West Mercia*
Malvern Wells *West Mercia*
Mamhilad *Gwent*
Manchester *Gtr Manchester*
Manea *Cambridgeshire*
Manfield *North Yorkshire*
Manley *Cheshire*
Manley Park *Gtr Manchester*
Manmoel *Gwent*
Manningham *West Yorkshire*
Mannings Heath *Sussex*
Mansel Lacy *West Mercia*
Manselton *South Wales*
Mansfield *Nottinghamshire*
Mansfield Woodhouse *Notts*
Manston *Dorset*
Manton *Leicestershire*
Manton *Nottinghamshire*
Maple Cross *Hertfordshire*
Mapledurham *Thames Valley*
Mapperley *Derbyshire*
Mapperton *Dorset*
Mappleton *Derbyshire*
Mapplewell *South Yorkshire*
Mappowder *Dorset*
Marazion *Devon & Cornwall*
Marbury *Cheshire*
Marbury-cum-Quoisley *Cheshire*
March *Cambridgeshire*
Marcham *Thames Valley*
Marchwiel *North Wales*
Marchwood *Hampshire*
Marcroft Gate *Gtr Manchester*
Marden *Kent*
Mardley Heath *Hertfordshire*
Mardy *Gwent*
Marefield *Leicestershire*
Mareham-le-Fen *Lincolnshire*
Marehay *Derbyshire*

Margam *South Wales*
Margaret Marsh *Dorset*
Margaretting *Essex*
Margate *Kent*
Marholm *Cambridgeshire*
Mark *Avon & Somerset*
Mark Cross *Sussex*
Market Bosworth *Leicestershire*
Market Deeping *Lincolnshire*
Market Drayton *West Mercia*
Market Harborough *Leicestershire*
Market Overton *Leicestershire*
Market Rasen *Lincolnshire*
Market Weighton *Humberside*
Markethill *PSNI*
Markfield *Leicestershire*
Markham *Gwent*
Markinch *Police Scotland*
Markland *Gtr Manchester*
Markyate *Hertfordshire*
Marland *Gtr Manchester*
Marlborough *Wiltshire*
Marlesford *Suffolk*
Marlingford *Norfolk*
Marlow *Thames Valley*
Marlpool *Derbyshire*
Marlston-cum-Lache *Cheshire*
Marnhull *Dorset*
Marple *Gtr Manchester*
Marple Bridge *Gtr Manchester*
Marpleridge *Gtr Manchester*
Marr *South Yorkshire*
Marsden *West Yorkshire*
Marsh Gibbon *Thames Valley*
Marsh Green *Gtr Manchester*
Marsh Lane *Derbyshire*
Marshfield *Avon & Somerset*
Marshfield *Gwent*
Marshland Green *Gtr Manchester*
Marshwood *Dorset*
Marske *North Yorks*
Marske-by-the-Sea *Cleveland*
Marston *Bedfordshire*
Marston *Cheshire*
Marston-on-Dove *Derbyshire*
Marston Magna *Avon & Somerset*
Marston Montgomery *Derbyshire*
Marston-St Lawrence *Northants*
Marston Trussell *Northants*
Marthall *Cheshire*
Martham *Norfolk*
Martin *Lincolnshire*
Martinsthorpe *Leicestershire*
Martinstown *PSNI*
Martlesham *Suffolk*
Martley *West Mercia*
Martock *Avon & Somerset*
Marton *North Yorkshire*
Marton *Lincolnshire*
Marton *Warwickshire*
Marton (Macclesfield) *Cheshire*
Marton (Northwich) *Cheshire*
Martons Both *North Yorkshire*
Mary Tavy *Devon & Cornwall*
Maryhill *Police Scotland*
Marylebone Lane *Metropolitan*
Maryport *Cumbria*
Masham *North Yorkshire*
Mastin Moor *Derbyshire*
Matfield *Kent*
Mathern *Gwent*
Matlock *Derbyshire*
Matlock Bath *Derbyshire*
Matthewstown *South Wales*
Mattingley *Hampshire*
Mattishall *Norfolk*
Mauchline *Police Scotland*
Maud *Police Scotland*
Maulden *Bedfordshire*

Maulds Meaburn *Cumbria*
Mawdesley *Lancashire*
Mewgan-in-Meneage *Devon & Cornwall*
Mawnan Smith *Devon & Cornwall*
Maxey *Cambridgeshire*
Mayals *South Wales*
Maybole *Police Scotland*
Maybury *Surrey*
Mayes Green *Surrey*
Mayfield *Police Scotland*
Mayfield *Sussex*
Mayford *Surrey*
Mayhill *South Wales*
Maynards Green *Sussex*
Meadowfield *Durham*
Meadows *Nottinghamshire*
Mealsgate *Cumbria*
Meanwood *West Yorkshire*
Mears Ashby *Northamptonshire*
Measham *Leicestershire*
Medbourne *Leicestershire*
Medlock *Gtr Manchester*
Medomsley *Durham*
Meerside *Gtr Manchester*
Meesden *Hertfordshire*
Meigle *Police Scotland*
Meir *Staffordshire*
Melbourn *Cambridgeshire*
Melbourne *Derbyshire*
Melbourne Park *Essex*
Melbury Abbas *Dorset*
Melbury Bubb *Dorset*
Melbury Osmond *Dorset*
Melbury Sampford *Dorset*
Melcombe Horsey *Dorset*
Melcombe Regis *Dorset*
Meldreth *Cambridgeshire*
Meliden *North Wales*
Melksham *Wiltshire*
Mellor *Cheshire*
Mellor Moor *Gtr Manchester*
Mells *Avon & Somerset*
Melmerby *Cumbria*
Melmerby (Leyburn) *North Yorks*
Melmerby (Wath) *North Yorkshire*
Northaw *Hertfordshire*
Melrose *Police Scotland*
Meltham *West Yorkshire*
Melton *Suffolk*
Melton Mowbray *Leicestershire*
Menai Bridge *North Wales*
Menston *West Yorkshire*
Meopham *Kent*
Mepal *Cambridgeshire*
Meppershall *Bedfordshire*
Mercaston *Derbyshire*
Merchants Square *Gtr Manchester*
Mere *Cheshire*
Mere *Wiltshire*
Mereworth *Kent*
Meriden *West Midlands*
Merilees *Leicestershire*
Merriott *Avon & Somerset*
Merrow *Surrey*
Merstham *Surrey*
Merston *Sussex*
Merthyr Tydfil *South Wales*
Merthyr Vale *South Wales*
Messingham *Humberside*
Metal Bridge *Cumbria*
Metheringham *Lincolnshire*
Methil *Police Scotland*
Methihill *Police Scotland*
Methley *West Yorkshire*
Methwold *Norfolk*
Methven *Police Scotland*
Mevagissey *Devon & Cornwall*
Mexborough *South Yorkshire*

Mey *Police Scotland*
Meynell Langley *Derbyshire*
Michaelstone-y-vedw *Gwent*
Micheldever *Hampshire*
Mickle Trafford *Cheshire*
Micklefield *West Yorkshire*
Mickleham *Surrey*
Micklehurst *Gtr Manchester*
Mickleover *Derbyshire*
Mickleton *Durham*
Mickley *Derbyshire*
Mickley *North Yorkshire*
Mickley Square *Northumbria*
Mid Calder *Police Scotland*
Middle Healey *Gtr Manchester*
Middle Hulton *Gtr Manchester*
Middle Rasen *Lincolnshire*
Middleham *North Yorkshire*
Middleport *Staffordshire*
Middlesbrough *Cleveland*
Middlestown *West Yorkshire*
Middleton *Derbyshire*
Middleton *Gtr Manchester*
Middleton *Norfolk*
Middleton *Northamptonshire*
Middleton *Sussex*
Middleton *West Yorkshire*
Middleton Cheney *Northants*
Middleton-St-George *Durham*
Middleton & Smerrill *Derbyshire*
Middleton Stoney *Thames Valley*
Middleton-in-Teesdale *Durham*
Middleton (Pickering) *North Yorks*
Middleton Quernhow *North Yorks*
Middleton Tyas *North Yorkshire*
Middleton (Wharfdale) *North Yorks*
Middleton-on-Leven *North Yorks*
Middleton-on-the-Wolds *Humberside*
Middlewich *Cheshire*
Midgley *West Yorkshire*
Midhurst *Sussex*
Midloe & Southoe *Cambridgeshire*
Midway *Derbyshire*
Milber *Devon & Cornwall*
Milborne Port *Avon & Somerset*
Milborne St Andrew *Dorset*
Milby *North Yorkshire*
Mildenhall *Suffolk*
Mile End *Gloucestershire*
Miles Blatting *Gtr Manchester*
Milfield *Northumbria*
Milford *Derbyshire*
Milford *Hampshire*
Milford *Surrey*
Milford Haven *Dyfed-Powys*
Milking Nook *Cambridgeshire*
Mill Brow *Gtr Manchester*
Mill Green *Hertfordshire*
Mill Hill *Gtr Manchester*
Mill Hill *Metropolitan*
Mill Shaw *West Yorkshire*
Millbridge *Surrey*
Millbrook *Gtr Manchester*
Millgarth *West Yorkshire*
Millhouse *South Yorkshire*
Millington *Cheshire*
Millom *Cumbria*
Millport *Police Scotland*
Mills Hill *Gtr Manchester*
Milnathort *Police Scotland*
Milngavie & Bearsden *Police Scotland*
Milnrow *Gtr Manchester*
Milnthorpe *Cumbria*
Milton *Cambridgeshire*
Milton *Derbyshire*

Milton *Staffordshire*
Milton Abbas *Dorset*
Milton of Campsie *Police Scotland*
Milton Ernest *Bedfordshire*
Milton Keynes *Thames Valley*
Milton Malsor *Northamptonshire*
Milverton *Avon & Somerset*
Minchinhampton *Gloucestershire*
Minehead *Avon & Somerset*
Minshull Vernon *Cheshire*
Minster (Sheppey) *Kent*
Minster (Thanet) *Kent*
Minster Lovell *Thames Valley*
Minsterley *West Mercia*
Mintern Magna *Dorset*
Mintlaw *Police Scotland*
Mirfield *West Yorkshire*
Miskin (Aberdare) *South Wales*
Miskin (Pontypridd) *South Wales*
Misson *Nottinghamshire*
Misterton *Avon & Somerset*
Misterton *Leicestershire*
Misterton *Nottinghamshire*
Mistley *Essex*
Mitcham *Metropolitan*
Mitchel Troy *Gwent*
Mitcheldean *Gloucestershire*
Mobberley *Cheshire*
Mochdre *North Wales*
Modbury *Devon & Cornwall*
Moffat *Police Scotland*
Moira *Leicestershire*
Moira *PSNI*
Mold *North Wales*
Mollington *Cheshire*
Moneymore *PSNI*
Monifieth *Police Scotland*
Monikie *Police Scotland*
Monk Fryston *North Yorkshire*
Monks Coppenhall *Cheshire*
Monks Eleigh *Suffolk*
Monks Green *Hertfordshire*
Monkswood *Gwent*
Monkton *Police Scotland*
Monmouth *Gwent*
Monsal Dale *Derbyshire*
Montacute *Avon & Somerset*
Montcliffe *Gtr Manchester*
Montgomery *Dyfed-Powys*
Montrose *Police Scotland*
Monyash *Derbyshire*
Moor Park *Hertfordshire*
Moorbarns *Leicestershire*
Moordown *Dorset*
Moore *Cheshire*
Moorends *South Yorkshire*
Moorside *Gtr Manchester*
Moortown *West Yorkshire*
Morborne *Cambridgeshire*
Morcott *Leicestershire*
Morden *Dorset*
Morden *Surrey*
More Crichel *Dorset*
Morecambe *Lancashire*
Moresby *Cumbria*
Moreton *Dorset*
Moreton *Essex*
Moreton *Merseyside*
Moreton-cum-Alcumlow *Cheshire*
Moreton-in-the-Marsh *Glos*
Moretonhampstead *Devon & Cornwall*
Moreton Pinkney *Northants*
Morfa Nefyn *North Wales*
Morgans Vale *Wiltshire*
Morley *Derbyshire*
Morley *West Yorkshire*
Morpeth *Northumbria*

Morriston *South Wales*
Mortimer *Thames Valley*
Morton *Derbyshire*
Morton *Gtr Manchester*
Morton *Lincolnshire*
Morton *West Yorkshire*
Morton-on-Swale *North Yorkshire*
Morville *West Mercia*
Mosborough *South Yorkshire*
Mosley Common *Gtr Manchester*
Moss Brow *Gtr Manchester*
Moss Gate *Gtr Manchester*
Moss Nook *Gtr Manchester*
Moss Side *Gtr Manchester*
Mossley *Gtr Manchester*
Mosterton *Dorset*
Moston *Cheshire*
Moston *Gtr Manchester*
Mostyn *North Wales*
Motcombe *Dorset*
Motherby *Cumbria*
Motherwell *Police Scotland*
Mottram-in-Longendale *Gtr Manchester*
Mottram St Andrews *Cheshire*
Mouldsworth *Cheshire*
Moulsford *Thames Valley*
Moulsham Lodge *Essex*
Moulton *Cheshire*
Moulton *Lincolnshire*
Moulton *Northamptonshire*
Moulton *North Yorkshire*
Moulton Chapel *Lincolnshire*
Mount Pleasant *Staffordshire*
Mountain *West Yorkshire*
Mountain Ash *South Wales*
Mountpottinger *PSNI*
Mountsorrel *Leicestershire*
Mousehole *Devon & Cornwall*
Mowmacre Hill *Leicestershire*
Mowsley *Leicestershire*
Moy *PSNI*
Much Hadham *Hertfordshire*
Much Marcle *West Mercia*
Much Wenlock *West Mercia*
Muckhart *Police Scotland*
Mudeford *Dorset*
Mudford *Avon & Somerset*
Mugginton *Derbyshire*
Muir of Ord *Police Scotland*
Muirhead *Police Scotland*
Muirkirk *Police Scotland*
Mullion *Devon & Cornwall*
Mullock *Dyfed-Powys*
Mumbles *South Wales*
Mumps *Gtr Manchester*
Mundesley *Norfolk*
Mundford *Norfolk*
Munslow *West Mercia*
Murrow *Cambridgeshire*
Murton *Durham*
Murton (Helmsley) *North Yorks*
Murton (York) *North Yorkshire*
Musgrave Street *PSNI*
Musselburgh *Police Scotland*
Muston *Leicestershire*
Mustow Green *West Mercia*
Muswell Hill *Metropolitan*
Muthill *Police Scotland*
Mytchett *Surrey*
Mytholmroyd *West Yorkshire*
Nacton *Suffolk*
Nafferton *Humberside*
Nailsea *Avon & Somerset*
Nailstone *Leicestershire*
Nailsworth *Gloucestershire*
Nairn *Police Scotland*
Nancledra *Devon & Cornwall*
Nannerch *North Wales*

Nanpantan *Leicestershire*
Nantgarw *South Wales*
Nantglyn *North Wales*
Nantwich *Cheshire*
Nantybwch *Gwent*
Nantyderry *Gwent*
Nantyffyllon *South Wales*
Nantyglo *Gwent*
Nantymoel *South Wales*
Naphill *Thames Valley*
Napton-on-the-Hill *Warwickshire*
Narberth *Dyfed-Powys*
Narborough *Leicestershire*
Narborough *Norfolk*
Narth *Gwent*
Naseby *Northamptonshire*
Nash *Gwent*
Nash Mills *Hertfordshire*
Nassington *Northamptonshire*
Navenby *Lincolnshire*
Nawton *North Yorkshire*
Nayland *Suffolk*
Nazeing *Essex*
Neath *South Wales*
Neath Abbey *South Wales*
Nechells Green *West Midlands*
Necton *Norfolk*
Needham Market *Suffolk*
Nefyn *North Wales*
Neilston *Police Scotland*
Nelson *Gwent*
Nelson *Lancashire*
Nelson Street *Avon & Somerset*
Ness *Cheshire*
Nesscliffe *West Mercia*
Neston *Cheshire*
Nether Alderley *Cheshire*
Nether Broughton *Leicestershire*
Nether Cerne *Dorset*
Nether Compton *Dorset*
Nether Haddon *Derbyshire*
Nether Heyford *Northamptonshire*
Netherlee *Police Scotland*
Nether Padley *Derbyshire*
Nether Peover *Cheshire*
Nether Stowey *Avon & Somerset*
Netheravon *Wiltshire*
Netherbury *Dorset*
Netherfield *Sussex*
Netherhall *Leicestershire*
Netherseal *Derbyshire*
Netherton *Police Scotland*
Netherton *West Yorkshire*
Nethybridge *Police Scotland*
Netley *Hampshire*
Netley Hill *Hampshire*
Netley Marsh *Hampshire*
Nettlebank *Staffordshire*
Nettlebed *Thames Valley*
Nettleden *Hertfordshire*
Nettleham *Lincolnshire*
Neville Holt *Leicestershire*
Neville's Cross *Durham*
New Addington *Metropolitan*
New Birmingham *Derbyshire*
New Brighton *Merseyside*
New Brighton *North Wales*
New Buckenham *Norfolk*
New Bury *Gtr Manchester*
New Chapel *Surrey*
New Cumnock *Police Scotland*
New Deer *Police Scotland*
New Delph *Gtr Manchester*
New Ferry *Merseyside*
New Fryston *West Yorkshire*
New Haw *Surrey*
New Hey *Gtr Manchester*
New Holland *Humberside*
New Inn *Gwent*

New Leake *Lincolnshire*
New Longton *Lancashire*
New Malden *Metropolitan*
New Mill *West Yorkshire*
New Mills *Derbyshire*
New Milton *Hampshire*
New Moston *Gtr Manchester*
New Parks *Leicestershire*
New Pitsligo *Police Scotland*
New Quay *Dyfed-Powys*
New Radnor *Dyfed-Powys*
New Romney *Kent*
New Sawley *Derbyshire*
New Springs *Gtr Manchester*
New Stevenson *Police Scotland*
New Town *Derbyshire*
New Tredegar *Gwent*
New Tupton *Derbyshire*
Newall Green *Gtr Manchester*
Newark *Nottinghamshire*
Newarthill *Police Scotland*
Newbattle *Police Scotland*
Newbiggin-in-Teesdale *Durham*
Newbold *Leicestershire*
Newbold Astbury *Cheshire*
Newbold-on-Avon *Warwickshire*
Newbold Verdon *Leicestershire*
Newborough *Cambridgeshire*
Newborough *North Wales*
Newbottle *Northamptonshire*
Newbridge *Gwent*
Newbridge-on-Wye *Dyfed-Powys*
Newburgh *Police Scotland*
Newburgh *Police Scotland*
Newburn *Northumbria*
Newbury *Thames Valley*
Newby Bridge *Cumbria*
Newby (Ingleton) *North Yorkshire*
Newby (Stokesley) *North Yorks*
Newby Wiske *North Yorkshire*
Newcastle *PSNI*
Newcastle-under-Lyme *Staffordshire*
Newcastle-upon-Tyne *Northumbria*
Newcastle Emlyn *Dyfed-Powys*
Newcastleton *Police Scotland*
Newchurch-in-Pendle *Lancashire*
Newdigate *Surrey*
Newent *Gloucestershire*
Newfield *Durham*
Newgate Street *Hertfordshire*
Newhall *Cheshire*
Newhall *Derbyshire*
Newhaven *Sussex*
Newington (Channel Ports) *Kent*
Newington (Sittingbourne) *Kent*
Newlay *West Yorkshire*
Newley Bridge *Cumbria*
Newlyn *Devon & Cornwall*
Newmains *Police Scotland*
Newmarket *Suffolk*
Newmills *Police Scotland*
Newmilns *Police Scotland*
Newnham *Hertfordshire*
Newnham *Kent*
Newnham *Northamptonshire*
Newnham Bridge *West Mercia*
Newport *Essex*
Newport *Gloucestershire*
Newport *Gwent*
Newport *Hampshire*
Newport *Humberside*
Newport *West Mercia*
Newport-on-Tay *Police Scotland*
Newport Pagnell *Thames Valley*
Newquay *Devon & Cornwall*
Newry *PSNI*

Newsham (Richmond) *North Yorks*
Newsham (Northallerton) *North Yorks*
Newstead *Nottinghamshire*
Newthorpe *Nottinghamshire*
Newton *Cambridgeshire*
Newton *Northamptonshire*
Newton *Derbyshire*
Newton *Gtr Manchester*
Newton (Bridgend) *South Wales*
Newton (Exelby) *North Yorkshire*
Newton (Malton) *North Yorkshire*
Newton Abbot *Devon & Cornwall*
Newton Aycliffe *Durham*
Newton Burgoland *Leicestershire*
Newton-by-Malpas *Cheshire*
Newton-by-Tattenhall *Cheshire*
Newton Ferrers *Devon & Cornwall*
Newton Grange *Derbyshire*
Newton Harcourt *Leicestershire*
Newton Heath *Gtr Manchester*
Newton Hill *West Yorkshire*
Newton-in-Bowland *Lancashire*
Newton Kyme *North Yorkshire*
Newton-le-Willows *Merseyside*
Newton-le-Willows *North Yorks*
Newton Mearns *Police Scotland*
Newton Moor *Gtr Manchester*
Newton Morrell *North Yorkshire*
Newton Mulgrave *North Yorkshire*
Newton-on-Ouse *North Yorkshire*
Newton Poppleford *Devon & Cornwall*
Newton Solney *Derbyshire*
Newton Stewart *Police Scotland*
Newton Wood *Gtr Manchester*
Newtonmore *Police Scotland*
Newtown *Dyfed-Powys*
Newtown *South Wales*
Newtown (Manchester) *Gtr Manchester*
Newtown (Swinton) *Gtr Manchester*
Newtown (Wigan) *Gtr Manchester*
Newtown Linford *Leicestershire*
Newtown St Boswells *Police Scotland*
Newtown Unthank *Leicestershire*
Newtownabbey *PSNI*
Newtownards *PSNI*
Newtownbutler *PSNI*
Newtownhamilton *PSNI*
Newtownstewart *PSNI*
Newtyle *Police Scotland*
Neyland *Dyfed-Powys*
Nidd *North Yorkshire*
Nimble Nook *Gtr Manchester*
Nine Elms *Metropolitan*
Ninfield *Sussex*
Niton *Hampshire*
Noctorum *Merseyside*
Nop End *Gtr Manchester*
Noranside *Police Scotland*
Norbury *Cheshire*
Norbury *Derbyshire*
Norbury *Metropolitan*
Norbury Moor *Gtr Manchester*
Norden *Gtr Manchester*
Norham *Northumbria*
Norley *Cheshire*
Normacot *Staffordshire*
Normanby *North Yorkshire*
Normandy *Surrey*
Normanton *Derbyshire*
Normanton *Leicestershire*
Normanton *West Yorkshire*
Normanton-le-Heath *Leicestershire*

Normanton Turville *Leicestershire*
North Ashton *Gtr Manchester*
North Berwick *Police Scotland*
North Cerney *Gloucestershire*
North Charlton *Northumbria*
North Curry *Avon & Somerset*
North Elmham *Norfolk*
North Elmsall *West Yorkshire*
North Featherstone *West Yorkshire*
North Ferriby *Humberside*
North Holmwood *Surrey*
North Hykeham *Lincolnshire*
North Kilworth *Leicestershire*
North Luffenham *Leicestershire*
North Malvern *West Mercia*
North Molton *Devon & Cornwall*
North Muskham *Nottinghamshire*
North Mymms *Hertfordshire*
North Ormsby *Cleveland*
North Petherton *Avon & Somerset*
North Poorton *Dorset*
North Queensferry *Police Scotland*
North Reddish *Gtr Manchester*
North Rode *Cheshire*
North Shields *Northumbria*
North Tawton *Devon & Cornwall*
North Walsham *Norfolk*
North Waltham *Hampshire*
North Weald *Essex*
North Wingfield *Derbyshire*
North Woolwich *Metropolitan*
North Wootton *Dorset*
Northallerton *North Yorkshire*
Northaw *Hertfordshire*
Northborough *Cambridgeshire*
Northbourne *Kent*
Northchapel *Sussex*
Northchurch *Hertfordshire*
Northenden *Gtr Manchester*
Northern Moor *Gtr Manchester*
Northfleet *Kent*
Northiam *Sussex*
Northleach *Gloucestershire*
Northill *Bedfordshire*
Northlew *Devon & Cornwall*
Northop *North Wales*
Northrepps *Norfolk*
Northwich *Cheshire*
Northwold *Norfolk*
Northwood *Metropolitan*
Northwood *Staffordshire*
Norton *Cheshire*
Norton *Hertfordshire*
Norton *Northamptonshire*
Norton *West Mercia*
Norton Bridge *South Wales*
Norton by Gaulby *Leicestershire*
Norton Conyers *North Yorkshire*
Norton Fitzwarren *Avon & Somerset*
Norton Green *Staffordshire*
Norton Juxta Twycross *Leicestershire*
Norton-in-the-Moors *Staffordshire*
Norton-le-Clay *North Yorkshire*
Norton-on-Derwent *North Yorks*
Norwich *Norfolk*
Norwood *North Yorkshire*
Norwood Green *Metropolitan*
Norwood Green *West Yorkshire*
Norwood Hill *Surrey*
Noseley *Leicestershire*
Notting Dale *Metropolitan*
Notting Hill *Metropolitan*
Nuffield *Thames Valley*
Nuneaton *Warwickshire*

Nuneham Courtenay *Thames Valley*
Nunney *Avon & Somerset*
Nunton *Wiltshire*
Nutfield *Surrey*
Nuthall *Nottinghamshire*
Nuthampstead *Hertfordshire*
Nutley *Sussex*
Nutsford Vale *Gtr Manchester*
Nuttal *Gtr Manchester*
Nuttall Lane *Gtr Manchester*
Oadby *Leicestershire*
Oak Gate *Gtr Manchester*
Oakdale *Dorset*
Oakdale *Gwent*
Oakengates *West Mercia*
Oakenshaw *West Yorkshire*
Oakerthorpe *Derbyshire*
Oakham *Leicestershire*
Oakhill *Avon & Somerset*
Oakhill *Staffordshire*
Oakington *Cambridgeshire*
Oaklands *Hertfordshire*
Oakley *Police Scotland*
Oakley *Hampshire*
Oakley Bank *Northamptonshire*
Oakmere *Cheshire*
Oaks-in-Charnwood *Leicestershire*
Oakthorpe *Leicestershire*
Oakwood *Surrey*
Oakworth Hill *West Yorkshire*
Oatlands (Harrogate) *North Yorkshire*
Oatlands Park *Surrey*
Oban *Police Scotland*
Oborne *Dorset*
Ockbrook *Derbyshire*
Ockham *Surrey*
Ockley *Surrey*
Odd Rode *Cheshire*
Odiham *Hampshire*
Odsal *West Yorkshire*
Odsey *Cambridgeshire*
Odstone *Leicestershire*
Offcote *Derbyshire*
Offenham *West Mercia*
Offerton *Derbyshire*
Offerton *Gtr Manchester*
Offerton Green *Gtr Manchester*
Offham *Kent*
Offley *Hertfordshire*
Offord Cluny *Cambridgeshire*
Offord D'Arcy *Cambridgeshire*
Offwell *Devon & Cornwall*
Ogbourne *Wiltshire*
Ogmore Vale *South Wales*
Okeford Fitzpaine *Dorset*
Okehampton *Devon & Cornwall*
Old *Northamptonshire*
Old Bilton *Warwickshire*
Old Brampton *Derbyshire*
Old Colwyn *North Wales*
Old Dalby *Leicestershire*
Old Fletton *Cambridgeshire*
Old Hall Green *Hertfordshire*
Old Hill *West Midlands*
Old Leake *Lincolnshire*
Old Milverton *Warwickshire*
Old Sawley *Derbyshire*
Old Stratford *Northamptonshire*
Old Trafford *Gtr Manchester*
Old Tupton *Derbyshire*
Old Western *Cambridgeshire*
Old Windsor *Thames Valley*
Old Working *Surrey*
Oldbury *West Midlands*
Oldcastle *Cheshire*
Oldcastle *Gwent*
Oldcotes *Nottinghamshire*

Oldfield Brow *Gtr Manchester*
Oldham *Gtr Manchester*
Oldham Edge *Gtr Manchester*
Oldhurst *Cambridgeshire*
Oldmeldrum *Police Scotland*
Oldpark *PSNI*
Olivers Battery *Hampshire*
Ollerset *Derbyshire*
Ollerton *Cheshire*
Ollerton *Nottinghamshire*
Olney *Thames Valley*
Olveston *Avon & Somerset*
Omagh *PSNI*
Ombersley *West Mercia*
Onchan *Isle of Man*
Ongar *Essex*
Onslow Village *Surrey*
Ordsall *Gtr Manchester*
Ordsall *Nottinghamshire*
Orford *Suffolk*
Orlingbury *Northamptonshire*
Ormesbury-St-Margaret *Norfolk*
Ormskirk *Lancashire*
Orrell *Gtr Manchester*
Orton *Northamptonshire*
Orton Longueville *Cambridgeshire*
Orton-on-the-Hill *Leicestershire*
Orton Waterville *Cambridgeshire*
Orwell *Cambridgeshire*
Osbaldwick *North Yorkshire*
Osbaston *Leicestershire*
Osgathorpe *Leicestershire*
Osgodby *Lincolnshire*
Osliston *Derbyshire*
Osmaston *Derbyshire*
Osmington *Dorset*
Osmondthorpe *West Yorkshire*
Osmotherley *North Yorkshire*
Ossett *West Yorkshire*
Oswaldkirk *North Yorkshire*
Oswestry *West Mercia*
Otford *Kent*
Othery *Avon & Somerset*
Otley *West Yorkshire*
Otterbourne *Hampshire*
Otterburn *Northumbria*
Otterburn *North Yorkshire*
Ottershaw *Surrey*
Ottery St Mary *Devon & Cornwall*
Oughtibridge *South Yorkshire*
Oulton *West Yorkshire*
Oundle *Northamptonshire*
Outseats *South Yorks*
Outward Gate *Gtr Manchester*
Outwell *Cambridgeshire*
Outwell *Norfolk*
Outwood *Surrey*
Outwood *West Yorkshire*
Ovenden *West Yorkshire*
Over *Cambridge*
Over Alderley *Cheshire*
Over Compton *Dorset*
Over Haddon *Derbyshire*
Overseal *Derbyshire*
Overstone *Northamptonshire*
Overton *Hampshire*
Overton *Lancashire*
Overton *North Wales*
Overton *North Yorkshire*
Overton *Wiltshire*
Overton-by-Frodsham *Cheshire*
Overton-by-Malpas *Cheshire*
Overtown *Police Scotland*
Ovingham *Northumbria*
Owermoigne *Dorset*
Owston *Leicestershire*
Oxenthorpe *West Yorkshire*
Oxford *Thames Valley*
Oxgangs *Police Scotland*

Oxhey *Hertfordshire*
Oxlode *Cambridgeshire*
Oxted *Surrey*
Oxton *Nottinghamshire*
Oxton *North Yorkshire*
Oxwich *South Wales*
Packington *Leicestershire*
Packmoor *Staffordshire*
Padbury *Thames Valley*
Paddington Green *Metropolitan*
Paddock Wood *Kent*
Padfield *Derbyshire*
Padgate *Cheshire*
Padiham *Lancashire*
Padstow *Devon & Cornwall*
Padworth *Thames Valley*
Pagham *Sussex*
Paignton *Devon & Cornwall*
Pailton *Warwickshire*
Painshill *Surrey*
Painswick *Gloucestershire*
Painthorpe *West Yorkshire*
Paisley *Police Scotland*
Palgrave *Suffolk*
Pamphill *Dorset*
Pampisford *Cambridgeshire*
Pandy *Gwent*
Pangbourne *Thames Valley*
Pannal *North Yorkshire*
Papplewick *Nottinghamshire*
Papworth Everard *Cambridgeshire*
Papworth St Agnes *Cambridgeshire*
Parbold *Lancashire*
Park Bridge *Gtr Manchester*
Park Gate *Hampshire*
Park Lane *Gtr Manchester*
Park Street *Hertfordshire*
Parkend *Gloucestershire*
Parkgate E Port *Cheshire*
Parklands *Gtr Manchester*
Parkmill *South Wales*
Parkstone *Dorset*
Parr Brow *Gtr Manchester*
Parr Fold *Gtr Manchester*
Parson Drove *Cambridgeshire*
Partington *Gtr Manchester*
Parton *Cumbria*
Partridge Green *Sussex*
Parwich *Derbyshire*
Passmands *Gtr Manchester*
Pateley Bridge *North Yorkshire*
Patricroft *Gtr Manchester*
Patrington *Humberside*
Patterdale *Cumbria*
Pattishall *Northamptonshire*
Paulerspury *Northamptonshire*
Paulton *Avon & Somerset*
Pavenham *Bedfordshire*
Peacehaven *Sussex*
Peak Dale *Derbyshire*
Peak Forest *Derbyshire*
Peakirk *Cambridgeshire*
Peasedown St John *Avon & Somerset*
Peaslake *Surrey*
Peasmarsh *Surrey*
Peasmarsh *Sussex*
Peatling Magna *Leicestershire*
Peatling Parva *Leicestershire*
Peckforton *Cheshire*
Peckham *Metropolitan*
Peckleton *Leicestershire*
Pedmore *West Midlands*
Peebles *Police Scotland*
Peel *Isle of Man*
Peel Green *Gtr Manchester*
Peel Hall *Gtr Manchester*
Pelton *Durham*

Pelynt *Devon & Cornwall*
Pemberton *Gtr Manchester*
Pembrey *Dyfed-Powys*
Pembroke *Dyfed-Powys*
Pembroke Dock *Dyfed-Powys*
Pembury *Kent*
Penalt *Gwent*
Penarth *South Wales*
Pencader *Dyfed-Powys*
Pencaerau *South Wales*
Penclawdd *South Wales*
Pencoed *South Wales*
Penderyn *South Wales*
Pendine *Dyfed-Powys*
Pendlebury *Gtr Manchester*
Pendleton *Gtr Manchester*
Pendre *South Wales*
Pengam *Gwent*
Pengam *South Wales*
Penge *Metropolitan*
Penhow *Gwent*
Penicuik *Police Scotland*
Penistone *South Yorkshire*
Penketh *Cheshire*
Penkhull *Staffordshire*
Penkridge *Staffordshire*
Penlan *South Wales*
Penllergaer *South Wales*
Penmachno *North Wales*
Penmaenmawr *North Wales*
Penn *Thames Valley*
Pennal *North Wales*
Pennard *South Wales*
Pennington *Hampshire*
Pennington *Gtr Manchester*
Pennington Green *Gtr Manchester*
Penparcau *Dyfed-Powys*
Penpedhairheol *Gwent*
Penpergwym *Gwent*
Penrhiwceiber *South Wales*
Penrhos *Gwent*
Penrhyn Bay *North Wales*
Penrhyndeudraeth *North Wales*
Penrith *Cumbria*
Penryn *Devon & Cornwall*
Pensarn *Dyfed-Powys*
Pensarn *North Wales*
Pensby *Merseyside*
Pensford *Avon & Somerset*
Penshurst *Kent*
Pensilva *Devon & Cornwall*
Penton Hook *Surrey*
Pentraeth *North Wales*
Pentre Broughton *North Wales*
Pentrefoelas *North Wales*
Pentremeurig *South Wales*
Pentrich *Derbyshire*
Pentridge *Dorset*
Pentwynmawr *Gwent*
Pentyrch *South Wales*
Penwortham *Lancashire*
Penybank *Dyfed-Powys*
Penybontfawr *Dyfed-Powys*
Penycae *North Wales*
Penyffordd *North Wales*
Penygarn *Gwent*
Penygraig *South Wales*
Penygroes *Dyfed-Powys*
Penygroes *North Wales*
Penylan *South Wales*
Penyrheol (Caerphilly) *South Wales*
Penyrheol (Swansea) *South Wales*
Penywaun *South Wales*
Penzance *Devon & Cornwall*
Peover Inferior *Cheshire*
Peover Superior *Cheshire*
Peperharrow *Surrey*
Peppard *Thames Valley*

Pepperstock *Hertfordshire*
Peppsal End *Hertfordshire*
Perranporth *Devon & Cornwall*
Perry Green *Hertfordshire*
Pershore *West Mercia*
Perth *Police Scotland*
Peterborough *Cambridgeshire*
Peterchurch *West Mercia*
Peterhead *Police Scotland*
Peterlee *Durham*
Petersfield *Hampshire*
Peterston *South Wales*
Peterstone Wentlooge *Gwent*
Petham *Kent*
Petworth *Sussex*
Pevensey Bay *Sussex*
Pewsey *Wiltshire*
Philips Park *Gtr Manchester*
Phillipstown *South Wales*
Piccotts End *Hertfordshire*
Pickering *North Yorkshire*
Pickmere *Cheshire*
Pickwell *Leicestershire*
Pickworth *Leicestershire*
Picton *Cheshire*
Picton *North Yorkshire*
Piddlehinton *Dorset*
Piddletrenthide *Dorset*
Pidley-cum-Fenton
    Cambridgeshire
Piercebridge *Durham*
Pilgrims Hatch *Essex*
Pill *Gwent*
Pill *Avon & Somerset*
Pilling *Lancashire*
Pilning *Avon & Somerset*
Pilsdon *Dorset*
Pilsgate *Cambridgeshire*
Pilsley (Alfreton) *Derbyshire*
Pilsley (Buxton) *Derbyshire*
Pilton *Leicestershire*
Pilton *Northamptonshire*
Pilton *Avon & Somerset*
Pimperne *Dorset*
Pinchbeck *Lincolnshire*
Pinhole *Gtr Manchester*
Pinner *Metropolitan*
Pinvin *West Mercia*
Pinxton *Derbyshire*
Piper Clough *Gtr Manchester*
Pipers End *Hertfordshire*
Pirbright *Surrey*
Pirton *Hertfordshire*
Pitch Place *Surrey*
Pitlochry *Police Scotland*
Pitsea *Essex*
Pitses *Gtr Manchester*
Pitsford *Northamptonshire*
Pittshill *Staffordshire*
Plains *Police Scotland*
Plaistow *Metropolitan*
Plank Lane *Gtr Manchester*
Plasycoed *Gwent*
Platt *Kent*
Platt Bridge *Gtr Manchester*
Platts Common *South Yorkshire*
Plawsworth *Durham*
Plaxtol *Kent*
Plean *Police Scotland*
Pleasley *Derbyshire*
Pleasley Hill *Nottinghamshire*
Plompton *North Yorkshire*
Pluckley *Kent*
Plumbridge *PSNI*
Plumley *Cheshire*
Plumpton *Cumbria*
Plumpton *Sussex*
Plumstead *Metropolitan*
Plungar *Leicestershire*

Plymouth *Devon & Cornwall*
Plymstock *Devon & Cornwall*
Pochin *Gwent*
Pock Nook *Gtr Manchester*
Pockington *Humberside*
Podington *Bedfordshire*
Polebrook *Northamptonshire*
Polegate *Sussex*
Polesworth *Warwickshire*
Pollington *Humberside*
Pollokshaws *Police Scotland*
Polmont *Police Scotland*
Polruan *Devon & Cornwall*
Pomeroy *PSNI*
Ponders End *Metropolitan*
Ponsanooth *Devon & Cornwall*
Pontardawe *South Wales*
Pontardulais *South Wales*
Pontargothi *Dyfed-Powys*
Pontcanna *South Wales*
Pontefract *West Yorkshire*
Ponteland *Northumbria*
Pontesbury *West Mercia*
Ponthir *Gwent*
Pontllanfraith *Gwent*
Pontlliw *South Wales*
Pontlottyn *South Wales*
Pontnewydd *Gwent*
Pontnewynydd *Gwent*
Pontrhondda *South Wales*
Pontrhydycuff *South Wales*
Pontrhydyfen *South Wales*
Pontrhydyrun *Gwent*
Pontyates *Dyfed-Powys*
Pontyberem *Dyfed-Powys*
Pontyclun *South Wales*
Pontycymmer *South Wales*
Pontygwaith *South Wales*
Pontypool *Gwent*
Pontypridd *South Wales*
Pool *Devon & Cornwall*
Pool *West Yorkshire*
Poole *Cheshire*
Poole *Dorset*
Pooley Bridge *Cumbria*
Poolsbrook *Derbyshire*
Poplars Green *Hertfordshire*
Poringland *Norfolk*
Porlock *Avon & Somerset*
Port Bannatyne *Police Scotland*
Port Ellen *Police Scotland*
Port Erin *Isle of Man*
Port Eynon *South Wales*
Port Glasgow *Police Scotland*
Port Isaac *Devon & Cornwall*
Port St Mary *Isle of Man*
Port Sunlight *Mersey*
Port Talbot *South Wales*
Port Tennant *South Wales*
Portadown *PSNI*
Portaferry *PSNI*
Portchester *Hampshire*
Portdinorwic *North Wales*
Portesham *Dorset*
Portglenone *PSNI*
Port *South Wales*
Porthcawl *South Wales*
Porthleven *Devon & Cornwall*
Porthyrhyd *Dyfed-Powys*
Portishead *Avon & Somerset*
Portland *Dorset*
Portmadoc *North Wales*
Portobello *Police Scotland*
Portpatrick *Police Scotland*
Portree *Police Scotland*
Portrush *PSNI*
Portscatho *Devon & Cornwall*
Portskewet *Gwent*
Portsmouth *Hampshire*

Portsoy *Police Scotland*
Portstewart *PSNI*
Portswood *Hampshire*
Portwilliam *Police Scotland*
Postern *Derbyshire*
Pott Shrigley *Cheshire*
Potten End *Hertfordshire*
Potter Heigham *Norfolk*
Potterne *Wiltshire*
Potters Bar *Hertfordshire*
Potters Heath *Hertfordshire*
Potters Marston *Leicestershire*
Potterspury *Northamptonshire*
Potto *North Yorkshire*
Potton *Bedfordshire*
Poulton *Gloucestershire*
Poulton *Lancashire*
Poulton *Merseyside*
Poulton-with-Fearnhead *Cheshire*
Poundswick *Gtr Manchester*
Povey Cross *Surrey*
Powburn *Northumbria*
Powerstock *Dorset*
Powick *West Mercia*
Pownall Green *Gtr Manchester*
Poxwell *Dorset*
Poyntington *Dorset*
Poynton-with-Worth *Cheshire*
Preesall *Lancashire*
Prenton *Merseyside*
Prescot *Merseyside*
Prestatyn *North Wales*
Prestbury *Cheshire*
Presteigne *Dyfed-Powys*
Prestlee *Gtr Manchester*
Preston *Dorset*
Preston *Hertfordshire*
Preston *Kent*
Preston *Lancashire*
Preston *Leicestershire*
Preston Brook *Cheshire*
Preston Capes *Northamptonshire*
Preston Candover *Hampshire*
Preston Under Scar *North Yorks*
Prestonpans *Police Scotland*
Prestwich *Gtr Manchester*
Prestwick Park *Gtr Manchester*
Prestwick *Police Scotland*
Prestwold *Leicestershire*
Prestwood *Thames Valley*
Prickwillow *Cambridgeshire*
Priestcliffe *Derbyshire*
Primethorpe *Leicestershire*
Princes Risborough *Thames Valley*
Princetown *Devon & Cornwall*
Prior's Heys *Cheshire*
Probus *Devon & Cornwall*
Prudhoe *Northumbria*
Puckeridge *Hertfordshire*
Puddington *Cheshire*
Puddletown *Dorset*
Pudds Cross *Hertfordshire*
Pudsey *West Yorkshire*
Pulborough *Sussex*
Pulford *Cheshire*
Pulham *Dorset*
Pulloxhill *Bedfordshire*
Pulrose *Isle of Man*
Pumsaint *Dyfed-Powys*
Puncknowle *Dorset*
Puriton *Avon & Somerset*
Purleigh *Essex*
Purse Caundle *Dorset*
Purston *West Yorkshire*
Purton *Wiltshire*
Pusey *Thames Valley*
Putney *Metropolitan*
Putnoe *Bedfordshire*

Puttenham *Hertfordshire*
Puttenham *Surrey*
Pwlldu *Gwent*
Pwllheli *North Wales*
Pyle *South Wales*
Pymore *Cambridgeshire*
Pyrford *Surrey*
Pytchley *Northamptonshire*
Pyworthy *Devon & Cornwall*
Quadring *Lincolnshire*
Quainton *Thames Valley*
Quarndon *Derbyshire*
Quarrington Hill *Durham*
Queen Adelaide *Cambridgeshire*
Queenborough *Kent*
Queensbury *West Yorkshire*
Queensferry *Police Scotland*
Queens Road *West Midlands*
Quenby *Leicestershire*
Queniborough *Leicestershire*
Quick Bridge *Gtr Manchester*
Quickwood *Gtr Manchester*
Quinton *West Midlands*
Quinton *Northamptonshire*
Quorndon *Leicestershire*
Rabley Heath *Hertfordshire*
Raby *Merseyside*
Rachub *North Wales*
Radbourne *Derbyshire*
Radcliffe-on-Trent *Nottinghamshire*
Radcliffe *Gtr Manchester*
Radford Semele *Warwickshire*
Radlett *Hertfordshire*
Radstock *Avon & Somerset*
Radstone *Northamptonshire*
Radwell *Hertfordshire*
Radyr *South Wales*
Ragdale *Leicestershire*
Raglan *Gwent*
Rain Shore *Gtr Manchester*
Rainford *Merseyside*
Rainham *Metropolitan*
Rainow *Cheshire*
Rainsough *Gtr Manchester*
Rainton *North Yorkshire*
Rainworth *Nottinghamshire*
Rake *Sussex*
Rakewood *Gtr Manchester*
Ralston *Police Scotland*
Rame *Devon & Cornwall*
Rampisham *Dorset*
Rampside *Cumbria*
Rampton *Cambridgeshire*
Ramsbottom *Gtr Manchester*
Ramsbury *Wiltshire*
Ramsey *Essex*
Ramsey *Cambridgeshire*
Ramsey Forty-Foot *Cambridgeshire*
Ramsey Heights *Cambridgeshire*
Ramsey Mereside *Cambridgeshire*
Ramsgate *Kent*
Ramsgill *North Yorkshire*
Ramsnest *Surrey*
Ranby *Nottinghamshire*
Randalstown *PSNI*
Ranmore *Surrey*
Ranskill *Nottinghamshire*
Raploch *Police Scotland*
Raskelf *North Yorkshire*
Rassau *Gwent*
Rastrick *West Yorkshire*
Ratby *Leicestershire*
Ratcliffe-on-the-Wreake *Leics*
Ratcliffe Culey *Leicestershire*
Rathfriland *PSNI*
Rattray *Police Scotland*
Raunds *Northamptonshire*

Ravenglass *Cumbria*
Ravensdale Park *Derbyshire*
Ravensden *Bedfordshire*
Ravensthorpe *Northamptonshire*
Ravenstone *Leicestershire*
Ravenstonedale *Cumbria*
Ravensworth *North Yorkshire*
Rawcliffe *Humberside*
Rawcliffe *North Yorkshire*
Rawdon *West Yorkshire*
Rawmarsh *South Yorkshire*
Rawtenstall *Lancashire*
Raydon *Suffolk*
Rayleigh *Essex*
Rayne *Essex*
Raynham *Norfolk*
Reach *Cambridgeshire*
Reading *Thames Valley*
Rearsby *Leicestershire*
Reay *Police Scotland*
Red Lumb *Gtr Manchester*
Red Moss *Gtr Manchester*
Red Rook *Gtr Manchester*
Redbourn *Hertfordshire*
Redcar *Cleveland*
Redding *Police Scotland*
Reddish *Gtr Manchester*
Reddish Vale *Gtr Manchester*
Redditch *West Mercia*
Redhill *Avon & Somerset*
Redhill *Surrey*
Redland *Avon & Somerset*
Redmile *Leicestershire*
Redmire *North Yorkshire*
Rednal *West Mercia*
Redruth *Devon & Cornwall*
Redvales *Gtr Manchester*
Redwick *Gwent*
Reed *Hertfordshire*
Reedham *Norfolk*
Reepham *Norfolk*
Reeth *North Yorkshire*
Reigate *Surrey*
Remenham *Thames Valley*
Renfrew *Police Scotland*
Renishaw *Derbyshire*
Repton *Derbyshire*
Resolven *South Wales*
Retford *Nottinghamshire*
Rettendon *Essex*
Reynoldston *South Wales*
Rhayader *Dyfed-Powys*
Rhiconich *Police Scotland*
Rhigos *South Wales*
Rhiwbina *South Wales*
Rhiwderin *Gwent*
Rhodes *Gtr Manchester*
Rhoose *South Wales*
Rhos *South Wales*
Rhos-on-Sea *North Wales*
Rhosddu *North Wales*
Rhosllanerchrugog *North Wales*
Rhosneigr *North Wales*
Rhossilli *South Wales*
Rhostyllen *North Wales*
Rhosymedre *North Wales*
Rhuallt *North Wales*
Rhuddlan *North Wales*
Rhydymwyn *North Wales*
Rhyl *North Wales*
Rhymney *Gwent*
Ribchester *Lancashire*
Richmond *North Yorkshire*
Richmond-on-Thames *Metropolitan*
Rickmansworth *Hertfordshire*
Riddings *Derbyshire*
Ridge *Hertfordshire*
Ridge Hill *Gtr Manchester*

Ridgeway *Derbyshire*
Ridgmont *Bedfordshire*
Riding Mill *Northumbria*
Ridley *Cheshire*
Ridlington *Leicestershire*
Rievaulx *North Yorkshire*
Rigside *Police Scotland*
Rillington *North Yorkshire*
Ringland *Gwent*
Ringley *Gtr Manchester*
Ringley Brow *Gtr Manchester*
Ringmer *Sussex*
Rings End *Cambridgeshire*
Ringshall *Hertfordshire*
Ringstead *Northamptonshire*
Ringway *Gtr Manchester*
Ringwood *Hampshire*
Ripley *Derbyshire*
Ripley *Surrey*
Ripley *North Yorkshire*
Ripon *North Yorkshire*
Ripple *West Mercia*
Ripponden *West Yorkshire*
Risby *Suffolk*
Risca *Gwent*
Riseley *Bedfordshire*
Rising Bridge *Lancashire*
Risinghurst *Thames Valley*
Risley *Derbyshire*
Riverside *South Wales*
Rixton *Cheshire*
Rixton-with-Glazebrook *Cheshire*
Roade *Northamptonshire*
Roadhead *Cumbria*
Roath *South Wales*
Robertsbridge *Sussex*
Robin Hood *West Yorkshire*
Robin Hood's Bay *North Yorkshire*
Rocester *Staffordshire*
Rochdale *Gtr Manchester*
Rochester *Kent*
Rochester Row *Metropolitan*
Rochford *Essex*
Rock *West Mercia*
Rock Ferry *Merseyside*
Rock Hill *West Mercia*
Rockcliffe *Cumbria*
Rockfield *Gwent*
Rockingham *Northamptonshire*
Rockland-St-Mary *Norfolk*
Rodborough *Gloucestershire*
Rode Heath *Cheshire*
Roden Street *PSNI*
Rodley *West Yorkshire*
Rodmel *Sussex*
Rodsley *Derbyshire*
Roe Cross *Gtr Manchester*
Roe Green *Hertfordshire*
Roe Green *Gtr Manchester*
Roebuck Low *Gtr Manchester*
Rogerstone *Gwent*
Roggiett *Gwent*
Rollerston *Leicestershire*
Rolvenden *Kent*
Romaldkirk *Durham*
Romford *Metropolitan*
Romiley *Gtr Manchester*
Romsey *Hampshire*
Romsley *West Mercia*
Rooley Moor *Gtr Manchester*
Rope *Cheshire*
Ropley *Hampshire*
Rosehearty *Police Scotland*
Rose Hill *Gtr Manchester*
Rosehill *Northumbria*
Rosemount *PSNI*
Rosliston *Derbyshire*
Ross-on-Wye *West Mercia*

Rossett *North Wales*
Rossington *South Yorkshire*
Rosslea *PSNI*
Rostherne *Cheshire*
Roston *Derbyshire*
Rosyth *Police Scotland*
Rothbury *Northumbria*
Rotherby *Leicestershire*
Rotherham *South Yorks*
Rotherhithe *Metropolitan*
Rotherstorpe *Northamptonshire*
Rothes *Police Scotland*
Rothesay *Police Scotland*
Rothley *Leicestershire*
Rothwell *Northamptonshire*
Rothwell *West Yorkshire*
Rougham *Suffolk*
Roundhay *West Yorkshire*
Rowarth *Derbyshire*
Rowhedge *Essex*
Rowland *Derbyshire*
Rowlands Castle *Hampshire*
Rowlatts Hill *Leicestershire*
Rowledge *Surrey*
Rowley Regis *West Midlands*
Rownhams *Hampshire*
Rowsley *Derbyshire*
Rowstock *Thames Valley*
Rowton *Cheshire*
Roxbury *Gtr Manchester*
Roxby (Ripon) *North Yorkshire*
Roxby (Whitby) *North Yorkshire*
Roxwell *Essex*
Roydon *Essex*
Roydon *Gtr Manchester*
Royle Green *Gtr Manchester*
Royley *Gtr Manchester*
Royston *Hertfordshire*
Royston *South Yorkshire*
Royton *Gtr Manchester*
Ruabon *North Wales*
Ruardean *Gloucestershire*
Rubery *West Mercia*
Rudby *North Yorks*
Ruddington *Nottinghamshire*
Rudgwick *Sussex*
Rudheath *Cheshire*
Rudry *Gwent*
Rufford *Lancashire*
Rufford *North Yorkshire*
Rufford *Nottinghamshire*
Rugby *Warwickshire*
Rugeley *Staffordshire*
Ruins *Gtr Manchester*
Ruinslip *Metropolitan*
Rumney *South Wales*
Runcorn *Cheshire*
Runfold *Surrey*
Runton *Norfolk*
Rushden *Hertfordshire*
Rushden *Northamptonshire*
Rushmere *Suffolk*
Rusholme *Gtr Manchester*
Rushton *Cheshire*
Rushton *Northamptonshire*
Ruskington *Lincolnshire*
Ruspidge *Gloucestershire*
Rustington *Sussex*
Rutherglen *Police Scotland*
Ruthin *North Wales*
Ryde *Hampshire*
Rye *Sussex*
Ryhall *Leicestershire*
Ryhill *West Yorkshire*
Ryme Intrinseca *Dorset*
Ryton-on-Dunsmore *Warwickshire*
Sabden *Lancashire*
Sacombe *Hertfordshire*

Sacriston *Durham*
Sadberge *Durham*
Saddington *Leicestershire*
Saddleworth *Gtr Manchester*
Saffron Lane *Leicestershire*
Saffron Walden *Essex*
Sageston *Dyfed-Powys*
Saighton *Cheshire*
St Agnes *Devon & Cornwall*
St Albans *Hertfordshire*
St Andrews *Police Scotland*
St Annes *Lancashire*
St Anns *Nottinghamshire*
St Ann's Road *Metropolitan*
St Arvans *Gwent*
St Asaph *North Wales*
St Athan *South Wales*
St Austell *Devon & Cornwall*
St Bees *Cumbria*
St Blazey *Devon & Cornwall*
St Boswells *Police Scotland*
St Briavels *Gloucestershire*
St Brides Wentlooge *Gwent*
St Clears *Dyfed-Powys*
St Columb *Devon & Cornwall*
St Cyrus *Police Scotland*
St Davids *Dyfed-Powys*
St Day *Devon & Cornwall*
St Dennis *Devon & Cornwall*
St Dials *Gwent*
St George *Avon & Somerset*
St Georges Hill *Surrey*
St Germans *Devon & Cornwall*
St Fagans *South Wales*
St Fillans *Police Scotland*
St Helens *Hampshire*
St Helens *Merseyside*
St Ippolytts *Hertfordshire*
St Ives *Cambridgeshire*
St Ives *Devon & Cornwall*
St Ives *Dorset*
St Johns *Surrey*
St John's (Colchester) *Essex*
St John's Wood *Metropolitan*
St Julians *Gwent*
St Just *Devon & Cornwall*
St Keverne *Devon & Cornwall*
St Kew *Devon & Cornwall*
St Leonards *Dorset*
St Margaret's *Kent*
St Margaret's Hope *Police Scotland*
St Martins *Cambridgeshire*
St Martins *North Yorkshire*
St Martins *West Mercia*
St Mary Cray *Metropolitan*
St Mary-in-the-Marsh *Kent*
St Maughans *Gwent*
St Mawes *Devon & Cornwall*
St Mellons *South Wales*
St Michaels *Lancashire*
St Minver *Devon & Cornwall*
St Monance *Police Scotland*
St Neot *Devon & Cornwall*
St Neots *Cambridgeshire*
St Nicholas *Kent*
St Nicholas *South Wales*
St Ninians *Police Scotland*
St Pauls Walden *Hertfordshire*
St Stephens *Devon & Cornwall*
St Thomas *South Wales*
St Twynnells *Dyfed-Powys*
St Weonards *West Mercia*
Saddleworth *Gtr Manchester*
Saintfield *PSNI*
Salcombe *Devon & Cornwall*
Sale *Gtr Manchester*
Salem *Gtr Manchester*
Salen (Mull) *Police Scotland*

Salford *Gtr Manchester*
Salfords *Surrey*
Saline *Police Scotland*
Salisbury *Wiltshire*
Salsburgh *Police Scotland*
Saltash *Devon & Cornwall*
Saltburn *Cleveland*
Saltby *Leicestershire*
Saltcoats *Police Scotland*
Saltford *Avon & Somerset*
Saltney *North Wales*
Salton *North Yorkshire*
Samlesbury *Lancashire*
Sandbach *Cheshire*
Sandbank *Police Scotland*
Sandbanks *Dorset*
Sandbeds *West Yorkshire*
Sandfields *South Wales*
Sandford *Thames Valley*
Sandford Hill *Staffordshire*
Sandford Oreas *Dorset*
Sandhead *Police Scotland*
Sandhills *Surrey*
Sandhurst *Kent*
Sand Hutton (Flaxton) *North Yorks*
Sand Hutton (Thirsk) *North Yorks*
Sandiacre *Derbyshire*
Sandon *Hertfordshire*
Sandown *Hampshire*
Sandridge *Hertfordshire*
Sandringham *Norfolk*
Sandwell *West Midlands*
Sandwich *Kent*
Sandy *Bedfordshire*
Sandy Lane *West Yorkshire*
Sandy Lane *Wiltshire*
Sandycroft *North Wales*
Sandyford *Staffordshire*
Sandygate *South Yorkshire*
Sankey *Cheshire*
Sanquhar *Police Scotland*
Sapcote *Leicestershire*
Sapperton *Gloucestershire*
Saracen *Police Scotland*
Sarisbury *Hampshire*
Sarn *North Wales*
Sarn *South Wales*
Sarratt *Hertfordshire*
Sauchie *Police Scotland*
Saughall *Cheshire*
Saughall Massie *Merseyside*
Saundersfoot *Dyfed-Powys*
Sawbridgeworth *Hertfordshire*
Sawley *Derbyshire*
Sawley *North Yorkshire*
Sawston *Cambridgeshire*
Sawtry *Cambridgeshire*
Saxby *Leicestershire*
Saxelby *Leicestershire*
Saxilby *Lincolnshire*
Saxmundham *Suffolk*
Saxon Street *Cambridgeshire*
Scalby *North Yorkshire*
Scaldwell *Northamptonshire*
Scalford *Leicestershire*
Scalloway *Police Scotland*
Scamblesby *Lincolnshire*
Scampton *Lincolnshire*
Scarborough *North Yorkshire*
Scarcliffe *Derbyshire*
Scarcroft *West Yorkshire*
Scarisbrick *Lancashire*
Scawthorpe *South Yorkshire*
Scholes (Dewsbury) *West Yorkshire*
Scholes (Tadcaster) *West Yorkshire*

School Aycliffe *Durham*
Scissett *West Yorkshire*
Scone *Police Scotland*
Scopwick *Lincolnshire*
Scorton *North Yorkshire*
Scotby *Cumbria*
Scotch Corner *North Yorkshire*
Scotland End *Gtr Manchester*
Scotlandwell *Police Scotland*
Scotsgap *Northumbria*
Scotter *Lincolnshire*
Scottow *Norfolk*
Scouthead *Gtr Manchester*
Scraptoft *Leicestershire*
Scremerston *Northumbria*
Scriven *North Yorkshire*
Scropton *Derbyshire*
Scruton *North Yorkshire*
Scunthorpe *Humberside*
Seaborough *Dorset*
Seacombe *Merseyside*
Seacroft *West Yorkshire*
Seaford *Sussex*
Seaforth *Merseyside*
Seagrave *Leicestershire*
Seaham *Durham*
Seaham Harbour *Durham*
Seahouses *Northumbria*
Seal *Kent*
Sealand *North Wales*
Seale *Surrey*
Seamer (Scarborough) *North Yorks*
Seamer (Stokesley) *North Yorks*
Seasalter *Kent*
Seascale *Cumbria*
Seaton *Cumbria*
Seaton Delaval *Northumbria*
Seaton (Exmouth) *Devon & Cornwall*
Seaton (St Austell) *Devon & Cornwall*
Seaton *Leicestershire*
Seaton Sluice *Northumbria*
Seaview *Hampshire*
Seavington St Mary *Avon & Somerset*
Sebastopol *Gwent*
Sebergham *Cumbria*
Sedbergh *Cumbria*
Sedgeberrow *West Mercia*
Sedgefield *Durham*
Sedgley *West Midlands*
Sedgley Park *Gtr Manchester*
Sedlescombe *Sussex*
Seedfield *Gtr Manchester*
Seedley *Gtr Manchester*
Seend *Wiltshire*
Seghill *Northumbria*
Selborne *Hampshire*
Selby *North Yorkshire*
Selkirk *Police Scotland*
Sellindge *Kent*
Selling *Kent*
Selsey *Sussex*
Selston *Nottinghamshire*
Send *Surrey*
Senghenydd *Gwent*
Sennen *Devon & Cornwall*
Sennybridge *Dyfed-Powys*
Settle *North Yorkshire*
Sevenoaks *Kent*
Seven Sisters *South Wales*
Severn Stoke *West Mercia*
Severn Tunnel Junction *Gwent*
Sewstern *Leicestershire*
Shackleford *Surrey*
Shackcliffe *Gtr Manchester*
Shackerstone *Leicestershire*

Shadow Moss *Gtr Manchester*
Shadwell *West Yorkshire*
Shaftesbury *Dorset*
Shafton *South Yorkshire*
Shakerley *Gtr Manchester*
Shalbourne *Wiltshire*
Shaldon *Devon & Cornwall*
Shalford *Essex*
Shalford *Surrey*
Shamley Green *Surrey*
Shangton *Leicestershire*
Shanklin *Hampshire*
Shap *Cumbria*
Shapwick *Dorset*
Shard End *West Midlands*
Shardlow *Derbyshire*
Sharlston *West Yorkshire*
Sharnbrook *Bedfordshire*
Sharnford *Leicestershire*
Sharpness *Gloucestershire*
Sharston Green *Gtr Manchester*
Sharston Mount *Gtr Manchester*
Shatterford *West Mercia*
Shatton *Derbyshire*
Shavington *Cheshire*
Shaw *Gtr Manchester*
Shaw Moor *Gtr Manchester*
Shaw Side *Gtr Manchester*
Shawclough *Gtr Manchester*
Shawell *Leicestershire*
Shawfield *Gtr Manchester*
Shawsburn *Police Scotland*
Shawbury *West Mercia*
Shearsby *Leicestershire*
Shebbear *Devon & Cornwall*
Shedfield *Hampshire*
Sheepy Magna *Leicestershire*
Sheepy Parva *Leicestershire*
Sheerness *Kent*
Sheffield *South Yorks*
Shefford *Bedfordshire*
Shefford *Thames Valley*
Sheldon *Derbyshire*
Sheldon *West Midlands*
Shelf *West Yorkshire*
Shelley *West Yorkshire*
Shellingford *Thames Valley*
Shelton *Staffordshire*
Shelver *Gtr Manchester*
Shenley *Hertfordshire*
Shenton *Leicestershire*
Shepherds Bush *Metropolitan*
Shepherdswell *Kent*
Shepley *West Yorkshire*
Shepperton *Metropolitan*
Shepreth *Cambridgeshire*
Shepshed *Leicestershire*
Shepton Mallet *Avon & Somerset*
Sherborne *Dorset*
Sherborne *Hampshire*
Sherburn *North Yorkshire*
Sherburn-in-Elmet *North Yorks*
Shere *Surrey*
Sherfield-on-Lodden *Hampshire*
Sheriff Hutton *North Yorkshire*
Sheringham *Norfolk*
Sherringham Avenue *Northumbria*
Sherston *Wiltshire*
Shettleston *Police Scotland*
Shevington *Gtr Manchester*
Shevington Moor *Gtr Manchester*
Shevington Vale *Gtr Manchester*
Shieldhall *Police Scotland*
Shifnal *West Mercia*
Shilbottle *Northumbria*
Shildon *Durham*
Shillingford *Thames Valley*
Shillingstone *Dorset*
Shillington *Bedfordshire*

Shilton *Warwickshire*
Shinfield *Thames Valley*
Shingay-cum-Wendy *Cambridgeshire*
Shiplake *Thames Valley*
Shipley *Derbyshire*
Shipley *West Yorkshire*
Shipley Bridge *Surrey*
Shippea Hill *Cambridgeshire*
Shipston-on-Stour *Warwickshire*
Shipton *North Yorkshire*
Shipton Bellinger *Hampshire*
Shipton Gorge *Dorset*
Shipton-under-Wychwood *Thames Valley*
Shirebrook *Derbyshire*
Shirenewton *Gwent*
Shireoaks *Nottinghamshire*
Shirland *Derbyshire*
Shirley *Derbyshire*
Shirley *Hampshire*
Shirley *West Midlands*
Shoby *Leicestershire*
Shocklach Oviatt *Cheshire*
Shoeburyness *Essex*
Shooters Hill *Metropolitan*
Shore *Gtr Manchester*
Shoreham *Kent*
Shoreham *Sussex*
Shorne *Kent*
Shotley *Suffolk*
Shotley Bridge *Durham*
Shottermill *Surrey*
Shottle *Derbyshire*
Shotts *Police Scotland*
Shotwick *Cheshire*
Shotwick Park *Cheshire*
Shouldham *Norfolk*
Shrewsbury *West Mercia*
Shrewton *Wiltshire*
Shrivenham *Thames Valley*
Shrub End *Essex*
Shudy Camps *Cambridgeshire*
Shutlanger *Northamptonshire*
Shuttlewood *Derbyshire*
Shuttleworth *Gtr Manchester*
Sibbertoft *Northamptonshire*
Sibsey *Lincolnshire*
Sibson *Leicestershire*
Sibson-cum-Stibbington *Cambs*
Sibton *Suffolk*
Sicklinghall *North Yorkshire*
Sidcup *Metropolitan*
Siddick *Cumbria*
Siddington *Cheshire*
Side-of-the-Moor *Gtr Manchester*
Sidebottomfold *Gtr Manchester*
Sidemoor *West Mercia*
Sidford *Devon & Cornwall*
Sidlesham *Sussex*
Sidlow Bridge *Surrey*
Sidmouth *Devon & Cornwall*
Sigglesthorne *Humberside*
Silchester *Hampshire*
Sileby *Leicestershire*
Silecroft *Cumbria*
Silloth *Cumbria*
Silkstone *South Yorkshire*
Silpho *North Yorkshire*
Silsden *West Yorkshire*
Silsoe *Bedfordshire*
Silton *Dorset*
Silver End *Essex*
Silverdale & Warton *Lancashire*
Silverstone *Northamptonshire*
Silverton *Devon & Cornwall*
Simistar *Gtr Manchester*
Simonstone *Lancashire*
Sinfin *Derbyshire*

Sinfin Moor *Derbyshire*
Singleton *Lancashire*
Singleton *Sussex*
Sinnington *North Yorkshire*
Sittingbourne *Kent*
Six Bells *Gwent*
Six Mile Bottom *Cambridgeshire*
Skeffington *Leicestershire*
Skegby *Nottinghamshire*
Skegness *Lincolnshire*
Skellingthorpe *Lincolnshire*
Skellow *South Yorkshire*
Skelmanthorpe *West Yorkshire*
Skelmersdale *Lancashire*
Skelmorlie *Police Scotland*
Skelton *Cleveland*
Skelton (Ripon) *North Yorkshire*
Skelton (York) *North Yorkshire*
Skene *Police Scotland*
Sketchley *Leicestershire*
Sketty *South Wales*
Skewen *South Wales*
Skinningrove *Cleveland*
Skipton *North Yorkshire*
Skipton-on-Swale *North Yorkshire*
Skirbeck *Lincolnshire*
Skirlaugh *Humberside*
Slackcote *Gtr Manchester*
Slaidburn *Lancashire*
Slaithwaite *West Yorkshire*
Slaley *Northumbria*
Slamannan *Police Scotland*
Slapton *Northamptonshire*
Slattocks *Gtr Manchester*
Slawston *Leicestershire*
Sleaford *Lincolnshire*
Slebech *Dyfed-Powys*
Sleights *North Yorkshire*
Slimbridge *Gloucestershire*
Slindon *Sussex*
Slinfold *Sussex*
Slingsby *North Yorkshire*
Slip End *Bedfordshire*
Slipton *Northamptonshire*
Slough *Thames Valley*
Smallbridge *Gtr Manchester*
Smalley *Derbyshire*
Smallfield *Surrey*
Smallford *Hertfordshire*
Smallthorne *Staffordshire*
Smallwood *Cheshire*
Smarden *Kent*
Smedley *Gtr Manchester*
Smeeth *Kent*
Smeeton Westerby *Leicestershire*
Smerrill *Derbyshire*
Smethwick *West Midlands*
Smisby *Derbyshire*
Smithfield *Cumbria*
Smithy Bridge *Gtr Manchester*
Smithy Green *Gtr Manchester*
Snailwell *Cambridgeshire*
Snainton *North Yorkshire*
Snarestone *Leicestershire*
Snatchwood *Gwent*
Sneinton Hermitage *Nottinghamshire*
Snelson *Cheshire*
Snelston *Derbyshire*
Snettisham *Norfolk*
Sneyd Green *Staffordshire*
Snibston *Leicestershire*
Snitterfield *Warwickshire*
Snitterton *Derbyshire*
Snodland *Kent*
Snow Hill *City of London*
Soham *Cambridgeshire*
Solihull *West Midlands*
Solva *Dyfed-Powys*

Somerby *Leicestershire*
Somercotes *Derbyshire*
Somerford *Cheshire*
Somerford *Dorset*
Somerford Booths *Cheshire*
Somerleyton *Suffolk*
Somersal Herbert *Derbyshire*
Somersham *Cambridgeshire*
Somerton *Avon & Somerset*
Sonning Common *Thames Valley*
Soothill *West Yorkshire*
Sopley *Hampshire*
Sound *Cheshire*
Southall *Metropolitan*
Southam *Warwickshire*
Southampton *Hampshire*
Southborough *Kent*
Southbourne *Dorset*
Southbourne *Sussex*
Southend-on-Sea *Essex*
Southend *Police Scotland*
Southerndown *South Wales*
Southfleet *Kent*
Southgate *Metropolitan*
Southill *Bedfordshire*
Southminster *Essex*
Southorpe *Cambridgeshire*
Southowram *West Yorkshire*
Southport *Merseyside*
Southsea *Hampshire*
Southsea *North Wales*
Southwark *Metropolitan*
Southwater *Sussex*
Southwell *Nottinghamshire*
Southwick *Hampshire*
Southwick *Northamptonshire*
Southwold *Suffolk*
Sowerby Bridge *West Yorkshire*
Sowood *West Yorkshire*
Soyland *West Yorkshire*
South Anston *South Yorkshire*
South Bank *Cleveland*
South Brent *Devon & Cornwall*
South Cave *Humberside*
South Cerney *Gloucestershire*
South Clifton *Nottinghamshire*
South Creake *Norfolk*
South Croxton *Leicestershire*
South Elmsall *West Yorkshire*
South Godstone *Surrey*
South Hiendley *West Yorkshire*
South Holmwood *Surrey*
South Killingholme *Humberside*
South Kilworth *Leicestershire*
South Kirkby *West Yorkshire*
South Leverton *Nottinghamshire*
South Luffenham *Leicestershire*
South Merstham *Surrey*
South Milford *North Yorkshire*
South Molton *Devon & Cornwall*
South Normanton *Derbyshire*
South Norwood *Metropolitan*
South Ockendon *Essex*
South Perrot *Dorset*
South Petherton *Avon & Somerset*
South Queensferry *Police Scotland*
South Reddish *Gtr Manchester*
South Shields *Northumbria*
South Walsham *Norfolk*
South Wigston *Leicestershire*
South Wingfield *Derbyshire*
South Zeal *Devon & Cornwall*
Sowerby *North Yorkshire*
Sowerby Bridge *West Yorkshire*
Spalding *Lincolnshire*
Spaldwick *Cambridgeshire*
Sparkhill *West Midlands*
Sparsholt *Hampshire*
Speanbridge *Police Scotland*

Spelthorne *Surrey*
Spencers Wood *Thames Valley*
Spennymoor *Durham*
Spetchley *West Mercia*
Spetisbury *Dorset*
Spexhall *Suffolk*
Spilsby *Lincolnshire*
Spinkhill *Derbyshire*
Spital *Merseyside*
Spittalfield *Police Scotland*
Splott *South Wales*
Spofforth *North Yorkshire*
Spondon *Derbyshire*
Spotland Bridge *Gtr Manchester*
Spratton *Northamptonshire*
Springburn *Police Scotland*
Springfield *Essex*
Springfield *Police Scotland*
Springfield *Gtr Manchester*
Springfield Road *PSNI*
Springhead *Gtr Manchester*
Springhill *Gtr Manchester*
Sproston *Cheshire*
Sprotborough *South Yorkshire*
Sproughton *Suffolk*
Sprowston *Norfolk*
Sproxton *Leicestershire*
Spurstow *Cheshire*
Stadhampton *Thames Valley*
Stafford *Staffordshire*
Stags End *Hertfordshire*
Stainborough *South Yorkshire*
Staincliffe *West Yorkshire*
Staindrop *Durham*
Staines *Surrey*
Stainforth *North Yorkshire*
Staining *Lancashire*
Stainland *West Yorkshire*
Staithes *North Yorkshire*
Stakeford *Northumbria*
Stakehill *Gtr Manchester*
Stalbridge *Dorset*
Stalham *Norfolk*
Stallingborough *Humberside*
Stalybridge *Gtr Manchester*
Stamford *Lincolnshire*
Stamford Bridge *Humberside*
Stamfordham *Northumbria*
Stamford St Martins *Cambs*
Stamperland *Police Scotland*
Stanborough *Hertfordshire*
Stanbridge *Bedfordshire*
Stand *Gtr Manchester*
Standish *Gtr Manchester*
Standlake *Thames Valley*
Standon *Hertfordshire*
Standon Green End *Hertfordshire*
Stanford *Northamptonshire*
Stanford Rivers *Essex*
Stanford-in-the-Vale *Thames Valley*
Stanground *Cambridgeshire*
Stanhope *Durham*
Stanhope Bretby *Derbyshire*
Stanion *Northamptonshire*
Stank *North Yorkshire*
Stanks *West Yorkshire*
Stanley *Derbyshire*
Stanley *Durham*
Stanley *Police Scotland*
Stanley Ferry *West Yorkshire*
Stanley Green *Gtr Manchester*
Stanningley *West Yorkshire*
Stannington *Northumbria*
Stannington *South Yorkshire*
Stanstead Abbotts *Hertfordshire*
Stanstead St Margarets *Herts*
Stansted *Essex*
Stansted *Kent*

Stanthorne *Cheshire*
Stanton *Derbyshire*
Stanton *Gloucestershire*
Stanton *Suffolk*
Stanton-by-Bridge *Derbyshire*
Stanton-by-Dale *Derbyshire*
Stanton-in-the-Peak *Derbyshire*
Stanton Hill *Nottinghamshire*
Stanton St Gabriel *Dorset*
Stanton St John *Thames Valley*
Stanton-under-Bardon *Leicestershire*
Stanway *Essex*
Stanwick *Northamptonshire*
Stanwick St John *North Yorkshire*
Stapeley *Cheshire*
Staple Cross *Sussex*
Staple Hill *Avon & Somerset*
Stapleford *Cambridgeshire*
Stapleford *Hertfordshire*
Stapleford *Leicestershire*
Stapleford *Nottinghamshire*
Stapleford *Wiltshire*
Stapleford Abbots *Essex*
Staplehurst *Kent*
Stapleton *Leicestershire*
Starkholmes *Derbyshire*
Starling *Gtr Manchester*
Starmore *Leicestershire*
Startforth *Durham*
Stathern *Leicestershire*
Staunton *Gloucestershire*
Staunton Harold *Leicestershire*
Staveley *Cumbria*
Staveley *Derbyshire*
Staveley *North Yorkshire*
Staverton *Northamptonshire*
Stebbing *Essex*
Stechford *West Midlands*
Steelhouse Lane *West Midlands*
Steeple *Dorset*
Steeple Ashton *Wiltshire*
Steeple Bumpstead *Essex*
Steeple Claydon *Thames Valley*
Steeple Gidding *Cambridgeshire*
Steeple Morden *Cambridgeshire*
Steepleton Iwerne *Dorset*
Steetley *Derbyshire*
Steeton *West Yorkshire*
Stelling Minnis *Kent*
Stenhousemuir *Police Scotland*
Stenson *Derbyshire*
Stepping Hill *Gtr Manchester*
Stepps *Police Scotland*
Stetchworth *Cambridgeshire*
Stevenage *Hertfordshire*
Stevenston *Police Scotland*
Steventon *Thames Valley*
Stewartby *Bedfordshire*
Stewarton *Police Scotland*
Stewartstown *PSNI*
Stewkley *Thames Valley*
Steyning *Sussex*
Stickcross *Thames Valley*
Sticker *Devon & Cornwall*
Stickford *Lincolnshire*
Stickney *Lincolnshire*
Stiffkey *Norfolk*
Stilton *Cambridgeshire*
Stinsford *Dorset*
Stirling *Police Scotland*
Stisted *Essex*
Stoak *Cheshire*
Stock *Essex*
Stockbridge *Hampshire*
Stock Brook *Gtr Manchester*
Stockbury *Kent*
Stockcross *Thames Valley*
Stockerston *Leicestershire*

Stocking Farm *Leicestershire*
Stocking Pelham *Hertfordshire*
Stockingford *Warwickshire*
Stockport *Gtr Manchester*
Stocksbridge *South Yorkshire*
Stocksfield *Northumbria*
Stockton *Cleveland*
Stockton Heath *Cheshire*
Stockton Malpas *Cheshire*
Stockton-on-Forest *North Yorks*
Stockwood *Dorset*
Stoke *Derbyshire*
Stoke *Kent*
Stoke *Surrey*
Stoke Abbot *Dorset*
Stoke Albany *Northamptonshire*
Stoke Bruerne *Northamptonshire*
Stoke-by-Nayland *Suffolk*
Stoke Doyle *Northamptonshire*
Stoke Dry *Leicestershire*
Stoke Fleming *Devon & Cornwall*
Stoke Golding *Leicestershire*
Stoke Mandeville *Thames Valley*
Stoke (Nantwich) *Cheshire*
Stoke Newington *Metropolitan*
Stoke Poges *Thames Valley*
Stoke Row *Thames Valley*
Stoke-St-Mary *Avon & Somerset*
Stoke-St-Michael *Avon & Somerset*
Stoke-sub-Hamdon *Avon & Somerset*
Stoke Trister *Avon & Somerset*
Stoke-upon-Trent *Staffordshire*
Stoke Wake *Dorset*
Stoke Works *West Mercia*
Stokenchurch *Thames Valley*
Stokesley *North Yorkshire*
Stone *Staffordshire*
Stone *Thames Valley*
Stonea *Cambridgeshire*
Stonebroom *Derbyshire*
Stoneclough *Gtr Manchester*
Stonehaven *Police Scotland*
Stonehouse *Gloucestershire*
Stonehouse *Police Scotland*
Stoneleigh *Warwickshire*
Stonesby *Leicestershire*
Stoney Middleton *Derbyshire*
Stoney Stanton *Leicestershire*
Stony Stanton *West Midlands*
Stoneycliffe *Gtr Manchester*
Stoneyfield *Gtr Manchester*
Stonham Parva *Suffolk*
Stonton Wyville *Leicestershire*
Storeton *Merseyside*
Stormont *PSNI*
Stornoway *Police Scotland*
Storrington *Sussex*
Stotfold *Bedfordshire*
Stoughton *Leicestershire*
Stoughton *Surrey*
Stour Paine *Dorset*
Stour Provost *Dorset*
Stourbridge *West Midlands*
Stourport *West Mercia*
Stourton *West Yorkshire*
Stourton Caundle *Dorset*
Stow-cum-Quy *Cambridgeshire*
Stow Longa *Cambridgeshire*
Stow-on-the-Wold *Glos*
Stowe Nine Churches *Northants*
Stowmarket *Suffolk*
Stowupland *Suffolk*
Strabane *PSNI*
Strachur *Police Scotland*
Stradbroke *Suffolk*
Stradishall *Suffolk*
Strandtown *PSNI*

Strangeways *Gtr Manchester*
Strangford *PSNI*
Stranraer *Police Scotland*
Stratford-upon-Avon
  Warwickshire
Stratford-St-Mary *Suffolk*
Strathaven *Police Scotland*
Strathdon *Police Scotland*
Strathmiglo *Police Scotland*
Strathpeffer *Police Scotland*
Stratton *Dorset*
Stratton-on-the-Fosse *Avon &*
  Somerset
Stratton-St-Margaret *Wiltshire*
Strawberry *Gtr Manchester*
Streatham *Metropolitan*
Street *Avon & Somerset*
Streethouse *West Yorkshire*
Streetly End *Cambridgeshire*
Streetside *West Yorkshire*
Strelley *Nottinghamshire*
Strensall *North Yorkshire*
Strete *Devon & Cornwall*
Stretford *Gtr Manchester*
Stretham *Cambridgeshire*
Stretton *Derbyshire*
Stretton *Leicestershire*
Stretton-on-Dunsmore
  Warwickshire
Stretton (Runcorn) *Cheshire*
Stretton Sugwas *West Mercia*
Stretton (Tarvin) *Cheshire*
Stretton-en-le-Field *Leicestershire*
Strichen *Police Scotland*
Strines *Gtr Manchester*
Strixton *Northampton*
Stromness *Police Scotland*
Strood *Kent*
Stroud *Gloucestershire*
Stroud *Hampshire*
Stubbington *Hampshire*
Stubbins *Lancashire*
Stubshaw Grass *Gtr Manchester*
Studley *Warwickshire*
Studley Roger *North Yorkshire*
Studley Royal *North Yorkshire*
Stuntney *Cambridgeshire*
Sturminster Marshall *Dorset*
Sturminster Newton *Dorset*
Sturry *Kent*
Styal *Cheshire*
Stydd *Derbyshire*
Sudborough *Northampton*
Sudbrook *Gwent*
Sudbury *Suffolk*
Sudbury *Derbyshire*
Sudden *Gtr Manchester*
Sulby *Northamptonshire*
Sulgrave *Northamptonshire*
Sully *South Wales*
Summerhill *North Wales*
Summerley *Derbyshire*
Sunbury *Metropolitan*
Sunderland *Northumbria*
Sunderland Green *Gtr Manchester*
Sundridge *Kent*
Sundon Park *Bedfordshire*
Sunningdale *Surrey*
Sunningdale *Thames Valley*
Sunninghill *Thames Valley*
Sunnyside *South Yorkshire*
Surbiton *Metropolitan*
Surfleet *Lincolnshire*
Sutterton *Lincolnshire*
Sutton *Metropolitan*
Sutton *Nottinghamshire*
Sutton *Suffolk*
Sutton *Wiltshire*
Sutton (Dover) *Kent*

Sutton (Macclesfield) *Cheshire*
Sutton (Runcorn) *Cheshire*
Sutton-at-Home *Kent*
Sutton Bassett *Northamptonshire*
Sutton Bonington
  Nottinghamshire
Sutton Bridge *Lincolnshire*
Sutton Cheney *Leicestershire*
Sutton Coldfield *West Midlands*
Sutton Courtenay *Thames Valley*
Sutton-cum-Duckmanton
  Derbyshire
Sutton Grange *North Yorkshire*
Sutton Green *Surrey*
Sutton Hill, Telford *West Mercia*
Sutton-in-Ashfield
  Nottinghamshire
Sutton-in-Craven *North Yorkshire*
Sutton-in-the-Elms *Leicestershire*
Sutton-on-Forest *North Yorkshire*
Sutton-on-Sea *Lincolnshire*
Sutton-on-the-Hill *Derbyshire*
Sutton-on-Trent *Nottinghamshire*
Sutton-St-James *Lincolnshire*
Sutton Scotney *Hampshire*
Sutton-under-Whitestone Cliffe
  North Yorkshire
Sutton Valence *Kent*
Sutton Veny *Wiltshire*
Sutton Waldron *Dorset*
Sutton-with-Howgrave *North
  Yorkshire*
Swadlincote *Derbyshire*
Swaffham *Norfolk*
Swaffham Bulbeck
  Cambridgeshire
Swaffham Prior *Cambridgeshire*
Swainby *North Yorkshire*
Swainswick *Avon & Somerset*
Swalecliffe *Kent*
Swallownest *South Yorkshire*
Swanage *Dorset*
Swanley *Kent*
Swanmore *Hampshire*
Swannington *Leicestershire*
Swannington *Norfolk*
Swanton Morley *Norfolk*
Swanwick *Derbyshire*
Swansea *South Wales*
Swarkestone *Derbyshire*
Swarthmoor *Cumbria*
Swavesey *Cambridgeshire*
Sway *Hampshire*
Swepstone *Leicestershire*
Swettenham *Cheshire*
Swillington *West Yorkshire*
Swinden *North Yorkshire*
Swinderby *Lincolnshire*
Swindon *North Yorkshire*
Swindon *Wiltshire*
Swinefleet *Humberside*
Swineshead *Lincolnshire*
Swinford *Leicestershire*
Swinton *Police Scotland*
Swinton *Gtr Manchester*
Swinton *North Yorkshire*
Swinton *South Yorkshire*
Swinton-with-Warthermarske
  North Yorks
Swithland *Leicestershire*
Swyre *Dorset*
Sydenham *Metropolitan*
Syderstone *Norfolk*
Sydling-St-Nicholas *Dorset*
Syke *Gtr Manchester*
Symington *Police Scotland*
Symondsbury *Dorset*
Syresham *Northamptonshire*
Sysonby *Leicestershire*

Syston *Leicestershire*
Sywell *Northamptonshire*
Tabley Inferior *Cheshire*
Tabley Superior *Cheshire*
Tadcaster *North Yorkshire*
Taddington *Derbyshire*
Tadley *Hampshire*
Tadlow *Cambridgeshire*
Taffs Well *South Wales*
Taibach *South Wales*
Tain *Police Scotland*
Takeley *Essex*
Talbot Green *South Wales*
Talgarth *Dyfed-Powys*
Talybont *Dyfed-Powys*
Talybont-on-Usk *Dyfed-Powys*
Talycoed *Gwent*
Talysarn *North Wales*
Talywain *Gwent*
Tamworth *Staffordshire*
Tandle Hill *Gtr Manchester*
Tandle Hill Park *Gtr Manchester*
Tandragee *PSNI*
Tandridge *Surrey*
Tanners Lane End *Gtr
  Manchester*
Tansley *Derbyshire*
Tansor *Northamptonshire*
Tanworth-in-Arden *Warwickshire*
Tarbert *Police Scotland*
Tarbolton *Police Scotland*
Tarden *Gtr Manchester*
Tarland *Police Scotland*
Tarleton *Lancashire*
Tarporley *Cheshire*
Tarrant Crawford *Dorset*
Tarrant Gunville *Dorset*
Tarrant Hinton *Dorset*
Tarrant Keynston *Dorset*
Tarrant Launceston *Dorset*
Tarrant Monkton *Dorset*
Tarrant Rawstone *Dorset*
Tarrant Rushton *Dorset*
Tarrington *West Mercia*
Tarves *Police Scotland*
Tarvin *Cheshire*
Tatling End *Thames Valley*
Tatsfield *Surrey*
Tattenhall *Cheshire*
Tatton *Cheshire*
Taunton *Avon & Somerset*
Tavarnaubach *Gwent*
Taverham *Norfolk*
Tavistock *Devon & Cornwall*
Tayinloan *Police Scotland*
Taynuilt *Police Scotland*
Tayport *Police Scotland*
Tea Green *Hertfordshire*
Tealby *Lincolnshire*
Tealing *Police Scotland*
Tebay *Cumbria*
Tedburn-St-Mary *Devon &
  Cornwall*
Teddington *Metropolitan*
Teeton *Northamptonshire*
Teigh *Leicestershire*
Teignmouth *Devon & Cornwall*
Telford *West Mercia*
Temple *Police Scotland*
Temple Cloud *Avon & Somerset*
Temple Hirst *North Yorkshire*
Temple Newsam *West Yorkshire*
Temple Normanton *Derbyshire*
Templecombe *Avon & Somerset*
Templepatrick *PSNI*
Temple Sowerby *Cumbria*
Tempo *PSNI*
Tempsford *Bedfordshire*
Tenby *Dyfed-Powys*

Tenbury *West Mercia*
Tennent Street *PSNI*
Tenterden *Kent*
Ternhill *West Mercia*
Terrington *North Yorkshire*
Terrington St John *Norfolk*
Teston *Kent*
Tetbury *Gloucestershire*
Tetney *Lincolnshire*
Tetsworth *Thames Valley*
Tetworth *Cambridgeshire*
Tettenhall *West Midlands*
Tetton *Cheshire*
Teversal *Nottingham*
Teversham *Cambridgeshire*
Tewin *Hertfordshire*
Tewkesbury *Gloucestershire*
Teynham *Kent*
Thackley *West Yorkshire*
Thame *Thames Valley*
Thatcham *Thames Valley*
Thaxted *Essex*
The Green *Cumbria*
The Lee *Thames Valley*
The Lizard *Devon & Cornwall*
Theale *Thames Valley*
Theddingworth *Leicestershire*
Thelwall *Cheshire*
Thenford *Northamptonshire*
Therfield *Hertfordshire*
Thetford *Norfolk*
Theydon Bois *Essex*
Thingwall *Merseyside*
Thirsk *North Yorkshire*
Thistleton *Leicestershire*
Thorley *Hertfordshire*
Thornaby *Cleveland*
Thornbury *Avon & Somerset*
Thornbury *West Yorkshire*
Thornby *Northamptonshire*
Thorncombe *Dorset*
Thorndon *Suffolk*
Thorne *South Yorkshire*
Thorner *West Yorkshire*
Thorney *Cambridgeshire*
Thorney Toll *Cambridgeshire*
Thornford *Dorset*
Thornhaugh *Cambridgeshire*
Thornhill *Cumbria*
Thornhill *Derbyshire*
Thornhill *Police Scotland*
Thornhill Road *West Midlands*
Thornley *Durham*
Thornliebank *Police Scotland*
Thornsett *Derbyshire*
Thornton *Police Scotland*
Thornton *Leicestershire*
Thornton *Merseyside*
Thornton *West Yorkshire*
Thornton Bridge *North Yorkshire*
Thornton-Cleveleys *Lancashire*
Thornton Hough *Merseyside*
Thornton-in-Craven *North Yorks*
Thornton-le-Beans *North Yorks*
Thornton-le-Clay *North Yorkshire*
Thornton-le-Dale *North Yorkshire*
Thornton-le-Moor *North Yorkshire*
Thornton-le-Moors *Cheshire*
Thornton-le-Street *North Yorks*
Thornton-on-the-Hill *North Yorks*
Thornton Riseborough *North Yorks*
Thornton Rust *North Yorkshire*
Thornton Steward *North Yorkshire*
Thornton Watlass *North Yorkshire*
Thorp *Gtr Manchester*
Thorpe *Derbyshire*

Thorpe *North Yorkshire*
Thorpe *Surrey*
Thorpe *West Yorkshire*
Thorpe Achurch *Northamptonshire*
Thorpe Arnold *Leicestershire*
Thorpe Bassett *North Yorkshire*
Thorpe-by-Water *Leicestershire*
Thorpe Langton *Leicestershire*
Thorpe-le-Soken *Essex*
Thorpe-le-Willows *North Yorks*
Thorpe Malsor *Northamptonshire*
Thorpe Mandeville *Northants*
Thorpe Satchville *Leicestershire*
Thorpeacre *Leicestershire*
Thrapston *Northamptonshire*
Threapwood *Cheshire*
Three Crosses *South Wales*
Three Mile Cross *Thames Valley*
Threlkeld *Cumbria*
Thringstone *Leicestershire*
Thriplow *Cambridgeshire*
Throckley *Northumbria*
Throwley *Kent*
Thrussington *Leicestershire*
Thrybergh *South Yorkshire*
Thurcaston *Leicestershire*
Thurcroft *South Yorkshire*
Thurgoland *South Yorkshire*
Thurlaston *Leicestershire*
Thurleigh *Bedfordshire*
Thurlestone *South Yorkshire*
Thurmaston *Leicestershire*
Thurnby *Leicestershire*
Thurnby Lodge *Leicestershire*
Thurning *Northamptonshire*
Thurnscoe *South Yorkshire*
Thursby *Cumbria*
Thursley *Surrey*
Thurso *Police Scotland*
Thurstaston *Merseyside*
Thurston Clough *Gtr Manchester*
Thurvaston *Derbyshire*
Tibshelf *Derbyshire*
Ticehurst *Sussex*
Tickencote *Leicestershire*
Tickhill *South Yorkshire*
Ticknall *Derbyshire*
Tiddington *Thames Valley*
Tideswell *Derbyshire*
Tidmarsh *Thames Valley*
Tidworth *Hampshire*
Tidworth (North) *Wiltshire*
Tiffield *Northamptonshire*
Tighnabruaich *Police Scotland*
Tilbrook *Cambridgeshire*
Tilbury *Essex*
Tilehurst *Thames Valley*
Tilford *Surrey*
Tillicoultry *Police Scotland*
Tillingham *Essex*
Tilshead *Wiltshire*
Tilston *Cheshire*
Tilstone Fearnall *Cheshire*
Tilsworth *Bedfordshire*
Tilton-on-the-Hill *Leicestershire*
Timperley *Gtr Manchester*
Timsbury *Avon & Somerset*
Timsbury *Hampshire*
Tincleton *Dorset*
Tingewick *Thames Valley*
Tinsley Green *Surrey*
Tintern *Gwent*
Tintwistle *Derbyshire*
Tinwell *Leicestershire*
Tipton *West Midlands*
Tiptree *Essex*
Tiree *Police Scotland*
Tirphil *South Wales*

Tiryberth *Gwent*
Tisbury *Wiltshire*
Tissington *Derbyshire*
Titchfield *Hampshire*
Titchmarsh *Northamptonshire*
Titsey *Surrey*
Tiverton *Devon & Cornwall*
Tiveton *Cheshire*
Tixover *Leicestershire*
Tobermory *Police Scotland*
Tockwith *North Yorkshire*
Todber *Dorset*
Todmorden *West Yorkshire*
Toft *Cheshire*
Toft *Cambridgeshire*
Tolethorpe *Leicestershire*
Toll Bar *South Yorkshire*
Toller Fratrum *Dorset*
Toller Lane *West Yorkshire*
Toller Porcorum *Dorset*
Tollesbury *Essex*
Tolleshunt D'Arcy *Essex*
Tollpuddle *Dorset*
Tomintoul *Police Scotland*
Tonbridge *Kent*
Tondu *South Wales*
Tong *West Mercia*
Tong *West Yorkshire*
Tonge *Leicestershire*
Tonge Fold *Gtr Manchester*
Tonge Moor *Gtr Manchester*
Tongham *Surrey*
Tong Park *West Yorkshire*
Ton Pentre *South Wales*
Tonna *South Wales*
Tonwell *Hertfordshire*
Tonypandy *South Wales*
Tonyrefail *South Wales*
Toomebridge *PSNI*
Tooting *Metropolitan*
Topcliffe *North Yorkshire*
Top-of-the-Brow *Gtr Manchester*
Top Hagley *West Mercia*
Top of Heben *Gtr Manchester*
Top of Th'Meadows *Gtr Manchester*
Top of Pyke *Gtr Manchester*
Top Rock *Gtr Manchester*
Top of Turton *Gtr Manchester*
Toppings *Gtr Manchester*
Torpoint *Devon & Cornwall*
Torquay *Devon & Cornwall*
Torrance *Police Scotland*
Toseland *Cambridgeshire*
Totland *Hampshire*
Totnes *Devon & Cornwall*
Toton *Nottinghamshire*
Tottenham *Metropolitan*
Tottenham Court Rd *Metropolitan*
Tottenhill *Norfolk*
Totternhoe *Bedfordshire*
Tottington *Gtr Manchester*
Totton *Hampshire*
Tow Law *Durham*
Towcester *Northamptonshire*
Tower Bridge *Metropolitan*
Tower View *Northumbria*
Town Green *Gtr Manchester*
Town Lane *Gtr Manchester*
Town of Lowton *Gtr Manchester*
Townhill *Police Scotland*
Townhill *South Wales*
Townsend *Staffordshire*
Townville *West Yorkshire*
Towyn-with-Kinmel Bay *North Wales*
Trafford Park *Gtr Manchester*
Trallwn *South Wales*

Tranent *Police Scotland*
Tranmere *Cheshire*
Tranmere Park *West Yorkshire*
Trawden *Lancashire*
Trawsfynydd *North Wales*
Trealaw *South Wales*
Trearddur *North Wales*
Trebanog *South Wales*
Trebanos *South Wales*
Trecastle *Dyfed-Powys*
Trecenydd *South Wales*
Tredegar *Gwent*
Tredington *Warwickshire*
Tredunnock *Gwent*
Treeton *South Yorkshire*
Trefnant *North Wales*
Treforest *South Wales*
Trefriw *North Wales*
Tregare *Gwent*
Tregaron *Dyfed-Powys*
Tregarth *North Wales*
Tregony *Devon & Cornwall*
Trehaford *South Wales*
Treharris *South Wales*
Treherbert *South Wales*
Trelawnyd *North Wales*
Trelewis *South Wales*
Trellech *Gwent*
Trellech Grange *Gwent*
Tremadoc *North Wales*
Tremorfa *South Wales*
Trent *Dorset*
Trent Vale *Staffordshire*
Trentham *Staffordshire*
Treorchy *South Wales*
Trethomas *Gwent*
Trevethin *Gwent*
Trevil *Gwent*
Triangle *West Yorkshire*
Trimdon Colliery *Durham*
Trimsaran *Dyfed-Powys*
Trinant *Gwent*
Tring *Hertfordshire*
Trinity Road *Avon & Somerset*
Troedrhiwgwair *Gwent*
Troedyrhiw *South Wales*
Troon *Devon & Cornwall*
Troon *Police Scotland*
Trotton *Sussex*
Troway *Derbyshire*
Trowbridge *Wiltshire*
Trowell *Nottinghamshire*
Trowley Bottom *Hertfordshire*
Trowse *Norfolk*
Truro *Devon & Cornwall*
Trusley *Derbyshire*
Tuddenham *Suffolk*
Tudeley *Kent*
Tugby *Leicestershire*
Tullibody *Police Scotland*
Tumble *Dyfed-Powys*
Tummel Bridge *Police Scotland*
Tunbridge Wells *Kent*
Tunsh *Gtr Manchester*
Tunstall *Kent*
Tunstall *North Yorkshire*
Tunstall *Staffordshire*
Tunstall *Suffolk*
Tunstead *Gtr Manchester*
Tunstead M'tn *Derbyshire*
Tupton *Derbyshire*
Tur Langton *Leicestershire*
Turnchapel *Devon & Cornwall*
Turnditch *Derbyshire*
Turners Hill *Sussex*
Turners Puddle *Dorset*
Turnhurst *Staffordshire*
Turn Village *Lancs*
Turnworth *Dorset*

Turiff *Police Scotland*
Turton *Lancashire*
Turvey *Bedfordshire*
Tushingham *Cheshire*
Tutshill *Gloucestershire*
Tuxford *Nottinghamshire*
Twemlow *Cheshire*
Twickenham *Metropolitan*
Twycross *Leicestershire*
Twyford *Derbyshire*
Twyford *Hampshire*
Twyford *Leicestershire*
Twyford (Berks) *Thames Valley*
Twyford (Bucks) *Thames Valley*
Twywell *Northamptonshire*
Tycoch *South Wales*
Tycroes *Dyfed-Powys*
Tydd Gote *Cambridgeshire*
Tydd St Giles *Cambridgeshire*
Tydd St Mary *Lincolnshire*
Tyersal *West Yorkshire*
Ty Graig *Gwent*
Tyldesley *Gtr Manchester*
Tylorstown *South Wales*
Tynan *PSNI*
Tyneham *Dorset*
Tynewydd *South Wales*
Tynygroes *North Wales*
Tynygongl *North Wales*
Tysoe *Warwickshire*
Tytherington *Cheshire*
Tyttenhangar Green *Hertfordshire*
Tywardreath *Devon & Cornwall*
Tywyn *North Wales*
Uckfield *Sussex*
Uddingston *Police Scotland*
Uffculme *Devon & Cornwall*
Uffington *Thames Valley*
Ufford *Cambridgeshire*
Uig *Police Scotland*
Ulceby *Humberside*
Ulcombe *Kent*
Uley *Gloucestershire*
Ullapool *Police Scotland*
Ulleskelf *North Yorkshire*
Ullesthorpe *Leicestershire*
Ulverscroft *Leicestershire*
Ulverston *Cumbria*
Underbank *West Yorkshire*
Undercliffe *West Yorkshire*
Underwood *Nottinghamshire*
Undy *Gwent*
University *Gtr Manchester*
Unstone *Derbyshire*
Unsworth *Gtr Manchester*
Up Cerne *Dorset*
Upavon *Wiltshire*
Upchurch *Kent*
Upend *Cambridgeshire*
Upham *Hampshire*
Uphill *Avon & Somerset*
Uplands *South Wales*
Uplawmoor *Police Scotland*
Upnor *Kent*
Upper Bangor *North Wales*
Upper Basildon *Thames Valley*
Upper Boat *South Wales*
Upper Cwmbran *Gwent*
Upper Hale *Surrey*
Upper Haugh *South Yorkshire*
Upper Heyford *Thames Valley*
Upper Heyford *Northamptonshire*
Upper Hopton *West Yorkshire*
Upper Killay *South Wales*
Uppermill *Gtr Manchester*
Uppingham *Leicestershire*
Upminster *Metropolitan*
Upton *Cambridgeshire*
Upton *Cheshire*

Upton *Leicestershire*
Upton *Northamptonshire*
Upton *West Yorkshire*
Upton Bishop *West Mercia*
Upton-upon-Severn *West Mercia*
Upton *Merseyside*
Upware *Cambridgeshire*
Upwell *Cambridgeshire*
Upwell *Norfolk*
Upwey *Dorset*
Upwood & The Raveleys *Cambs*
Urmston *Gtr Manchester*
Urswick *Cumbria*
Usk *Gwent*
Uskmouth *Gwent*
Utkington *Cheshire*
Uttoxeter *Staffordshire*
Uxbridge *Metropolitan*
Valley *North Wales*
Varteg *Gwent*
Vaynor *South Wales*
Velindre *Dyfed-Powys*
Velindre *South Wales*
Velindre *South Wales*
Ventnor *Hampshire*
Verwood *Dorset*
Veryan *Devon & Cornwall*
Victoria *PSNI*
Victoria Park *Gtr Manchester*
Victory *Gtr Manchester*
Viewpark *Police Scotland*
Vine Street *Metropolitan*
Virginia Water *Surrey*
Vyse Street *West Midlands*
Vyse Street *West Yorkshire*
Waddington *Lancashire*
Waddington *Lincolnshire*
Waddesdon *Thames Valley*
Wadebridge *Devon & Cornwall*
Wadenhoe *Northamptonshire*
Wadesmill *Hertfordshire*
Wadhurst *Sussex*
Wadworth *South Yorkshire*
Waenfawr *North Wales*
Wainfleet *Lincolnshire*
Waingroves *Derbyshire*
Wainscot *Kent*
Wakefield *West Yorkshire*
Wakerley *Northamptonshire*
Walbottle *Northumbria*
Walcote *Leicestershire*
Walderslade *Kent*
Waldingfield *Suffolk*
Walesby *Nottinghamshire*
Walgherton *Cheshire*
Walgrave *Northamptonshire*
Walkden *Gtr Manchester*
Walkeringham *Nottinghamshire*
Walkern *Hertfordshire*
Wallasey Village *Merseyside*
Wallbank *Gtr Manchester*
Wallingford *Thames Valley*
Wallington *Hertfordshire*
Wallington *Metropolitan*
Wallness *Gtr Manchester*
Wallop *Hampshire*
Walmersley *Gtr Manchester*
Walpole-St-Peter *Norfolk*
Walsall *West Midlands*
Walsall Road *West Midlands*
Walshford *North Yorkshire*
Walsden *West Yorkshire*
Walsham-le-Willows *Suffolk*
Walshaw *Gtr Manchester*
Walsoken *Norfolk*
Walsworth *Hertfordshire*
Waltham *Essex*
Waltham *Humberside*
Waltham Abbey *Essex*

Waltham Cross *Hertfordshire*
Waltham-St-Lawrence *Thames Valley*
Waltham-on-the-Wolds *Leics*
Walthamstow *Metropolitan*
Walton *Cheshire*
Walton *Derbyshire*
Walton *Essex*
Walton *Leicestershire*
Walton *West Yorkshire*
Walton-le-Dale *Lancashire*
Walton-on-Thames *Surrey*
Walton-on-the-Wolds *Leicestershire*
Walton-on-Trent *Derbyshire*
Wanborough *Surrey*
Wandsworth *Metropolitan*
Wandsworth Common *Metropolitan*
Wangford *Suffolk*
Wanlip *Leicestershire*
Wansford *Cambridgeshire*
Wanstead *Metropolitan*
Wanstrow *Avon & Somerset*
Wantage *Thames Valley*
Wappenham *Northamptonshire*
Wapping *Metropolitan*
Warboys *Cambridgeshire*
Warburton *Gtr Manchester*
Warburton Green *Gtr Manchester*
Ward Green *South Yorkshire*
Wardle *Gtr Manchester*
Wardley *Gtr Manchester*
Wardley *Leicestershire*
Wardlow *Derbyshire*
Wardy Hill *Cambridgeshire*
Ware *Hertfordshire*
Wareham *Dorset*
Wareham-St-Martin *Dorset*
Wareside *Hertfordshire*
Waresley *Cambridgeshire*
Wargrave *Thames Valley*
Waringstown *PSNI*
Wark *Northumbria*
Warkton *Northamptonshire*
Warkworth *Northamptonshire*
Warkworth *Northumbria*
Warlingham *Surrey*
Warmfield *West Yorkshire*
Warmingham *Cheshire*
Warmington *Northamptonshire*
Warminster *Wiltshire*
Warmsworth *South Yorkshire*
Warmwell *Dorset*
Warnham *Sussex*
Warrenpoint *PSNI*
Warrington *Cheshire*
Warsash *Hampshire*
Warslow *Staffordshire*
Warsop *Nottinghamshire*
Warsop Vale *Nottinghamshire*
Warth Fold *Gtr Manchester*
Wartnaby *Leicestershire*
Warton *Lancashire*
Warwick *Warwickshire*
Washington *Northumbria*
Washington *Sussex*
Watchet *Avon & Somerset*
Watchfield *Thames Valley*
Waterbeach *Cambridgeshire*
Watercombe *Dorset*
Water End *Hertfordshire*
Water Newton *Cambridgeshire*
Waterfoot *Lancashire*
Waterford *Hertfordshire*
Waterhead *Gtr Manchester*
Waterhouses *Durham*
Waterhouses *Staffordshire*
Wateringbury *Kent*

Waterloo *Derbyshire*
Waterloo *Gtr Manchester*
Waterloo Pier *Metropolitan*
Watersheddings *Gtr Manchester*
Waterside *PSNI*
Watford *Hertfordshire*
Watford *Northamptonshire*
Wath (Malton) *North Yorkshire*
Wath (Ripon) *North Yorkshire*
Wath-in-Niddersdale *North Yorks*
Wath-on-Dearne *South Yorkshire*
Watlington *Thames Valley*
Watnall *Nottinghamshire*
Watten *Police Scotland*
Watthill Mudd *Gtr Manchester*
Watton *Norfolk*
Watton-at-Stone *Hertfordshire*
Wattstown *South Wales*
Wattsville *Gwent*
Waunarlwydd *South Wales*
Waunfawr *North Wales*
Waunllwyd *Gwent*
Waverley *Surrey*
Waverton *Cheshire*
Weald *Kent*
Wealdstone *Metropolitan*
Weaste *Gtr Manchester*
Weaverham *Cheshire*
Webheath *West Mercia*
Wedmore *Avon & Somerset*
Wednesbury *West Midlands*
Wednesfield *West Midlands*
Weedon Bec *Northamptonshire*
Weeke *Hampshire*
Weekley *Northamptonshire*
Weeley *Essex*
Weeting *Norfolk*
Weeton *Lancashire*
Weetwood *West Yorkshire*
Welbeck Village *Nottinghamshire*
Welby *Leicestershire*
Welburn *North Yorkshire*
Welburn (Kirkbymoorside) *North Yorkshire*
Welburn (Malton) *North Yorkshire*
Weldon *Northamptonshire*
Welford *Northamptonshire*
Welham *Nottinghamshire*
Welham Green *Hertfordshire*
Welham *Leicestershire*
Well *North Yorkshire*
Welland *West Mercia*
Wellbank *Police Scotland*
Wellesbourne *Warwickshire*
Well House *West Yorkshire*
Wellingborough *Northamptonshire*
Wellington *Avon & Somerset*
Wellington (S) *West Mercia*
Wellow *Nottinghamshire*
Wellow *Avon & Somerset*
Wellpond Green *Hertfordshire*
Wells *Avon & Somerset*
Wells-next-Sea *Norfolk*
Wellsborough *Leicestershire*
Wellsushes *Gtr Manchester*
Welshpool *Dyfed-Powys*
Welton *Lincolnshire*
Welton *Northamptonshire*
Welton-le-Wold *Lincolnshire*
Welwyn *Hertfordshire*
Welwyn Garden City *Hertfordshire*
Wem *West Mercia*
Wembley *Metropolitan*
Wemys Bay *Police Scotland*
Wendover *Thames Valley*
Wennington *Cambridgeshire*
Wensley *Derbyshire*

Wensley *North Yorkshire*
Wentworth *Cambridgeshire*
Wentworth *South Yorkshire*
Wentworth *Surrey*
Wenvoe *South Wales*
Weobley *West Mercia*
Werneth *Gtr Manchester*
Werwin *Cheshire*
Wessington *Derbyshire*
West Auckland *Durham*
West Ayton *North Yorkshire*
West Bergholt *Essex*
West Bradford *Lancashire*
West Bridgford *Nottinghamshire*
West Bromwich *West Midlands*
West Byfleet *Surrey*
West Calder *Police Scotland*
West Challow *Thames Valley*
West Chelborough *Dorset*
West Chiltington *Sussex*
West Clandon *Surrey*
West Coker *Avon & Somerset*
West Compton *Dorset*
West Cornforth *Durham*
West Cowes *Hampshire*
West Denton *Northumbria*
West Didsbury *Gtr Manchester*
West Drayton *Metropolitan*
West End *Hampshire*
West End *North Yorkshire*
West End *Staffordshire*
West End *Surrey*
West End Central *Metropolitan*
West Felton *West Mercia*
West Gorton *Gtr Manchester*
West Haddon *Northamptonshire*
West Hagley *West Mercia*
West Hallam *Derbyshire*
West Ham *Metropolitan*
West Hampstead *Metropolitan*
West Hendon *Metropolitan*
West Hoathly *Sussex*
West Horrington *Avon & Somerset*
West Horsley *Surrey*
West Houghton *Gtr Manchester*
West Humble *Surrey*
West Hyde *Hertfordshire*
West Keal *Lincolnshire*
West Kilbride *Police Scotland*
West Kingsdown *Kent*
West Kirby *Merseyside*
West Knighton *Dorset*
West Langton *Leicestershire*
West Lavington *Wiltshire*
West Lulworth *Dorset*
West Lynn *Norfolk*
West Malling *Kent*
West Meon *Hampshire*
West Mersea *Essex*
West Monkton *Avon & Somerset*
West Moors *Dorset*
West Orchard *Dorset*
West Parley *Dorset*
West Pennard *Avon & Somerset*
West Pinchbeck *Lincolnshire*
West Row *Suffolk*
West Stour *Dorset*
West Stafford *Dorset*
West Thurrock *Essex*
West Vale *West Yorkshire*
West Wellow *Hampshire*
West Wemyss *Police Scotland*
West Wickham *Cambridgeshire*
West Wickham *Metropolitan*
West Winch *Norfolk*
West Wratting *Cambridgeshire*
West Wycombe *Thames Valley*
Westborough *Surrey*
Westbourne *Dorset*

Westbourne *Sussex*
Westbury *Thames Valley*
Westbury *West Mercia*
Westbury *Wiltshire*
Westbury-on-Severn *Gloucestershire*
Westcliff *Essex*
Westcombe Park *Metropolitan*
Westcott *Surrey*
Westerham *Kent*
Westerhope *Northumbria*
Westfield *Surrey*
Westham *Dorset*
Westham *Sussex*
Westhoughton *Gtr Manchester*
Westhulme *Gtr Manchester*
Westland Green *Hertfordshire*
Westleigh *Gtr Manchester*
Westleton *Suffolk*
Westley Waterless *Cambridgeshire*
Westmill *Hertfordshire*
Weston *Hertfordshire*
Weston *Lincolnshire*
Weston (Crewe) *Cheshire*
Weston (Runcorn) *Cheshire*
Weston and Weedon *Northants*
Weston Colville *Cambridgeshire*
Weston Coyney *Staffordshire*
Weston-on-the-Green *Thames*
Weston-on-Trent *Derbyshire*
Weston Rhyn *West Mercia*
Weston-sub-Edge *Gloucestershire*
Weston-super-Mare *Avon & Somerset*
Weston-under-Penyard *West Mercia*
Weston-under-Wetherley *Warwicks*
Weston-under-Wood *Derbyshire*
Westrill *Leicestershire*
Westward Ho! *Devon & Cornwall*
Westwicke *Cambridgeshire*
Westwood Park *Gtr Manchester*
Wetheral *Cumbria*
Wetherby *West Yorkshire*
Wetheringsett *Suffolk*
Wethersfield *Essex*
Wettenhall *Cheshire*
Wetwang *Humberside*
Wexham *Thames Valley*
Weybread *Suffolk*
Weybridge *Surrey*
Weyhill *Hampshire*
Weymouth *Dorset*
Whaddon *Cambridgeshire*
Whaddon *Thames Valley*
Whaley Bridge *Derbyshire*
Whaley Thorns *Derbyshire*
Whalley Range *Gtr Manchester*
Whaplode *Lincolnshire*
Whaplode Drove *Lincolnshire*
Wharncliffe *South Yorkshire*
Whatborough *Leicestershire*
Whatcroft *Cheshire*
Whatfield *Suffolk*
Whatstandwell *Derbyshire*
Whatton *Nottinghamshire*
Wheathampstead *Hertfordshire*
Wheatley *Thames Valley*
Wheatley *South Yorkshire*
Wheatley Hill *Durham*
Wheeldon Mill *Derbyshire*
Wheelock *Cheshire*
Wheelton *Lancashire*
Whelley *Gtr Manchester*
Whelnetham *Suffolk*
Wherstead *Suffolk*
Wheston *Derbyshire*
Whetstone *Metropolitan*

Whetstone *Leicestershire*
Whickham *Northumbria*
Whiddon Down *Devon & Cornwall*
Whinmoor *West Yorkshire*
Whilton *Northamptonshire*
Whipsnade *Bedfordshire*
Whirley *Cheshire*
Whissendine *Leicestershire*
Whiston *South Yorkshire*
Whiston Upper *South Yorkshire*
Whitburn *Police Scotland*
Whitby *North Yorkshire*
Whitchurch *Avon & Somerset*
Whitchurch *Hampshire*
Whitchurch *South Wales*
Whitchurch *West Mercia*
Whitchurch *Thames Valley*
Whitchurch-on-Thames *Thames Valley*
Whitchurch Canonicorum *Dorset*
Whitcombe *Dorset*
White City *South Wales*
White Gate *Gtr Manchester*
White Lye *Gwent*
White Waltham *Thames Valley*
Whitebrook *Gwent*
Whitecastle *Gwent*
Whitecross *Police Scotland*
Whitefield *Gtr Manchester*
Whitehaven *Cumbria*
Whitehead *PSNI*
Whitehill *Hampshire*
Whitehurst *North Wales*
Whiteley Village *Surrey*
Whiteparish *Wiltshire*
Whiteshill *Gloucestershire*
Whitfield *Kent*
Whitfield *Northamptonshire*
Whitfield *Northumbria*
Whithorn *Police Scotland*
Whiting Bay *Police Scotland*
Whitkirk *West Yorkshire*
Whitland *Dyfed-Powys*
Whitley *Gtr Manchester*
Whitley *North Yorkshire*
Whitley Bay *Northumbria*
Whitley Bridge *North Yorkshire*
Whitminster *Gloucestershire*
Whitmoor Common *Surrey*
Whitnash *Warwickshire*
Whitson *Gwent*
Whitstable *Kent*
Whittaker *Gtr Manchester*
Whittingham *Northumbria*
Whittington (S) *West Mercia*
Whittington (W) *West Mercia*
Whittington Moor *Derbyshire*
Whittle *Derbyshire*
Whittle *Gtr Manchester*
Whittle Brook *Gtr Manchester*
Whittlebury *Northamptonshire*
Whittlesey *Cambridgeshire*
Whittlesford *Cambridgeshire*
Whittonstall *Northumbria*
Whitwell *Derbyshire*
Whitwell *Hertfordshire*
Whitwell *Leicestershire*
Whitwell *North Yorkshire*
Whitwell-on-the-Hill *North Yorks*
Whitwick *Leicestershire*
Whitwood *West Yorkshire*
Whitwood Mere *West Yorkshire*
Whitworth *Lancashire*
Whyteleafe *Surrey*
Wibsey *West Yorkshire*
Wick *Police Scotland*
Wick *South Wales*
Wicken *Cambridgeshire*

Wicken *Northamptonshire*
Wicken Lane *Gtr Manchester*
Wickersley *South Yorkshire*
Wickford *Essex*
Wickham *Hampshire*
Wickhambrook *Suffolk*
Wickham Bishops *Essex*
Wickham Market *Suffolk*
Wickwar *Avon & Somerset*
Widdrington *Northumbria*
Widecombe *Devon & Cornwall*
Widford *Hertfordshire*
Widnes *Cheshire*
Wigan *Gtr Manchester*
Wiganthorpe *North Yorkshire*
Wiggengall St Germans *Norfolk*
Wiggenhall St Mary Magdalen *Norfolk*
Wigginton *Hertfordshire*
Wighill *North Yorkshire*
Wigland *Cheshire*
Wigsthorpe *Northamptonshire*
Wigston East *Leicestershire*
Wigston Fields *Leicestershire*
Wigston Magna *Leicestershire*
Wigston Parva *Leicestershire*
Wigtoft *Lincolnshire*
Wigton *Cumbria*
Wigtown *Police Scotland*
Wilbarston *Northamptonshire*
Wilberfoss *Humberside*
Wilburton *Cambridgeshire*
Wilby *Northamptonshire*
Wild Hill *Hertfordshire*
Wildboarclough *Cheshire*
Wilden *West Mercia*
Wildon Grange *North Yorkshire*
Willand *Devon & Cornwall*
Willaston *Isle of Man*
Willaston (Nantwich) *Cheshire*
Willaston (Wirral) *Cheshire*
Willenhall *West Midlands*
Willenhall (Coventry) *West Midlands*
Willerby *North Yorkshire*
Willesden Green *Metropolitan*
Willersley *Leicestershire*
Williamstown *South Wales*
Willian *Hertfordshire*
Willingham *Cambridgeshire*
Willingham Green *Cambridgeshire*
Willington *Cheshire*
Willington *Derbyshire*
Willington *Durham*
Williton *Avon & Somerset*
Willorghbys *Gtr Manchester*
Willoughby-on-the-Wolds *Notts*
Willoughby Waterless *Leicestershire*
Willowfield *PSNI*
Willows *Gtr Manchester*
Willstrop *North Yorkshire*
Wilmslow *Cheshire*
Wilne *Derbyshire*
Wilsden *West Yorkshire*
Wilsford *Lincolnshire*
Wilson *Leicestershire*
Wilstead *Bedfordshire*
Wilstone *Hertfordshire*
Wilton *North Yorkshire*
Wilton *Wiltshire*
Wimbledon *Metropolitan*
Wimblington *Cambridgeshire*
Wimbolds Trafford *Cheshire*
Wimboldsley *Cheshire*
Wimborne Minster *Dorset*
Wimborne-St-Giles *Dorset*
Wimpole *Cambridgeshire*
Wincanton *Avon & Somerset*

Wincham *Cheshire*
Winchcombe *Gloucestershire*
Winchelsea *Sussex*
Winchester *Hampshire*
Winchmore Hill *Metropolitan*
Wincle *Cheshire*
Windermere *Cumbria*
Windlehurst *Gtr Manchester*
Windlesham *Surrey*
Windley *Derbyshire*
Windmill Hill *Sussex*
Windmill Hill *West Midlands*
Windrush *Gloucestershire*
Windsor *Thames Valley*
Windsor Park *Thames Valley*
Windygates *Police Scotland*
Windy Hill *Gtr Manchester*
Winford *Avon & Somerset*
Winfrith Newburgh *Dorset*
Wing *Leicestershire*
Wing *Thames Valley*
Wingate *Durham*
Wingates *Gtr Manchester*
Wingerworth *Derbyshire*
Wingham *Kent*
Winkleigh *Devon & Cornwall*
Winnall *Hampshire*
Winnersh *Thames Valley*
Winscombe *Avon & Somerset*
Winsford *Cheshire*
Winsford *Avon & Somerset*
Winsley *North Yorkshire*
Winsley *Wiltshire*
Winslow *Thames Valley*
Winstanley *Gtr Manchester*
Winster *Derbyshire*
Winterborne Abbas *Dorset*
Winterbourne Came *Dorset*
Winterbourne Clenston *Dorset*
Winterbourne Gunner *Wiltshire*
Winterbourne Herringston *Dorset*
Winterbourne Houghton *Dorset*
Winterbourne Kingston *Dorset*
Winterbourne Monkton *Dorset*
Winterbourne St Martin *Dorset*
Winterbourne Steepleton *Dorset*
Winterbourne Stickland *Dorset*
Winterbourne Whitchurch *Dorset*
Winterbourne Zelston *Dorset*
Winterburn *North Yorkshire*
Winteringham *Lincolnshire*
Winterslow *Wiltshire*
Winterton *Humberside*
Winton *Dorset*
Winton *Gtr Manchester*
Winton *North Yorkshire*
Wintringham *North Yorkshire*
Winwick *Cambridgeshire*
Winwick *Cheshire*
Winwick *Northamptonshire*
Wirksworth *Derbyshire*
Wirswall *Cheshire*
Wisbech *Cambridgeshire*
Wisbech-St-Mary *Cambridgeshire*
Wisborough Green *Sussex*
Wishaw *Police Scotland*
Wisley *Surrey*
Wistaston *Cheshire*
Wistow *Leicestershire*
Wistow *North Yorkshire*
Wistow *Cambridgeshire*
Witcham *Cambridgeshire*
Witchampton *Dorset*
Witchford *Cambridgeshire*
Witham *Essex*
Witham-on-the-Hill *Lincolnshire*
Withcote *Leicestershire*
Witheridge *Devon & Cornwall*
Witherley *Leicestershire*

Withernsea *Humberside*
Withington *Gtr Manchester*
Witley *Surrey*
Witney *Thames Valley*
Wittering *Cambridgeshire*
Witterings *Sussex*
Witton *West Mercia*
Witton Gilbert *Durham*
Wiveliscombe *Avon & Somerset*
Wivelsfield *Sussex*
Wivenhoe *Essex*
Woburn *Bedfordshire*
Woburn Sands *Thames Valley*
Woking *Surrey*
Wokingham *Thames Valley*
Woldingham *Surrey*
Wollaston *Northamptonshire*
Wollaston *West Midlands*
Wollaton *Nottinghamshire*
Wollescote *West Midlands*
Wolsingham *Durham*
Wolsington *Northumbria*
Wolstanton *Staffordshire*
Wolstenholme *Gtr Manchester*
Wolston *Warwickshire*
Wolverhampton *West Midlands*
Wolverley *West Mercia*
Wolverton *Thames Valley*
Wolvey *Warwickshire*
Wombourne *Staffordshire*
Wombwell *South Yorkshire*
Womersley *North Yorkshire*
Wonersh *Surrey*
Wooburn Green *Thames Valley*
Wood End *Gtr Manchester*
Wood Green *Metropolitan*
Wood Street *Surrey*
Woodbank Park *Gtr Manchester*
Woodborough *Wiltshire*
Woodbridge *Suffolk*
Woodbridge Road *West Midlands*
Woodbury *Devon & Cornwall*
Woodchurch *Merseyside*
Woodchurch *Kent*
Woodcott *Cheshire*
Woodcroft *Cambridgeshire*
Woodditton *Cambridgeshire*
Woodend *Northamptonshire*
Woodford *Gtr Manchester*
Woodford *Metropolitan*
Woodford Halse
  Northamptonshire
Woodford-cum-Membris
  Northants
Woodgate Hill *Gtr Manchester*
Woodhall Spa *Lincolnshire*
Woodham *Surrey*
Woodham Ferrers *Essex*
Woodhey *Gtr Manchester*
Woodhill *Gtr Manchester*
Woodhouse *South Yorkshire*
Woodhouse *West Yorkshire*
Woodhouse Eaves *Leicestershire*
Woodhouse Park *Gtr Manchester*
Woodhouses *Gtr Manchester*
Woodhurst *Cambridgeshire*
Woodland *Durham*
Woodlands *Dorset*
Woodlands *North Yorkshire*
Woodley *Gtr Manchester*
Woodley *Thames Valley*
Woodnesborough *Kent*
Woodnewton *Northamptonshire*
Woodplumpton *Lancashire*
Woodrow *West Mercia*
Woods Moor *Gtr Manchester*
Woodsetts *South Yorkshire*
Woodsford *Dorset*
Woodside *Hertfordshire*

Woodstock *Thames Valley*
Woodston *Cambridgeshire*
Woodthorpe *Derbyshire*
Woodthorpe *Leicestershire*
Woodville *Derbyshire*
Woodwalton *Cambridgeshire*
Woofferton *West Mercia*
Wookey *Avon & Somerset*
Wool *Dorset*
Woolacombe *Devon & Cornwall*
Woolaston *Gloucestershire*
Wooldale *West Yorkshire*
Wooler *Northumbria*
Woolford *Gtr Manchester*
Woolfox *Leicestershire*
Woolhampton *Thames Valley*
Woolland *Dorset*
Woolley *Cambridgeshire*
Woolley *West Yorkshire*
Woolmer Green *Hertfordshire*
Woolpit *Suffolk*
Woolstanwood *Cheshire*
Woolston *Cheshire*
Woolverstone *Suffolk*
Woolwich *Metropolitan*
Woore *West Mercia*
Wootton *Bedfordshire*
Wootton *Hampshire*
Wootton *Northamptonshire*
Wootton (Berks) *Thames Valley*
Wootton (Oxon) *Thames Valley*
Wootton Bassett *Wiltshire*
Wootton Fitzpaine *Dorset*
Wootton Glanville *Dorset*
Wootton Wawen *Warwickshire*
Worcester City *West Mercia*
Worfield *West Mercia*
Workington *Cumbria*
Worksop *Nottinghamshire*
Worleston *Cheshire*
Worlingham *Suffolk*
Wormald Green *North Yorkshire*
Wormhill *Derbyshire*
Wormley *Hertfordshire*
Wormley *Surrey*
Worplesdon *Surrey*
Worral *South Yorkshire*
Worsbrough *South Yorkshire*
Worsbrough Bridge *South Yorks*
Worsley *Gtr Manchester*
Worsley Menes *Gtr Manchester*
Worsthorne *Lancashire*
Worth *Kent*
Worth Matravers *Dorset*
Worthing *Sussex*
Worthington *Gtr Manchester*
Worthington *Leicestershire*
Wortley *South Yorkshire*
Wortley *West Yorkshire*
Worton *North Yorkshire*
Wothorpe *Cambridgeshire*
Wotton *Surrey*
Wotton-under-Edge *Glos*
Wouldham *Kent*
Wragby *Lincolnshire*
Wragby *West Yorkshire*
Wrangaton *Devon & Cornwall*
Wrangle *Lincolnshire*
Wraxall *Dorset*
Wray *Lancashire*
Wraysbury *Thames Valley*
Wrea Green *Lancashire*
Wrecclesham *Surrey*
Wrelton *North Yorkshire*
Wrenbury *Cheshire*
Wrentham *Suffolk*
Wrenthorpe *West Yorkshire*
Wrestlingworth *Bedfordshire*
Wrexham *North Wales*

Writtle *Essex*
Wrose *West Yorkshire*
Wrotham *Kent*
Wroughton *Wiltshire*
Wroxall *Hampshire*
Wroxham *Norfolk*
Wroxton *Thames Valley*
Wyaston *Derbyshire*
Wyberton *Lincolnshire*
Wyboston *Bedfordshire*
Wybunbury *Cheshire*
Wychbold *West Mercia*
Wychough *Cheshire*
Wycomb *Leicestershire*
Wyddiall *Hertfordshire*
Wye *Kent*
Wyke *Surrey*
Wyke *West Yorkshire*
Wyke Regis *Dorset*
Wykeham *North Yorkshire*
Wykin *Leicestershire*
Wylam *Northumbria*
Wyllie *Gwent*
Wylye *Wiltshire*
Wymeswold *Leicestershire*
Wymington *Bedfordshire*

Wymondham *Leicestershire*
Wymondham *Norfolk*
Wynford Eagle *Dorset*
Wythall *West Mercia*
Wythenshawe *Gtr Manchester*
Yafforth *North Yorkshire*
Yalding *Kent*
Yapton *Sussex*
Yarcombe *Devon & Cornwall*
Yardley Gobion *Northamptonshire*
Yardley Hastings *Northants*
Yarm *Cleveland*
Yarmouth *Hampshire*
Yarnbrook *Wiltshire*
Yarnton *Thames Valley*
Yarwell *Northamptonshire*
Yateley *Hampshire*
Yattendon *Thames Valley*
Yatton *Avon & Somerset*
Yaxley *Cambridgeshire*
Yaxley *Suffolk*
Yeadon *West Yorkshire*
Yealand *Lancashire*
Yearsley *North Yorkshire*
Yeaveley *Derbyshire*
Yedingham *North Yorkshire*

Yeldersley *Derbyshire*
Yelling *Cambridgeshire*
Yelvertoft *Northamptonshire*
Yelverton *Devon & Cornwall*
Yeovil *Avon & Somerset*
Yetholm *Police Scotland*
Yetminster *Dorset*
Ynysddu *Gwent*
Ynysforgan *South Wales*
Ynyshir *South Wales*
Ynystawe *South Wales*
Ynysybwl *South Wales*
Youlton *North Yorkshire*
York *North Yorkshire*
York Road *PSNI*
York Town *Surrey*
Yorkely *Gloucestershire*
Youlgreave *Derbyshire*
Yoxford *Suffolk*
Ystalyfera *South Wales*
Ystrad Fawr *South Wales*
Ystrad Mynach *Gwent*
Ystrad Rhondda *South Wales*
Ystradgynlais *Dyfed-Powys*
Ystradowen *Dyfed-Powys*
Ystradowen *South Wales*

ACTS OF PARLIAMENT

TABLE FOR ASCERTAINING DATES

Acts of Parliament were dated by the year of the Monarch's reign in which they were passed, and each is numbered, within each year of the reign, from one upwards in the order of its Chapter or appearance on the Statute Book. The starting date of each reign is given below. Since 19 July 1962 Acts of Parliament have been dated by the Calendar Year.

William I	14 Oct 1066	Mary	6 July 1553
William II	9 Sept 1086	Elizabeth I	17 Nov 1558
Henry I	2 Aug 1096	James I	24 March 1603
Stephen	1 Dec 1139	Charles I	27 March 1625
Henry II	25 Oct 1155	Charles II	30 Jan 1649
Richard I	9 July 1184	James II	6 Feb 1685
John	6 April 1199	William III & Mary	13 Feb 1689
Henry III	19 Oct 1219	William III (alone)	28 Dec 1694
Edward I	16 Nov 1272	Anne	28 March 1702
Edward II	7 July 1307	George I	1 Aug 1714
Edward III	25 Jan 1327	George II	11 June 1727
Richard II	21 June 1377	George III	25 Oct 1760
Henry IV	29 Sept 1399	George IV	29 Jan 1820
Henry V	20 March 1414	William IV	26 June 1830
Henry VI	31 Aug 1422	Victoria	20 June 1837
Edward IV	4 March 1460	Edward VII	22 Jan 1901
Edward V	9 April 1483	George V	6 May 1910
Richard III	22 June 1483	Edward VIII	20 Jan 1936
Henry VII	22 Aug 1485	George VI	10 Dec 1936
Henry VIII	22 April 1508	Elizabeth II	6 Feb. 1952
Edward VI	28 Jan 1547		

INDEX